The

CHEMICAL BIOLOGY

of

FISHES

The
CHEMICAL BIOLOGY
of
FISHES

With a Key to the Chemical Literature

R. MALCOLM LOVE
Torry Research Station, Aberdeen
Scotland

1970
ACADEMIC PRESS
LONDON AND NEW YORK

ACADEMIC PRESS INC. (LONDON) LTD.
Berkeley Square House,
Berkeley Square,
London, W1X 6BA

U.S. Edition published by
ACADEMIC PRESS INC.
111 Fifth Avenue,
New York, New York 10003

Library of Congress Catalog Card Number: 72–92397
Standard Book Number: 12–455850–X

PRINTED IN GREAT BRITAIN BY
THE WHITEFRIARS PRESS LTD, LONDON & TONBRIDGE

この著書を日本の
水産学を研究して
いる友達に捧げます

*This work is dedicated to my friends, the
Fisheries Scientists of Japan.*

PREFACE

This book is a biology of fish seen through chemical analysis. Like Caesar's Gaul, it is divided into three parts. The first contains the text proper, which describes the dynamic aspects of fish chemistry, and the other two are bibliographical indexes of chemical composition, firstly by chemical substance and secondly by name of fish. Since one of the purposes of the first part is to show the futility of single chemical determinations in the tissues of fish of unknown history, it might be wondered why the second two parts have been compiled at all, but from the number of enquiries received from colleagues, it is clear that a need for such an index exists. Investigators such as nutritionists often want to know the order of concentration of a substance, or what sort of figure to expect if they should carry out analysis themselves. The index also serves as a reference list for methods of analysis which have been found suitable for fish tissue—it is often difficult to know where to look for such information, and a perusal of two or three papers on, say, the calcium content of fish blood will soon show the technique most in vogue. After some thought I decided not to compile a list of 'best methods' of analysis, since direct experience was lacking in most instances, and the reliability of hearsay tends to vary.

I have deliberately avoided the term 'biochemistry' in the title, because in recent years this word has acquired a rather restricted meaning as the study of isolated systems, without much reference to the animal as a whole. In addition, a good deal of present-day biochemical investigation is carried out on rats or other small mammals kept under constant conditions in a colony. The stresses, such as severe depletion, which most fish undergo as part of their normal living, have such a profound effect on the composition of the body that fish chemistry requires a special approach. Fishery biologists usually realize this, but may not be familiar with the range of techniques available to biochemists which could profitably be applied to biological problems.

One aim of the book, then, is to try and combine the outlooks of both disciplines, to mutual advantage. Furthermore it is hoped that the indexes will prove useful to anyone dipping into fisheries science who wishes to find chemical information without having to hunt through a mass of literature to do so.

In making the compilation, I have drawn not only on conventional biochemical literature, but also on that from the nutrition and food technology fields, which can be surprisingly useful. For example, while the chemical constituents of salted, dried or canned material are not usable in the present instance, many investigators give figures for the 'controls', that is, the fresh fish before processing. These are usually valid for the present purpose.

It is a fact that many research problems cannot be solved until the phenomenon under investigation can be measured, and this with some degree of accuracy. It is also usually necessary to attack a problem from several different angles, so that the greatest ingenuity must be brought to bear in devising novel techniques of measurement. In the study of fish, even the armoury of conventional biochemistry is sometimes inadequate, and extra techniques need to be devised—one should not, for example, be ashamed of chewing the fish in order to detect any differences in the mechanical properties of the muscle during the spawning season. As an instance of 'biological' information emerging from technological research, Castell and Maclean (1964) discovered that there was a seasonal variation in the rate of development of rancidity in the muscle of cod stored after death. They also found that the muscle from the tail section became rancid more quickly than that from the head section. Observations such as these can be very valuable in the study of chemical biology, and it is possible to find clues in a variety of literature.

Since very little chemical work has been done from a biological standpoint, it follows that most of the information set out in the following pages was originally obtained with other motives, frequently technological, in mind; it has often been the little 'asides' in the discussions of such papers which have proved to be of most value. From one point of view, then, there may seem to have been an imbalance of research effort, which has not necessarily been concentrated on the most biologically interesting species. In fish chemistry, the counterpart of the University Rat is the goldfish, *Carassius auratus*, which has often been investigated not because of its intrinsic interest or economic value, but because it is cheap to maintain and readily available. However, the over-riding motive behind most of the work has been economic: Riedel (1961) showed that of all the fish landed in the world, the greatest weight was of herring, *Clupea harengus*, and cod, *Gadus morhua*. Examination of Part III (p. 295) shows that the intensity of research effort has been very high in these two species, and, similarly, the rainbow trout, *Salmo gairdnerii*, and the carp, *Cyprinus carpio*, have been much investigated as the principal species used in artificial culture; breeders have wished to find out, for example, the effect of different diets on the composition and condition of the stock.

Where writers have attempted to relate their chemical findings to some inherent characteristic of the fish, one can often sense in their accounts a frustration engendered by trying to formulate something tidy or clear-cut. So often, having uncovered a statistically sound relationship between the concentration of a substance and some characteristic of the fish, they have had to end lamely by admitting that one wretched species does not fit into the scheme at all, but shows the relationship in reverse. It is hoped that, in this present discussion of factors which can influence fish chemistry, a way may occasionally be found to explain why the 'awkward' species behave as they do. So incomplete is the present state of relevant knowledge, however, that the attempt can be only a modest one.

My coverage of the literature on lipids, hormones and enzymes is not by any means complete, since the first field is so vast that a non-specialist simply cannot do it justice, and the literature of the other two fields is at present expanding rapidly and is difficult to assess as a whole.

Some clumsiness in the text may strike the reader, since, in addition to putting the author's name and date in parenthesis after an observation, it is usually desirable to specify the name in Latin of the species investigated. Unwieldy though it is, this practice has had to be followed, because there is often such diversity between the chemistry of different species that one rarely dares to generalize about any property whatsoever, and local names of fish cannot be relied upon as exclusive to a single species. Surprisingly, some of the Latin names are not above criticism either, since alternatives exist in a number of cases (for example, *Gadus morhua*, *Gadus morrhua* and *Gadus callarias* for cod). *Squalus suckleyi* is now thought to be the same fish as *Squalus acanthias*, and the names of the different species of tuna are even more in doubt. Since systematists are not agreed as to the correct Latin names for all of the fish, my practice in the text, apart from correcting very many spelling mistakes, has been to leave the names as they were given by the authors, even though this sometimes results in a fish's appearance under two or more aliases. Among fish commonly investigated, however, I have rendered *Gadus callarias* as *Gadus morhua* unless it refers specifically to cod from the Baltic Sea, *Salmo fario* as *Salmo trutta*, *Salmo irideus* as *Salmo gairdnerii* and *Melanogrammus aeglefinus* as *Gadus aeglefinus*. *Hippoglossus vulgaris*, *Tinca vulgaris* and a few other similar names have also been transcribed as *Hippoglossus hippoglossus*, *Tinca tinca* and so on. In addition, the sorting out of synonyms has been attempted in Part III (p. 295), where the different names of single species have been cross-referenced. Trivial names of most of the fish mentioned in the text can be found in part III if required.

Sometimes the concentrations of constituents have been reported for more than one species, and whether or not the values diverge it may be useful to know whether the fish are related to each other. For this purpose, an appendix (p. 406) has been compiled using Starr Jordan's classification (1963) to show the inter-relationships of many of the generic names mentioned in the text. For example, among the cyclostomes, *Entosphenus* is shown to be more closely related to *Petromyzon* than to *Polistotrema*. I am indebted to Mr. Noel Wilkins for his advice in this matter.

I have attempted to simplify a little of the specialized vocabulary of both biochemistry and biology in an effort to make it more comprehensible to the general reader. The penchant of 19th Century scientists for deriving words, almost impossible to pronounce, from the Greek in order to describe rather ordinary phenomena makes some of the older biological literature tedious for the non-specialist—for example 'sympiezospondyly' for 'bone compression' (Howes, 1894)— and the present habit of biochemists of using initial letters of the names of complex substances to produce 'words' such as NADH and DNAP is also upsetting for the uninitiated. How one would like to write a treatise in Anglo-Saxon English, which would be completely comprehensible to scientist and non-scientist alike, rather than in the ponderous words of Graeco-Roman English! While I always prefer to 'look at' fish rather than 'submit them to macroscopic examination,' the use of a substantial proportion of words of Greek or Latin origin is, alas, inevitable in work of this kind.

Since the text has been written for a wide readership, I have deliberately not adopted the most recent changes in Biochemical nomenclature, but have adhered to more familiar designations, assuming that the new versions will not be in general use for a few years yet.

Some facts are discussed under more than one heading. While I have tried by cross-referencing to keep actual duplication to a minimum and avoid irritating those who read the work right through, my aim has been to make each section complete in itself.

The indexing is such that the reader can obtain information in several ways. The general index (p. 543) lists topics in the text, but any species of fish may be looked up under its Latin name (obtainable from the trivial name, if necessary, in Appendix B, p. 410) in Part III. Here its occurrences in the text are noted, in addition to the bibliographical references to its constituents. Similarly, data on an individual constituent can be found in Part II, which shows where each substance is mentioned in the text and also gives the bibliographical reference to its concentration in various organs. By suitable use of Parts II and III one can in most cases identify papers showing the level of a constituent in a certain organ of a certain fish. Finally, the bibliography is combined with an author index.

All temperatures quoted are in centrigrade (Celcius) units.

October, 1969   MALCOLM LOVE
East Silverburn,
Kingswells,
Aberdeenshire

ACKNOWLEDGEMENTS

A number of colleagues and friends who are marine biologists or biochemists have kindly read parts of the manuscript, and their comments have been extremely helpful, especially in correcting the howlers one is liable to make when wandering into unfamiliar areas of research. I should like to record my sincere thanks for such help to A. C. Burd, J. R. Burt, R. N. Farragut, P. T. Grant, June Olley, M. Walker, C. Wardle, N. P. Wilkins, R. S. Wright, K. Zama, and Professors G. A. D. Haslewood and F. G. T. Holliday. I am also greatly indebted to T. Motohiro for the considerable pains he took in photographing a section of a puffer fish, Fig. 19. Finally I would like to thank J. A. Lovern, until recently Director of Torry Research Station, for his interest and encouragement throughout the work.

CONTENTS

Part I

I. TOWARDS A VALID SAMPLING TECHNIQUE

2. THE LIFE CYCLE

5. DEPLETION

Part II

INDEX OF CHEMICAL SUBSTANCES

Part III

CHAPTER 1

TOWARDS A VALID SAMPLING TECHNIQUE

A. Chemistry and Anatomy

Discussing the ash in fish tissues, Vinogradov (1953) stated that the largest amount is to be found in the sturgeons and pikes, but that "these results may be too high due to the presence of skin or bones . . . the descriptions by investigators often make it impossible to tell how the material was prepared for analysis, thus making their data of relatively little value for scientific problems".

While we may smile at the thought of analysing muscle for minerals without first removing the bones, it should be pointed out that the musculature of fish is itself a heterogeneous mixture of structures which differ widely in their chemical make-up. Although no one submits random mixtures of skin and bones to chemical analysis, investigators have for years cheerfully chopped or minced up whole fish fillets, or, worse, unspecified parts of fillets, prior to investigation. The purpose of this section is to examine the validity of such a procedure by taking a closer look at the anatomy of fish muscle in relation to the proportions of its constituents. So many factors influence the composition of fish muscle that chemical analysis can be a tool of great versatility for studying the life and habits of the fish, but a faulty sampling technique can easily obliterate clues that might have emerged.

1. Cell Dimensions

Figure 1 is a diagrammatic representation of a fillet of cod (*Gadus morhua*), looking at the surface removed from the backbone. The lines represent sheets of connective tissue (myocommata) which separate the blocks of muscle tissue proper (myotomes) from each other. They do not simply run vertically from 'bone' side to 'skin' side, but curve towards the tail end within the thickness of the fillet in a complex way —as Ganguly and Nag (1964) put it: "The problem of the nature and arrangement of the myomeric musculature is a most vexatious one". Yes indeed. More will be said of the connective tissue later (p. 4).

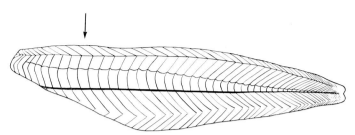

FIG. 1. Appearance of the musculature of *Gadus morhua* after removal from the skeleton. The lines represent connective tissue, and the arrow indicates the region where the contractile cells are longest.

The muscle cells run approximately from left to right in Fig. 1, so that the longest cells in the central bands of muscle are to be found at about the place indicated by the arrow. Actual measurements of myotome widths show that the widest ones (i.e. the longest cells) are 11–14 myotomes from the point of severance of the head. The widths drawn in Fig. 1 were based on these measurements. More interestingly, the diameters of the individual cells (Fig. 2) follow the same pattern.*

This finding is of great importance in sampling muscle tissue, since that from the region of myotome 12 will contain a smaller *number* of cells in a gramme than that taken from a more anterior or posterior position (Love, 1958a).

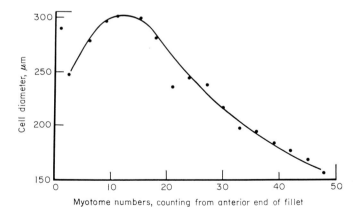

FIG. 2. Average diameters of muscle cells from different parts of the musculature from a specimen of *Gadus morhua* 95 cm long. The myotomes are numbered from the point of severance of the head. Each point is the mean of 200 cells. After Love (1958a), reproduced by courtesy of the Society of Chemical Industry.

* The cells of dark muscle, to be discussed fully later (p. 17) appear to reach their largest diameter in the region of the last dorsal fin, where maximum flexure occurs (M. Walker, private communication).

The deoxyribose nucleic acid (DNA) content of one cell nucleus is usually constant, so taking account of the above observation the concentration of DNA in muscle from the head or tail ends where the cells are narrower should be higher than that near myotome 12. Experiments confirm this (Fig. 3), whether or not the muscle is dissected free from connective tissue (Love, 1958b). Since the proportions of extracellular fluid to intracellular material are affected by the sizes of the cells, this size distribution is bound to influence the concentrations of certain ions in muscle from different parts of the fillet, as most of the sodium and chloride is found outside the cell and most of the potassium inside. Love, Robertson and Strachan (1968) showed that the muscle of *Gadus morhua* from the head end of the fillet, freed from connective tissue, contains 24 mg sodium per 100 g, while that from the tail end contains 34 mg. This isolated observation is consistent with there being

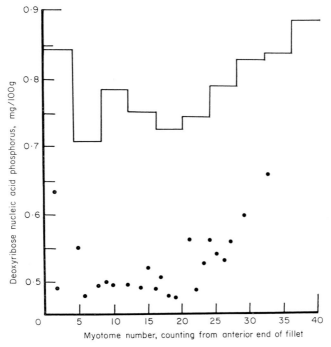

FIG. 3. Concentration of deoxyribose nucleic acid (expressed as phosphorus) in different parts of the musculature from a 90 cm *Gadus morhua*. The upper part refers to whole tissue (myotomes plus myocommata) while the lower part shows the concentration in myotomes (contractile muscle) alone, freed from myocommata (connective tissue). The myotomes are numbered from the point of severance of the head. After Love (1958b), reproduced by courtesy of the Society of Chemical Industry.

a larger proportion of extracellular fluid in the tail region, due to the smaller size of the cells. The proportion of cell wall material (mostly collagen, see pp. 8 and 12) presumably alters in the same way. Thurston and MacMaster (1960) showed that dark muscle, which consists of smaller cells than white muscle (Fig. 14) also contains a higher concentration of sodium. While there are many other chemical differences between dark and white muscle, the mechanism in this instance may be the same again.

Thus the first precept for sampling is to decide on one particular region of the fish, and use none other for all samples which are to be compared. Myotome no. 12 from the point of severance of the head is suitable for *Gadus morhua*; other myotomes may be more appropriate for other species.

2. *Connective Tissue (myocommata)*

(a) *Separation of connective tissue from muscle*

It is clear from Fig. 1 that the proportion of connective tissue to contractile muscle varies enormously in different parts of the fillet, being particularly high at the tail end. The myocommata look so thin that it is tempting to ignore them and simply chop or mince the fish from the chosen portion of the fillet. However, an examination of its chemical properties shows that this approach is inappropriate. For

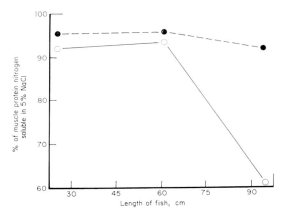

Fig. 4. Proportion of protein (nitrogen) which is extractable by 5% NaCl at 0°, from myotomes nos. 8 to 16 of *Gadus morhua* of different sizes. After Ironside and Love (1958), reproduced by courtesy of the Society of Chemical Industry. ○ Whole muscle (myotomes plus myocommata); ● Myotomes only, from same region of fillet.

example, the muscle cells proper, which are made up largely of the contractile proteins actin and myosin, dissolve to the extent of more than 90% in 5% sodium chloride, and variations in the solubility can be used in the study of starvation (Ironside and Love, 1958; Love and Robertson, 1967: *Gadus morhua*) (see p. 235). However, only about 30% of the proteins of the myocommata of this species will dissolve in the same solvent (Ironside and Love, 1958), so variations in the proportion of the two types of tissue will affect the solubility of the mixture.

Figure 4 shows the solubility in 5% sodium chloride of myotomes 8–16, inclusive, after chopping the mixed tissue—myotomes plus myocommata—with scissors (lower curve) and after dissecting the

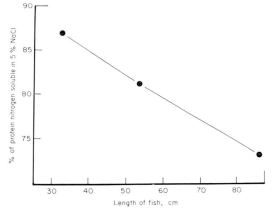

Fig. 5. Proportion of protein (nitrogen) which is extractable by 5% NaCl at 0°, from complete skinned fillets of *Gadus morhua* of various sizes. After Ironside and Love (1958), reproduced by courtesy of the Society of Chemical Industry.

myotomes free from myocommata (upper curve). Clearly, the solubility is much lower in the biggest fish when whole tissue is used. The apparent relationship between solubility of mixed tissue and the size of the fish was even closer when complete fillets, without skin, from fish of different sizes, were passed through a domestic mincer and then extracted with sodium chloride solution (Fig. 5). Again, this effect was eliminated by dissecting free from connective tissue.

The explanation appears to lie in the increase in thickness of myo-commata as the fish grow in length. Figure 6 shows how myocomma no. 12 of the same species increases in thickness. A doubling of fish size results in a roughly three-fold increase in myocomma thickness, but in only a doubling of the spacing in between (Fig. 43, p. 87).

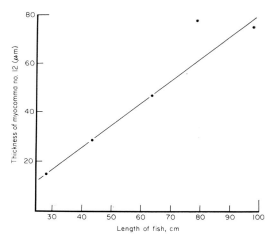

Fig. 6. Average thickness of myocomma no. 12 (counting from point of severance of the head) at the 'skeleton' side of fillets from *Gadus morhua* of different sizes. After Love (unpublished).

The myocommata are also very rich in DNA, so make the value for 'muscle' tissue too high if left in place (Fig. 3).

The concentration of lipid in whole flesh of *Gadus morhua* is low, ranging from about 0·85 to over 1%, according to season (Dambergs, 1964). However, the lipid content of myocommata is higher than that of 'dissected' myotomes (0·84—0·98% as against 0·59—0·62%: Love and Lavéty, 1969, unpublished). This almost certainly accounts for most of the differences found in the lipid of the head, middle and tail sections of the same species, which over the year averages 0·96, 0·93 and 1·13%, respectively (Dambergs, 1963). The 'concentrations' of myocommata in these regions (Fig. 1, p. 2) correspond with the same pattern. Dark muscle, which is more abundant in the tail region, may also contribute measurably to the higher tail lipid content.

Thurston and his colleagues have analysed different regions of fish fillets for inorganic constituents. In *Hippoglossus hippoglossus* there is a decrease of potassium from 454 to 425 mg% and an increase in sodium from 48 to 63 mg% towards the tail (Thurston and MacMaster, 1960). A similar pattern was seen in *Oncorhynchus gorbuscha* (Thurston, 1958a; Thurston and Groninger, 1959), and in this species it was also noted that sodium is higher, potassium lower, at the head end compared with the middle section. The siscowet trout (*Salvelinus namaycush siscowet*) on the other hand shows increases of both sodium and potassium at the tail end (Thurston, 1962).

Kruchakova (1952) analysed seven species of fish from the Black Sea and found increases in sodium, potassium and calcium at the tail ends, magnesium being little affected by locality. In this case, however, it was taken as established fact that the reason for the increased concentration was an increase in the metabolic activity of the muscle at the tail end. Nothing was presented in support, and it is perhaps worth pausing for a moment to examine what evidence there is.

The concentrations of chemical compounds which supply energy (glucose phosphates, fructose phosphates and other intermediates of the carbohydrate cycle) do not seem to be preferentially raised in any one part of the musculature (Nagayama, 1961a: *Lateolabrax japonicus*). Glycogen increases from the head to the middle part, then decreases at the tail end in unexercised *Gadus morhua* (Fraser, Dyer *et al.*, 1966) and *Auxis tapeinosoma* (Amano, Bito and Kawabata, 1953). Nagayama (1961a) found a higher concentration of glycogen and free glucose in the tail of one batch of *Lateolabrax japonicus*, but not of a second batch. Black, Connor *et al.* (1962) studied *Salmo gairdnerii* which had been strenuously exercised, and noted that while both glycogen and lactic acid concentrations increase towards the tail end, the ratio of lactate/glycogen decreases; this they interpreted as showing no indication of greater muscular activity in the tail section. In *Auxis tapeinosoma* which have died after struggling, the highest lactic acid concentration, as indicated by the lowest pH, is in the mid-section, not the tail (Amano, Bito and Kawabata, 1953). Thus it is not at all certain that the tail muscle is in fact the most metabolically active. It is possible that the tail muscle is more concerned with the continuous slow swimming of some fish, rather than in sudden energetic bursts. Fraser, Mannan and Dyer (1961) showed that the brown lateral muscle (see A4, p. 17) makes up about 8% of the flesh of the tail of *Gadus aeglefinus*, but only 1% of the middle section, and dark muscle is intimately concerned with continuous swimming (p. 33).

Although the available evidence is thus somewhat confused, it seems reasonably certain that changes in the properties of the proteins and increases in the concentrations of DNA, sodium, lipid and probably other substances towards the tail end of the fillets of some fish are the results of increases both in the number of cells per gramme and in the proportion of connective tissue, rather than in metabolic activity.

Our second precept for sampling, therefore, is to use muscle tissue from which the connective tissue has been removed by dissection.

Just how valid is this step? Is any connective tissue left behind in the 'muscle' tissue? Careful study of the fine anatomy of cod muscle shows that thin processes of connective tissue leave the myocomma and grow

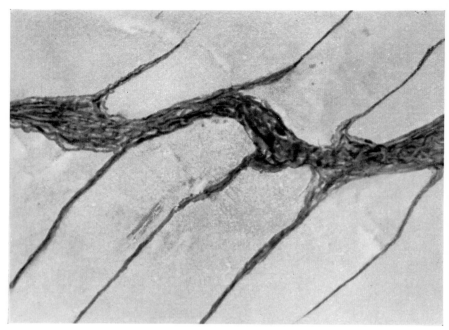

Fig. 7. Histological preparation of part of a myocomma (stained dark) in among the muscle cells of *Gadus morhua*, showing the processes of connective tissue growing in between the cells (light areas). Stained with van Gieson's picro-fuchsin by the 'bleaching' method of Lavéty, quoted by Love, Lavéty and Steel (1969), in whose paper the illustration appears. The diameters of the muscle cells are about 250 μ. Reproduced by courtesy of the Journal of Food Technology.

between each cell along its length; they are shown up by differential staining in Fig. 7, and may well be tubular—as Love, Lavéty and Steel (1969) have pointed out, the distinction between these processes and the cell wall disappears a short distance away from the myocomma.

The processes (or tubes) extend such a long way between the cells that one may guess that they join up with the next myocomma. One can envisage a thin three-dimensional parallel scaffolding of connective tissue linking the faces of adjacent myocommata together, the spaces in between being filled with contractile muscle and extracellular fluid. Any sample of muscle tissue dissected free from myocommata must therefore contain some connective tissue, quite apart from any collagen there may be in the cell walls proper. For this reason, 'dissected' muscle tissue contains 0·2—0·4% of hydroxyproline, an amino acid found only in collagen. The hydroxyproline content of myocommata is 1—2% (Love and Lavéty, unpublished).

Figures 4 and 5 showed that much of the sampling error due to the inclusion of connective tissue was eliminated by dissecting the muscle, so the procedure is obviously valuable. However, it is as well to bear in mind that a small quantity of connective tissue is still present.

(b) *Heterogeneity of connective tissue itself*

Figure 8 shows a myocomma from a fillet of a large cod after scraping the muscle tissue away from one face. The point of attachment to the bone is at the upper left corner. It can be seen that the connective tissue fibrils are thickest at this point and spread out like a net, becoming thinner and progressively more difficult to distinguish towards the bottom of the picture. It is well known that the chemical and physical

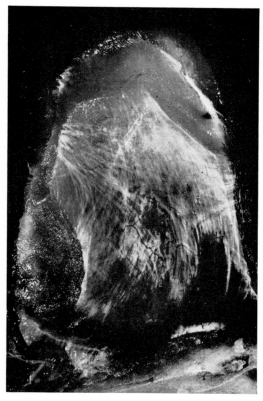

FIG. 8. Sheet of connective tissue (myocomma) with one side scraped free from muscle, in place at the anterior end of the musculature of *Gadus morhua*. The convergence of thicker and thicker collagen fibres towards the upper left side can be seen; this is thought to be the point of attachment to the skeleton. After Love (unpublished).

properties of thick connective tissue fibres are different from those of thin ones, and so it proves to be in the present instance. Love and Lavéty (unpublished) showed that the fractionation of collagen in different solvents differs according to the locality of the myocomma (Table I), and that whole myocommata from the tail region are different again. The material nearer the bone, which consists of larger fibres, appears to be more salt-soluble than the material nearer the skin. This result is surprising, since the finer fibrils or fibril precursors of connective tissue, rather than fully-formed collagen fibres, are thought

TABLE I. SALT FRACTIONATION OF COLLAGEN IN MYOCOMMATA FROM
DIFFERENT PARTS OF GADUS MORHUA
(after Love and Lavéty, unpublished)

	µg Hydroxyproline per mg wet tissue		
	Head end		*Tail end*
	Near to skeleton	*Near to skin*	
Soluble in 0·2 M NaCl	8·9	1·6	1·2
Soluble in citrate buffer pH 3·5	2·2	6·2	4·8
Insoluble	3·0	4·4	7·5
Total	14·1	12·2	13·5

to be richest in salt-soluble collagen (Gross, Highberger and Schmitt, 1955), which would therefore be expected to predominate in the part of the myocomma nearer the skin. More work is needed here. There is at present no other information on myocommata, but Chvapil and Hruza (1962) showed that the physical properties of rat tail tendon fibres of the same diameter differ according to their location in the tail. Further, the hydroxyproline content of collagen varies from organ to organ, for example between scale, swim bladder and skin in *Cyprinus carpio* (Piez and Gross, 1960) and between skeleton and skin in *Squalus suckleyi* (Geiger, Roberts and Tomlinson, 1962). The results of Table I are in line with these observations. Clearly, sampling of myocommata for chemical investigation must be done with discrimination.

The thickness of myocommata varies in different parts of the cod fillet. Figure 9 shows the average thicknesses in a large fish, at the surface nearest to the bone. A slight increase in thickness at the tail can be seen, and then as one passes forwards the dimensions remain almost constant at a lower level until at the head end a marked thickening occurs. If we regard the myocommata as the means whereby the force of muscle contraction is transmitted to the backbone, this makes

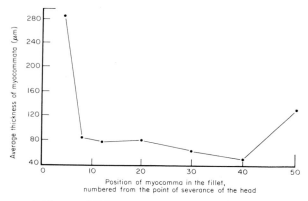

FIG. 9. Average thickness of different myocommata at the cut surface of a fillet (next to bone) from *Gadus morhua* 1 metre long. The myocommata were taken from the block of muscle immediately dorsal to the lateral line. After Love (unpublished).

sense—fish such as cod show the greatest bending about two thirds of the way between snout and tail during swimming, so the greatest force will be exerted at the extremities of the actual musculature, where the points of attachment will presumably need strengthening. The mode of swimming of various fish in relation to the complicated pattern of muscle segments, and the role of the tail in swimming are discussed in detail by Nursall (1956) and Bainbridge (1963), respectively.

This observation still does nothing to identify the region of greatest metabolic activity, but it is probably correct to regard the greatest contractile force as acting just behind the head, where, incidentally, the musculature is thickest. The effect of this on the chemistry of the connective tissue, or of the muscle for that matter, remains to be investigated.

3. *Heterogeneity of 'pure' Muscle Tissue*

We have seen that even when the true muscle tissue (myotome) is dissected free from visible myocommata, it still contains some connective tissue. Is it heterogeneous in other ways?

Each muscle cell is separated from the next by a channel of extra-cellular fluid, which usually comprises 10–20% of the weight of the tissue and is thought to be similar in composition to blood plasma. It is the medium through which nutrient materials are supplied to the cells and catabolites are removed (Manery, 1954), and is shown in an electron photomicrograph (Fig. 10). A similar picture for the same species has been shown in a paper by Bishop and Odense (1967). This

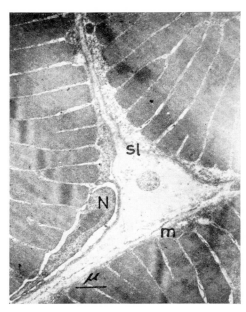

Fig. 10. Electron photomicrograph of a cross-section of muscle of newly-killed *Gadus morhua*, showing the margins of three cells with extracellular fluid between them. Sl = sarcolemma. N = nucleus. M = mitochondria. After Liljemark (1969), reproduced by courtesy of the author and Mr. Arthur J. Heighway.

fluid is much richer in sodium and chloride and poorer in potassium than the cell contents, and has a very different protein composition. Since the proportion of extracellular fluid probably varies, for instance with the diameters of the cells, we appear once more to be faced with a mixed tissue of variable proportions.

Although the cell wall (sarcolemma) is relatively thin, it also differs markedly from 'cellular' material in being composed largely of collagen fibrils. A very beautiful electron micrograph has been published by Kono, Kakuma *et al.*, (1964, plate F), showing the collagen fibrils and their cross-banding in the sarcolemma from a rat.

It is possible to eliminate this heterogeneity, too, by dissection, although the quantity of material so obtained is necessarily small (Love, 1962a). Figure 11 shows the 'plough' used in micro-dissection, which removes material from within the cells after the sides have been opened up by a wide knife). The large diameter (up to 300μ) of cod muscle cells (Fig. 40, p. 85) renders them very suitable for this treatment, which yields enough material for analysis. The sodium and potassium concentrations were found to be 43·3 and 719 mg% , respectively. From

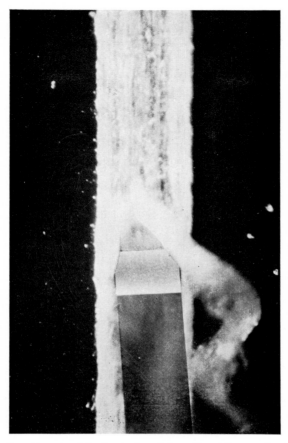

FIG. 11. The dissection at −20° of a single cell from the white muscle of *Gadus morhua*. The cell, about 200 μ wide, was removed from the fish, frozen rapidly on a glass slide and stored at −80° until required. The top edge was sliced off with a wide knife, after which this narrow steel blade scooped out the contents, uncontaminated by cell walls or extracellular fluid apart from that in the T-system. The ice crystals were rather large in this specimen. Quicker freezing produces a completely homogeneous-looking cell. After Love (1962a), reproduced by courtesy of MacMillan (Journals) Ltd.

the value of intracellular sodium and total muscle sodium from the same fish, it should therefore be possible to calculate the extracellular space of the muscle. However, the applications of this technique are more limited than they would seem, and some recent work has shown that, for example, amino acid analysis of cell contents would not be profitable.

The reason is that the fish muscle cell is not in fact a sealed-off sac, but is penetrated in many places by tubules, known collectively as the

'T' system, through which extracellular fluid appears to flow. Figure
12 shows a thin section through a single fibre of a black mollie (*Mollienesia*
sp.), and the tucking-in of the cell wall can be clearly seen. While
Peachey (1965) has calculated that the transverse tubule system of the
frog occupies only about 0·3% of the cell volume, this finding clearly
reduces the advantage to be obtained from dissecting the interiors from
individual cells, since the material is now seen to be unavoidably
'contaminated'. Zadunaisky (1966) has demonstrated that there is a
high concentration of sodium in the transverse tubules, confirming the
presence of extracellular fluid.

Figure 11 showed the limit of what could be achieved by direct
dissection. The isolation of smaller constituents for the purposes of
homogeneity (or 'meaningfulness') can be achieved only by liquid
separation. Cell walls have been isolated from muscle tissue for chemical
analysis by homogenizing the muscle, extracting the cell fragments
with salt solutions to remove the contractile proteins, and then separat-

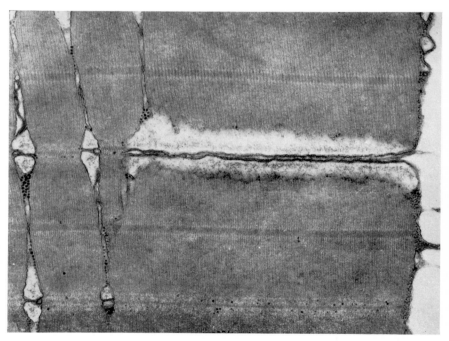

Fig. 12. Electron photomicrograph of a longitudinal section through a muscle cell of
Mollienesia sp., showing how the cell wall becomes tucked in to form a long tubule,
part of the 'T-system'. After Franzini-Armstrong and Porter (1964), reproduced by
courtesy of the authors and the Rockefeller University Press.

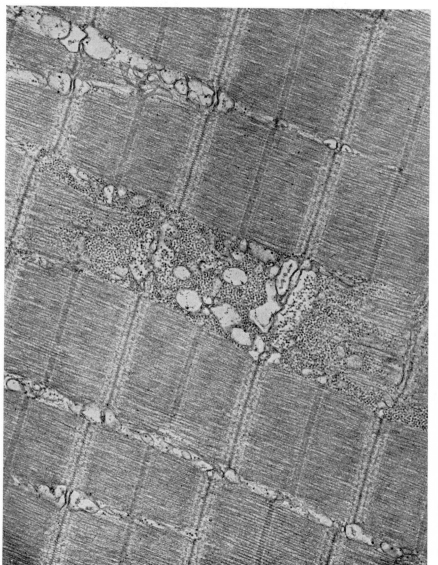

FIG. 13. Electron photomicrograph of a longitudinal section through part of one 'white' muscle cell of *Gadus morhua*, showing four fibrils. Note the I bands (light striations), which are narrower in fish than in mammalian muscle. The granular material among the sarcoplasmic reticulum in the centre of the picture is glycogen. Unpublished photograph by Mr. P. Howgate, reproduced by courtesy of Dr. J. J. Connell.

ing the resulting tubular membranes by differential centrifugation in potassium bromide solution (Kono and Colowick, 1961, using rat muscle). However, no such separation from fish muscle has come to the writer's attention so far.

The chemical constituents which can be investigated after such treatment are limited: inorganic ions, salt-soluble proteins and other smaller-molecule materials would obviously be removed during the extraction, but Kono and Colowick (1961) were able to perform analyses of lipid, insoluble protein and amino acids.

The results of ultra-high-power microscopy of mammalian muscle tissue are now well known, and good pictures showing the alternating thick and thin filaments (myosin and actin, respectively) have been shown by a number of authors, e.g. Huxley (1957).

Fish muscle is similar (Fig. 13), and in *Gadus morhua* the filaments of actin and myosin make up about 75% of the total protein (Bailey, 1954). Further pictures of muscle from this species under high power have been published by Bishop and Odense (1967). The proteins of the two types of fibril can be isolated in a reasonably pure state. Actin is prepared from fish by extracting coarsely minced muscle with acetone,

TABLE II. AMINO ACID COMPOSITION OF THE ACTIN AND MYOSIN OF COD MUSCLE (after Connell and Howgate, 1959a)

	g of N/100g protein N	
	Myosin	*Actin*
Alanine	6·03	5·80
Arginine	12·99	14·22
Aspartic acid	7·21	6·08
Cystine/2	0·61	0·97
Glutamic acid	12·31	7·56
Glycine	3·77	5·51
Histidine	3·33	5·26
Isoleucine	2·95	4·89
Leucine	6·52	5·50
Lysine	12·14	7·37
Methionine	1·67	2·42
Phenylalanine	1·98	2·30
Proline	2·51	4·35
Serine	3·87	4·71
Threonine	3·04	4·81
Tryptophan	0·62	1·29
Tyrosine	1·26	2·77
Valine	3·75	4·22

air-drying, and then extracting with water, myosin by extracting finely minced fish muscle with a slightly acid salt solution containing pyrophosphate ions. These dissociate the actin-myosin bonds and allow the myosin to dissolve, leaving most of the actin behind (Connell, 1960). Connell and Howgate (1959a) were able to analyse these separated constituent proteins for amino acids (Table II).

This final procedure probably comes nearest to the ideal of separating a recognizable single tissue structure from the heterogeneous mass of other material and then analysing it. However, for our present purpose it is extremely limited, and would reveal nothing, for instance, of the effect of environment or development on the composition of the muscle. The most useful procedure for practical purposes appears to be the straightforward freeing of pieces of muscle from associated sheets of connective tissue and taking them from the same part of the musculature each time. More elaborate separation, while possible, is of narrower application.

Depending on the information sought by means of chemical analysis, it is also sometimes necessary to limit the fish to one particular size (p. 84), season (p. 169) or fishing ground (p. 172), but these aspects will be discussed fully later on.

4. Dark Muscle

(a) Properties and distribution

The muscle of most fish is not uniform, but is often coloured brown or reddish in places, especially along the side of the body just under the skin. Many early workers believed that darkening of the muscle in various animals was caused merely by blood, and there was much discussion on the point before any experimental work was done (Needham, 1926). However, when Kühne (1865, quoted by Stirling, 1886) washed out the vascular system of rabbits with saline and found that subsequent extracts of the dark muscle were still red, it became clear that a different tissue was involved.

The cells of dark muscle are narrower than those of white muscle (Stirling, 1886). The difference is illustrated in Fig. 14 (*Scomber scombrus*), and a smaller diameter has also been noted for the cells of *Carassius auratus* (36 μ compared with 49·4 μ: Nishihara, 1967), *Labeo rohita* (25 to 45 μ compared with about 135 μ: George and Bokdawala, 1964), *Rastrelliger kanagurta* (32 μ compared with 65 μ: George, 1962), seven species of freshwater fish (Boddeke, Slijper and van der Stelt, 1959) and *Ophiodon elongatus* (Buttkus, 1963).

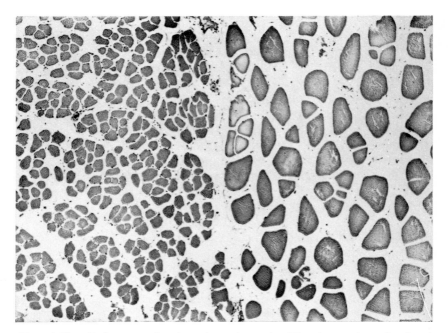

FIG. 14. Magnified cross section through trunk muscle of *Scomber scombrus*, showing the difference in cell sizes between white muscle, on the right, and dark muscle on the left of the picture. After Braekkan (1959), reproduced by courtesy of the author.

The chemical differences are numerous, and have been summed up in Table III.

Although there are often differences between dark and light muscle in the concentrations of major constituents, the differences do not seem to extend to the further breakdown of such material. Thus, there is a difference in protein content but apparently not in the distribution of amino acids, and a difference in lipid content but not in individual fatty fractions.

Cholesterol, glycogen, histidine, niacin, protein and water have been listed as being both more concentrated and less concentrated in dark muscle, according to different workers, but it will be appreciated that the number of chemical differences is still formidable, and would cause error if mixed tissue were used for sampling. For emphasis it should be added that the proportion of dark muscle differs continually along the body. The manner in which this occurs in *Katsuwonus pelamis* (Fig. 15) has been illustrated by Kishinouye (1923) who also shows the distribution in other scombroid fish. Braekkan (1959) deals similarly with various European species.

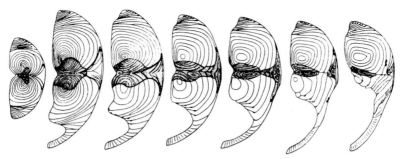

Fig. 15. Sections through the right half of the body of *Katsuwonus pelamis*, showing the distribution of dark muscle in the musculature from the tail (left) to the head (right). After Kishinouye (1923), reproduced by courtesy of the Faculty of Agriculture, University of Tokyo.

As explained more fully in 4c (p. 26), the proportion of dark to white muscle varies between species, increasing with the swimming activity of the fish. It can be very great: 48% of the body weight of *Sardinia melanosticta*, for example, is dark muscle (Fujikawa and Naganuma, 1936).

These facts underline the undesirability of chopping up whole fillets or parts of fillets for analysis without separating the dark muscle from the white.

(b) Deep and superficial dark muscle

The dark muscle of the majority of fish lies immediately under the skin along the side of the body. However, certain very active fish possess an additional band of it near the spine. An example of this was illustrated in Fig. 15 (*Katsuwonus pelamis*), which shows deep-seated dark muscle to be present all along the body, although the superficial dark muscle could not always be seen. Perhaps for this reason, the cell-widths of superficial dark muscle have been reported (Kafuku, 1950) to be the same as those of ordinary white muscle where deep-seated dark muscle is present (normally they are narrower, see p. 18).

Chemical differences exist between these two types of dark muscle. The deep-seated muscle is richer in haemoglobin, myoglobin, cytochrome C (Matsuura and Hashimoto, 1954) and in choline (Mori, Konosu and Miyagawa, 1957). The white muscle of fish contains virtually no arginase, while the superficial dark muscle has appreciable activity: however, in fish where both types of dark muscle are present, the superficial dark muscle has little or no arginase, while the deep-seated dark muscle shows definite activity (Matsuura, Baba and Mori, 1953). In *Parathunnus sibi* and *Katsuwonus vagans*, the distribution of

TABLE III. CHEMICAL DIFFERENCES BETWEEN DARK AND
ORDINARY MUSCLE

(a) *Constituent is more concentrated in the dark muscle*

Constituent	Species	Reference
Alanine	*Engraulis japonicus*	Arakaki and Suyama (1966b)
Arginase	(general)	Matsuura, Baba and Mori (1953)
Biotin	*Brosme brosme*	Braekkan and Boge (1965)
	Gadus morhua	
	Gadus virens	
	Molva molva	
Cerebroside	*Seriola quinqueradiata*	Tsuyuki and Naruse (1962)
Cholesterol	*Gadus morhua*	Igarashi, Zama and Katada (1957b)
	Thunnus orientalis	
Choline	*Parathunnus sibi*	Mori, Konosu and Miyagawa (1957)
	Seriola quinqueradiata	
Cholinesterase	*Trachurus trachurus*	Pora, Sildan and Wittenberger (1965)
Cytochrome C	*Cololabis saira*	Matsuura and Hashimoto (1954)
	Katsuwonus vagans	
	Makaira mazara	
	Makaira mitsukurii	
	Neothunnus macropterus	
	Parathunnus sibi	
	Scomber japonicus	
	Seriola quinqueradiata	
	Thunnus orientalis	
Glutathione	*Carassius auratus*	Nishihara (1967)
	Cyprinus carpio	Okada, Osakabe *et al.* (1953)
Glycogen	*Ophiodon elongatus*	Buttkus (1963)
	Scyliorhinus canicula	Bone (1966)
	Thunnus thynnus	Braekkan (1956)
Haemoglobin	*Cololabis saira*	Matsuura and Hashimoto (1954)
	Katsuwonus vagans	
	Makaira mazara	
	Makaira mitsukurii	
	Neothunnus macropterus	(also Brown, 1962)
	Parathunnus sibi	
	Scomber japonicus	
	Seriola quinqueradiata	
	Thunnus orientalis	
Histidine	*Sardinia melanosticta*	Amano and Bito (1951)
	Thunnus orientalis	
Hypoxanthine	*Salmo gairdnerii*	Saito, Arai and Yajima (1959)

TABLE III—*continued*

(a) *Constituent is more concentrated in the dark muscle*

Constituent	Species	Reference
Iron	(general)	Parks and Rose (1933)
	(general)	Vinogradov (1953)
	Labeo rohita	Alexander (1955)
	Sardinia melanosticta	Fujikawa and Naganuma (1936)
	Scatophagus argus	Alexander (1955)
Lecithin	*Seriola quinqueradiata*	Tsuyuki, Naruse and Shionoya (1961)
Lipid	*Clupea harengus*	Braekkan (1959)
	Clupea pallasii	Zama (1963a)
	Gadus morhua	Bligh and Scott (1966)
		Ackman and Cormier (1967)
	Gadus virens	Braekkan (1959)
	Hippoglossus hippoglossus	Braekkan (1959)
		Thurston and MacMaster (1960)
	Labeo rohita	Alexander (1955)
		George and Bokdawala (1964)
	Lamna cornubica	Braekkan (1959)
	Lamna nasus	Dyer, Fraser and Tibbo (1963)
	Rastrelliger kanagurta	George (1962)
	Salmo salar	Braekkan (1959)
	Salvelinus namaycush siscowet	Thurston (1962)
	Sardinia melanosticta	Fujikawa and Naganuma (1936)
	Scatophagus argus	Alexander (1955)
	Scomber scombrus	Braekkan (1959)
	Thunnus orientalis	Zama (1963a)
	Thunnus thynnus	Braekkan (1959)
Lipase	*Rastrelliger kanagurta*	George (1962)
Methionine	*Cololabis saira*	Matsuura, Kogure and Fukui
	Katsuwonus vagans	(1952)
	Neothunnus macropterus	
	Scomber japonicus	
Mitochondria	*Rastrelliger kanagurta*	George (1962)
Myoglobin	*Cololabis saira*	Matsuura and Hashimoto (1954)
	Cyprinus carpio	Hamoir (1953)
	Katsuwonus vagans	Matsuura and Hashimoto (1954)
	Makaira mazara	
	Makaira mitsukurii	
	Neothunnus macropterus	(also Brown, 1962)
	Parathunnus sibi	
	Scomber japonicus	
	Seriola quinqueradiata	
	Thunnus orientalis	

TABLE III—*continued*

(a) *Constituent is more concentrated in the dark muscle*

Constituent	Species	Reference
Niacin	*Clupea harengus*	Braekkan (1959)
	Gadus virens	
	Lamna cornubica	
Pantothenic acid	*Clupea harengus*	Braekkan (1959)
	Gadus virens	
	Hippoglossus hippoglossus	
	Lamna cornubica	
	Salmo salar	
	Scomber scombrus	
	Thunnus thynnus	
Phosphatase	(general)	Ogata and Mori (1963)
Phospholipid	*Squalus acanthias*	Olley, Pirie and Watson (1962)
	Thunnus orientalis	Katada, Zama and Igarashi (1960)
Phosphorylase	(general)	Ogata and Mori (1963)
Long chain poly-ethylenic acids	*Thunnus orientalis*	Igarashi, Zama and Katada (1957b)
Protein	*Labeo rohita*	Alexander (1955)
	Scatophagus argus	
Riboflavin	(many species)	Tomoda and Hotta (1957)
	Clupea harengus	Braekkan (1959)
	Gadus virens	
	Hippoglossus hippoglossus	
	Lamna cornubica	
	Salmo salar	
	Scomber scombrus	
	Thunnus thynnus	
Sodium	*Hippoglossus hippoglossus*	Thurston and MacMaster (1960)
Sphingomyelin	*Seriola quinqueradiata*	Tsuyuki and Naruse (1962)
Sulphur	*Sardinia melanosticta*	Fujikawa and Naganuma (1936)
Taurine	*Engraulis japonicus*	Arakaki and Suyama (1966b)
Thiamine	*Caprinus aoratus*	Masukawa, Sako and Nagata (1957)
	Clupea harengus	Braekkan, 1959
	Cololabis saira	Masukawa, Sako and Nagata (1957)
	Cyprinus carpio	
	Decapterus muroadsi	
	Gadus virens	Braekkan (1959)
	Hippoglossus hippoglossus	
	Lamna cornubica	
	Leuciscus hakonensis	Masukawa, Sako and Nagata (1957)
	Makaira sp.	
	Mugil japonicus	
	Pagrosomus major	
	Salmo salar	Braekkan (1959)

TABLE III—*continued*

(a) *Constituent is more concentrated in the dark muscle*

Constituent	Species	Reference
Thiamine—continued	*Sardinia melanosticta*	Masukawa, Sako and Nagata (1957)
	Scomber scombrus	Braekkan (1959)
	Scomberomorus niphonius	Masukawa, Sako and Nagata (1957)
	Seriola quinqueradiata	
	Thunnus orientalis	
	Thunnus thynnus	Braekkan (1959)
	Trichodon stelleri	Masukawa, Sako and Nagata (1957)
Trimethylamine oxide	*Thunnus albacares*	Yamagata, Horimoto and Nagaoka (1968)
Uric acid	*Cololabis saira*	Arai and Saito (1963)
	Scomber japonicus	
Vitamin A	majority of teleost fish	Higashi (1961)
Vitamin B_{12}	*Clupea harengus*	Braekkan (1959)
	Gadus virens	
	Hippoglossus hippoglossus	
	Lamna cornubica	
	Salmo salar	
	Scomber scombrus	
	Thunnus thynnus	
Vitamin E	*Gadus morhua*	Ackman and Cormier (1967)
Water	*Lamna nasus*	Dyer, Fraser and Tibbo (1963)
Zinc	(general)	Vinogradov (1953)

(b) *Constituent is less concentrated in dark muscle*

Adenosine diphosphate	*Salmo gairdnerii*	Saito, Arai and Yajima (1959)
Adenosine monophosphate		
Adenosine triphosphate	*Salmo gairdnerii*	
	Scomber japonicus	Nakano (1961)
Amino peptidase	(general)	Ogata and Mori (1963)
Anserine	*Brevoortia tyrannus*	Lukton and Olcott (1958)
	Pneumatophorus diego	
	Sardinops caerulea	
Ash	*Clupea harengus*	Braekkan (1959)
	Gadus virens	
	Hippoglossus hippoglossus	
	Labeo rohita	Alexander (1955)
	Lamna cornubica	Braekkan (1959)
	Lamna nasus	Dyer, Fraser and Tibbo (1963)

TABLE III—*continued*

(b) *Constituent is less concentrated in the dark muscle*

Constituent	Species	Reference
Ash—	*Salmo salar*	Braekkan (1959)
continued	*Scatophagus argus*	Alexander (1955)
	Scomber scombrus	Braekkan (1959)
	Thunnus thynnus	
Carnosine	*Brevoortia tyrannus*	Lukton and Olcott (1958)
	Pneumatophorus diego	
	Sardinops caerulea	
Cholesterol	*Sardinia melanosticta*	Fujikawa and Naganuma (1936)
Creatin	(general)	Kutscher and Ackermann (1933)
Creatinine	*Engraulis japonicus*	Arakaki and Suyama (1966b)
Creatin phosphate	*Scomber japonicus*	Nakano (1961)
Diphosphopy-ridine nucleotide (= nicotinamide adenine dinucleotide)	*Cololabis saira*	Arai and Saito (1963)
	Scomber japonicus	
Esterase	(general)	Ogata and Mori (1963)
β-galactosidase		
β-glucuronidase		
α-glycerophosphate dehydrogenase	*Myxine glutinosa*	Mellgren and Mathisen (1966)
Glycogen	*Lateolabrax japonicus*	Nagayama (1961)
Histidine	*Clupea harengus*	Hughes (1964)
	Engraulis japonicus	Arakaki and Suyama (1966b)
Inosine mono-phosphate	*Salmo gairdnerii*	Saito, Arai and Yajima (1959)
Lactic acid	(general)	Tsuchiya and Kunii (1960)
	Lateolabrax japonicus	Nagayama (1961a)
	Thunnus thynnus	Braekkan (1956)
Lactic dehydro-genase	*Myxine glutinosa*	Mellgren and Mathisen (1966)
Lysine	*Sardinia melanosticta*	Fujikawa and Naganuma (1936)
Niacin	*Hippoglossus hippoglossus*	Braekkan (1956, 1959)
	Salmo salar	
	Scomber scombrus	
	Thunnus thynnus	
Pentose	*Lateolabrax japonicus*	Nagayama (1961a)
Phosphate (inorganic)	*Gadus morhua*	Fraser, Dyer *et al.* (1966)
	Lateolabrax japonicus	Nagayama (1961a)
Potassium	*Hippoglossus hippoglossus*	Thurston and MacMaster (1960)
Protein	*Clupea harengus*	Braekkan (1959)
	Gadus virens	

Table III—*continued*

(b) Constituent is less concentrated in the dark muscle

Constituent	Species	Reference
Protein— continued	*Hippoglossus hippoglossus* *Lamna cornubica* *Lamna nasus* *Salmo salar* *Sardinia melanosticta* *Scomber scombrus* *Thunnus thynnus*	Dyer, Fraser and Tibbo (1963) Braekkan (1959) Fujikawa and Naganuma (1936) Braekkan (1959)
Vitamin A	Elasmobranchs	Higashi (1961)
Water	*Clupea harengus* *Gadus virens* *Hippoglossus hippoglossus* *Labeo rohita* *Lamna cornubica* *Salmo salar* *Scatophagus argus* *Scomber scombrus* *Thunnus thynnus*	Braekkan (1959) Alexander (1955) Braekkan (1959) Alexander (1955) Braekkan (1959)

(c) No consistent difference between dark and ordinary muscle

Adenosine triphosphate	*Gadus morhua* (unexercised)	Fraser, Dyer *et al.* (1966)
Amino acids	*Katsuwonus vagans* *Parathunnus sibi* *Scomber japonicus* *Seriola quinqueradiata*	Matsuura, Konosu *et al.* (1955)
Calcium	(general)	Vinogradov (1953)
Creatin		Sakaguchi, Fujita and Simidu (1964)
Creatinine		
Glycogen	*Gadus morhua* (unexercised)	Fraser, Dyer *et al.* (1966)
Hexose (total)	*Lateolabrax japonicus*	Nagayama (1961)
Lactic acid	*Gadus morhua* (unexercised)	Fraser, Dyer *et al.* (1966)
Lipid composition	*Gadus morhua*	Bligh and Scott (1966) Ackman and Cormier (1967)
Niacin	(general)	Higashi (1961a)
Pyridoxine	*Brosme brosme* *Gadus morhua* *Gadus virens* *Molva molva*	Braekkan and Boge (1965)
Vitamin C	*Cyprinus carpio*	Pora, Wittenberger and Gábos (1964)

Lisovskaya and Petkovitch (*Ryb. Khoz.* **44**, 65–66. 1968) found that silicon and almost all the trace elements were more concentrated in dark muscle, while K, Na, Ca and Mg were about the same in dark and white.

amino acids appeared to be relatively uniform between the white and superficial dark muscle, but small differences were noted between the deep-seated dark muscle and the white muscle, with glycine, leucine and phenylalanine having the greater concentration in the former and aspartic and glutamic acids, histidine and lysine in the latter (Matsuura, Konosu *et al.*, 1955).

These differences, and no doubt there are others, emphasize the need for further information on the true function of dark muscle. It is surprising that after so many years of investigation there is still no general agreement on its nature, and recent discussions by the writer with many workers in the field has revealed a roughly equal distribution of opinions between the two main lines of thought. No comment on dark muscle would be complete without an attempt to clarify the issue.

(c) *The function of dark muscle*

Dark muscle is related in some way to the activity of the fish. Figure 16 shows that there is much less of it in the three gadoid fish, which

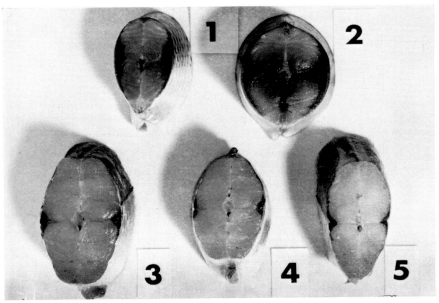

FIG. 16. Sections through the trunk of several species of fish, showing the lateral bands of dark muscle. Fish were of approximately the same length, and the body was cut in the same place, near the tail. (a) Active fish: 1. herring, *Clupea harengus*; 2. mackerel, *Scomber scombrus*. (b) Less active fish: 3. haddock, *Gadus aeglefinus*; 4. cod, *Gadus morhua*; 5. whiting, *Gadus merlangus*.

often rest on the sea bottom, than in the pelagic fish which swim continuously throughout their lives.

Much of the controversy on the function of dark muscle stems from the work of Braekkan (1956) and of Mori, Hashimoto and Komata (1956). After carrying out many analyses of vitamins of the B group, they chanced to notice that the concentrations in dark muscle, which differ from those in white muscle, bear a marked resemblance to those in the liver of the same fish. It was therefore postulated that dark muscle takes over some of the functions of the liver, its close proximity to the white muscle being an obvious advantage for the transfer of metabolites. Braekkan pointed out other similarities and expounded his argument at greater length in a subsequent publication (Braekkan, 1959).

Since the dark muscle has a much higher lipid content than ordinary muscle, he considered that it is not suited to strenuous activity, and also

TABLE IV. PRINCIPAL CONSTITUENTS OF DARK AND ORDINARY
MUSCLE IN COMPARISON WITH THOSE OF LIVER
(after Braekkan, 1959)

Species		Percent wet tissue. Protein $= N \times 6.25$			
		Water	Protein	Lipid	Ash
Clupea harengus	L	78·0	18·1	1·8	1·60
	D	57·8	15·5	28·2	1·30
	O	74·0	22·0	13·0	1·40
Gadus virens	L	41·8	13·3	42·2	1·30
	D	77·8	18·6	2·5	1·13
	O	78·4	19·9	0·5	1·27
Hippoglossus hippoglossus	L	49·6	10·8	38·2	1·15
	D	62·0	11·3	27·3	0·82
	O	77·7	14·5	7·0	1·10
Lamna cornubica	L	14·1	2·8	84·2	0·44
	D	75·6	23·7	1·2	1·58
	O	76·4	23·9	0·7	1·50
Salmo salar	L	75·8	17·2	7·4	1·87
	D	66·3	16·2	15·1	1·66
	O	73·7	22·6	2·0	1·72
Scomber scombrus	L	69·8	19·8	7·7	1·90
	D	54·2	14·9	29·7	1·18
	O	65·5	21·2	13·1	1·24
Thunnus thynnus	L	63·4	17·0	17·5	1·09
	D	66·4	22·9	6·7	1·16
	O	68·5	25·1	4·6	1·34

L = Liver, D = Dark Muscle, O = Ordinary Muscle.

thought that the anatomical location of the dark muscle prevents it from taking part in serious muscular work.

Notwithstanding Lankester's suggestion, as long ago as 1871, that red pigmentation is found in muscles from which the most persistent and prolonged activity is required, the evidence that dark muscle is not so much a contractile substance as a tissue resembling liver is impressive, and the concept has received support from a number of other sources as we shall see.

Table IV shows the main constituents of the dark and white muscle and the liver of seven species of fish. There is no obvious similarity here between liver and dark muscle, but in Table V (the B-vitamins) the analogy is often striking, values for liver and dark muscle occurring close together and differing from those of white muscle. Niacin does not fit into the same scheme, its concentration usually being higher in the white muscle.

TABLE V. VITAMINS IN DARK AND ORDINARY MUSCLE IN COMPARISON
WITH THOSE OF LIVER (after Braekkan, 1959)

Species		Thiamine	Riboflavin	Pantothenic acid	Vitamin B_{12}
		mg% in wet tissue			
Clupea harengus	L	0·16	0·59	2·10	0·034
	D	0·11	1·27	3·00	0·054
	O	0·003	0·11	0·28	0·007
Gadus virens	L	0·30	0·63	0·80	0·025
	D	0·80	0·70	1·39	0·020
	O	0·05	0·09	0·20	0·003
Hippoglossus hippoglossus	L	0·25	0·73	1·08	0·100
	D	0·04	0·25	0·52	0·005
	O	0·04	0·06	0·36	0·001
Lamna cornubica	L	0·09	0·25	0·56	0·004
	D	0·60	0·64	3·30	0·037
	O	0·08	0·10	1·50	0·003
Salmo salar	L	0·40	0·80	1·73	0·045
	D	0·43	0·88	2·80	0·022
	O	0·13	0·09	1·00	0·004
Scomber scombrus	L	—	1·13	3·33	0·052
	D	0·37	1·37	3·00	0·047
	O	0·02	0·14	0·38	0·002
Thunnus thynnus	L	0·37	4·60	2·60	0·310
	D	0·43	0·79	3·28	0·038
	O	0·25	0·15	0·50	0·005

L = Liver, D = Dark Muscle, O = Ordinary Muscle.

Braekkan also drew attention to the higher level of creatin in ordinary muscle (see Table III), indicating a higher physical activity there than in dark muscle, and a lower ultimate pH in ordinary muscle following death with struggling. The pH of muscle tissue falls after death owing to the accumulation of lactic acid, which is the end-product of carbohydrate metabolism in the absence of oxygen. The apparently greater metabolism of carbohydrates in white muscle again indicated greater physical activity, just as the greater enzymatic activity of dark muscle (see under various authors in Table III) indicated a greater metabolic turnover than would have been justified by mere contraction. Tsuchiya and Kunii (1960) confirmed the higher ultimate concentration of lactic acid in white muscle and concluded with Braekkan and the other writers that the function of the dark muscle is probably similar to that of an internal organ.

There is, however, some doubt about the relative concentrations of energy-rich compounds. Although creatin has been reported (Kutscher and Ackermann, 1933; Nakano, 1961) to be more concentrated in ordinary than in dark muscle (creatin phosphate supplies the energy for muscular contraction), Nakano and Tsuchiya (1960) determined a number of high-energy phosphate compounds, all links in the same chain, in the two tissues of ten species of fish, and found too much random variation to be certain either way. Sakaguchi, Fujita and Simidu (1964) also reported no distinctive distribution of creatin, and Fraser, Dyer et al. (1966) found the same with adenosine triphosphate, so the issue should be left open at present, although Hamoir (1955) stated definitely that dark muscle has a higher capacity for the resynthesis of energy-rich phosphate under aerobic conditions than white muscle.

Zama (1963a) analysed the lipids of Thynnus orientalis, and found that the composition of conjugated lipid and the distribution of cholesterol in the deep-seated dark muscle are similar to those in liver, suggesting again a function different from that of ordinary skeletal muscle. However, in contrast to Braekkan, he considered that the mechanical usefulness of the superficial dark muscle is significant. More recently (personal communication, 1967) he has concluded that while the fatty acid composition of dark muscle does resemble that of liver, it is definitely not the same.

Physiological evidence can also be interpreted as supporting the 'liver' concept. Barets (1961) showed that the motor nerve system of the superficial muscle of Tinca tinca and Ameiurus nebulosus resembles that of the smooth muscle of the frog. When dark muscle was immersed in a solution of acetyl choline, it contracted in the manner of slow muscle, not like quick striated muscle. The electrophysiological properties of the dark muscle of *Carassius auratus* also resemble slow muscle from the frog, while white muscle resembles the fast muscle (Nishihara, 1967). Wittenberger (1960) studied the dark muscle of teleost fish, and concluded that it is completely deprived of tetanic features. The very low excitability level, weak contractility and high metabolic rate seem to indicate that the function of this muscle is not of a contractile nature. Wittenberger and Oros (1961) showed that the amplitude of isotonic contraction of dark muscle is about ten times less than that of neighbouring white muscle. They concluded also that there is a negative correlation between the degree of development of dark muscle and the size of the liver : 'generally', the pelagic fish, which have abundant dark muscle, have a liver much reduced in size compared with that of fish living on the sea bed. Wittenberger and Vitca (1966) found that the maximum amount of work (stimuli until exhausted) of white muscle from *Cyprinus carpio* is very low, but that it increases if still joined to the dark muscle. The glycogen content of the white muscle decreases by about 25% during stimulation, but when dark and white muscle are stimulated together there is a fall in the glycogen content of the dark muscle of 7% and an increase of 18% in that of the white muscle. This again suggests that the dark muscle supplies energy compounds to the white muscle—though it might simply mean that the dark muscle is doing all the work.

The opposing view of dark muscle is that it functions like the muscle of the heart, with the ability to work continuously for long periods. This still fits in with the fact that pelagic fish (Fig. 16, p. 26), which never stop swimming, contain a large proportion of dark muscle. Matsuura (private communication, 1967) noted that histological preparations of dark muscle strongly resemble those of heart muscle. Unlike Braekkan (1959), Mellgren and Mathisen (1966) felt that the anatomical location of dark muscle suits it admirably for active work, and unlike Wittenberger (1960), Buttkus (1963) found that in *Ophiodon elongatus* the rigor contraction and isometric tension in dark muscle is about three times greater than that in white muscle, and concluded that the dark muscle is the active component of a fish's muscular equipment, especially designed for rapid acceleration. His electron photomicrographs showed that all the usual structures for muscular contraction are in fact present, the main difference from white being the large numbers of mitochondria—a conclusion endorsed by Nishihara (1967) in the case of *Carassius auratus*.

It has already (p. 29) been stated that some doubt exists about the relative concentrations of energy-rich compounds in dark and white muscle. Hamoir (1955) deduced that dark muscle has a higher capacity for the resynthesis of energy-rich compounds under aerobic conditions, adding that dark muscle is probably capable of enduring more prolonged muscular exertion than white muscle. There seems, however, to be less doubt about the relative concentrations of glycogen, the parent energy-substance that gives rise to the high-energy phosphate compounds. This substance was found to be considerably more concentrated in the dark muscle of *Ophiodon elongatus* (Buttkus, 1963) and *Labeo rohita* (George and Bokdawala, 1964). Fraser, Dyer *et al.* (1966) found that the glycogen contents of dark and white muscle of rested *Gadus morhua* are similar, but that after severe exercise the glycogen level is much higher in the dark muscle—breakdown of glycogen in dark muscle is evidently rather slow. Similar observations were made on *Cyprinus carpio* by Wittenberger and Diaciuc (1965), who found that exhausting effort, which greatly reduces white muscle glycogen, hardly affects that of the dark muscle. However, an enormous rise in lactate concentration in the latter surely shows that in fact much carbohydrate has been metabolized there. Perhaps the dark muscle is able to resynthesize glycogen very rapidly. Kishinouye (1923 : scombroid fishes) pointed out that it receives a copious blood supply compared with white muscle, and Stevens (1968 : *Salmo gairdnerii*) supported this view, calculating that there is 2·6 times as much blood present in dark as in white muscle. Buttkus' observation (1963) that the ultimate pH after death never falls very low could be explained by the efficient removal of lactate up to the moment of death by means of the better vascularity. Because of this difference in blood supply, it is probably unsafe to deduce a greater mechanical activity in white muscle from the lower pH seen after the death-struggle by Amano, Bito and Kawabata (1953).

Lipase activity is greater in dark muscle (George, 1962 ; George and Bokdawala, 1964), and it has been concluded that dark muscle is well adapted for aerobic metabolism, using lipid as its chief fuel,* while white muscle uses mostly glycogen, which it metabolizes anaerobically (George, 1962). The same author concluded that quick, darting movements are possible through the action of white muscle, while dark muscle is used for continuous, slower movement. A similar distribution of function is suggested by Marshall (1965). Mellgren and Mathisen (1966), noting the poor vascularity of the white muscle of *Myxine*, concluded also that its metabolism was mainly anaerobic, while Gordon (1968) found that isolated dark muscle from *Katsuwonus pelamis* and *Thunnus obesus* consumes over six times as much oxygen as the corresponding white muscle.

---

* Bilinski (1963: *Salmo gairdnerii*) found that the ability of dark muscle to oxidize fatty acids was much greater than that of ordinary muscle.

Boddeke, Slijper and van der Stelt (1959) pointed out that the staying-power of a muscle is increased by good vascularization. They did not agree with Braekkan's thesis, and drew attention to the fact that the musculature of the pectoral fins of those species that use them is entirely built up of narrow, red fibres which are identical with those in the superficial dark muscle band. This at least suggests that dark muscle can be used for normal work. Summing up a well-reasoned paper, they concluded that the broad white muscle cells possess the qualities required for the sprinter (that is, fish requiring sudden, powerful bursts of energy) while the narrow dark cells principally

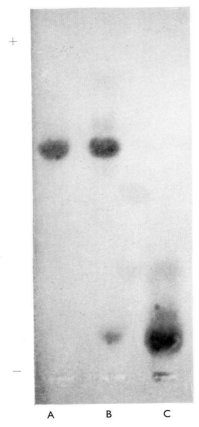

A   B   C

FIG. 17. Starch gel electropherogram of lactic dehydrogenase of *Scomber scombrus*. A. Heart muscle lactic dehydrogenase; B. Dark muscle lactic dehydrogenase; C. White muscle lactic dehydrogenase. All samples were from the same fish. Photograph kindly supplied by Mr. N. P. Wilkins.

show the qualities of the stayer. It is clear from this that most fish hold the larger part of their body musculature in reserve for that frantic dash needed to escape from a predator, or suddenly to seize prey, while 'cruising' is done with their relatively small proportion of dark muscle, using lipid as fuel.

There is a distinct resemblance between the lactic dehydrogenase from dark muscle and that from heart when the electropherograms are compared. Although two faint bands are common to dark and white muscle, large amounts of a fast fraction, absent from white muscle, are found in both dark muscle and heart (Fig. 17). Here again there seems to be a link between the two types of tissue.

Making a balanced assessment of the whole situation is far from easy, since there are contradictions in the findings of like experiments carried out by the protagonists of the rival theories, presumably resulting from seasonal or species differences. The key to the problem seems to be whether dark muscle is mechanically more active or less active than white. In most intact fish, the performance of each kind of muscle cannot be assessed separately, since they are intimately associated, and the behaviour of strips of muscle separated from the parent animal may not be typical. What is needed is a fish containing nothing but dark muscle, so that there would be no doubt about its contribution to the movement through the water.

While visiting an aquarium in Shirahama, Japan, the writer was struck by the unusual mode of swimming shown by the puffer fish, *Fugu* sp., which seemed likely to offer a solution to the problem. This fish (Fig. 18) hardly ever bends its body, but keeps it rigid while swimming. Near the tail, thick upper and lower fins thresh vigorously from side to side in contrary motion, providing all the motive power for sending the body through the water—the nearest thing imaginable to a propeller-driven fish. Here at least there was no doubt as to which muscles were the active ones.

After a specimen had been caught from the sea with rod and line, a dissection was stealthily carried out with a razor blade in a sumptuous hotel room, aided and abetted by Dr. T. Motohiro—and there was the answer: the body muscle, not normally used for swimming, was entirely white, while the muscle at the base of the active fins was dark red (see Fig. 19).

From the literature, the sunfish (*Masturus lanceolatus*) seems to have fin-propulsion even more highly developed (Raven, 1939), but there has been no opportunity to examine a fresh specimen of this species.

Support for the notion of mechanically active dark muscle is found in the work of Bone (1966), who inserted electrodes into the muscle of

FIG. 18. Japanese puffer fish (*Fugu* sp.), which propels itself along by side-to-side movement of the large dorsal and ventral fins, and rarely bends the body. A clue as to the function of dark muscle has been obtained by examining its distribution in this species. From a postage stamp. Original picture kindly supplied by the Central Post Office, Tokyo.

living but acraniate elasmobranchs, and found that only dark muscle fibres generate currents during slow swimming, whereas during vigorous movement the white fibres come into play. In this case it was not possible to determine whether dark muscle was also used during vigorous movement, because the relatively small potentials were swamped by the much larger potentials of the white muscle, but it is clear that these results point in the same direction. Rayner and Keenan (1967) made a similar investigation on tranquillized *Katsuwonus pelamis* which showed that, in a species where both types of dark muscle are present, it is the deep-seated tissue which provides most of the motive power in gentle swimming.

Bone (1966) also supplies the final comment on the dual muscular system in fish, remarking that for these animals it is but a light penalty to carry around a large mass of normally inactive muscle, though it would be impractical for terrestrial vertebrates. The advantage seems

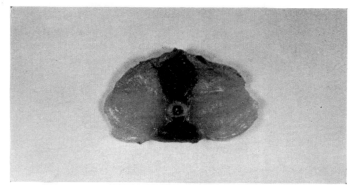

FIG. 19a.

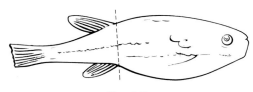

FIG. 19b.

FIG. 19a. Section through the body of 'mafugu', a puffer fish (*Fugu vermicularis porphyreus*) cut just anteriorly to the two propellant fins, showing the dorso-ventral placing of the dark muscle which supplies power to the fins. 19b: Diagram showing where the section was cut. Photograph kindly prepared by Dr. T. Motohiro. A second photograph from the same source was used in the preparation of the diagram (19b).

to be a more efficient use of metabolites, plus a 'coiled spring' (the white muscle) waiting to supply instant energy to the fish in case of emergency.

5. Miscellaneous Studies

So far we have seen that variation in the size or the type of muscle cells, or in the proportion of connective tissue, influences the concentration of some constituents in different parts of the musculature. A number of published reports describe variations in other constituents according to locality, but without relating them to anatomical or physiological features.

(a) Principal constituents: protein, lipid and water

In the round-bodied fish, as distinct from the flat-fish (see Vitamin A and riboflavin, p. 38) no consistent difference has ever been found between constituents in the left and right fillets of the same fish. When a systematic study of the protein of *Gadus morhua* was carried out by six independent laboratories, it was specifically noted that differences between left and right do not occur, but that there is a decline in protein nitrogen from head to tail (Anon., 1966a), a decline which, incidentally, does not occur in *Gadus virens*, a closely related species (R. Pirie, Torry Research Station, unpublished).

The concentrations of lipids vary enormously in different parts of the body. In fatty fish, there is usually a high concentration immediately under the skin, and Olley and Lovern (1960) showed that in this locality of *Gadus morhua*, a non-fatty species, the lipid is richer in cholesterol (relative to phospholipid) than is lipid from other parts of the body. In the surface layers of tunnies and marlins, fast-swimming fish, oily tissues are sandwiched between layers of connective tissue, an arrangement which is thought to damp the turbulence of the water passing over the surface of the body, and so to reduce drag (Marshall, 1965). The belly wall of fatty species, for example *Oncorhynchus kisutch* (Karrick and Thurston, 1964), often shows the highest concentration of lipid, perhaps because it cannot take an active part in swimming anyway and so makes a convenient lipid storehouse. It has also been found to be rich in lipid in *Hippoglossus hippoglossus*, a flat fish, where the concentration in the belly wall, 4·8%, exceeds that in the general musculature which ranges from 3·1% in the thick part to 1·2% towards the tail (Mannan, Fraser and Dyer, 1961). The grotesquely fatty Siscowet trout, *Salvelinus namaycush siscowet*, shows a higher concentration in the ventral part (89%) as distinct from the dorsal part (86·2%), while the belly wall at 74·5% is least fatty of all (Thurston, 1962), but anomalous behaviour is to be expected in such an unusual species anyway. It is conceivable that the low specific gravity resulting from so much lipid along the lower side might cause the fish to float upside-down, but, in some species at least, it is partly counterbalanced by a high concentration along the upper surface of the fish. The now classical analysis of lipids in different parts of *Clupea harengus* carried out by Brandes and Dietrich (1953a), Fig. 20, shows the highest concentration, apart from in the belly wall, to be just forward of the dorsal fin. Like the belly wall, tissue lying along the upper (dorsal) apex of the fish would not be well placed for muscular activity.

The preferential accumulation of lipid in the dorsal and ventral positions may not be universal for 'round' fish. Kanemitsu and Aoe (1958) reported that there is no consistent distribution pattern of lipid between upper, lower and tail muscle in the five species of Pacific salmon (*Oncorhynchus* spp.).

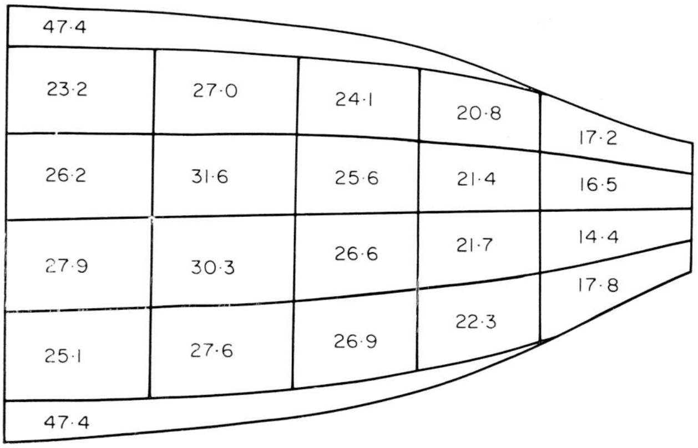

FIG. 20. Percentage of lipid in different parts of the musculature of *Clupea harengus*. After Brandes and Dietrich (1953a), reproduced by courtesy of Dr. C. H. Brandes.

Since there is an approximate inverse relationship between the lipid and water contents of fatty fish muscle tissue (see p. 226), the distributional characteristics of lipid are reflected in those of water among the fatty species, as, for example, in Fig. 21 (*Clupea harengus*), where the second most anterior region has the highest lipid and least water, and the situation is reversed in the tail region.

However, in non-fatty genera such as the Gadidae, where muscle lipid concentration is only about 0·5%, the water content is instead related inversely to the protein (see p. 229) and so presumably shows a different distribution.

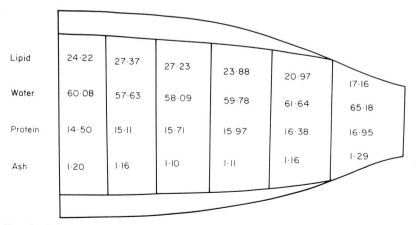

FIG. 21. Distribution of lipid, water, protein and ash in six regions of *Clupea harengus* musculature. In contrast to Fig. 20, there are no longitudinal sub-divisions. After Brandes and Dietrich (1953a), reproduced by courtesy of Dr. C. H. Brandes.

(b) *Minor constituents*

There are a few isolated observations on the distribution of single substances within fish tissues. Thus, *lecithin* in *Sardinia melanosticta* is most concentrated in the dark muscle, less in the belly and least of all in the dorsal flesh (Matsumoto, 1950). *Astaxanthin* (Kanemitsu and Aoe, 1958: *Oncorhynchus* sp.) and *trimethylamine oxide* (Koizumi, Kawakami and Nonaka, 1967: *Thunnus albacares*) in the muscle have both been found to increase in concentration towards the tail end, and the same progression has been found concerning the ribose nucleic acid (Edström, 1964) of the nervous system, which was more concentrated at the tail end of the Mauthner axon of *Carassius auratus* than at the brain end. In flat fish, it has been found that *riboflavin* is more concentrated in the upper flesh than the lower (Higashi, 1961).

The physiological significance of these observations is unknown, but the discovery that skin from different parts of the body of *Prionace glauca* contains different proportions of elastin (Takahashi and Yokoyama, 1954a) could perhaps be related to the differing extensibility required of the skin according to the mode of swimming.

Several workers have studied the distribution of vitamin A, although it seems to be subject to unpredictable variations, and the exact locality in the flesh where it is richest varies from fish to fish of the same species (Hirao, Yamada and Kikuchi, 1954a: *Oncorhynchus* sp.). The vitamin A content of the liver, between species, varies markedly depending on whether the liver lies on the right or the left side of the body (Higashi, 1961). Within the liver, which in *Squalus suckleyi* is shaped like a horse-shoe, the vitamin A is least concentrated at the two tips, and increases in concentration towards the place where the organ joins the body (Yamamura, 1949a; Yamamura and Kondo, 1949). In the same species it is more concentrated in the inner layers of the liver than nearer the surface (Yamamura, 1949b). Similarly, in *Oncorhynchus* sp. the vitamin A is more concentrated in the deeper layers of the muscle than in the muscle near the skin (Hirao, Yamada and Kikuchi, 1954a). There is often a decrease in concentration from the head to the tail end of the musculature of *Thunnus obesus* (Hirao, Yamada and Kikuchi, 1954a) and *Entosphenus japonicus* (Higashi, Hirao *et al.*, 1957, 1958). The latter species (Japanese lamprey) is interesting in that the concentration of vitamin A in the muscle is for some reason far greater than in any other species of fish.

In the case of a number of Japanese flat fish, there is always more vitamin A in the flesh from the upper ('eyed') side than in the 'blind' side (Hirao, Yamada and Kikuchi, 1954b). This phenomenon seems to be governed by a difference in the skin: in *Paralichthys olivaceus*, the difference in vitamin A between sides is great near the surface, but there is only a small difference in the inner layers (Hirao, Yamada and Kikuchi, 1954b). Also, the skin itself from the upper surface contains more than twice as much as the lower skin (Hirao, Yamada and Kikuchi, 1955c).

Some of the observations on locational differences in vitamin A may be explained by differences in oil content: a high level of oil usually results in a low concentration of vitamin A, and vice versa. However, in *Paralichthys olivaceus*, although the quantity of oil varies there is always more vitamin A in the oil on the uppermost side (Hirao, Yamada and Kikuchi, 1955c).

B. The Effects of Stress

We have seen that fish tissues are heterogeneous, so that meaningful chemical results can be obtained only if a special sampling technique is followed.

Apart from blood, which can be taken from the living fish, most other tissues are taken for analysis after death. Samples most likely to yield results of physiological significance are therefore those taken from the fish immediately after capture, which are nearest to those obtaining during life. Or are they? Capture by net or hook involves various degrees of desperate struggle, followed by a period of asphyxiation after the fish has been landed. In this section we shall examine the effects of stress on fish chemistry, and then go on to consider what steps can be taken to reduce them.

What are the 'true' chemical values in any case? Are they the concentrations characteristic of gentle swimming without undue stress? The further one looks into the question, the more difficult it is to be certain, since the activity of some fish varies at different times of the day, and is enhanced during spawning migration. As usual we end with a compromise which, it is hoped, will enable us to arrive at values most nearly related to the biology of the fish.

1. *Exercise and Anoxia*

As an introduction, some experimental values are quoted in Table VI, to show the range of substances investigated and the extent of change possible under stress produced by forced swimming. The big disparity between authors can sometimes be explained by differences in the amount of stress caused. Forced exercise in some sort of apparatus for 15 minutes is a common technique (Black, 1955; Miller, Sinclair and

TABLE VI. THE EFFECT OF EXERCISE (FORCED SWIMMING) ON THE CONCENTRATIONS OF SOME CONSTITUENTS (mg%)

Substance	Species	Before exercise	After exercise	Reference
Blood				
Adrenaline	*Salmo gairdnerii*	0·0005	0·132	Nakano and Tomlinson (1967)
Cortisol	*Oncorhynchus nerka*	0·005	Great increase	Fagerlund (1967)
Lactic acid	*Cyprinus carpio*	0·007–0·012	0·012–0·036	Leloup-Hatey (1960)
	Ameiurus melas melas	6–11	26–49	Black (1955)
	Catostomus catostomus	13–22	51–60	
	Cyprinus carpio	8–11	50–82	
	Micropterus salmoides	11–23	57–89	
	Oncorhynchus nerka	19·5	103	Black (1957)
	Ptychocheilus oregonensis	19	94	Black (1955)
	Salmo gairdnerii	5·1	69·7	Black, Manning and Hayashi (1966)
		10·8	45·3	Miller, Sinclair and Hochachka (1959)
			551% increase	Nakatani (1957)
			1000% increase	Stevens and Black (1966)
	Salmo gairdnerii kamloops	7–18	72–106	Black (1955)
	Tinca tinca	15·7	53·2	Secondat and Diaz (1942)
Noradrenaline	*Salmo gairdnerii*	0·0003	0·0025	Nakano and Tomlinson (1967)
Phosphate (inorganic)			58% increase	Nakatani (1957)
Pyruvic acid		0·45	0·69	Black, Manning and Hayashi (1966)

In addition, an increase in lactic dehydrogenase activity has been reported in elasmobranchs by Rasmussen and Rasmussen (1967)

Substance	Species	Before exercise	After exercise	Reference
Dark muscle				
Glycogen	*Cyprinus carpio*	1700	1570	Wittenberger and Diaciuc (1965)
Lactic acid		111	246	
Pyruvic acid		0·29	0·38	
Kidney (anterior)				
Adrenaline	*Salmo gairdnerii*	0·372	0·469	Nakano and Tomlinson (1967)
Noradrenaline		0·410	0·555	
Liver				
Glycogen	*Cyprinus carpio*	13800	14600	Wittenberger and Diaciuc (1965)
	Ictalurus melas	2210	1390	Dean and Goodnight (1964)

Compound	Species			Reference
Lepomis macrochirus as				
	Micropterus salmoides	3060	1870	Black, Bosomworth and Docherty (1966)
	Pomoxis annularis	830	1090	
	Salmo gairdnerii	3661	3506	
		3910	4780*	Miller, Sinclair and Hochachka (1959)
		3910	2810†	
		no change		Stevens and Black (1966)
Lactic acid	*Cyprinus carpio*	32·6	31·7	
Pyruvic acid		0·21	0·25	Wittenberger and Diaciuc (1965)
Muscle				
Adenosine diphosphate	*Gadus morhua*	24·5	18·1	Jones and Murray (1957, 1960)
Adenosine monophosphate		23·9	19·8	
Adenosine triphosphate		272	13·3	
Adenosine triphosphate P	*Salmo gairdnerii*	36·7	14·2	Tomlinson, Geiger and Kay (1965)
Creatin phosphate P		29·3	6·5	
Dihydroxyacetone phosphate	*Gadus morhua*	0·3–2·9	1·2–3·2	Burt and Stroud (1966)
Diphosphopyridine nucleotide (=nicotinamide adenine dinucleotide)		7·2	22·4	Jones and Murray (1960)
Fructose-1,6-diphosphate		85·0	28·9	Burt (1961); Burt and Jones (1961)
Fructose-1-phosphate		5·2 }	2·1	
Fructose-6-phosphate			2·1	
Glucose		37·8–39·6	8–33	Jones (1958c); Burt (1961)
Glucose-1-phosphate		24·4	5·7	Burt (1961); Burt and Jones (1961)
Glucose-6-phosphate		16·9	22·9	
L-α-glycerophosphate		4·6–12·5	8·6–12·7	Burt and Stroud (1966)
Glycogen	*Cyprinus carpio*	230	200	Wittenberger and Diaciuc (1965)
	Ictalurus melas	128	72	Dean and Goodnight (1964)
	Lepomis macrochirus	104	79	
	Micropterus salmoides	97	56	
	Pomoxis annularis	38	16	
	Salmo gairdnerii	167	21	Black, Bosomworth and Docherty (1966)
		80% decrease		Stevens and Black (1966)

TABLE VI—*continued*

Substance	Species	Before exercise	After exercise	Reference
Guanosine triphosphate	*Gadus morhua*	0·131	0	Jones and Murray (1960)
Inosine monophosphate		43·9	204	Jones and Murray (1957, 1960)
Lactic acid	*Cyprinus carpio*	158	295	Wittenberger and Diacinc (1965)
	Gadus morhua	6–48	84–150	Burt and Stroud (1966)
	Platichthys stellatus	49	226	Tomlinson, Arnold *et al.* (1961)
	Salmo gairdnerii	126	434	Black, Bosomworth and Docherty (1966)
			124% increase	Nakatani (1957)
			350% increase	Stevens and Black (1966)
		238	484	Tomlinson, Arnold *et al.* (1961)
		59	460	Tomlinson, Geiger and Kay (1965)
Magnesium		26	32	
Phosphate (inorganic)			22% increase	Nakatani (1957)
3-phosphoglyceric acid	*Gadus morhua*	1·6–4·3	0·4–3·7	Burt and Stroud (1966)
Potassium	*Salmo gairdnerii*	516	555	Tomlinson, Geiger and Kay (1965)
Pyruvic acid	*Cyprinus carpio*	1	0·55	Wittenberger and Diacinc (1965)
Ribose	*Gadus morhua*	0	0	Jones (1958c); Burt (1961)
Ribose-1-phosphate		0	0	Burt (1961); Burt and Jones (1961)
Ribose-5-phosphate		—	0	Burt and Jones (1961)
Sodium	*Salmo gairdnerii*	38	28	Tomlinson, Geiger and Kay (1965)
Triphosphopyridine nucleotide (=nicotinamide adenine dinucleotide phosphate)	*Gadus morhua*	0·05	0·036	Jones and Murray (1960)
Uridine triphosphate		0·174	0	

* Exercise for 15 minutes: † exercise for 24 hours.

Hochachka, 1959; Black, Manning and Hayashi, 1966), but values are also quoted after exercise for 2 minutes (Black, Bosomworth and Docherty, 1966) and 30 minutes (Leloup-Hatey, 1960), while several authors exercise the fish to the point of exhaustion (Jones and Murray, 1960; Tomlinson, Arnold et al., 1961; Wittenberger and Diaciuc, 1965; Tomlinson, Geiger and Kay, 1965). The effects of stress from other causes, for example asphyxia, will be described later.

The table shows that the stimulant hormone, adrenalin, increases in the blood during activity, and that energy-rich compounds such as adenosine triphosphate and creatin phosphate are broken down and decrease markedly, as does the 'parent' carbohydrate, glycogen, break-down of which results in the synthesis of more high-energy phosphates. However, there is a difference here between liver and muscle. Muscle shows a considerable decrease in glycogen and increase in lactic acid, the final anaerobic product of carbohydrate metabolism, while the liver, which is the chief storehouse of glycogen, is but little depleted by this period of exercise—indeed, the glycogen appears to increase in some cases, no doubt through fish-to-fish variation. Glycogen is evidently rapidly utilized at the site of energy requirement, and can be replaced there only by a relatively slow mobilization in the liver. A significant reduction in liver glycogen *is* brought about if the fish are made to swim for 24 hours instead of 15 minutes (Miller, Sinclair and Hochkachka, 1959: *Salmo gairdnerii*). The increase in blood phosphate with exercise probably reflects the temporary breakdown of creatin phosphate and adenosine triphosphate.

The relatively small change in the glycogen and lactic acid of dark muscle, as compared with ordinary muscle, is probably because the energy for dark muscle contraction is derived mostly from lipid, not carbohydrate (see under dark muscle, p. 31).

The single observation on muscle sodium and potassium deserves comment, because of the decrease in the former and increase in the latter with exercise. This is the opposite to previous experience with mammalian or amphibian muscle, where it has been found that exercise causes potassium to leave the muscle and sodium to accumulate in it, the change being reversed during subsequent rest (Fenn and Cobb, 1936; Fenn, 1939; Sréter and Friedman, 1958; Schleusing and Nöcker, 1960; Bachelard, Campbell and McIlwain, 1962; Voronova, 1962; Sréter, 1963; Hodgkin and Horowicz, 1959). No mechanism for the shift has been postulated as far as the writer is aware, but since sodium appears to be kept out of the muscle by a mechanism that requires energy (the "sodium pump") it is not unreasonable to suppose that exercise allows sodium to enter by using for a while all the available 'pump' energy. Whatever the mechanism, it is clear that further work is needed to establish whether these atypical results are true of fish in general, and if so why they should differ from other animals.

The dynamics of the change of blood constituents during stress are of interest but not brought out in the table. Figure 22 shows that blood lactic acid, which increases in *Gadus aeglefinus* above the resting level by the stress of capture in an otter trawl, continues to increase afterwards as the fish rest in a tank, before eventually returning to the resting level. Lactic acid is probably not produced from carbohydrate precursors in the blood itself, but released into it from the tissues. There is therefore a delay before the tissues have shed their lactic acid and we can see it, as it were, in transit.

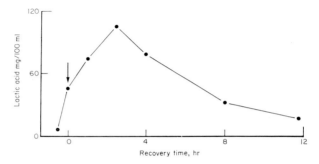

FIG. 22. Concentration of lactic acid in the blood of *Gadus aeglefinus* following capture by otter trawl in the month of July. Arrow shows value immediately after capture. The resting level (lowest point on the graph) was determined on fish maintained in the laboratory. After Beamish (1966), reproduced by courtesy of the author and the Fisheries Research Board of Canada.

If a fish is taken out of water, the delay in the rise of lactic acid in the blood may be more pronounced. Leivestad, Andersen and Scholander (1957) showed that when *Gadus morhua* are left to struggle in air for 4 minutes, there is an almost immediate reduction in the heart rate, analogous to that shown by diving mammals and birds when submerged in water. Due to the violent threshing about, there is a sharp increase in muscle lactic acid, but since the circulation through the muscles has been strongly depressed, little of it enters the blood. The phenomenon appears to be a protection against damage by asphyxia, during which the muscles are left to rely largely on anaerobic resources; as we shall see, a high level of blood lactic acid can kill the fish.

When the fish are replaced in the water, normal heart rate is restored, circulation increases and lactic acid pours into the blood. With the restoration of the oxygen supply, however, it is soon oxidized to carbon dioxide and eliminated through the gills. The changes in lactic acid in muscle and blood under these circumstances are shown in Fig. 23, the space between the arrows indicating the period out of water. The behaviour in the muscle during this period contrasts strongly with that in the blood.

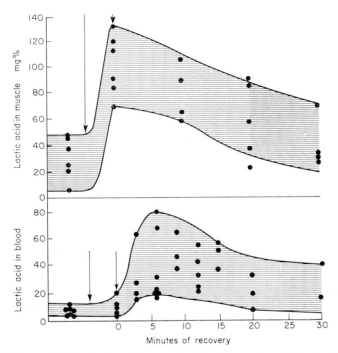

FIG. 23. Changes in the lactic acid concentration of muscle and blood when *Gadus morhua* were taken out of the water for 4 minutes and then replaced and allowed to recover. Time out of water is denoted by the space between the arrows. After Leivestad, Andersen and Scholander (1957), reproduced by courtesy of Dr. P. F. Scholander and the American Association for the Advancement of Science.

During asphyxia there is also a rise in blood sugar (Menten, 1927; Gray and Hall, 1930; Al-Gauhari, 1958) probably mobilized from liver glycogen in readiness for use by the muscles after the restoration of the circulation. In the seven species of fish examined by Menten (1927), the rise in blood sugar began less than 15 minutes after the onset of asphyxial conditions, and its degree depended on the initial level in the blood, which again was largely determined by the amount of food recently ingested.

Exercise unconnected with asphyxial conditions can also cause a rise in blood glucose (Kiermeir, 1939; Dean, 1962; Falkmer and Winbladh, 1964; Nakano and Tomlinson, 1967; Black and Tredwell, 1967). This does not occur in every case (Dean, 1962). It was suggested by Kiermeir (1939) that if the exercise is suited to the normal mode of living of the fish, there will be no marked change in the blood sugar concentration, but if it is too strenuous or lasts too long, the blood sugar can rise to high values, the increase being mainly in the glucose fraction. Falkmer and Winbladh (1964) measured the blood glucose of the hagfish, *Myxine glutinosa*, the day the fish were caught, and found that it was less on the following day and less still 10 days later. Since the fish had not been fed, this could have been the result of starvation, but the authors pointed out that it might also represent a fading of the stress response produced during capture.

The effect of stress on the rise of these several blood constituents (glucose, lactic acid and perhaps some inorganic substances) has been reported also as a gross effect. McFarland and Munz (1958) showed that while the whole blood of *Polistotrema stoutii* is isotonic with sea-water, it can become hypertonic if the animals are disturbed. Capture stress, it was postulated, could therefore account for hypertonic values previously reported in the literature.

This could be true only if struggling were involved during capture. It should be noted, though, that there is a further effect specifically attributed to asphyxia rather than muscular effort. In this, the blood volume decreases by loss of water into the other tissues, and at the same time the spleen contracts, releasing iron (presumably as respiratory pigment) into the blood (Hall, Gray and Lepkovsky, 1926; Hall, 1928; Dawson, 1933). The potential combining power for oxygen is thus increased under conditions of oxygen lack, and the loss of water from the blood will cause increases in the concentrations of most of the other constituents, as shown in Fig. 24.

This effect is not enough to account for all of the increase in glucose concentration (Hall, Gray and Lepkovsky, 1926), the remainder being caused by muscular effort as described before. Recently it has been reported (Stevens, 1968: *Salmo gairdnerii*) that exercise without asphyxia also causes the blood to lose water to other tissues and become concentrated, but in this case it was considered that no extra blood cells were added to the circulatory system.

There is a considerable body of evidence that very severe stress, such as that caused during capture by trawling, can cause the death of the fish. Von Buddenbrock (1938), working with *Gadus morhua* and *Platessa limanda* believed that the cause of death was a flooding of the

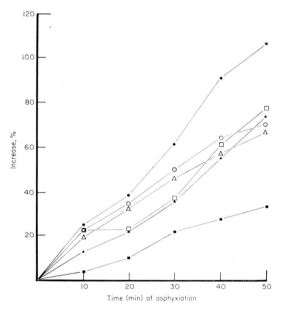

Fig. 24. Effect of asphyxia on the concentrations of various constituents in the blood of *Brevoortia tyrannus*. Results are average values from 100 fish placed in water in sealed jars in which the oxygen gradually became used up. ● Iron; □ Red blood cells; ▲ Haemoglobin; ○ Dry matter; △ Phosphorus; ■ Nitrogen. After Hall (1928), reproduced by courtesy of the American Society of Biological Chemists.

tissues with lactic acid, and Black (1958) pointed out that under these conditions both the oxygen- and carbon dioxide-carrying capacity of the blood would be seriously affected. The lactate ion, if injected as sodium lactate, is not in itself lethal. Fatalities in *Salmo gairdnerii* occur only if the pH is reduced by the lactic acid to the region of 6·8 to 6·9 (Jonas, Sehdev and Tomlinson, 1962). Secondat and Diaz (1942) observed frequent mortality in *Cyprinus carpio* and *Tinca tinca* (both freshwater fish) after severe exercise. Black (1957) reviewed several other papers on the same subject, and reported that *Oncorhynchus nerka* can also die in this way; however, he suggested that the cause of death might be osmotic, resulting from a loss of scales. Later (Black and Tredwell, 1967), it was shown, using *Salmo gairdnerii*, that the loss of scales and mucus does *not* contribute to the death of the animal here. Where trawling does not actually lead to death in salmon, it often gives rise later to a distressed condition, but neither distress nor death can be predicted by examining the fish at the time of capture (Parker, Black and Larkin, 1959). The latter authors showed that a mortality of 34 to

52% occurs in *Oncorhynchus kisutch* after trawling, and that the time of maximum death rate coincides with the period of maximum blood lactic acid. The fish survive if the level in the blood does not exceed 125 mg%, or if it reaches that value and then subsides. For some reason the same species of adult salmon in fresh water do not appear capable of lethal hyperactivity, and it was suggested that the cessation of feeding during spawning migration might therefore have survival value, by cutting down carbohydrate reserves and so cutting down possible high lactic acid levels. The delay in rise of blood lactic acid when cod are taken out of water (Fig. 23) can also be seen as a protective mechanism.

Is it possible to reduce the mortality of stress by training the fish as one trains an athlete? Hammond and Hickman (1966) habituated *salmo gairdnerii* to exercise and found that it is. Physically conditioned fish show a higher lactate concentration in muscle and plasma when fatigued, but it is more rapidly removed than in unconditioned fish, presumably by improved circulation. Plasma glucose shows no significant change during exercise, but rises slightly during the recovery of both groups. Training does not modify the increase in plasma and muscle phosphate that occurs with exercise: presumably a given energy output requires the breakdown of the same amounts of high-energy phosphate compounds regardless of physical condition. Pyle, Poston and Livingston (1967) found no significant differences between the protein, water, ash and lipid contents of *Salvelinus fontinalis* habituated to exercise for 20 weeks in a hatchery and the same constituents in unhabituated controls.

Great activity in tunnies (*Thunnus* sp.) and some species of perch (*Perca* sp.) generates heat faster than it can be conducted away, and the body temperature rises appreciably (Zharov, 1965). The effect of this would be to speed up enzymatic processes making further energy available, so it is probably useful to the fish.

A curious and unexplained effect of stress was described by Jakoubek and Edström (1965), who spun *Carassius auratus* round in an apparatus at about 60 revolutions per minute. On analysis they found a decrease in the ribose nucleic acid (RNA) content of a nerve, the 'Mauthner axon'. The RNA content diminished for at least 90 minutes, but returned to its initial value after 180 minutes. No significant changes were recorded for the myelin sheath.

2. *Resting the Fish before Sampling*

It is clear from the foregoing that the stress which fish undergo at the time of capture markedly changes the concentration of many constituents. We shall now consider the effects of trying to avoid such stress, and the procedures which might perhaps be helpful.

(a) Resting newly-caught fish in an aquarium

Newly-caught, exhausted fish cannot be used for meaningful determinations of muscle carbohydrates or of any intermediates in the carbohydrate cycle such as sugar phosphates. For such work it has been customary in one laboratory to rest the fish (Gadus morhua) in aquaria on a diet of squid for 4 weeks (Burt and Stroud, 1966) or 8 weeks (Jones and Murray, 1960). During this time, some of the reserves of liver carbohydrate replaced all or most of those of the muscle and brought them back to a satisfactorily stable level. Fish for analysis were subsequently lifted out of the aquarium and immobilized by a blow on the head, after which a sample of muscle could be rapidly dissected out and stabilized in liquid air.

However, the use of an aquarium brings a number of problems in its train.

First of all, the activity of the fish is almost certain to be different from that of a fish in the wild state. The relatively close confinement of the fish causes stress in the establishment of 'territories', in which one fish reserves a part of the tank for itself and vigorously repels intruders. This behaviour is especially noticeable at the spawning season (Brawn, 1961b). Other aggressive behaviour is also shown, which leads to a fairly stable social caste system, or 'peck order', among fish, similar to that seen in domestic animals (and of course man also) when they are kept together. Small fish repeatedly chased by the others eventually refuse food and die (Brawn, 1961a), though, incidentally, they are not enabled to thrive by removing them from the company of the dominant fish and placing them in a tank by themselves (Phillips, Podoliak et al., 1961: Salvelinus fontinalis). One would therefore expect a difference in carbohydrate patterns between the dominated and dominating fish. Something of the kind has in fact been demonstrated by Hochachka and Sinclair (1962) who found that the glycogen in the muscle of a group of captive fish falls if a second group (Salmo trutta) is introduced, presumably because of extra 'shunning' activity.

The accumulation of small quantities of waste products in an aquarium leads to changes in the fish. Burrows (1964) found that as little as $0\cdot7$ parts per million of ammonia in the aquarium water causes the lamellae of the gills of Oncorhynchus tschawytscha to fuse together after 6 weeks, and it is to be expected that this would cause the changes associated with asphyxia to occur (p. 45).

Keeping Tilapia mossambica, a freshwater fish, for even a short time

in an aquarium has been found to affect seriously the secretion of acid
in the stomach because of a shortage of salt; this species depends on
ingested salt from suitable food to maintain its digestive secretion
(Fish, 1960), so the particular trouble appears to be dietary. Changes in
the diet can also profoundly affect the pigmentation of fish kept in
aquaria. Specimens of *Serranus scriba* have been found to lose a quarter
of their fin and tail xanthophylls after only two days in captivity
(Bellamy, 1966). *Salmo trutta* lose most of their red and yellow pigments
(astaxanthene and lutein) if fed synthetic diets, and the situation is
remedied only by feeding 'natural' foods—supplements of pure
carotenoid added to the basal diet did not restore the colour of the
depigmented fish (Steven, 1948). However, Sumner and Fox (1935a)
found that the depigmentation of *Girella nigricans*, caused by loss of
xanthophylls, cannot be halted or reversed either by adding pure
carotenoid to the diet or by feeding xanthophyll-rich algae, though the
fading is retarded by placing the fish on a yellow background. Vellas
(1965) claimed that it was bad nutritional status that reduced the
enzymatic activity of mirror carp (*Cyprinus carpio*) kept in an aquarium:
after six months in captivity the activities of uricase, allantoicase and
allantoinase in the liver were lower than those of carp newly removed
from an outside pond.

The stomachs of fish feeding in the natural state are presumed to be
full nearly all the time, so that a stream of nutrients diffuses into the
blood. It is therefore as well to remember that in aquarium-kept fish,
fed at the customary fixed intervals, the nutrients in the blood rise and
fall according to the feeding period. An example of the manner in which
this can occur is shown in Fig. 25, where blood glucose suddenly shows
a three-fold increase at an appropriate time after the last meal.

Where artificial feeding is very frequent, a natural rhythm supervenes
in the blood glucose, which shows a minimum in the late morning just
before the period of greatest food intake (Bellamy, 1968: *Rooseveltiella*

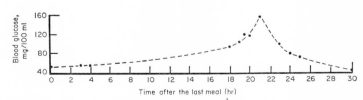

Fig. 25. Level of glucose in the blood of *Clarias lazera* at different times after feeding a
mixture of bread and earthworms. After Al-Gauhari (1958), reproduced by courtesy of
Springer-Verlag.

nattereri), so it is unlikely that a constant level of glucose can ever be guaranteed under artificial conditions. However, Dean and Goodnight (1964) have observed that no large fluctuations in glucose or lactic acid occur in the blood of four other fish species at different times of the day.

While a moderate change of diet can bring about detectable modifications in the chemistry of the fish, an unfortunate characteristic of newly-caught fish placed into an aquarium after capture is that they may refuse food altogether for a while. If *Gadus morhua* starve, a redistribution of the protein fractions takes place, so that some which had previously dissolved in 5% sodium chloride now cease to do so, perhaps as a prelude to mobilization (Love and Robertson, 1967). The insolubility rises to a maximum (Fig. 92) 2–4 weeks after the beginning of starvation. When fish which were intentionally starved in an aquarium were compared with 'fed' controls, it was found that *both* groups exhibited the protein change, because the 'fed' fish had not in fact consumed the proffered food for 10–14 days, a period long enough to trigger off the protein shift, to be described in greater detail later (p. 235). Thus the proteins of cod, and perhaps other fish as well, alter when the fish are placed to 'rest' in an aquarium.

The fact that carp kept in an aquarium differed from those kept in a pond (see above) immediately raises the subject of fish kept in ponds, and of artificial rearing generally. How do fish reared from birth by man compare with 'wild' ones? Diet would immediately be suspect as a factor causing differences, as would water temperature. There is also a considerable weight of direct evidence.

(b) Using hatchery-reared fish

Rested fish from the comparatively shallow depths of a hatchery can readily be whisked out of the water with a net and stunned for the purpose of determining resting levels of constituents. Unfortunately, though, there are many chemical differences between such fish and those living in the wild state.

The importance of diet is immediately made clear by Martin's study (1966) of wild *Salvelinus namaycush*, which may feed on plankton or fish according to the state of the food supply in the summer months. He found that plankton feeders grow slowly, do not reach as great a size or age as fish-feeders and mature at a smaller size and lower age. Where plankton-feeding trout are transferred to a natural fish-feeding environment, they increase their growth rate and span of life.

As with fish held in an aquarium, dietary insufficiency causes a shortage of astaxanthin in the skins of fish cultivated in ponds (Katayama, Ikeda and Harada, 1965: *Chrysophrys major*).

Disillusion at the effects of feeding rich and expensive hatchery food to *Salvelinus fontinalis* was expressed by Phillips, Lovelace *et al.* (1956), who hopefully remarked "previous experiments have shown that hatchery foods are nutritionally superior (in the chemical constituents analysed) to the natural food of brook trout. In general, superior foods produce a superior product and therefore, a chemical comparison of hatchery and wild trout should provide a measure of the production efficiency of the two types of food." These authors then went on to assess their findings, which showed, alas, that in the body of wild trout, the natural food with only half the protein of hatchery food produces a higher level of body protein, and a greater level of body ash although it contains only one-fifth of the ash of the artificial food, and with twice the water content it gives rise to a significantly *lower* level of body water in the fish! The lipid content of the hatchery fish is higher than that to be expected by the difference in lipid contents of the two types of food. The findings are summed up in Table VII. The differences shown in the table are statistically significant, and the fish from both groups are of roughly the same sizes.

TABLE VII. BODY COMPOSITION OF SALVELINUS FONTINALIS FROM A
HATCHERY AND FROM A NATURAL ENVIRONMENT
(after Phillips, Lovelace *et al.*, 1956)

Substance	Percent wet tissue	
	Wild (21 fish analysed)	*Hatchery* (27 fish analysed)
Water	71·5	77·2
Protein	21·2	13·7
Ash	3·3	2·0
Lipid	3·4	5·5

The lipid of the fish on a hatchery diet is more saturated than that of wild fish, and therefore, by analogy with Hoar and Cottle's results (1952a) on *Carassius auratus* it is likely that the hatchery fish would be less resistant to temperature changes.

As discussed earlier (p. 49), any differences in the amount of exercise performed by groups of fish can alter their chemical composition, although Phillips, Lovelace *et al.* (1956) showed that there are no outstanding differences in certain constituents in trout from still lakes, as compared with those from flowing streams. Later (Phillips, Podoliak *et al.*, 1958) it was shown that forced exercise of hatchery trout for

4 hours per day does not alter the chemical composition either. However, rearing in a hatchery, like placing in an aquarium, confines the fish in smaller parcels of 'territory' than they would occupy in the wild state, and one result is that they become very aggressive. They tend to dominate wild fish if both groups are transferred together to an aquarium. Fenderson, Everhart and Muth (1968), who observed this effect in the parr of *Salmo salar*, suggested that this high level of aggressiveness might contribute to the mortality of hatchery-reared salmon planted in streams because of loss of feeding time, excessive use of energy, and increased exposure to predators.

Differences in composition have been found by Wood, Yasutake *et al.* (1957) between ten salmonid species reared in the two environments, and their average results, this time expressed on a dry-weight basis, are quoted in Table VIII. It was concluded that the differences are caused mainly by diet.

TABLE VIII. BODY COMPOSITION (AVERAGE) FROM TEN SALMONID SPECIES FROM NATURAL AND ARTIFICIAL ENVIRONMENTS
(after Wood, Yasutake *et al.*, 1957)

Substance	Percent Dry Matter	
	Wild (*42 fish*)	*Hatchery* (*87 fish*)
Protein	75·8	68·1
Ash	12·3	9·7
Lipid	13·4	22·5

Taking the three principal constituents in turn for more detailed examination, it appears that although there is more protein in the wild fish than in those kept in a hatchery, the nature of the protein itself is not appreciably different (Table IX).

The consequences of the lower ash contents, as shown in Tables VII and VIII, had already been observed by Mottram (1936, quoted by McCay and Tunison, 1937), who found that the skeletons of wild trout show a much denser X-ray picture than those of cultivated fish.

The increased lipid shown in the two tables seems to manifest itself mainly as an abnormal fatty degeneration of the liver (Hewitt, 1937; Wood, Yasutake *et al.*, 1957; Ono, Nagayama and Masuda, 1960; Ghittino and Leon, 1963; Weiser and Otte, 1964; Fowler and Wood, 1966) although Phillips, Podoliak *et al.* (1958) reported an increase also

TABLE IX. AMINO ACID COMPOSITION OF TOTAL PROTEINS OF SALVELINUS
FONTINALIS FROM A NATURAL ENVIRONMENT AND FROM TWO SEPARATE
HATCHERIES (after Block, 1959)

Amino acid	Percent		
	Wild	Hatchery 1	Hatchery 2
Alanine	8·6	7·8	8·6
Arginine	4·7	4·5	4·6
Aspartic acid	8·5	9·1	8·6
Cystine	1·9	1·7	1·7
Glutamic acid	10·9	10·9	10·7
Glycine	9·4	8·2	9·2
Hydroxyproline	1·4	1·4	1·6
Leucine ⎱ Isoleucine ⎰	13·4	13·3	13·0
Lysine	6·7	6·6	6·8
Methionine	2·0	2·0	2·3
Phenylalanine	3·8	3·9	3·6
Proline	5·0	4·5	4·6
Serine	4·6	4·5	4·8
Threonine	5·5	5·6	5·6
Tyrosine	3·1	3·0	2·9
Valine	5·0	5·2	4·9

in body lipid. Phillips, Lovelace et al. (1956) found a direct correlation between body lipid content in Salvelinus fontinalis and fish size which exists only in hatchery-reared fish, not in wild fish.

Clearly, the lipid contents of artificial diets vary enormously, and when Weiser and Otte (1964) kept Salmo gairdnerii on a low-lipid artificial diet they found that the body lipid dropped below that of the wild fish; nevertheless, the captive fish still showed the fatty degeneration in the liver. This lipid appears to be abnormal, and writers speak of waxy material (Ghittino and Leon, 1963) and 'ceroid substance', a brownish material (see review by Deuel, 1957, p. 714) being present in it (Weiser and Otte, 1964; Fowler and Wood, 1966). Its origin is unknown, but Ono, Nagayama and Masuda (1960) suggested that some symptoms commonly found in hatchery fish, comprising lipoid degeneration of the liver, anaemia, abnormal tissue structure in the kidney and deposition of cholesterol, are the result of feeding material which contains oxidized lipid.

Fowler and Wood (1966) found that if an all-meat diet is supplemented by peanut oil, the fish (Oncorhynchus tschawytscha) do not undergo lipoid infiltration of the liver, but that if hard fat from the meat is included, then the usual symptoms appear. They concluded that fish metabolize hard fat with difficulty, and found in addition that if fish showing liver degeneration are then transferred to a 'soft fat' diet, they show little, if any, recovery.

The same authors found that on a hard fat diet the spleen and haematopoietic tissues show degenerative changes, eventually resulting in anaemia. This symptom has also been seen by Marsh (1902), Wood, Yasutake et al. (1957), Ono, Nagayama and Masuda (1960) and Ghittino and Leon (1963), but was not observed in fish examined by Slicher (1961) or Piper and Stephens (1962)—presumably the degree of damage to the haematopoietic tissues depends on the length of time in captivity and the degree of unsuitability of the diet, whatever that involves.

Fatty degeneration of the pancreas is also reported by Wood, Yasutake et al. (1957), while Ghittino and Leon (1963) found that waxy material is sometimes deposited in the kidney (said to have an 'abnormal structure' by Ono, Nagayama and Masuda, 1960), spleen and lymphatic tissue. They also noticed an increase in connective tissue in the body.

Other differences between wild fish and those reared in a hatchery are reported from time to time, for example in the fatty acid composition of the muscle (Shimma and Taguchi, 1964b), the electrophoretic patterns of the blood serum proteins (Thurston, 1967), and in the vitamin A, which was shown to be poorer (Higashi, Hirao et al., 1960), more fluctuating (Higashi, Hirao et al., 1962) or richer (Steffens, 1964) in cultivated than in wild fish, presumably as a result of variations in the artificial diet. Phillips, Podoliak et al. (1958) found that various species of trout from hatcheries die in calcium-free water where wild fish survive. This they related to increased catabolism in the former group.

It is clear from this account that the differences between wild and cultivated fish are numerous and formidable. They become more extreme as the period of artificial rearing is increased (Wood, Yasutake et al., 1957) and some, at least, soon vanish if the hatchery fish are transferred to a natural environment (Wood, Yasutake et al., 1960).

The eggs and fry of cultivated fish, or those spawned from wild fish and artificially nurtured, also differ from normal ones. Bams (1967) found that the stamina of Oncorhynchus nerka fry is highest from naturally-propagated eggs, while the performance of those incubated in gravel or in hatchery baskets is not as good. Pleuronectes platessa reared from eggs in a hatchery show a very poor survival rate when released into the sea (Anon., 1966b). Only 7% of them are normally pigmented, so many more are eaten by predators than 'wild' youngsters of a similar age. The first signs of colouring abnormality appear at the beginning of metamorphosis, and from then on it is permanent, the growth rate showing a concomitant fall compared with normally pigmented fish at the hatchery. Bailey (1964) described the work of N. N. Disler, who had studied the mode of emergence of hatchery fry from their eggs, and had noticed that when the eggs are on the flat surfaces of trays or troughs, the fry emerge in a 'head-down' position. This causes the oil droplet of the yolk sac to occupy an unnatural posterior position, where it causes a temporary deformation of the intestine and prevents the passage of food. He observed that hatchery fry begin to swim and use up their body lipid earlier than wild fry (*Oncorhynchus keta*), and recommended that the young fish should be kept in a tank covered with pebbles, and that water should come into the tank through the pebbles.

The chemical differences between the eggs spawned by hatchery fish (averaged from 9 different hatcheries) and those from a lake are shown in Table X. The 'natural' eggs are much poorer in pantothenic acid, but richer in pyridoxine, vitamin B_{12}, iron and astaxanthin, and the experimenters, Murayama and Yanase (1961), found no correlation between hatching rate and any chemical constituent. However, other workers have found iron to be important in this respect (Hirao, Yamada and Kikuchi, 1955b: *Salmo gairdnerii*).

It should now be obvious that the greatest caution must be used in interpreting analytical results obtained from fish that have been kept under restraint of any kind. Sometimes what appears to be negligible restraint has a far-reaching effect. Near Shirahama, Japan, there is an

TABLE X. CHEMICAL CONSTITUENTS OF 'EYED' EGGS FROM WILD AND HATCHERY-REARED SALMO GAIRDNERII
(after Murayama and Yanase, 1961)

Substance	Average from 9 hatcheries	Wild from Lake Mashuu
Water %	62·4	66·4
Lipid %	4·6	5·4
Pyridoxine $\mu g\%$	120	240
Pantothenic acid $\mu g\%$	1039	400
Folic acid $\mu g\%$	12·6	14
Vitamin B_{12} $\mu g\%$	12·5	23
Biotin $\mu g\%$	12·4	12·3
Astaxanthin $\mu g\%$	228·7	1423
Calcium mg%	56·3	44·2
Iron mg%	2·6	4

enclosed lake several hundreds of metres in diameter, the water of which has direct contact and interchange with the sea at high tide. In spite of this near-natural environment, the yellowtail (*Seriola quinqueradiata*) kept there neither spawn nor build up gonads (Y. Shimizu, personal communication) and for that reason the water content of the muscle remains constant throughout the year, unlike that of their wild counterparts which exhibit the usual once-yearly rise and fall (as in Fig. 83, p. 227).

Avoiding or compensating for stress preparatory to sampling fish for chemical analysis must therefore be done with careful thought.

C. Conclusions

In this chapter we have seen that anatomical heterogeneity and stress, or unsuitable compensation for stress, can lead to almost worthless results. Let us be quite clear about this: it is pointless to carry out chemical analysis unless the results can be related in some way to the life of the fish. Nutritionists and food technologists obtain chemical data in order to evaluate the material as food, or to assess the effect of some processing procedure on composition, but beyond these and reports in which fish has been the experimental material for trying out new analytical techniques, there has been a surprising number of papers published reporting analyses which seem to have had no clear purpose in mind, but which seem to have been performed on the basis of "something done so something achieved". The whereabouts of some of this information can be found along with more useful material in Parts II and III, which does give it a humble *raison d'être*—one can learn from it the concentrations that might at times have been found in a tissue. However, this is no longer sufficient justification for doing expensive new work along the same lines, and analyses should always have physiological, nutritional or technological significance.

Phosphorus is a case in point. Many early papers quote values for total phosphorus in the muscle, but how should we regard such figures? The total phosphorus could have originated in nucleic acids and the nucleotides, high energy compounds like the phosphates of adenosine and creatin, phosphoprotein, phospholipid, inorganic phosphate—the list is long. In truth, total phosphorus values in muscle are without meaning, and as such have been omitted from Parts II and III. In the blood the situation appears to be somewhat different, since the phosphorus concentration increases during exercise, presumably

4*

through the splitting of high-energy phosphates in the muscle, and also during the maturation of some female fish, perhaps denoting the transport of phosphorus-rich protein from liver to gonad. The values might therefore be used as a 'marker' to study maturation.

The status of total muscle sulphate is little better, though since chondroitin sulphate appears to be absent from muscle, most of it probably comes from the amino acids methionine and cystine, the proportions of which may not change very much. However, it will be seen that the objections are similar in principle to those of phosphorus.

It is possible to eliminate much of the anatomical variation in chemical constituents by taking always the same myotome or group of myotomes for analysis, and by dissecting free from connective tissue. In spite of this, one's first reaction to seeing the many consequences of capture stress and the unsatisfactory results of resting the fish in an aquarium or hatchery may well be that one might as well give up and not try to find the 'true' values, whatever that really means. This view is unnecessary. With the information at our disposal it should be possible to arrive at a procedure giving values close to those we want, although sometimes a compromise procedure must be followed.

Hatchery fish are probably unsuitable for the determination of any constituents, apart perhaps from combined amino acids in the protein. The latter concession brings no real advantage: Beach, Munks and Robinson (1943) reckoned that the amino acid composition of muscle tissue would be uniform throughout the animal kingdom anyway, and a partly decomposed or frozen 'wild' fish will yield just as good results.

Protein, water, lipid and ash are not affected by stress, so can be usefully determined on freshly-caught 'wild' fish, as can all the vitamins as far as the writer is aware. If the fresh material is not available, then frozen or even canned material may be used for the four main constituents, although the separation of bones from canned fish may be difficult, resulting in high ash values. Protein and lipid can also be determined in fresh fish packed for a few days in melting ice, but this manner of temporary preservation soon significantly increases the water content and decreases the ash (Thurston, 1958d; Thurston and Groninger, 1959; Love, Robertson and Strachan, 1968).

The proportions of various protein fractions change and, indeed, the total protein nitrogen of the muscle increases (Fig. 90) if newly-caught fish are kept in an aquarium, so this treatment should not be carried out for more than two or three days if detailed information on the muscle proteins is sought.

Determinations of intermediates in the carbohydrate cycle really do require a resting fish. One might suppose that ideally the fish should be shot dead in its natural habitat by a diver, but the considerable time-lag between death, hauling to the surface and sampling would still allow catabolism to occur and invalidate this as a technique. As far as is known, resting in an aquarium for a few weeks yields reasonably authentic values, since the large carbohydrate reserves of the liver appear to make good the smaller resting levels of the various compounds in the muscle. Possibly, however, trap-caught fish would give truer values, provided the traps were large and did not stimulate the fish to unnatural activity.

It is conceded that some species of fish will probably elude for some time a satisfactory technique for determining authentic 'resting' values. The redfish, *Sebastes marinus*, does not normally survive capture owing to the eversion of the stomach caused by expansion of the swim bladder. There is, however, one living specimen in captivity in the Bergen aquarium, obtained by deflating the bladder with a hypodermic needle before raising the fish to the surface. No doubt there are other problems of this kind to be faced.

A valid sampling technique is therefore not impossible, but it does require considerable knowledge of the physiology of the fish.

Resting values of many constituents are not constant, but may be influenced by factors which are either built-in (Chapter III), come from the environment (Chapter IV) or depend on the age of the fish (Chapter II) or its nutritional status (Chapter V).

Chapter 2

THE LIFE CYCLE

A. Beginnings of Life

The progressive development and organization of a complete animal from a beginning represented by the fusion of two cells is an incredible and fascinating process. In man, the stage at which the mass of multiplying cells can really be regarded as a person with a Soul is considered to lie between the fourth and seventh months of gestation, according to different philosophies. In eggs, such as those of the domestic fowl, the little segments of the future spine can easily be observed early in the incubation period, followed by the dark patch which will become an eye and—wonder of wonders—by an actively beating heart.

In fish, one may clearly mark the advent of a number of systems through the medium of chemical analysis, which is sometimes more realistic than visual examination. An example is to be found in the ultracentrifuge pattern of the egg proteins of *Salmo gairdnerii*, in which, during development, a new protein suddenly appears. This is thought to be a blood protein corresponding with the beginnings of a circulatory system (Fig. 37, p. 73).

We shall now examine the chemistry of egg development and hatching, and also the stage before it, the growth of the germ cells in the ovary and testis before they are shed into the sea. Marine biologists sometimes need to measure objectively the degree of maturity of a fish, and although the quest has not so far been entirely successful, the following pages might hold a potential key.

1. *Growth of the Germ Cells**

Some constituents may be seen in the blood stream of the parent fish on their way to the developing ova. Hess, Bills *et al.* (1927) noticed that the serum calcium of *Gadus morhua* and *Fugu* sp. is higher in the

---

* This section deals only with the developing eggs or sperm. The chemistry of the rest of the fish body during maturation and spawning is to be found on p. 97.

female than in the male, and that it is especially high when the roe is well developed. An exception is the female dogfish (Latin name not specified), which does not lay eggs but bears live young within her body; the authors found that in this species the serum calcium is high both in males and females, and does not vary seasonally. However, the former relationship seems to hold in most of the egg-laying fish.

Actual values found in *Salvelinus fontinalis* can be seen in Fig. 26: high levels of serum calcium are found throughout the period when the female fish usually spawns. In individual fish, the values are highest

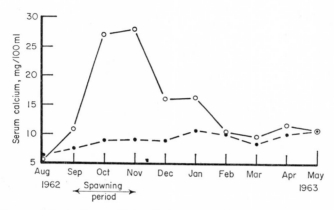

FIG. 26. Seasonal fluctuation in the level of serum calcium in male and female *Salvelinus fontinalis*. ● Males; ○ Females. After Phillips, Podoliak *et al.* (1964), reproduced by courtesy of Professor A. M. Phillips.

when the ovaries are ripe (A. D. Woodhead and P. M. J. Woodhead, 1965). That the period of high blood calcium can be considerably longer than this is shown in Fig. 27, which illustrates the blood calcium changes in *Fundulus kansae*. Again, the difference between male and female is striking, though in *Gadus morhua*, while the calcium maximum is greater in the female, both sexes show an annual cycle (Woodhead, 1968).

The phenomenon is controlled by oestradiol, one of the sex hormones, and a high blood calcium level can be induced outside the breeding season by injecting it into the fish (Bailey, 1957; A. D. Woodhead and P. M. J. Woodhead, 1965; Oguri and Takada, 1967). As a corollary, A. D. Woodhead and P. M. J. Woodhead (1965) noted that there is no change in the concentration of plasma calcium in cod of either sex throughout the year if they are immature.

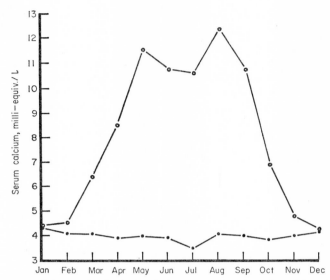

FIG. 27. Seasonal fluctuation in the level of serum calcium in male and female *Fundulus kansae*. ● Males; ○ Females. After Fleming, Stanley and Meier (1964), reproduced by courtesy of Dr. Fleming and Academic Press.

Part of the increase in calcium consists of an increase in colloidal calcium phosphate, so blood phosphate increases at the same time. The remainder of the non-ultrafilterable calcium is bound to vitellin, a phosphoprotein (Bailey, 1957). This compound appears to be formed in the liver and released into the blood, which transports it to the ovaries to be deposited in the developing eggs. Total serum protein concentration has in fact been measured in *Salvelinus fontinalis*, and the results (Fig. 28) show a rise during the breeding season similar to that in calcium.

An elevation in serum magnesium during sexual activity has also been reported (Oguri and Takada, 1967), but its role is not at present clear.

Gross changes in the liver have been indicated by Krivobok (1964), who showed that the weight in Baltic herring (*Clupea harengus membranus*) increases in the female until gonad maturation has definitely started, but then declines with progressive maturation up to the stage when the ova are ripe (stage VI). How much of the weight loss is due to vitellin and how much to other compounds is not known. Krivobock's results are shown in Fig. 29.

It appears also that phospholipid is mobilized for egg production, and lipid phosphorus determinations on the serum of *Salmo trutta* have

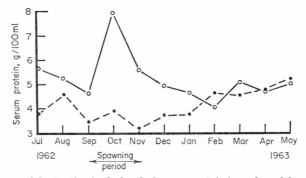

Fɪɢ. 28. Seasonal fluctuation in the level of serum protein in male and female *Salvelinus fontinalis*. ●————● Male; ○————○ Female. After Phillips, Podoliak *et al.* (1964), reproduced by courtesy of Professor A. M. Phillips.

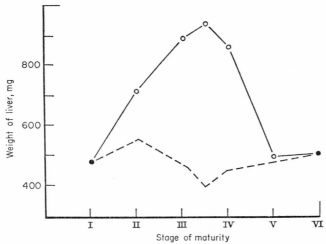

Fɪɢ. 29. Weight of liver in male (lower curve) and female (upper) *Clupea harengus membranus*, 17 cm in length, at different stages of maturation. I = immature. II = beginning to ripen. III-V = ripening. VI = ripe and spawning. VII = spent. After Krivobok (1964), reproduced by courtesy of the author.

shown a high level during gonad build-up and a drop to lower values after spawning. The figures then remain steady for the remainder of the year, until the next breeding cycle begins (Fig. 30). The changes in the male follow the same pattern, but are less pronounced than those in the female.

A different situation arises in the case of serum cholesterol, which is *minimal* during the period of greatest sexual activity (Fig. 31). The concentration patterns are thought (McCartney, 1967) to be related

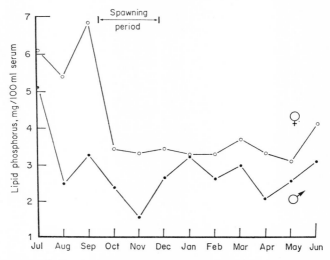

Fig. 30. Seasonal fluctuation in the level of serum phospholipid in male and female *Salmo trutta*, expressed as phosphorus. After McCartney (1967), reproduced by courtesy of Professor A. M. Phillips.

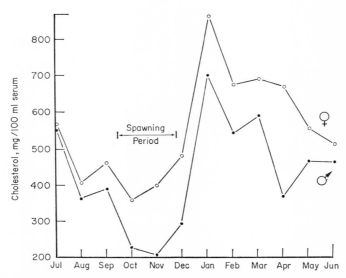

Fig. 31. Seasonal fluctuation in the level of serum cholesterol in male and female *Salmo trutta*. Unlike so many other constituents it is minimal at the time of greatest sexual activity. After McCartney (1967), reproduced by courtesy of Professor A. M. Phillips.

to changes in cholesterol metabolism associated with the formation of sex hormones, which have a steroid structure. This diagram is not strictly related to the genesis of germ cells, but was apposed to Fig. 30 to emphasize the contrast in behaviour between two fat-soluble constituents.

So much for changes in the blood of the parent fish. Turning now to the gonads themselves as the eggs or sperm develop, we can find several distinct trends in the concentrations of the four principal constituents. In *Sardinella longiceps*, the ovaries, which have a dark reddish colour in the immature stage, change with maturity to a yellowish tint because of the deposition of yolk in individual eggs (Hornell and Nayudu, 1923). The lipid is of a special type; Lovern (1934a) found that when the body lipid of *Salmo salar* is transferred to the developing ovaries, a high selectivity of individual fatty acids is shown. Presumably those fatty acids mobilized but not laid down in the ovaries are used to supply energy to the fish. As the ova of this species mature, the relative proportions of fatty acids change within the lipid, unsaturated acids with 18 carbon atoms ('C_{18} acids') showing a steady increase while C_{16} acids, both saturated and unsaturated, decline (Lovern, 1942). On the other hand, the fatty acid pattern of *Gadus morhua* ovaries does not alter during the course of development (Jangaard, Ackman and Sipos, 1967), so no general rule can be stated.

Care is needed in interpreting concentrations of constituents made on a fresh weight basis, since the ovaries, at least in *Gadus morhua*, take up a considerable weight of water just before spawning (Braekkan and Boge, 1962c), so there is an apparent decrease in some constituents. Similarly, the increase in yolk earlier on during development leads to a relative decrease in the proportion of water and minerals (Mengi, 1965: *Gadus morhua*).

Braekkan's measurements of water, protein and ash (1958b) in the developing ovaries of *Gadus morhua* are shown in Fig. 32. The decrease in mineral content is clearly shown, but that in water is barely detectable on the scale used; presumably these ovaries did not reach full ripeness. There is, however, a noticeable increase in the concentration of protein. No doubt because of this, there is a steady increase in the content of *free* amino acids in the latter part of the ripening process, independently of changes in the water content (Krishnamoorthi, 1958; Gjessing, 1963; Mengi, 1965). Gjessing's curves show a fall in 6 of the *free* amino acids at the very end of the ripening process, even on a dry weight basis, perhaps marking the completion of the deposition of protein. The content and proportions of *free* amino acids during maturation do not change in the muscle or blood (Cowey, Daisley and Parry, 1962: *Salmo salar*).

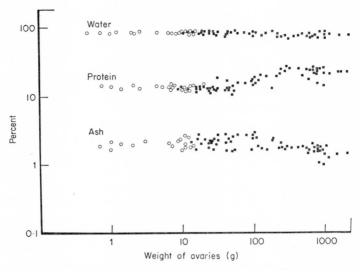

FIG. 32. Water, protein and ash in ovarian tissue of *Gadus morhua* during maturation. ○ Immature; ■ Mature. After Braekkan (1958b), reproduced by courtesy of the author and of the Office of the Director of Fisheries, Norway.

The proportions of combined amino acids in the gonad also change somewhat during maturation. In the five species of Pacific salmon (*Oncorhynchus*), the arginine, histidine and isoleucine all steadily increase in the ovary, while smaller changes occur in one or other direction in the remaining amino acids (Seagran, Morey and Dassow, 1954). In *Clupea sprattus*, arginine and histidine increase, while methionine, tryptophan and tyrosine all decrease in the ovary. In the testis (milt) there is an increase in methionine, in addition to that in arginine and histidine (Petrenko and Karasikova, 1958). Korzhenko (1966) found that in the ovary of *Oncorhynchus keta* there is an increase in alanine and leucine, while glycine progressively decreases during maturation. In the testis there is a rise in arginine, histidine, lysine, leucine, isoleucine and valine, and a fall in serine, proline and glycine (see Table XII, p. 76). The general impression is that in the testis there is an accumulation of amino acids having a high nitrogen content at the expense of nitrogen-poor compounds, and it was suggested that this is connected in some way with the synthesis of nucleic acids. The changes in amino acids occur only at the time of active spermatogenesis. Korzhenko's results are discussed further on p. 101.

Clearly during the creation of germ cells there must be a synthesis of nucleic acids, but little published evidence has come to the writer's notice. Creelman and Tomlinson (1959) reported that during the spawning migration of *Oncorhynchus nerka* there is an increase in deoxyribose nucleic acid (DNA) in both males and females, but a loss in ribose nucleic acid (RNA) occurring at the same time suggests that, at least in the females, the one is being synthesized at the expense of the other.

Vitamins play some part in the development of the germ cells, although the mechanism is not always known. Vitamin A (=retinol: Anon., 1965) would clearly be needed for the development of vision in the larva (vitamin A forms part of the visual pigments of the retina) since there is no dietary source for a considerable time after hatching. Plack, Woodhead and Woodhead (1961) found that vitamin A aldehyde (retinal) begins to accumulate in the ovary of *Gadus morhua* at the same time as the yolk is being deposited. After the fish have spawned in March, no retinal can be found in the ovary until vitellogenesis begins in the next batch of oocytes (egg precursor cells) the following November. The highest concentration is found just before spawning. Plack and Kon (1961) tabulated values for the different forms of vitamin A in a number of other species, and noted again that the aldehyde is found in the ovary only when it is ripe. Bearing in mind the behaviour of blood calcium in ripening females (Figs. 26 and 27), representing a calcium-protein complex in transit to the ovaries, it is not surprising that the level of vitamin A aldehyde in the serum of female *Gadus morhua* rises from a resting level of 2 μg/100 ml to 10 μg/100 ml at the spawning time, and that there is little change in the low concentration of this compound in the corresponding male fish (Plack and Woodhead, 1966).

Vitamin A precursors are also deposited in the ovary. In *Salmo trutta* the concentration of carotenoids, when expressed in micro grammes per gramme of tissue, remains almost constant during maturation. However, this represents an increase in the carotenoid content of each oocyte in proportion to its increase in size. It has been noted also that in the carotenoid fraction the proportions of β-carotene, lutein and astaxanthin remain approximately constant during this period (Steven, 1949).

The true function of the vitamins of the B group during maturation of the oocytes is not known, but from studying the changes in concentration it is clear that at least one of them plays a vital part in the process.

Vitamin B_{12} (cyanocobalamin) and biotin change little, the concentration of the former showing a slight but steady decline, the latter a slight increase during maturation (Braekkan and Boge, 1962a):

deposition here roughly keeps pace with growth, and a decrease in the liver biotin of *Salmo salar* has been observed to occur at the same time (Cowey, Daisley and Parry, 1962). Similarly, the absolute amounts of gonad inositol increase during the maturation of *Oncorhynchus nerka*, although the concentration actually shows a slight fall (Chang, Tsuyuki and Idler, 1960).

The values of pantothenic acid in the immature ovaries of *Gadus morhua* are of interest as the highest ever reported for a natural source of this vitamin (Braekkan, 1955). Here, however, little if any new material is laid down, and the concentration falls steeply as the ovaries increase in size (Fig. 33).

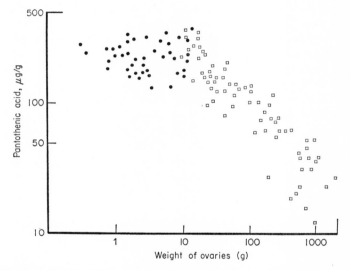

Fɪɢ. 33. Pantothenic acid in ovarian tissue of *Gadus morhua* during maturation. ● Immature; □ Mature. After Braekkan (1955), reproduced by courtesy of the author and of MacMillan (Journals) Ltd.

In contrast to the other vitamins of the B group, vitamin B_6 (pyridoxine) is unique in showing a large increase in concentration during maturation from $2 \cdot 3 \ \mu g\%$ in immature ovaries (*Gadus morhua*) to $320 \ \mu g\%$ at its maximum (Braekkan and Boge, 1962a). As these determinations are on a 'fresh weight' basis, it shows an apparent fall, just before spawning, caused by the uptake of water by the ovaries already mentioned.

2. *Development of Eggs and Fry*

(a) *Factors affecting development*

The eggs and fry of fish develop more rapidly at elevated temperatures (Embody, 1934: *Salmo trutta*; Forrester and Alderdice, 1966: *Gadus macrocephalus*; Alderdice and Forrester, 1968: *Parophrys vetulus*). Phillips, Podoliak *et al.* (1964) found that *Salmo trutta* eggs incubated at a higher temperature contain more water throughout their development, and so less protein on a wet weight basis. Protein on the basis of dry matter is not affected. Further papers relating development rate to water temperature are reviewed by Blaxter and Holliday (1963).

The eggs of *Clupea harengus* can develop successfully over a wide range of salinity, increasing in size at low salinity owing to increased uptake of water (Blaxter and Holliday, 1963). However, the rate of development of *Gadus macrocephalus* eggs is retarded by a reduction in salinity (Forrester and Alderdice, 1966) and that of *Cyprinodon macularius* eggs is retarded by an increase (Kinne and Kinne, 1962). *Parophrys vetulus* egg development is optimal at a salinity of 25‰ if the incubation temperature lies between 6 and 12°, but at 4° this concentration of salt appears to be the worst for development, and a change to a more concentrated or more dilute environment now encourages it (Alderdice and Forrester, 1968). Lowered oxygen tension in the water retards development also, or may cause the death of the embryo (Garside, 1959: *Salvelinus namaycush*), while a richly oxygenated environment accelerates it (Kinne and Kinne, 1962: *Cyprinodon macularius*). However, if development is already advanced, a decrease in the concentration of oxygen induces earlier hatching, and vice versa, in bony fish embryos, especially those of *Misgurnus* sp. (Buznikov, 1961, quoted by Kotlyarevskaya, 1967).

All of these factors interact (Kinne and Kinne, 1962). Both retardation of development by high salinity and acceleration by oxygen increase are accentuated by a rise in temperature. Lethal temperatures, too, are a function of salinity and oxygen. These observations may serve to remind anyone analysing eggs after different times of incubation that the stages of development may not always be the same after comparable times.

Little work appears to have been done on the proportion of a batch of fertilized eggs that grows successfully to the point of hatching, based on the composition of the eggs themselves. Hirao, Yamada and Kikuchi (1955b) found that the riboflavin (vitamin B_2) content of eggs of high hatching rate is slightly higher than those of low hatching rate (*Salmo gairdnerii*). The relationship between hatching rate and

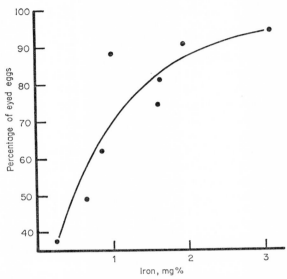

FIG. 34. The hatching rate of *Salmo gairdnerii* eggs in relation to their iron content. Graph drawn from data by Hirao, Yamada and Kikuchi (1955b).

iron content is more striking: the values quoted by these authors have been plotted in Fig. 34. Perhaps the critical factor here is the ability to form a sufficient quantity of blood pigment to support life.

(b) Changes in weight

Hayes (1930a) noted that the weight of the eggs of *Salmo salar* gradually increases before hatching. In the hatched larva the wet weight increases at first and then decreases, but the dry weight decreases continuously.

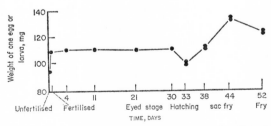

FIG. 35. Weight changes in an egg or larva of *Salmo gairdnerii* during early development. The swelling on fertilization, loss of egg capsule on hatching, and starvation after using up the yolk can all be seen in the diagram. After Suyama and Ogino (1958), reproduced by courtesy of Professor M. Suyama and the Japanese Society of Scientific Fisheries.

The changes in weight of *Salmo gairdnerii* eggs, which were studied by Suyama and Ogino (1958), are shown graphically in Fig. 35. On fertilization there is an almost immediate swelling with the formation of the 'fertilization membrane', which shows as a sudden increase in weight. Hatching is marked by a weight loss with the shedding of the egg case, and thereafter the weight increases, presumably by absorption of water, until the yolk is all used up, when starvation brings about a further loss for a short period. This is followed by a continuing gain as the little fish begin to feed.

(c) *Energy requirements*

Movement of the larva within the egg consumes energy, and the egg has been observed to respire right from the time of fertilization, implying that some of its substance is burning away. Hayes (1930b) reported that the oxygen consumption of *Salmo salar* eggs drops to a low level before hatching, then increases greatly in the free-swimming larva. On the other hand, Hayes, Wilmot and Livingstone (1951) found a steady increase in oxygen consumption from fertilization to hatching, and quoted the results of Privolniev (1938) in support of their own. Although the total weight of the egg does not change up to the point of hatching (see also Fig. 35), inert yolk material is presumably being converted into living tissue, and the authors related oxygen consumption to the amount of living material within the egg. Uesugi and Yamazoe (1964) also measured oxygen consumption, this time in *Salmo gairdnerii*, and found that while it increases steadily from low levels after fertilization, the greatest acceleration occurs after hatching.

Organic material is therefore consumed, and direct calorimetric measurements carried out by Faustov and Zotin (1965) on the eggs of *Misgurnus fossilis*, *Acipenser stellatus* and *Acipenser güldenstadti* showed that the calorie content of each egg declines steadily from the time of fertilization to the point of emergence of the embryo from its membrane.

Some of the weight loss is in the lipid fraction, but the loss in protein is the more important. In *Salmo gairdnerii* each of these constituents is reduced by half during development (Suyama and Ogino, 1958), and at the same time the non-protein nitrogen increases about 5-fold. While some of this may represent nitrogen excretion, it is likely that a further portion consists of *free* amino acids mobilized for combustion.

The manner in which the water content increases to compensate for protein loss during development, keeping the total weight approximately constant, is shown for *Salmo trutta* in Fig. 36. Further data of the same type are given by Ando (1962a) for *Salmo gairdnerii*. It will

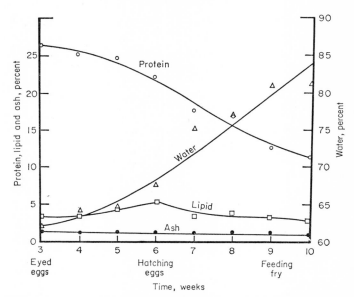

FIG. 36. Changes in the composition of eggs from first-spawning *Salmo trutta* during development. After Phillips, Podoliak *et al.* (1958), reproduced by courtesy of Professor A. M. Phillips.

be seen that the lipid rises to a peak and then declines. Hayes (1930b) made a similar observation on the lipid content of eggs, reporting peaks 10 days before hatching and 6 weeks after. He believed that the decrease in lipid after a peak signifies a change from protein to lipid as an energy source, but it would be unwise to put too much weight on this interpretation, bearing in mind the big changes in proportions of the other major constituents occurring at the same time. It is these changes that have led some workers to analyse eggs only on a dry weight basis, or even 'per egg'.

The utilization of yolk protein, either for energy or body growth, is not a steady process, but one in which periods of more rapid utilization alternate with less active periods. In Fig. 37, the yolk protein of *Salmo gairdnerii* eggs was separated by ultracentrifuging into two components, the proportions of which can be seen to vary considerably. Of especial interest is the appearance of a third component which coincides with the first recognizable formation of blood vessels: it may perhaps be a blood protein.

The relatively small proportion of carbohydrate in fish eggs has been studied in *Salmo gairdnerii* by Smith (1952), who showed that depletion of this constituent is especially noticeable during the establishment of

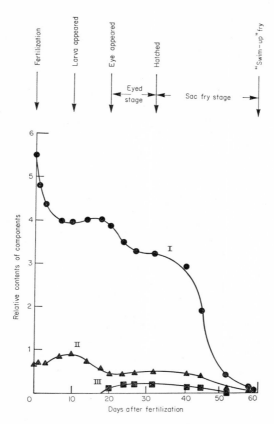

FIG. 37. Changes in the proportions of three ultracentrifuge components of yolk protein during the development of eggs of *Salmo gairdnerii*. After Ando (1965), reproduced by courtesy of the author and the National Research Council of Canada.

the blood circulation, hatching, and at the onset of starvation after the yolk has been absorbed.

Thus for a period the fish egg, like the sun, exists by burning up its own substance. This is not to say that it is completely sealed off from its environment, but evidence for the acquisition of material from the water is scanty. McCay, Tunison *et al.* (1936) found that before the yolk sac of *Salvelinus fontinalis* larvae is absorbed, that is, well before feeding has commenced, there is a marked increase in calcium, which must originate in the environment. In addition, Phillips, Podoliak *et al.* (1962) showed that *Salmo trutta* eggs absorb calcium from the water at a rate which increases as the eggs mature. However, these authors found no evidence for actual accumulation in the tissue, and supposed that a mere exchange of calcium takes place.

The possibility of the eggs acquiring other nutrients in this way should not be overlooked, in spite of the lack of experimental evidence at present. For example, the water of the Atlantic Ocean has been found to contain vitamin B_{12} to the extent of 0·1 milli-microgram or more per ml, depending on the locality and the season (Droop, 1957).

(d) Synthesis and conversion

Some materials laid down in the egg are used for the synthesis of others. While ascorbic acid (vitamin C) is present in the newly-shed eggs of *Esox lucius*, there is evidence that more of it is synthesized during the development of the embryo (Minakowski and Nowicka, 1962), presumably from sugar precursors.

Since deoxyribose nucleic acid (DNA) carries the genetic material in each cell, we would expect it to be synthesized to keep pace with cell division in the fertilized egg. Continuous synthesis of DNA has in fact been demonstrated in *Misgurnus fossilis*; this is apparently at the expense of the ribose nucleic acid (RNA), since the total of DNA + RNA does not change, but remains at 2·2 μg/egg until the end of gastrulation (Aitkhozin, Belitsina and Spirin, 1964).

Vitamin A is needed by the developing eyes, but is not synthesized in measurable amounts in the egg, being already there when the eggs were spawned. However, it is initially present as the ester form, and changes to the alcohol (retinol) during development (Yamamura and Muto, 1961). The content of astaxanthin, shown by Gross and Budowski (1966) to be a vitamin A precursor in fish, falls slightly, so possibly there is some synthesis of the vitamin, but since the total level of vitamin A falls during development there is at present no proof.

Acetylcholinesterase, the enzyme associated with nervous stimulation of the muscles, has been detected from the 10th day after fertilization in *Salmo gairdnerii* eggs. In the 'eye' stage the increase in activity is abrupt (Fig. 38), coinciding with the development of excitable tissues (Uesugi and Yamazoe, 1964). The activity is not inhibited by a homogenate of newly-fertilized eggs, so the lack of activity in the early stages is not caused by an inhibitor: the enzyme is evidently created at the appropriate time. The activity of six different phosphatases was studied by Noda (1967a) in the same species, and found to increase in all cases during development, the increase again being especially marked at the 'eye' stage.

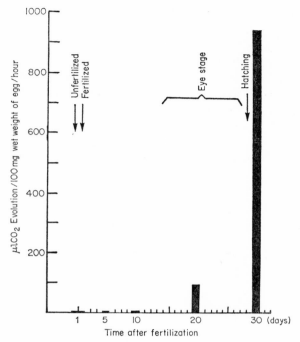

FIG. 38. Acetylcholinesterase activity of the eggs of *Salmo gairdnerii* during development. After Uesugi and Yamazoe (1964), reproduced by courtesy of Professor Yamazoe.

(e) *Amino acids, fatty acids and minor constituents*

Block and Weiss (1956) averaged the amino acid contents of fish eggs
as determined by several writers, so the resulting figures are a useful
base-line (Table XI).

Changes in the amino acid patterns during the development of the
eggs of *Salmo gairdnerii* and *Fugu niphobles* are shown in Tables XII

TABLE XI. AMINO ACID CONTENT OF FISH EGG PROTEINS
(averaged from several writers by Block and Weiss, 1956)

g per 16 g Nitrogen			
Arginine:	7·0	Methionine:	2·9
Cystine:	1·5	Phenylalanine:	4·8
Histidine:	2·4	Threonine:	5·7
Isoleucine:	7·2	Tryptophan	1·0
Leucine:	9·8	Tyrosine:	4·8
Lysine:	8·0	Valine:	7·3

and XIII, respectively. A considerable decrease in alanine is shown during development in Table XII, and Table XIII shows that the developmental stage resulting in the biggest all-round change in amino acids, especially in proline, is from egg to larva. Serine is shown by the data in both tables to be preferentially used up during development, and there is a consistent relative increase in glycine, methionine and lysine.

TABLE XII. CHANGES IN AMINO ACID COMPOSITION OF SALMO GAIRDNERII EGGS DURING DEVELOPMENT (after Suyama, 1958).

Amino acid	g per 16 g Nitrogen				
	Unfertilized egg	Eyed egg	Just after hatching	1/3 of Yolk absorbed	Fry
Alanine	8·24	8·23	8·20	7·73	5·30
Arginine	5·68	5·71	5·34	5·39	6·03
Aspartic acid	9·15	9·24	9·37	9·35	10·40
Cystine	1·05	1·00	1·13	1·34	1·10
Glutamic acid	11·70	12·00	12·30	12·40	13·90
Glycine	2·67	2·70	3·02	3·70	6·58
Histidine	2·45	2·48	2·50	2·48	2·36
Hydroxyproline	0·72	0·73	0·82	1·01	0·99
Isoleucine	4·89	4·52	4·50	4·15	3·52
Leucine	9·67	9·22	9·15	8·82	7·79
Lysine	7·25	7·34	7·44	7·40	7·91
Methionine	2·87	2·91	2·94	2·89	3·17
Phenylalanine	5·71	5·24	5·24	5·15	4·68
Proline	6·67	6·70	6·83	7·00	7·28
Serine	6·20	5·99	5·87	5·52	4·46
Threonine	4·89	4·75	4·77	4·70	4·48
Tryptophan	0·99	0·97	0·99	0·94	1·08
Tyrosine	4·14	4·32	4·28	4·19	4·00
Valine	6·26	6·19	6·15	5·58	4·52

As we might expect, there is no marked difference in the lipids and component fatty acids of the lecithins as between fertilized and unfertilized eggs (Zama, Katada and Igarashi, 1959: *Oncorhynchus keta*), but over the longer period up to the complete absorption of the yolk a change of sorts can be seen (Table XIV), the C_{20} unsaturated fatty acid being burned up to a greater extent than the others. It should be remembered that the figures in the table are relative to each other, and that the *absolute* amounts of all the fatty acids in one egg decrease during development.

Table XV shows the changes in inorganic constituents. Judging by the great increase in most of them in the lowest row of figures, the larval fish had begun to feed. Prior to that there was no sign of accumulation of calcium by absorption from the environment, but this is in line

TABLE XIII. CHANGES IN AMINO ACID COMPOSITION OF EGGS OF FUGU NIPHOBLES DURING DEVELOPMENT (after Suyama, 1966).

	g per 16 g Nitrogen					
Amino acid	2 Hours	2 Days	4 Days	6 Days	7 Days	
					Eggs	Larvae
Alanine	5·64	5·55	5·60	5·14	5·01	5·84
Arginine	6·63	6·72	6·93	6·72	6·42	6·51
Aspartic acid	10·4	10·3	10·3	10·4	10·1	9·88
Cystine	1·74	1·70	1·72	1·71	1·78	1·14
Glutamic acid	12·0	12·1	12·4	12·6	12·3	12·3
Glycine	3·33	3·47	3·49	3·78	3·97	4·71
Histidine	3·03	3·12	2·97	3·13	2·98	2·33
Isoleucine	5·20	5·17	5·12	4·86	4·73	4·73
Leucine	8·28	8·24	8·28	7·86	7·61	8·15
Lysine	7·93	7·92	7·67	7·57	7·13	8·17
Methionine	2·63	2·75	2·73	2·44	2·33	2·78
Phenylalanine	5·26	5·23	5·13	5·12	5·00	4·80
Proline	7·14	7·14	7·33	7·48	7·30	3·98
Serine	8·00	7·88	7·69	7·09	6·69	6·52
Threonine	5·78	5·58	5·88	5·77	5·30	4·83
Tryptophan	3·94	3·94	2·99	2·41	2·36	1·66
Tyrosine	5·00	5·02	5·28	5·38	5·08	3·01
Valine	6·95	6·87	6·70	6·73	6·22	6·20

with the observations of Phillips, Podoliak et al. (1962), that any calcium absorbed in this way merely exchanges with the egg's own calcium, and does not augment it.

Little can be said in summary on these last four tables, except that where some constituents are preferentially utilized, for example to supply energy, the percentages of all constituents must still add up to 100, so that the concentrations of some of them appear to increase, though real synthesis is rarely involved.

TABLE XIV. CHANGES IN THE FATTY ACID COMPOSITION OF THE LIPIDS OF SALMO GAIRDNERII EGGS DURING DEVELOPMENT (after Ando, 1962b)

Stage	Days after fertilization	Saturated acids, %				Unsaturated acids, %					
		%Total	C_{14}	C_{16}	C_{18}	%Total	C_{14}	C_{16}	C_{18}	C_{20}	C_{22}
Unfertilized egg	0	18·0	0·8	13·1	4·1	82·0	tr.	15·0	29·5	21·3	16·2
Fertilized egg	9	18·2	0·8	12·9	4·5	81·8	tr.	4·9	32·7	32·4	11·8
Just before eye stage	13	17·1	0·8	11·8	4·5	82·9	tr.	7·3	33·8	26·1	15·7
Eye stage	19	16·9	0·5	11·6	4·8	83·1	0·2	9·7	30·6	22·8	19·7
Just before hatching	26	16·4	0·8	10·9	4·7	83·6	tr.	11·0	30·0	24·6	18·2
Newly hatched fry	34	14·6	0·7	9·8	4·1	85·4	tr.	9·2	37·6	20·2	18·4
Half yolk absorbed	47	15·7	0·9	10·0	4·8	84·3	0·1	11·9	35·7	18·2	18·3
Swim-up fry	58	15·6	0·4	10·0	5·2	84·4	0·2	16·0	34·6	16·7	17·0

TABLE XV. CHANGES IN INORGANIC CONSTITUENTS OF SALMO GAIRDNERII EGGS DURING DEVELOPMENT
(after Ogino and Yasuda, 1962)

Stage	Days after fertilization	On basis of dry weight							
		Crude ash, %	Ca %	Mg %	K mg%	Na mg%	Fe mg%	Cu mg%	Si mg%
Unfertilized egg	0	3·66	0·182	0·135	58·7	19·2	13·8	0·66	5·8
Fertilized egg	5*	3·81	0·204	0·139	192	25·4	11·9	0·61	6·3
Fertilized egg	12	3·76	0·208	0·135	229	22·0	11·0	0·77	14·7
3–5 days before hatching	29	3·78	0·190	0·146	70·5	15·9	9·4	0·63	10·5
6–8 days after hatching	40	4·45	0·197	0·154	239	55·3	15·5	0·39	16·5
Larval fish	54	6·23	0·412	0·132	943	227	10·4	1·14	25·1

* hours

B. Metamorphosis

During development, a few species of fish change their form, and this short section deals with chemical changes that occur at the same time.

1. *Parr-smolt Change in Salmon*

Salmon eggs are laid in fresh water in rivers far from the sea. As the young fish grow and slowly move down towards the sea they are known in the English language, respectively, as fry, parr and smolt, and the young marine form, maturing and returning to spawn after one winter in the sea, is called grilse. There are some instances of salmon which have been permanently sealed into a freshwater system, migrating between rivers and lakes, but migration to the sea is more usual, and is the behaviour to be considered here.

The most obvious change is in the colour of the fish, which has been correlated with an increase in the purine content of the surface layers, silvery materials being laid down in the scales and deep in the dermis near the muscle (Johnston and Eales, 1967: *Salmo salar*). When the parr become silvery, there is a sharp increase in the guanine and hypoxanthine content of both scales and deeper layers, deposition being enhanced by a rise in temperature (Johnston and Eales, 1968). The silvery parrs later change to smolts, and these constituents again increase in the scales, though there is no further change deeper down. Markert and Vanstone (1966) chromatographed the pigments of the belly-skin of coho salmon (*Oncorhynchus kisutch*) during the next stage when the 'smolt' become 'grilse', and found that while the guanine, hypoxanthine and guanylic acid patterns remain the same throughout the period of observation, the two spots on the chromatogram corresponding with 'pterins' decrease from the pre-smolt to the smolt stage, and disappear altogether in the grilse.

Vanstone, Roberts and Tsuyuki (1964) submitted the haemoglobins of *Oncorhynchus kisutch* to starch gel electrophoresis, and found increases in some fractions, while other entirely new fractions emerge when parrs change to smolts. This change continues after the fish have entered salt water, and the authors tentatively suggested that the new haemoglobin fractions have a higher affinity for oxygen than those present at the parr stage, being an ecological adaptation to life in the ocean, with its poorer oxygen content compared with the mountain streams. This observation, therefore, is more relevant to the discussion of ecological factors (see p. 176) than to metamorphosis. The same can probably be said of the tissue water content of *Salmo salar*, which happens to decline between the parr and smolt stages (Houston and

Threadgold, 1963), but seems really to be related to the length of the fish as there is no sudden change between the forms, only a gradual shift.

Plasma chloride, however, also investigated by Houston and Threadgold (1963), appears to correlate with the physiological state. As the parr increase in size there is a sharp drop in plasma chloride while they remain parr. If on the other hand they become silvery, the level rises above the original level (Fig. 39). The writers interpreted this as a

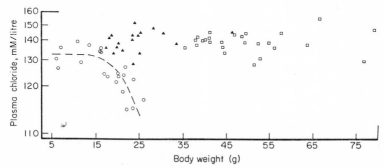

FIG. 39. Plasma chloride concentration in young *Salmo salar* during development. ○ Parr; ▲ Silvery parr; □ Smolt. After Houston and Threadgold (1963), reproduced by courtesy of Dr. A. H. Houston and the Fisheries Research Board of Canada.

temporary breakdown in ability to regulate plasma electrolyte concentrations during this physiological change. Changes in electrolyte composition bring about corresponding changes in the freezing point of the blood, which has been shown to rise during the smolt stage (that is, the electrolyte content has decreased) and to fall again at the marine stage (Kubo, 1955). That a change in osmoregulation occurs at this phase of the life of the salmon has also been shown by Koch, Evans and Bergström (1959), who found that parr abruptly transferred to full-strength sea water invariably die, the blood showing a steep rise in sodium, while smolts of the same age survive such treatment. Conte, Wagner *et al.* (1966) also noticed that the ability to adapt to sea-water precedes actual entry into the sea by several months.

There is a pronounced fall in the unsaturation (number of double bonds, hence 'reactivity') of the lipid of salmon smolts as compared with parrs. In discussing this fact, Lovern (1942) pointed out that relatively high unsaturation is typical of the lipids of juvenile forms, such as fish eggs, and it is possible that the more rapid metabolism of embryonic or larval forms requires a particularly reactive food reserve.

Cowey and Parry (1963) determined various *free* amino acids and dipeptides in the muscle of *Salmo salar* and noted that the decrease in taurine from 20·1 to 10·1 mg N/100 g wet tissue between parr and smolt was the only significant change. Since the value dropped further to 2·7 in adults in the sea, this change may again have been a specific adaptation to salt water, rather than being associated with the parr and smolt stages. The same may be true of anserine, which increased from 44·9 to 57·2 mg N/100 g between parr and smolt, and then to 137·8 mg N in the sea.

Although the change from parr to smolt is visually quite striking, it appears, casting one's eye back over the data, that only the change in the pigments and perhaps the sudden change in osmoregulatory ability can be specifically identified with this transformation. Other changes were already going on in the fry, or continuing in the grilse, so are more likely to be effects of gradual adaptation to salt water.*

2. *Lampreys and Eels*

The young of lampreys differ in appearance from adults, and are known as ammocoetes. So many factors such as growth (p. 94), parr-smolt transformation (p. 80) and sex differences (p. 121) result in changes in the electrophoretic patterns of the blood of other fish that it is quite in character that the metamorphosis of lampreys should also cause changes of this kind. It is as well to remember that the exact identity of many of the bands is completely unknown, but patterns are often constant under a given circumstance, so can be used in comparative work. As an interim generalization, then, we may say that the haemoglobin electropherograms reveal different kinds of pigment which sometimes show differing capacities for oxygen, while serum patterns depict different proportions of proteins such as α, β and γ globulins. The bands from muscle or muscle extracts are thought to be mostly enzymes, perhaps entirely so, and these patterns vary much less than those from the blood. The structural proteins, actin and myosin, do not take part in the electrophoresis, being too big to move in the supporting medium; the smaller protein molecules from muscle which separate out as bands are collectively known as myogens.

Uthe and Tsuyuki (1967) studied the electropherograms of three species of lamprey. *Petromyzon marinus, Ichthyomyzon unicuspis,* and *Lampetra lamottei,* and found that when plasma is used the ammocoete form of the animal is always characterized by an intense and slow-

---

* A fuller account of the specific effects of migration from fresh to salt water is given on p. 187.

moving band which is either faint or completely undetectable in the adult form.

Marked changes also occur in the haemoglobin electropherograms upon metamorphosis, both in the relative strengths of the bands and in their mobility, but the muscle extract patterns do not differ between ammocoetes and adults.

Carlson (1961) determined the amino acids in the muscle of two forms of lamprey, and some of his results are shown in Table XVI.

TABLE XVI. AMINO ACIDS IN THE MUSCLE OF AMMOCOETE AND ADULT LAMPREYS (after Carlson, 1961).

	Moles percent			
	Petromyzon marinus ammocoete (8 specimens)	Petromyzon marinus adult (8 specimens)	Entosphenus lamottei ammocoete (12 specimens)	Entosphenus lamottei adult (8 specimens)
Alanine	8·6	8·7	8·8	8·4
Arginine	6·9	6·5	6·9	6·5
Aspartic acid	7·6	8·4	9·6	8·2
Cystine	1·1	1·4	1·0	1·2
Glutamic acid	5·8	9·0	8·9	8·3
Histidine	3·7	1·8	1·7	2·0
Leucines (both)	15·9	14·9	16·5	16·1
Lysine	15·0	15·7	12·4	14·0
Methionine sulphoxide	2·1	2·5	1·4	2·5
Phenylalanine	3·6	3·3	3·0	4·2
Proline	5·1	4·7	4·2	4·9
Threonine	6·5	5·5	6·5	5·8
Tyrosine	1·7	1·7	0·9	2·1
Valine	6·2	5·6	6·8	6·1

No conclusive pattern emerges, as usually a change in one species is not matched in the other, and the consistent increases in cystine, lysine and methionine, and decreases in arginine, leucines and valine are modest anyway.

The European eel (*Anguilla anguilla*) is yellow in the immature form and later becomes silver. Sharratt, Chester Jones and Bellamy (1964) showed that the silver form of either sex contains more sodium in certain muscles. Those from sea water always contain more sodium than those from fresh water (see Table XXX, p. 192), but comparing the two morphological forms from either medium, the adult silver form always contains the more sodium. It is not known whether the increase in sodium signifies increased retention caused by a change in osmoregulation, or increased extracellular space, which causes an overall increase in muscle sodium (see p. 250). The corresponding potassium concentrations are not strikingly different. The sodium, potassium and calcium contents of the liver and kidney of the two forms are similar, apart from the liver sodium which increases in the silver form (Pequignot and Serfaty, 1966). Transfer of either form from fresh to salt water increases all three ions in both organs.

C. Growth

1. *General*

The attainment of increased size can of itself cause changes in the chemistry of the fish, but phenomena seen in larger specimens sometimes result from the onset of sexual maturity and it is not always possible to distinguish between the two factors.

The movement of a man running looks quite different from that of a child, largely because of the increasing inertia of his longer limbs. The mechanical stresses within the body of a swimming fish may also increase disproportionately with size, since the myocommata, which appear to transmit the power of the muscle contraction to the vertebral column, increase in thickness three-fold for a doubling of fish length (Fig. 6, p. 6). In some way, the swim bladder, too, appears to be subjected to greater stress during growth, since it shows a striking increase in weight (Lühmann and Mann, 1957: *Cyprinus carpio*).

As the scales become larger, the calcium content of the skin increases. A calcium concentration of 670 mg% was found in the skin of *Salvelinus fontinalis* which weighed 7 g, and this rose to 940 mg% in 28 g fish (Phillips, Lovelace *et al.*, 1953).

As mouths and gullets grow, so does the size of food which the fish is able to swallow. Thus, in growing *Gadus morhua* there is a gradual changeover in diet from decapod crustaceans to small fish (Rae, 1967a), which is likely to influence the composition of the predator, although no specific changes have so far been mentioned. The proportions of the different enzymes in the digestive tract also alter according to the nature of the diet (Fig. 76, p. 204), so it is to be expected that they will change with the size of the fish. Morishita, Noda *et al.* (1964) have in fact reported a reduction in the proteolytic and amylolytic activity of the alimentary canal of five species of Japanese fish with increasing size.

Enlargement of the bulk of the body will also slow the rate at which the temperature of the tissues can change if the fish is transferred to water of a different temperature. This may be why larger *Carassius auratus* show an increased rate of survival over smaller fish when they are subjected to severe cold shock, as reported by Hoar (1955).

2. *Cell Dimensions*

A variation in the distribution of cell sizes in different parts of the body causes changes in several constituents (p. 3). When fish grow, do the cells increase in size, or multiply in number? Measurements of cells from myotome 12, counting from the point of severance of the head, of *Gadus morhua* (Love, 1958a) leave no doubt that the diameters increase in direct proportion to the length of the fish (Fig. 40),

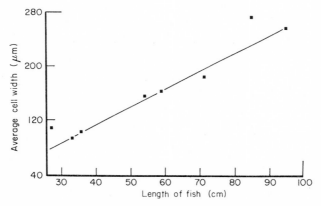

FIG. 40. Cell diameters in muscle from *Gadus morhua* of different sizes. The samples were taken from myotome no. 12, counting from the point of severance of the fillet from the head. Each point represents the mean value of 200 cells, apart from that relating to the largest fish (166 cells). After Love (1958a), reproduced by courtesy of the Society of Chemical Industry.

suggesting that over the range investigated the number of cells in the whole animal remains constant.

An increase in the size rather than the number of the cells has also been found sufficient to account for the increase in the bulk of cattle (Hiner, Hankins *et al.*, 1953) and sheep (Joubert, 1955) and a recent report (Bendall and Voyle, 1967) tells of an actual reduction in the number of cells (with a further increase in the diameters of the remainder) as cattle age. However, foetal sheep increase in weight from 8 to 800 g by actual multiplication of the muscle cells, which remain of roughly constant size. The formation of new cells presumably ceases

at a particular stage of growth, but this stage has not been identified in
fish—unless the levelling of cell diameters shown in the smallest fish
in Fig. 40 should chance to be significant.

Since doubling the body length results in halving the number of cells
in a given weight of muscle, it is to be expected that the deoxyribose
nucleic acid (DNA), which is usually constant in amount in each cell
nucleus, will be halved also. In actual fact the reduction is less than this,
so some synthesis of DNA probably occurs in the muscle during growth.
Figure 41 is representative of curves obtained in five different months

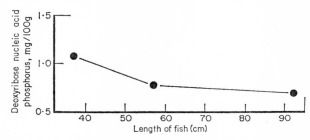

FIG. 41. Concentration of deoxyribose nucleic acid phosphorus in muscle tissue from
myotome no. 12 in *Gadus morhua* of different lengths. After Love (1958b), reproduced
by courtesy of the Society of Chemical Industry.

of the year, suggesting that the effect, a relative elevation of values in
the larger fish, is real.

Since DNA is a constituent of each cell nucleus, carrying the genetic
material, it is actively synthesized in the gonads, where the creation of
each new germ cell is accompanied by synthesis of an appropriate
amount of DNA. This synthesis makes complete nonsense of any
relationship that there might have been between the size of the organ
and the concentration of the DNA, as Fig. 42 shows; there is no question
here of the DNA being 'diluted' by an increase in cytoplasm.

With the increase in cell diameters in larger fish, we should also
expect a reduction in the proportion of cell-wall constituents, largely
collagen (Kono, Kakuma *et al.*, 1964), unless the cell-walls thicken at the
same time. This field is unexplored.

Figure 43 shows that the spaces between the myocommata, that is,
the lengths of the cells, double when the fish doubles in length. However,
as already shown (Fig. 6, p. 6), the proportion of connective tissue
in whole flesh actually increases, because the thickness of the myocommata has increased three-fold at the same time. Since myocommata
are also rich in sodium, there should be a tendency for the sodium
concentration to increase in larger fish, but this may be largely offset by

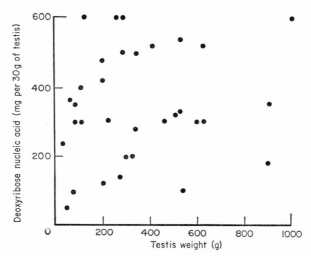

FIG. 42. Concentration of deoxyribose nucleic acid in the testis of *Thunnus obesus* with increase in size. After Fujii (1965), reproduced by courtesy of the author and the Director of the Tokai Regional Fisheries Laboratory.

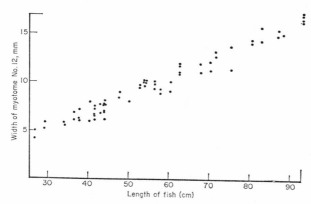

FIG. 43. Lengths of cells in myotome no. 12, counting from the point of severance of the head, in *Gadus morhua* of different sizes. After Love (1958a), reproduced by courtesy of the Society of Chemical Industry.

a decrease in the sodium content of the myotomes, which we shall now consider.

In earlier work, no consistent relationship between the size of a mammal and the mineral content of its musculature was found (some papers are reviewed by Love, Robertson and Strachan, 1968). In fish, the picture was also confused. The sodium and potassium content of

Anoplopoma fimbria showed wide variations, but in *Sebastodes alutus*, *Gadus macrocephalus*, and *Ophiodon elongatus* the mineral composition was seen to be relatively uniform, regardless of species, size, season or fishing ground (Thurston, 1961b). Comparing these constituents in *Oncorhynchus tschawytscha* of various sizes, McBride and MacLeod (1956a) found that the muscle sodium of small fish was greater than that in medium or large fish. However, this applied only to three small fish out of five examined, and in *Hippoglossus stenolepis* it was the larger fish that showed the higher values. MacLeod, Jonas and McBride (1958) reiterated that there was in fact a relationship between size and the concentration of mineral constituents, but added that the issue was complicated by the salmon spending part of their lives in salt water, part in fresh, and that there were additional fluctuations which could not be explained.

Recently the issue appears to have been clarified in *Gadus morhua*. The potassium concentration has been found not to alter according to the size of the fish, but the sodium always decreases as the fish grow, *provided they are not depleted* (Love, Robertson and Strachan, 1968). For a considerable portion of the year, the muscle of this species is depleted through the transfer of protein to the gonads for building up eggs or sperm, and also probably for repairing tissue after spawning. The subject will be considered in full later (p. 99), the point here being that the larger fish are more depleted than the smaller (Fig. 45, p. 91). Depletion causes the sodium in the muscle to rise (p. 246), and since in the spawning months there is great variation in the extent of depletion between fish, any clear relationship between sodium concentration and size is destroyed.

The total mineral content of cartilage from the pectoral girdle has been shown by Doyle (1968) to increase linearly with age in the elasmobranch *Squalus acanthias*. Changes in the ratio of the amino sugars in the same tissue as the fish grow appear to be unimportant.

It is possible that the proportion of extracellular fluid is greater in young fish at the stage when the cells are multiplying rather than increasing in size. It is well known, according to Dickerson and Widdowson (1960), that the water content of (mammalian) tissue falls during development, the fall being accompanied by a decrease in the extracellular ions sodium and chloride. Photomicrographs in their paper showed that the human foetus embodied much more extracellular space than did the young child after birth. Mezincescu and Strugali (1958) showed the same effect in young rabbits, and Parker and Vanstone (1966) in *Oncorhynchus gorbuscha*, the significant point being that these fish showing a decline in water content with growth were less than 7·5 cm long. Growth also causes a decrease in the water content of *Eptatretus stouti* (Munz and Morris, 1965).

Thus by analogy with measurements on mammals there is a likelihood that in the young stage of fish, when the cells are dividing, a higher proportion of extracellular space results in more net water, sodium and chloride, all of which diminish as the fish grows. When the number of cells has reached a stable figure the water content becomes constant, but smaller fish still have a higher sodium content than bigger fish, probably because of their smaller cells (see p. 3).

3. *Fecundity, Exhaustion and Reserves*

Not only in man does life become more of a strain with increasing age ; we may derive some pale comfort from the knowledge that many fish are similarly troubled, eventually to death. The earliest paper on this subject to come to the attention of the writer was by Orton (1929), who, reviewing several earlier papers, concluded that the ripe gonads of a fish formed a progressively larger proportion of the total body weight with increasing age. As we shall see in the section on aging (p. 126), some fish do become less fertile as they grow older, but this is true of only a few species.

Egg counts confirm Orton's hypothesis. Figure 44 shows that the number of eggs laid by *Gadus morhua* rises more and more steeply as the fish grow.

The build-up of gonads is often, perhaps always, accomplished at the expense of the body proteins. Dietary proteins seem to be unequal to the huge demands made by the sex organs while eggs and sperm are maturing. In non-fatty fish the whole process may be observed by means of water determinations. As protein is removed from the muscle, the water content rises steadily and so is a useful index of the state of depletion of the fish (Love, 1960; 1962b).

When *Gadus morhua* of different sizes were taken from one fishing ground in the North Sea at different times of the year, the water contents varied in an interesting way (Fig. 45). Immature fish maintained the same water content at all times, apart from a small peak in the month of March. Medium-sized fish, which were spawning for the first time, showed an increased water content, and took longer to recover. The largest fish, all of which had spawned at least once already, showed the highest water content at the spawning time, when they were physically weak as evidenced by their lack of struggling when landed on the deck. The most depleted fish ever caught in this area by the writer was 108 cm long and obviously moribund when landed on the

5*

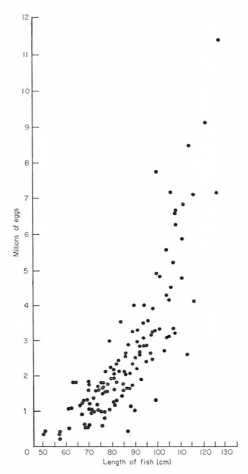

Fig. 44. Number of eggs laid by *Gadus morhua* with increase in length of the parent fish. After May (1967) reproduced by courtesy of the author and the Fisheries Research Board of Canada.

deck in the month of June. The huge water content of 87·2% made one wonder what was holding the fish together.

The small peak seen in immature fish may perhaps be the result of starvation at that time of the year, but there is also a possibility of some sort of 'dummy run', a modified hormone-controlled change analogous to the incomplete spawning migration undertaken by immature Svalbard cod, which start out with the mature fish but do not complete the journey to the spawning ground (Trout, 1957).

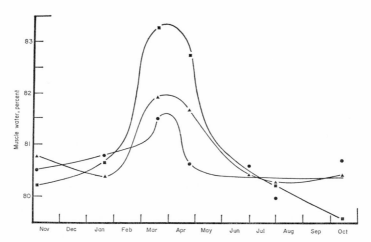

F<small>IG</small>. 45. Water content of the muscle of *Gadus morhua* caught on the Aberdeen Bank (N.E. Scotland) during the year 1959. ● Sexually immature; ▲ Spawning for the first time; ■ Spawned several times. Redrawn from Love (1960), reproduced by courtesy of MacMillan (Journals) Ltd. *Note:* A corollary is apparent in the work of Khawaja and Jafri (1967), who showed that there is a steady decline in lipid, protein and ash with increase in size of *Ophicephalus punctatus* captured just after spawning.

However, it is not clear what form this change would take, unless the immature gonads enlarge 'experimentally' at the spawning season.

'Over-reproduction' affects males as well as females: according to Hickling (1930) the burden of spawning in male *Merluccius merluccius* doubles for every 10 cm increase in body length.

Since larger fish, then, make greater demands on their resources, we should expect them to lay up greater energy reserves, and this in fact is the case.

Liver or muscle oil has been reported to increase during the growth of *Anguilla anguilla* (Lovern, 1938b), *Cyprinus carpio* (Naumann, 1927, quoted by Mann, 1961), *Gadus morhua* (Jangaard, Brockerhoff *et al.*, 1967), *Galeorhinus zyopterus* (Ripley and Bolomey, 1946), *Raja batis* (Fisher, 1964), *Sardinella longiceps* (Hornell and Nayudu, 1923) and *Trachurus trachurus* (Arevalo 1948). Hornell and Nayudu (1923) interpreted the relationship differently, concluding simply that older fish are able to lay down reserves more readily because their growth rate is then slower, but in the light of Orton's suggestion of 'over-reproduction" with age, the increased lipid seems more likely to act as an extra energy reserve at the spawning time to assist recovery.

The distribution of ages in *Gadus morhua* landed at Torry Research Station bears out the idea of 'over-reproduction' in this species at least : among the larger cod, otolith readings (see Figs. 64 and 65, p. 162) reveal ages of 6, 7 or 8 years . . . but no more. The fate of the 9-year-olds must be dramatic, since there is no obvious appearance of aging in those a year younger, and one sometimes hears of moribund cod lying in deep water. What tragedies are enacted beneath the waves —and the setting of the stage for this particular one is shown up starkly in Fig. 45 in mere determinations of water content!

The lipid reserves laid down by *Trachurus trachurus* with increasing size are shown in Fig. 46. The fall in value in the largest size group

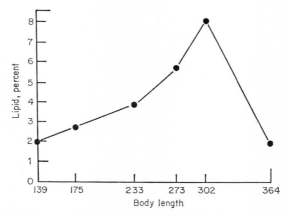

FIG. 46. Relationship between lipid content of *Trachurus trachurus* and body length. After Arevalo (1948), reproduced by courtesy of the Instituto Español de Oceanografia.

probably indicates spawning ; the point made by the author was that because of this relationship with size, lipid cannot be used as an index of nutritional state.

Krivobock (1964) showed (Fig. 29) that the relative size of the liver of Baltic herring (*Clupea harengus membranus*) increases as the fish grow, and it has also been demonstrated that as the size of the liver increases, so does the yield of oil per unit weight (Ali, Haq and Mahdihassan, 1958, using sharks caught off the coast of Karachi). Phillips, Lovelace *et al.* (1956) showed that the body lipid of *Salvelinus fontinalis* increases with size, but only in specimens reared in a hatchery ; the correlation does not exist in wild fish for some unexplained reason.

Kiermeir (1939) reported that the blood sugar levels of freshwater fish do not differ according to size, and Al-Gauhari (1958) came to a similar conclusion with *Clarias lazera*. However, the level of carbohydrate in transit, as this is, does not necessarily reflect that in the muscles or liver, and in fact there is some evidence that larger fish carry greater reserves of this constituent also. Both in the writer's laboratory and elsewhere (Kelly, 1969) it has been noticed that the muscle of large *Gadus morhua*, some time after death, tends to reach a lower minimum pH (pH drops for the first 24 hours or so post-mortem) than that of small fish. Low pH results from the accumulation of lactic acid, derived in turn from carbohydrates, so it is possible that larger fish hold larger reserves, again as a buffer against depletion. Patashnik (1966) also reported a lowering of pH with increasing size, in this case in *Hippoglossus hippoglossus*. Clearly there is scope for additional work here.

4. *Studies on Blood*

The blood volume of fish is relatively small, and counts of blood cells seem to show that larger fish require an increased oxygen-carrying capacity, though this may be a premature conclusion. Murachi (1959) found that the haematocrit value (volume of red blood cells after centrifuging) and haemoglobin content of the blood of *Cyprinus carpio* increase as the fish grow, and Preston (1960) found the same in *Pleuronectes platessa*. Values for two other species are shown in Table XVII. All values in the table show a clear upward trend with growth, apart from the haemoglobin of *Tilapia*.

TABLE XVII. BLOOD CONSTITUENTS IN FISH OF INCREASING SIZE (after Pradhan, 1961).

Species	*Body length* cm	*Red blood cells* $\times\ 10^{-6}$ *per cu. mm*	*Haematocrit* (*red cell vol.*)	*Haemoglobin* *g/100 ml*
Tilapia sp.	9·0–9·5	1·125–1·49	28–33	10–11
	10–11	1·04–1·6	30–37	9–10
	12–14	1·6–2·4	35–44	9–12
Ophiocephalus sp.	10–13	1·7–1·9	30–35	12–14
	14–15	2·0–2·52	44–56	15–16·5
	17–19	2·8–2·86	60–70	18–20

When fish haemoglobin is subjected to electrophoresis, it often separates into bands moving at different speeds (polymorphism), the proportions of which have been used to identify different races or stocks within a single species (p. 164). Juvenile and adult stages of fish are often similarly characterized by distinct forms of haemoglobin

(Hashimoto and Matsuura, 1960b: *Oncorhynchus keta*; Manwell, 1963: *Squalus suckleyi*; Golovanenko, 1964: *Acipenser güldenstadti*; Yamanaka, Yamaguchi *et al.*, 1967: salmonid species).

The clearest changes to have been described so far were found in *Salmo salar* by Koch, Bergström and Evans (1964) and in *Clupea harengus* by Wilkins and Iles (1966). These authors have demonstrated a series of patterns succeeding one another as the fish grow. Their results are shown in Fig. 47.

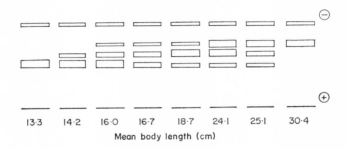

Fig. 47. Stylized reproductions of electropherograms of haemoglobin from *Clupea harengus* of different sizes. After Wilkins and Iles (1966), reproduced by courtesy of the authors and Pergamon Press.

The nature of these changes and their purpose can only be guessed, although by analogy with Table XVII a change in oxygen-carrying capacity is an obvious possibility—assuming as one usually does that any change, however small, is not fortuitous but benefits the animal in some way. At present it is not certain whether these different components are different haemoglobins, that is, have a different sequence of amino acids or result from various recombinations of polypeptide chains. The latter explanation is thought to be the more likely by Wilkins and Iles (1966).

Haemoglobin polymorphism related to growth is not a universal phenomenon: the electrophoretic patterns of the haemoglobins of *Gadus morhua* and *Gadus merlangus* do *not* change with the age of the fish (Sick, 1961).

There is evidence from several sources that the electrophoretic patterns of the serum proteins also change to some extent with the growth of the fish (Booke, 1964b), but the changes in haemoglobin are generally greater, so potentially more useful for estimating the stage of development.

5. Miscellaneous

Several substances have been shown to change with the growth of the fish, but information on any one of them in most cases has been confined to a single species, so the general applicability of the results is not known.

The increase of vitamin A in the liver, however, is well authenticated (Lovern, Edisbury and Morton, 1933: several species; MacPherson, 1933: *Gadus morhua*; Higashi, 1940, quoted by Higashi, 1961: several species; Ripley and Bolomey, 1946: *Galeorhinus zyopterus*; Fisher, 1964: *Squalus acanthias* and *Raja batis*). Higashi (1961) was of the opinion that bigger fish consume more vitamin A. Certainly, as they produce a larger number of eggs, more vitamin A will be required for the visual pigments of the larval eyes, so larger stores will have to be laid down at other seasons. Transport from the store to the developing ova was observed by Plack and Woodhead (1966), who found that the

TABLE XVIII. CHANGES IN VARIOUS CONSTITUENTS OF FISH WITH INCREASE IN SIZE

Substance	Change	Species	Reference
Amylase	Increase*	*Catla catla*	Das (1965)
Calcium	Decrease*		
Chloride	Increase*		
Cholesterol	Increase†	*Cyprinus carpio*	Ogino and Konno (1950)
Creatinine	Increase*	*Catla catla*	Das (1965)
Fatty acid, 20 carbon, mono-unsaturated ($=20:1$)			
	Increase	*Gadus morhua*	Jangaard, Ackman and Sipos (1967)
Fatty acid, 22:6			
	Decrease		
Glucose	Increase*	*Catla catla*	Das (1965)
Haemoglobin	Increase*		
Iodine, protein-bound	Increase‡	*Scarus guacamaia*	Matty (1959)
Lipid saturation	Increase	*Clupea harengus*	Lovern (1938a)
Phosphatase	Decrease*	*Catla catla*	Das (1965)
Phosphatide	Decrease†	*Cyprinus carpio*	Ogino and Konno (1950)
Protein	Increase*	*Catla catla*	Das (1965)
Trimethylamine oxide	Increase¶	*Clupea harengus*	Hughes (1959a)
Vitamin B_{12}	Decrease	*Tuna-like fishes*	Y. Simidu (1957) quoted by Higashi (1961)
Zinc	Increase§	(general)	Vinogradov (1953)

* in blood; † in brain; ‡ in thyroid, more in females than males; § tissues in general; ¶ in muscle.

vitamin A in the blood plasma of female *Gadus morhua* rises from a resting level of 2 μg/100 ml to 10 μg/100 ml at the spawning season. Little change occurs in the males, as vitamin A is probably not required by sperm. There is, however, no evidence that the stores of vitamin A in the females are actually greater than those of the males— in fact it is the reverse in *Squalus acanthias* and *Raja batis* (Fisher, 1964).

Carotenoids, some of which are precursors of vitamin A, were shown to increase in the liver of *Squalus acanthias* with growth, but to decrease in *Raja batis* (Fisher, 1964).

The remaining miscellaneous changes are shown in Table XVIII without further comment.

6. *Negative Findings*

A number of substances have been said to have no relationship with the size of the fish. These are summarized in Table XIX, but must be accepted with caution, since negative findings are more difficult to

TABLE XIX. CONSTITUENTS STATED TO HAVE HAD NO RELATIONSHIP WITH
THE SIZE OF THE FISH

Substance	Species	Reference
Free amino acids*	*Clupea harengus*	Hughes (1959b)
Astaxanthin	5 spp of salmon	Kanemitsu and Aoe (1958)
Cholesterol†	*Salmo trutta*	McCartney (1965)
Niacin	*Gadus morhua*	Braekkan (1959)
Pantothenic acid		
Protein‡		Anon (1966a)
Pyridoxine	(general)	Yanase (1956)
Riboflavin	(several species)	Hoar and Barberie (1945)
	Gadus morhua	Braekkan (1959)
Vitamin B_{12}		

* collectively or individually; † in serum; ‡ not true in spawning season. See text.

establish than positive ones, especially as positive but intermittent correlation sometimes occur. For example, it was the joint conclusion of six laboratories (Anon., 1966a) that the size of *Gadus morhua* has no significant influence on the nitrogen (protein) content of the flesh. However, bearing in mind that protein and water in this species are inversely related, Fig. 45 (p. 91) shows that this conclusion would not apply during the spawning season.

D. Maturity and Spawning

1. *Introduction*

There is a considerable body of literature on the chemical changes that occur when fish become sexually mature, and, in the case of salmon and related species, when they leave the sea and migrate upstream. In spite of this, the present section has not been easy to present as a self-sufficient account, because many of the phenomena described are not the direct result of maturation at all, but can be duplicated by straight-forward depletion on the one hand (described fully in a later section, p. 222), or by placing in water of a different salinity (see p. 187) on the other. Moreover, the changes that occur in the developing ova have already been described as preliminaries to the study of the growth of the larvae (p. 65).

What, then, is left? Alterations in the hormone pattern obviously belong to this section, and, as genetic material is proliferating during maturation, any studies on the concentrations of nucleic acids should be relevant. Certain amino acids may perhaps be mobilized preferentially from the muscle for the concoction of sex products, but they may also be mobilized during starvation, and no clear distinction has so far been made.

Many fish mature when they reach a critical size, rather than a particular age. Thus *Abramis brama* matures when it has grown to 27 cm in length, *Idus idus* to 18 cm (Vasnetsov, 1934, quoted by Nikolsky, 1963) and *Clupea harengus* to 21·6 cm (Burd, 1962). Since the growth rates of several species are known to be retarded in more Northerly latitudes, it follows that maturity is initiated in fish of progressively greater ages as one moves North. For example, *Rutilus rutilus* in Southern Europe becomes mature at 3 years, in Central Europe at 4–5 years, and in Finland at 5–6 years (Nikolsky, 1963).

We shall now consider the depletive effects of maturation and spawning, and if possible try to discover whether they are in any way different from the effects of merely withholding food at a time when the gonads are inactive.

2. *Depletion**

(a) *General*

The production of eggs or sperm always depletes a fish, but in salmon, ascending the rivers to spawn, the condition is exaggerated by a concurrent abstention from food. There seems to be a puzzle here,

---

* A detailed study of depletion is presented later (p. 222). This section deals with depletion only as reported in relation to maturation.

because as anglers know an ascending salmon will snap at a bait, but according to Gillespie (1898) even if the salmon swallowed food at this time, it could not digest it because of a marked decrease in the secretion of gastric enzymes. Gulland, also in 1898, described the breakdown of the whole stomach lining of migrating *Salmo salar* by a process he described vividly if unattractively as "desquamative catarrh". Extensive degeneration of the digestive tract has also been observed in *Oncorhynchus* sp. by Greene (1926).

Thus the salmon suffers an incredible amount of depletion, losing up to 99% of its lipid, 72% of its protein and 63% of its ash (Tilik, 1932). At the same time, the water content of all the tissues increases (Greene, 1926).

These extremes of depletion are not suffered by all fish: *Gadus morhua*, for example, feeds fairly intensively throughout the year (Rae, 1967a), so can compensate to some extent for the drain on its resources, at least in its earlier years. However, although *Clupea harengus* do not draw on their body proteins during the early stages of gonad development (Milroy, 1908), some depletion seems to be the invariable accompaniment of maturation in fish, and Siebert, Schmitt and Bottke (1964) suggested that that was the reason why fish muscle is so extraordinarily rich in proteolytic enzymes.

(b) Carbohydrates

Physical exhaustion can profitably be studied by means of carbohydrate analysis in mammals but not in fish. Most of the energy needed for spawning migration in salmonids is derived from lipids or from glucose recently derived from lipids (gluconeogenesis), and so the amount of glycogen in the muscles of salmon caught in fresh water is very small, irrespective of the degree of maturation (Fontaine and Hatey, 1953).

However, glycogen and glucose have both been reported to accumulate in the ovary during maturation (Greene, 1926: *Oncorhynchus tschawytscha*; Chang and Idler, 1960: *Oncorhynchus nerka*; Yanni, 1961: *Clarias lazera*), so in female fish the glycogen of the liver, the main carbohydrate storehouse, is preferentially depleted (Fontaine and Hatey, 1953: Chang and Idler, 1960). The difference is sometimes striking: in spawning *Salmo salar*, Fontaine and Hatey (1953) found an average of 24·9 mg glycogen/g of liver in the male fish, but only 0·5 mg in the female.

As with other constituents, the level in the blood does not reflect the situation in muscle or liver, and shows no consistent change during maturation. In *Myxine glutinosa*, no difference was detected between the blood glucose contents of egg-bearing and non-egg-bearing females (Falkmer and Winbladh, 1964). Nace, Moule and Schuh (1964) and Robertson, Krupp, Favour *et al.* (1961) observed a rise in the blood sugar of *Opsanus tau* and *Oncorhynchus tschawytscha*, respectively, during maturation of the gonads, but that of *Lampetra fluviatilis* (Bentley and Follett, 1965) and *Oncorhynchus nerka* (Jonas and MacLeod, 1960) showed a moderate fall, little difference showing between the sexes in the latter species.

In muscle, the glycogen content of *Lampetra fluviatilis* falls from 245 mg% at the mouth of the river to 222 mg% at the spawning ground (Bentley and Follett, 1965)—again little change.

Thus the changes in the carbohydrate reserves of the fish seem mostly to reflect the requirements of the developing ovaries.

(c) Amino acids and proteins

Gjessing (1963) showed that the concentrations of several *free* amino acids of the roe of *Clupea harengus* increase steadily with maturity, reflecting the activity of transfer from other sites. A corresponding activity in breakdown is not, however, indicated by the levels of *free* amino acids in the muscle, which show little change according to the stage of maturity (Hughes, 1959b: *Clupea harengus*; Cowey, Daisley and Parry, 1962: *Salmo salar*). Perhaps the amino acids are removed from the muscle as fast as they are liberated. The latter authors also noted little change in the amino acids of the blood during spawning migration, but Chance (1962) found big increases in l-methyl-histidine, beta-alanine, serine and taurine in *Oncorhynchus tschawytscha*, so the situation is somewhat confused. Wood (1958) and Wood, Duncan and Jackson (1960) noted a marked decrease in the *free* histidine of the muscle of *Oncorhynchus nerka* during spawning migration.

Table XX shows the variations in five of the combined amino acids, both in gonad and the corresponding muscle, for *Clupea sprattus* at various stages of maturity. The arginine shows a decline in the muscle of females and a corresponding increase in the gonads, but no other constituent behaves in such an exemplary manner, and Petrenko and Karasikova (1958) concluded that the changes were "complex".

The decrease in muscle arginine had been observed previously in six other species of fish by Sekiné (1921 and 1926, quoted by Geiger and Borgstrom, 1962), who also observed a decrease in histidine and cystine and an increase in lysine during maturation.

Korzhenko (1966) analysed a greater number of amino acids in the gonads of *Oncorhynchus keta* during maturation (Table XXI). In the

TABLE XX. CHANGES IN THE AMINO ACIDS OF CLUPEA SPRATTUS DURING MATURATION (after Petrenko and Karasikova, 1958).

	Percent raw protein								
	Muscle					Gonads			
	Females								
Stage of maturity	II	III	IV	V	VI	II	III	IV	V
Arginine	9·95	9·30	5·18	4·52	4·68	7·70	7·71	8·78	10·41
Histidine	1·21	1·41	1·65	0·90	1·23	1·30	1·35	1·38	1·48
Methionine	3·69	3·56	2·56	1·68	1·73	3·12	2·89	2·37	2·12
Tryptophan	2·73	1·77	1·33	1·17	1·02	2·20	1·98	1·61	1·58
Tyrosine	3·65	3·80	3·81	2·87	2·66	4·87	4·29	3·73	3·37
	Males								
Arginine	3·71	6·96	7·52			8·74	9·21	10·43	
Histidine	0·63	1·32	1·65			1·07	1·41	1·79	
Methionine	2·37	2·33	2·31			2·41	2·50	2·60	
Tryptophan	1·57	1·26	1·14	1·10	0·95	5·60	2·68	1·49	1·41
Tyrosine	4·23	3·86	3·46	3·04	2·87	6·21	4·18	2·68	0·74

II: beginning to mature. III-V: maturing. VI: ripe and spawning.

TABLE XXI. CHANGES IN THE AMINO ACIDS OF THE GONADS OF ONCORHYNCHUS KETA DURING MATURATION (after Korzhenko, 1966)

	Moles percent						
	Female					Male	
Stage of maturity	II	II-III	III	III-IV	II	II-III	III
Alanine	10·58	11·99	13·46	12·75	9·82	10·48	9·16
Arginine	4·35	4·29	3·87	4·48	5·00	5·37	6·88
Aspartic acid	10·06	9·12	9·18	9·22	8·69	8·47	8·15
Glutamic acid	10·83	10·17	10·41	10·46	10·47	10·80	10·47
Glycine	10·95	6·52	5·22	5·31	16·86	15·81	10·78
Histidine	2·15	2·42	1·94	1·82	1·62	1·76	2·31
Isoleucine	3·23	4·39	5·00	5·24	2·82	2·90	4·68
Leucine	6·97	8·78	9·70	9·22	6·45	6·73	8·26
Lysine	5·48	6·67	4·62	5·39	5·70	6·31	10·14
Methionine	2·06	2·42	2·41	2·41	2·51	2·08	2·13
Phenyl alanine	4·35	3·99	4·21	4·22	3·03	3·18	3·23
Proline	7·25	7·15	6·44	7·40	8·60	7·21	5·54
Serine	8·11	7·36	7·94	7·51	6·59	6·81	5·14
Threonine	6·72	5·79	5·93	5·61	4·61	5·03	4·97
Tyrosine	2·47	2·72	2·81	2·62	2·32	2·27	2·28
Valine	4·43	6·15	6·81	6·07	4·91	4·92	6·29

gonad of the female, proline and glycine declined and alanine increased, while in the male, proline and glycine declined, and lysine, histidine, arginine, leucine and isoleucine increased. Korzhenko found the increase in alanine and decrease in glycine to be consistent enough for him to use the ratio of the two as an index of maturity: in four species of fish, glycine/alanine ranged from 1·2 to 1·4 when immature, and from 0·3 to 0·6 when mature.

The reduction in the concentrations of proline and glycine is interesting, because it is now well established in different animals that collagen, the principal protein of connective tissue, is unusually rich in these amino acids (Harkness, Marko *et al.*, 1954; Bowes, Elliott and Moss, 1955; Damodaran, Sivaraman and Dhavalikar, 1956; Whitaker, 1959; Young and Lorimer, 1960; Manery, 1962; Asboe-Hansen, 1963; Lewis and Piez, 1964; Bornstein and Piez, 1964). It seems most likely therefore that proline and glycine decrease during maturation because of an increase in the proportion of eggs or sperm, which reduces the proportion of connective tissue (mostly collagen) in a given weight of sex organ. The only amino acid to occur exclusively in collagen, hydroxyproline, was not determined by Korzhenko.

The complementary picture is seen in Table XXII, where the muscle

TABLE XXII. AMINO ACIDS IN THE MUSCLE OF MIGRATING AND SPENT SALMO SALAR (after Cowey, Daisley and Parry, 1962)

	g N per 100 g protein N	
Amino acid	Migrating in sea water	Spent
Alanine	6·94	7·04
Arginine	12·6	12·1
Aspartic acid	7·45	7·58
Cystine/2	1·04	0·95
Glutamic acid	9·65	9·91
Glycine	5·90	6·34
Histidine	4·68	4·31
Isoleucine	3·81	3·48
Leucine	6·25	5·76
Lysine	12·25	12·98
Methionine	1·90	2·00
Phenylalanine	2·47	2·65
Proline	2·78	2·96
Serine	3·85	3·78
Threonine	3·81	3·85
Tryptophan	0·97	0·91
Tyrosine	2·00	1·87

of spent *Salmo salar* shows a small *increase* in proline and glycine, corresponding with preferential utilization of the more mobile proteins during spawning migration and so a relative increase in collagen. Korzhenko and Novikov (1967) observed no relationship between the amino acid composition of the muscle of *Oncorhynchus keta* or *Oncorhynchus gorbuscha* and the stage of maturation, but only marine forms of the fish were examined, so the development of the gonads would have been relatively slight.

Collagen is usually considered to be metabolically inert, and apart from such instances as the resorbing uterus after the birth of the young, or the disappearance of the tails of amphibian tadpoles at metamorphosis, one usually regards collagen newly laid down as being likely to remain there for the life of the individual. However, if mice are fed on a protein-free diet, some of the skin collagen is mobilized (Harkness, Harkness and James, 1958), so a certain amount of catabolism might be expected to occur in the collagen of maturing fish, especially as it is relatively easily broken down by heat (Fig. 79, p. 215). Actual measurements, though, have yielded some curious results: far from being mobilized, collagen seems to be actively deposited in the body of *Clupea pallasii* during maturation, since the fluid obtained from these fish during heat treatment was observed to contain progressively more gelatin (hydrolyzed collagen) as the spawning time approached (McBride, MacLeod and Idler, 1959a,b). Subsequent measurements of collagen in skin and scales showed a rise from 1·76% in June to 4·06% in February, the spawning time, and from 0·22 to 0·31% in the muscle. While the increase in muscle collagen can probably be dismissed as relative and due to the depletion of other constituents, the increase in the skin seems to be too large to be accounted for in this way. The collagen content of *Clupea harengus* has also been found to increase at the spawning time (Fig. 48), but the concentration increases more, later in the year, when the fish cease to feed (Hughes, 1963). Most of the increase is shown to be in the skin, and from histological sections Hughes showed that the skin really does become thicker.

The reason is not known, but it is logical to expect that the skin would need strengthening at a time when the body cavity is crammed full of eggs. However, Hughes' findings are complicated by the discovery of an increase caused by simple depletion. McBride, MacLeod and Idler (1960) noted that *Clupea pallasii* cease to feed during gonad development, so that much of the gonad tissue is built from proteins drawn from the musculature. They suggest that since the requirements for amino acids by the gonads are likely to be selective, the amino acids which are not needed might be made into collagen and deposited in the skin

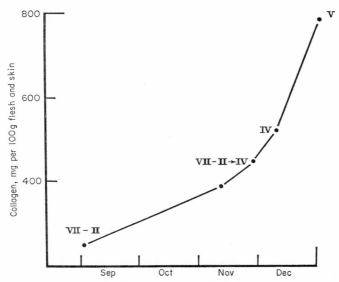

Fɪɢ. 48. Collagen content of flesh plus skin in *Clupea harengus* of different stages of maturity. For key to the Roman numerals see legend to Fig. 29 (p. 63). After Hughes (1963), reproduced by courtesy of the author and the Society of Chemical Industry.

(and perhaps in the jaw extensions and humped back of salmon species, see Fig. 51) which would be a sort of tidy waste-disposal unit—an ingenious suggestion which requires further investigation, as does this whole question of collagen (?)synthesis during periods of depletion.

In 1958, Ironside and Love examined the solubility characteristics of the muscle proteins of *Gadus morhua* at different seasons. Usually about 95% of them would dissolve in an excess of neutral 5% sodium chloride after homogenization at chill temperatures, but the survey revealed some interesting behaviour: in November, at the beginning of the maturation period, the insoluble protein nitrogen of sexually mature fish increased from a normal (summer) value of about 0·1 g per 100 g muscle to 0·45 g, while the value for immature fish remained at the 'resting' level (see Table XXXIV, p. 236). The total protein nitrogen was the same in both groups of fish, indeed it was slightly greater in the larger fish, so the change appeared to represent an insolubilization of protein that had previously dissolved, and was not just a preferential depletion. As the spawning season at the beginning of March approached, this insoluble fraction increased further in maturing fish and then declined to the resting level as spawning passed. In immature fish an increase was observed, but it was small and of short duration.

The phenomenon may have represented a change in the properties of the muscle proteins preparatory to being mobilized. In the light of their later findings, McBride, MacLeod and Idler (1960) considered that the insoluble fraction might be newly-synthesized collagen, but no direct evidence has yet been forthcoming.

Ironside and Love (1958) suggested that values for insoluble protein might be a sensitive indication of the biological condition of the fish. The important question was whether the change was controlled by the maturation process (hormones) or simply by depletion. A long series of experiments showed that the phenomenon could be reproduced at will by starving the fish at a time when the gonads were inactive (Love and Robertson, 1967). Figures 92 and 93 (pp. 236 and 237) show that the increase in insoluble protein occurs some two weeks after the onset of starvation, appearing much earlier than the overall loss of protein or gain in water, which is undetectable until some time afterwards. The important point, though, as concerns the present section is that the phenomenon is not specific to maturation, but can occur under other circumstances.

Some changes have been noted in the blood proteins during maturation. Naumov (1956, quoted by Blaxter and Holliday, 1963) found that the haemoglobin content of the blood of *Clupea harengus* is highest during early maturation, but falls sharply at spawning and in the spent stage. This finding may represent merely a change in plasma volume, but qualitative changes in the types of haemoglobin are free from this criticism, and Wilkins and Iles (1966) have found that the electrophoretic patterns of the haemoglobins of the same species can be correlated with the stages of maturity on the Hjort scale, which is described in the legend to Fig. 29, p. 63.

On the other hand, gross changes in the red blood cells do not occur during maturation. The content of haemoglobin in the blood does not vary between pre- and post-spawned fish (Sindermann and Mairs, 1961 : *Alosa pseudoharengus*), and there is no change in the sedimentation rate or red blood cell fragility. Similarly, Smirnova (1962) reported that the numbers of red and white blood cells do not correlate with the maturity of a number of freshwater fish.

The serum proteins do seem to show small changes with maturity, but as usual no one has so far attempted to distinguish between maturation and asexual depletion. Sindermann and Mairs (1959, quoted by Blaxter and Holliday, 1963) found no difference with maturity in the serum electrophoretic patterns of *Pomolobus pseudoharengus*, but Thurston (1967), studying *Salmo gairdnerii*, observed a band which is found only in sexually ripe females. He also noticed other variations in the pattern which he attributed to the degree of maturity. A less specific effect was observed by Drilhon (1954) in *Anguilla anguilla*, in which the globulin fractions cannot be separated in the serum of resting females, but can in mature females.

Analogous results have been obtained in the field of immunology. Ridgway, Klontz and Matsumoto (1962) found an antigenic component in the serum of *Oncorhynchus nerka* which is confined to mature females, later identified as a lipoprotein (perhaps ovovitellin, see p. 62) by Krauel and Ridgway (1963).

(d) *Lipids*

As already stated (p. 98), the maturation of salmonid species results in an extensive depletion of the lipid reserves of the flesh. Not all of the lipid is used for energy purposes: in *Oncorhynchus nerka* 8% of it is transferred to the female gonad and 0·5% to the male gonad during migration (Idler and Bitners, 1960).

The lipid in the white muscle of this species was observed to decrease from 9·7% to 1·8% during spawning migration, but from 27·4% to 6·8% in dark muscle—a higher final figure, though a similar proportional decrease (Thurston and Newman, 1962).

A reduction in lipid stores may cause an apparent increase in the concentration of lipid-soluble materials which are not being utilized. A case in point is vitamin A, which has been shown to become more concentrated in the liver of *Galeorhinus zyopterus* during maturation, owing to the depletion of oil in this organ (Ripley and Bolomey, 1946). In addition, the lipid remaining in the body of mature *Clupea harengus* has been observed by Lovern (1938a) to be more saturated than that of fish at an earlier stage of maturation, presumably through preferential utilization, though a change in body size or the nature of the diet could be important.

(e) *Inorganic ions*

At first glance it is difficult to make anything of the published information on inorganic ions in relation to maturation, which seems to show changes of a random nature. The reason is most probably that nearly all the work has been carried out on fish which ascend rivers to spawn, and the transfer from salt to fresh water, coupled with a loss of ability to osmoregulate after spawning (p. 106), causes an overall loss of ions which masks the effect caused by maturation.

The only two papers on non-migratory fish both relate to *Gadus morhua*. Maturation here is seen to be accompanied by an increase in the water content of the muscle (Fig. 45, p. 91), and concurrently the predominantly extracellular ions sodium and chloride increase, while the intracellular potassium, magnesium and phosphorus decline (Sutton, 1968).

Love, Robertson and Strachan (1968) showed that the effect is not confined to maturing cod, but can be reproduced by depleting these fish in an aquarium when the gonads are inactive. Their results are discussed in full under 'depletion' (p. 246), the point here being that hormonal control of inorganic ions in maturing fish, tentatively suggested by MacLeod, Jonas and McBride (1958), is unlikely. Photomicrographs (Fig. 99, p. 249) show that under these conditions the muscle cells shrink and the extracellular spaces enlarge, with corresponding diminution of the intracellular and increase of extracellular ions.

This, then, is probably the only positive consequence of maturation as regards inorganic substances, and again it is not exclusive to maturation but is merely a further consequence of depletion.

One indication of the same phenomenon has been reported in migrating salmon, in that the muscle sodium of *Oncorhynchus nerka* increases (Thurston and Newman, 1962), but Cowey (1965) showed that the sodium and potassium both decrease in *Salmo salar*, and MacLeod, Jonas and McBride (1958) showed that the sodium declines in the early part of the migration and then increases at the spawning ground (*Oncorhynchus tschawytscha*).

Parry (1961) and Cowey (1965) concluded that salmonids cannot maintain a proper ionic balance in fresh water for some time after spawning, and this probably accounts for the decrease in the blood constituents of spawning fish observed by several workers (Fontaine, Callamand and Vibert, 1950: calcium and chloride in *Salmo salar*; Robertson, Krupp, Favour *et al.*, 1961: sodium and potassium in *Oncorhynchus tschawytscha*; Sindermann and Mairs, 1961: chloride in *Alosa pseudoharengus*; Parry, 1961: sodium, potassium and chloride in *Salmo salar*; Cowey, 1965: sodium and potassium in *Salmo salar*).

This brings us to the end of the section on the depletive effects of maturation. The limited evidence leaves one unsatisfied, since there has been almost no indication of selective or specific depletion, apart from the curious hypothesis on the utilization of unwanted amino acids for the synthesis of collagen. Even this effect can apparently be brought about by mere starvation, as can the changes in the solubility of the proteins and in the relative concentrations of intracellular and extracellular ions.

The other alterations in the levels of amino acids seem to be 'concentration' effects in the more stable collagen as mobile amino acids are removed from the tissue, and with the possible exception of arginine they give no sign of selective depletion from the reserves or selective build-up in the gonads.

There is research potential here in the study of accumulation by the gonads of their special requirements from food or other tissues.

3. *Nucleic Acids*

Little information exists on changes in the nucleic acid content of tissues during maturation, although the fact that the deoxyribose nucleic acid (DNA) carries the genetic material from generation to generation makes this substance of great interest.

Creelman and Tomlinson published in 1959 an extensive set of analyses of DNA and of RNA (ribose nucleic acid, which controls protein synthesis in the cytoplasm) in *Oncorhynchus nerka* taken from Lummi Island, at the beginning of the spawning run, Lillooet, some distance upstream, and Forfar Creek, the spawning ground. They found a net increase in DNA and decrease in RNA in the whole fish of both sexes. Major losses in RNA occurred in the flesh, alimentary tract and male gonad, while the gonads of both sexes gained large amounts of DNA. The *concentrations* of these compounds in different organs were less informative. In the liver, the RNA was more concentrated in the female than in the male, perhaps because of greater depletion of liver oil from the female (see sex differences, p. 118).

The results on muscle and gonad are shown in Table XXIII. The muscle shows a small fall in RNA, but the results for this tissue are not striking. The much lower values of nucleic acid in the female gonad than the male are the consequence of the large volume of yolk in the former, which dilutes the genetic material.

Bhushana Rao (1965) reported the concentrations of nucleic acids in the muscle of *Caranx sexfasciatus*. In this instance (Table XXIV) there is a considerable increase in muscle DNA as well as a loss in RNA.

The two tables taken together may serve as a warning, since the discrepancy in the behaviour of DNA in the two species seems to be a sampling artefact and not a species difference. When a fish becomes ripe the musculature may shrivel through the depletion of the cells, which would cause an apparent increase in the concentration of DNA by bringing the cell nuclei into greater proximity. Also, the sheets of connective tissue (myocommata) are much richer than the muscle cells in DNA (2·4 mg% DNAP as compared with 0·5 mg%: Love, 1958b, *Gadus morhua*), so that again when the muscle shrinks the proportion of myocommata in a given weight increases and so does the DNA. Love (1958b) reported the concentrations of DNA in the muscle of *Gadus*

TABLE XXIII. CONCENTRATION OF DNA PHOSPHORUS AND RNA PHOSPHORUS
IN MUSCLE AND GONAD OF ONCORHYNCHUS NERKA DURING SPAWNING
MIGRATION (after Creelman and Tomlinson, 1959)

| | | mg% | | |
		Lummi Island (entering river)	Lillooet	Forfar Creek (spawning ground)
Muscle				
RNAP	male	6·4	4·7	4·7
	female	7·0	5·2	5·1
DNAP	male	2·7	2·5	2·4
	female	2·1	2·1	3·3
Gonad				
RNAP	male	43·5	34·5	17·4
	female	3·9	3·6	2·0
DNAP	male	236·0	268·0	226·0
	female	2·9	2·6	2·1

The nucleic acid molecule consists of an organic base, a sugar (ribose or deoxyribose) and phosphate. Assay can be carried out by measurement of any of these substances, since the proportions are constant, but, while a few workers have used sugar analysis in this way, it is usually by phosphate analysis that nucleic acids are estimated. Thus in this table the results are expressed as nucleic acid phosphorus, without conversion to the weights of nucleic acids.

morhua throughout the year, but in this case freed the muscle from myocommata and showed that the concentration in the spawning season was similar to that in the autumn when the gonads were inactive. It is probably better, therefore, always to consider the net gain or net loss per fish, rather than the concentration, of these substances.

TABLE XXIV. THE CONCENTRATION OF DNA PHOSPHORUS AND RNA
PHOSPHORUS IN THE MUSCLE AND DARK MUSCLE OF CARANX
SEXFASCIATUS (after Bhushana Rao, 1965)

| | $\mu g\%$ | |
	Immature	Ripe
Muscle		
RNAP	725·6	202·5
DNAP	136·6	184·0
Dark muscle		
RNAP	493·6	206·1
DNAP	129·5	187·0

Creelman and Tomlinson (1959) also investigated the individual nucleotides (nucleic acid fractions containing different bases) in the RNA during maturation, and found that in the male gonad the proportion of guanine increases with maturity, suggesting that in the depletion of RNA the guanylic acid is broken down less than the other nucleotides. Berdyshev, Korotaev *et al.* (1967) found that the 5-methyl cytosine content of DNA from the body of *Oncorhynchus gorbuscha* is reduced by 35–40% with the advance of spawning migration. Much more work needs to be done before anything definite can be stated here.

4. *Hormones*

Hormones from the pituitary, thyroid, adrenal and gonad are intimately concerned with maturation. The overall control originates in the pituitary, but a suitable water temperature as well as adequate illumination is essential if the pituitary is to initiate ripening and the release of sexual cells (Marshall, 1965).

The thyroid seems to be important in initiating spawning migration. A. D. Woodhead and P. M. J. Woodhead (1965) assessed the activity of the gland by histological measurement of the height of the follicular cells which produce the thyroxine: their results are shown in Fig. 49. It will be seen that in addition to the expected change in mature fish, immature cod also show an increase in thyroid activity, and at the same time they engage in a trial 'spawning migration', although they do not swim the whole way to the spawning grounds. The Woodheads

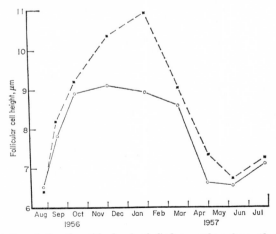

FIG. 49. Activity of the thyroid gland of *Gadus morhua* from the Barents Sea at different times of the year. ■————■ Mature; ○————○ Immature. After A. D. Woodhead and P. M. J. Woodhead (1965), reproduced by permission of the authors and the International Council for North Atlantic Fisheries (ICNAF).

found that the 'dummy run' of the immature fish towards Norway
continues just as long as the thyroid remains active, but that when the
follicular cells decrease in height they drift homewards towards
Svalbard.

The effect of thyroxine, the hormone of the thyroid gland, is to
stimulate locomotory activity, and to increase the excitability of the
animal to external stimuli. Artificial treatment of the fish with thyroxine
would therefore be expected to affect their swimming behaviour, and
this in fact happens. Baggerman (1962) dissolved synthetic thyroxine in
the sea water in which young sticklebacks (*Gasterosteus aculeatus*)
were swimming, and found that after six days they show a preference
for fresh water, to which under natural conditions they would migrate
for spawning. Four days after discontinuing the thyroxine treatment,
the original salt-water preference returns. Adult fish injected with
thyroid-stimulating hormone from the pituitary behave similarly, and
adult fish in fresh water show a strong preference for sea water 1 day
after an anti-thyroid compound (thio-urea) has been added to the water.
Baggerman (1962) considered that the thyroid is stimulated into
activity by sex hormones from the gonads, so that maturity and the
urge to migrate occur together, but it is also likely that the whole
process is controlled by the hormones from the pituitary.

Many hormones have a steroid structure, and their source appears to
be cholesterol from the diet and from stocks already present in the
fish. It has been shown earlier (Fig. 31, p. 64) that the serum cholesterol
level of *Salmo trutta* decreases at the time of maximum sexual activity
(McCartney, 1967), and the same has been found in the cholesterol of
serum (Idler and Tsuyuki, 1958), gonad and liver (Idler and Bitners,
1960) of both sexes of *Oncorhynchus nerka*, although that in the muscle
of this species shows a slight increase (Idler and Bitners, 1958). The
latter authors concluded that cholesterol is not used for energy purposes.

A. D. Woodhead and P. M. J. Woodhead (1965) showed that the
adrenal tissue of *Gadus morhua* undergoes histological changes during
spawning migration, and in addition the hormones produced by the
adrenal cortex have been shown to increase in various species of salmon.
For example, in female *Oncorhynchus nerka*, the cortisone increases from
41 μg/100 ml plasma in the pre-spawning fish to 44 μg after spawning,
while the cortisol increases from 26 μg to 141 μg/100 ml plasma. The
corresponding figures for the male fish are 22 increasing to 27, and 11
increasing to 66, respectively, so it is in the cortisol that the most
striking increase takes place (Idler, Ronald and Schmidt, 1959b).
Schmidt and Idler (1962) and Fagerlund (1967) also demonstrated an
increased level of plasma cortisol in this species at the spawning time,

and increases in the combined levels of cortisol and cortisone were found in *Salmo gairdnerii* (Hane and Robertson, 1959; Robertson, Krupp, Thomas *et al.*, 1961) and *Oncorhynchus tschawytscha* (Hane and Robertson, 1959; Robertson, Krupp, Favour *et al.*, 1961). As we shall see (p. 114), these high levels of cortisol are thought to presage death in these species.

Big changes have been observed in the sex hormones. The increases in the plasma oestrogens of female *Ictalurus punctatus* with gonad growth are shown in Fig. 50, and in *Salmo salar* it has been shown that

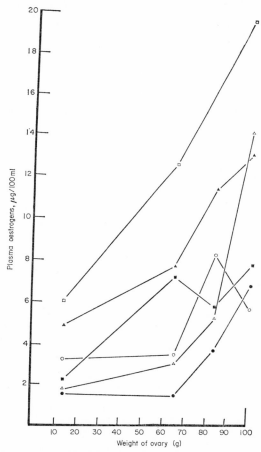

Fig. 50. Increase in plasma oestrogens with increase in ovarian size in *Ictalurus punctatus*. □ 16-keto-oestradiol; ▲ Oestriol; △ Oestradiol-17β; ■ Epi-oestriol; ○ Oestrone; ● Oestradiol-17α. After Eleftheriou, Boehlke and Tiemeier (1966), reproduced by courtesy of Dr. B. E. Eleftheriou and the Society for Experimental Biology and Medicine.

the levels fall again after spawning (Cedard, Fontaine and Nomura, 1961). The *concentrations* of ovarian oestradiol and oestrone in *Scyliorhinus canicula* have been shown to remain constant as the eggs grow, so the absolute amounts increase with maturity (Simpson, Wright and Hunt, 1963).

In male *Oncorhynchus nerka*, the plasma level of testosterone falls from 5 μg/100 ml before spawning to 1 μg/100 ml after spawning (Schmidt and Idler, 1962). In the male gonad itself, testosterone increases steadily in concentration as well as in absolute amount, from 4·1 μg/100 g at the start of the spawning run to 10·6 up the river and to 13·3 μg at the spawning ground.

Thus the sex hormones of fish behave more or less as one would expect during maturation, that is, they show steady increases, and then decline after spawning.

5. *Spawning Death*

While many fish spawn contentedly year after year, a few species spawn only once and then die. The most important of these are the five species of Pacific salmon, *Oncorhynchus**, eel (*Anguilla*) and lamprey (*Lampetra*) and a few lesser species reviewed by Robertson, Krupp, Favour *et al.* (1961). The degeneration of the salmon is striking, and while Nikolsky (1963) accepts it as a means of providing nourishment for the offspring from the corpses of the adults, one cannot but regret the inexorable decay of such a splendid fish. Figure 51 shows the sequence of events in *Oncorhynchus tschawytscha*, where the jaw becomes prolonged and hooked (incidentally making any further feeding difficult or impossible), the back becomes humped, and finally extensive fungal infection sets in. Lampreys are in prime physical condition just before spawning, but they too show rapid degeneration afterwards and soon die (McCay, 1931).

Belding (1934) considered that the cause of death in salmon was simply excessive depletion, noting that death occurs in starving man after the loss of about 40% of the body weight, in dog 31% and guinea pig 38%. The loss of 31 to 44% of its initial weight by the salmon thus brings it within the lethal range, and it seemed likely to him that the Pacific salmon die because of the greater lengths of the rivers of the Pacific Coast of America, and hence the greater distance to return to the sea. Certainly the carbohydrate reserves of lampreys are much reduced at the time of death: the blood glucose has been reported to fall from 123 mg% at the time of spawning to 54 mg% when dying

---

* *Salmo salar* usually survives spawning on the American continent, but all the males and a high proportion of the females die in the rivers of Europe.

(a)

(b)

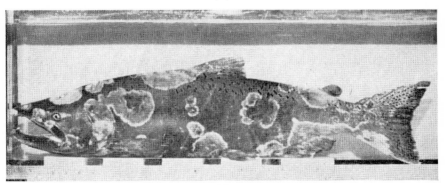

(c)

Fig. 51. Degeneration associated with the spawning of male *Oncorhynchus tschawytscha*. (a) Taken during spawning migration; testes in early stages of development. Silver coloured: (b) Taken on spawning ground. Jaws prolonged and hooked. Back shows a well marked hump. Skin has darkened, and fungus infection has started on the eye and posterior flank: (c) Taken on spawning ground. Fungus infection far advanced. After Robertson, Krupp, Favour *et al.* (1961), reproduced by courtesy of Dr. M. A. Krupp and the Editor of *Endocrinology*.

(McCay, 1931), whilst liver glycogen has been shown to fall from 126 mg% when *Lampetra fluviatilis* enter the river to only 14 mg% at the point of death (Bentley and Follett, 1965). It might appear that salmon are unable to replenish their reserves, because the stomach (Gulland, 1898), intestine and pyloric caecae (Greene, 1926) atrophy markedly, but in fact some absorption of food is possible, and the degeneration can be largely reversed if the fish are fed. McBride, Fagerlund *et al.* (1965) found that all *Oncorhynchus nerka* die within two weeks of spawning if they are unfed, but that feeding can prolong life for as much as 13 weeks. However, although the fed fish are somewhat restored in vigour, sooner or later they inevitably become diseased. after which they deteriorate rapidly and resemble the unfed fish in outward appearance. The muscle cells also continue to degenerate during re-feeding (Tomlinson, McBride and Geiger, 1967), causing the sodium to increase and potassium to decrease (p. 245). Thus depletion is not the sole cause of death in spawned salmon.

Robertson and Wexler (1957) noted that the pituitary glands of mature salmon resemble those of senescent mammals, showing a reduction in the number of cells and an increase in the connective tissue. Study by these workers of the other internal organs revealed a widespread degeneration of a degree which seemed to be "incompatible with life". Such behaviour of the pituitary suggests that hormones may play a part in the death of the fish.

Idler, Ronald and Schmidt (1959b) observed that the plasma cortisol of *Oncorhynchus nerka* increases 6-fold at the spawning time, and suggested that the excessive activity of the adrenal gland may contribute to the death of the fish. Robertson, Krupp, Favour *et al.* (1961) showed that there are many similarities between the changes in the fish at the spawning time and those occurring in man in a condition known as Cushing's syndrome, which is known to result from hyperactivity of the adrenal cortex.

Salmo gairdnerii usually survive spawning, and Robertson, Krupp, Thomas *et al.* (1961) showed that the degenerative changes of the internal organs are less pronounced than those occurring in Pacific salmon, although the adrenal hormones still increase to a high level. Van Citters and Watson (1968) studied the coronary arteries of *Salmo gairdnerii* and found that they undergo marked degeneration at the spawning period. However, unlike the salmon which also exhibit widespread vascular degeneration, the process is reversed when these fish re-enter salt water after spawning, and the arteries of those entering rivers for the second time to spawn are as sound as those of immature fish. The cause of death in Pacific salmon may therefore be an inability

to excrete the excess cortisol after spawning, rather than overproduc-
tion. This was demonstrated by Idler, Truscott *et al.* (1963), who
injected both cortisone and cortisol into *Oncorhynchus nerka*, and found
that it is cleared from the plasma of mature or spawned fish much
more slowly than from that of the immature fish or from spawned
Canadian *Salmo salar*, which are not killed by spawning (see footnote to
p. 112). Dying mature *Gadus morhua* are also found to have an
abnormally high concentration of cortisol in the blood (Idler and
Freeman, 1965), and it was again suggested that inability to excrete is
the cause of death.

While further work is needed on the way in which cortisol acts, an
investigation by Robertson, Hane *et al.* (1963) has shown that it is
almost certainly the lethal agent and its presence in high concentrations
at the time of death is not just coincidence. Pellets of cortical hormone
were implanted in immature *Salmo gairdnerii*, so that cortisol was
released continuously into the blood stream. The fish lost weight,
developed infections of the skin and died within 5–9 weeks. Death
occurred much more rapidly and with smaller doses of the corticoid
when the water temperature was raised from 13° to 17°.

Fagerlund (1967) noted that while maturation and spawning in
Oncorhynchus nerka does not induce *sustained* increases in plasma
cortisol if the fish are healthy, physical stress can do so and cause
death. It is therefore possible that physical activity at the time of
spawning induces the lethal over-secretion of cortical hormones in
Pacific salmon.

The phenomenon does not occur in the absence of gonad maturation :
Robertson (1961) castrated *Oncorhynchus nerka kennerlyi*, and found
that instead of maturing and dying in 2–4 years, some actually live to
9 years of age, provided that no gonad tissue has regenerated. Thus
the death of *Oncorhynchus* species is not fixed according to the age of the
fish, but to maturation.

6. *Sex Differences*

Since the levels of several constituents change at the onset of
maturity, we may expect that they will also differ between the sexes.
In this section we shall look for *consistent* differences in composition,
and also establish which sex is the more depleted at the spawning time :
to find this out would immediately establish a body of chemical
information (see 'depletion', p. 222).

Differences are likely to disappear at times of the year when the
gonads are inactive, so we shall pay particular attention to values
obtained at the spawning time.

Unlike terrestrial animals, it is not possible to distinguish the sex of many species of fish from their external appearance. The man who said in a letter to *Science** that he was able to use a colorimetric test to distinguish the sexes of human babies in hospital (pink bootees = girl, blue bootees = boy) was lucky ; with fish it is often more difficult. Nuptial tubercles appear on the males of some species to indicate the sex, and males are often brighter in colour (Lagler, Bardach and Miller, 1962). In *Gadus aeglefinus* two extra pigment spots appear on each side of the male at the spawning period (Hawkins, Chapman and Symonds, 1967) but in *Gadus morhua*, with which the writer is most familiar, the two sexes seem to be identical in appearance, and, as an act of mating occurs in this species, it is a matter of some wonder that the fish themselves know the difference.

The question has now been resolved : apart from there being a slight shape and colour difference (Brawn, 1961b; Marshall, 1965), cod discover the sex of a visitor from its behaviour. In a fascinating account, Brawn (1961a,b) describes how a female cod enters the territory of a male in a relaxed way, swimming very slowly and showing no fear. If the male rushes at her, she ignores the sally and continues to swim slowly. On the other hand, another male intruding on the same territory will swim in a more lively manner, changing speed more often and turning quickly. If attacked, it usually turns tail and flees. A quietly swimming female evokes a flaunting display in the other fish at an appropriate moment, enabling her in turn to recognize it as a male.

The most frequent secondary sex character is a difference in size : the female of many species is larger than the male, thus ensuring the largest fecundity of the stock (Nikolsky, 1963). The female has been reported the larger of the two sexes in *Brevoortia tyrannus* (Westman and Nigrelli, 1955, quoted by Blaxter and Holliday, 1963), *Cyprinus carpio* (Mann, 1961), *Gadus morhua* (Otterbech, 1953; Fleming, 1960), *Hippoglossus stenolepis* (Dunlop, 1955), *Merluccius merluccius* (Hickling, 1933), *Perca fluviatilis* (Le Cren, 1958) and *Sardinella longiceps* (Hornell and Nayudu, 1923).

Most of these writers noted that the males mature one or more years earlier than the females, and presumably this is sufficient to slow their growth rate : Nomura (1963) showed that *Salmo gairdnerii* grow more slowly as soon as the gonads have become active. Earlier maturation of the males has also been reported in *Clupea harengus* (Iles, unpublished, quoted by Blaxter and Holliday, 1963), *Gadus morhua* (A. D. Woodhead, personal communication; Chrzan, 1950), *Salmo trutta* (McCartney,

---

* I have unfortunately not been able to rediscover this letter, which was published several years ago.

1967) and both fresh- and salt-water fish in general (Alm, 1959). However, Ancellin (1953) found that the growth rate of *Gadus morhua* from Labrador and Terra Nova is roughly the same for both sexes, and in *Clupea harengus* from the southern North Sea (Hickling, 1940, quoted by Blaxter and Holliday, 1963) and *Salvelinus fontinalis* (Haskell and Griffiths, 1956) it is the males that are the larger of the two. In general, the males are larger in those species where they are required to protect the offspring (Nikolsky, 1963).

An odd fact about sex differences in relation to size is that 'female' *Oncorhynchus nerka kennerlyi* grow to a larger size than 'males' even when the fish have been castrated (Robertson, 1961). Nothing is known about the mechanism of this; perhaps the pituitary secretions differ.

Thus if many species of fish of like *age* are analysed, some differences in composition by sex emerge owing to differences in cell size and other consequences of growth (p. 85). They are, however, unlikely to be important.

In addition to growing faster, females also live longer (K. S. Ketchen, unpublished, quoted by Hoar, 1957 : six species of fish) and since males may have slightly more stamina (Pyle, 1965 : *Salvelinus fontinalis*) there is a recognizable parallel here with the human situation. Female fish adapt better both to cold (Stroganov, 1956 : *Gambusia holbrooki*) and to heat (Tsukuda, 1961 : *Lebistes reticulatus* and *Oryzias latipes*) but if they are kept in salt-water the salinity of which is gradually reduced, they are more susceptible to the low salinity and die before the males (Odense, Bordeleau and Guilbault, 1966 : *Gadus morhua*).

When a fish spawns, the proteins of the body fluids change, and affect the pattern of materials laid down in the otolith, a small calcareous body found in the ear-chamber (described in more detail p. 159 and Figs. 64 and 65). Thus if the spawning habits differ between the sexes, a different otolith pattern will emerge. An example is to be found in *Neogobius melanostomus*, where active growth starts earlier in the year in males than in females. The annual rings in the otoliths of female fish lie closer together than those of the males, and the non-synchronous sexual maturity of the two sexes, single spawning of the males and repeated spawning of the females results in otolith patterns so different that the fish may be sexed by examination of the otoliths once they are more than two years old (Kostuichenko, 1961).

Considering now the relative depletion suffered by the two sexes, it is likely that if the gonad of one sex takes up a greater proportion of the body weight than that of the other, that sex will become the more depleted. A difference in the proportion of male and female gonads has in fact been known in fish for a long time. In the Encyclopedia Londiniensis (1801) we read "The desire of reproduction, which is always performed near the shores, impels them, at the return of spring, to quit the main ocean, and repair to the banks and shallows . . . the females arrive first, being more eager to get rid of their load *which is greater*; the males follow." (my italics). In more modern times, Chrzan (1950) found that in Baltic cod caught in the gulf of Gdansk the gonad of the female forms up to 28% of the weight of the fish, while the male gonad takes up only 13%. Idler and Bitners (1958) measured the lipid and protein consumed by *Oncorhynchus nerka* during their spawning migration, in mg per mile, and found that in almost all cases the females consume more than the males, since in addition to components being burned up to supply energy, more are needed to build up the female gonad than the male : over the whole distance, the ovaries consume 8% of the energy expended by the fish, while the testes account for only 0·5%. It is possible for other factors to complicate the issue. In spite of the difference in gonad size, more body lipid is used up by the *males* of *Salmo salar* because they fight repeatedly among themselves while ascending the rivers (Lovern, 1942).

The growth of the gonads in the two sexes of *Salmo gairdnerii* is illustrated in Fig. 52, where the greater size of the female gonad is clearly shown.

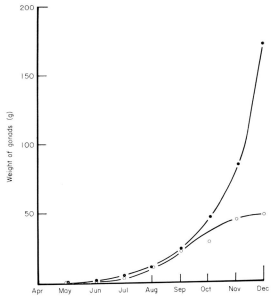

Fɪɢ. 52. Increase in weight of male and female gonads in *Salmo gairdnerii* during maturation. ● Female; ○ Male. After Sano (1960b), reproduced by courtesy of the author.

The chemical effects of this sex difference have been shown in a number of instances. Greene (1904) found the blood of female *Oncorhynchus tschawytscha* to be less concentrated than that of the male, as measured by freezing point depression, although writers quoted by Vinogradov (1953) showed that this phenomenon is the result of a lower mineral content only—the organic matter in the blood is greater in females (we shall return to this in a moment). Female *Salmo salar* have been shown to lose more lipid and protein from muscle and viscera (Belding, 1934) and the same has been shown for lipid and protein of *Tinca tinca* in the period just before spawning (Ziecik and Slawinski, 1965). Female *Gadus morhua* at various stages of maturity contain relatively less protein in the muscle, and less lipid in the liver (Kordyl, 1951) as have female *Lampetra fluviatilis* (Bentley and Follett, 1965). Female *Clupea harengus* at an advanced stage of maturity contain slightly less lipid, although in the earlier stages there is no difference between the sexes (Kordyl, 1951).

Female *Salmo salar* lose more carbohydrate from the muscle and viscera than do males (Belding, 1934), and the level in the blood of *Oncorhynchus tschawytscha* is also less in the females (Robertson, Krupp, Favour *et al.*, 1961). An exception is found in *Oncorhynchus nerka*, where blood glucose in the female is higher at the spawning ground (Jonas and MacLeod, 1960), but in this case the starting level is also slightly higher. As already stated (p. 98), glycogen is unimportant as an energy reserve in fish, but since it is deposited in the ovaries during development, it is withdrawn from other parts of the body preferentially in the females. Thus the concentration is lowered in the liver of female *Salmo salar*—0·5 mg glycogen per g liver as compared with 24·9 mg in the male (Fontaine and Hatey, 1953)—and *Oncorhynchus nerka* (Chang and Idler, 1960), the difference between the sexes being consistent throughout the spawning migration in the latter species.

It has been shown in *Gadus morhua* that the sex differences resulting from depletion do not occur outside the spawning season (Dambergs, 1963): three months after spawning the concentration of lipid, "water-solubles", protein and water do not differ markedly between the sexes.

Lampetra fluviatilis has similar reserves of both carbohydrate and lipid at the time of death in both sexes, but at the spawning time a few weeks earlier the female is the more depleted in having less lipid in the liver (Bentley and Follett, 1965).

Several writers quoted by Vinogradov (1953), also Pora (1936a: *Labrus bergylta*), Phillips, Podoliak *et al.* (1964: *Salvelinus fontinalis*) and Yamashita (1967: *Sebastiscus marmoratus*) have shown that the concentration of proteins in the blood is always greater in the females

during the spawning period (not at other times). This can be satisfactorily explained as protein in transit from other organs to the larger
gonad of the female. Figures 26 and 27 (pp. 61 and 62) show a rise
in the blood calcium of the females, and it has been suggested (Bailey,
1957) that this represents the mobilization of the protein ovovitellin,
which has calcium linked to the molecule, from the liver.

However, if female fish really are more depleted than the males at
the spawning time, then a number of published values for body
constituents are at first sight harder to explain: there appears to be
contradiction in a substantial proportion of the literature.

Thus the weights of the livers of *Clupea harengus membranus* are
relatively greater in the females during the early stages of maturity
(Fig. 29, p. 63) and the same has been observed in *Gadus morhua*
(Graham, 1924). Fattening has been reported to be greater in females
than males (Keiz, 1959: *Cyprinus carpio*; Herrera and Muñoz, 1963:
Mullus barbatus) and Yanni (1961) showed that the liver glycogen of
Clarias lazera, which varies during the year, reaches the highest value
in the female (318 mg%), the maximum observed in the male being
only 250 mg%. The muscle of female *Labrus bergylta* has been reported
to contain more organic material and ash, and less water than the male
(Pora, 1936a) and a muscle from female *Anguilla anguilla*, to have less
sodium than that of the male, whether in fresh- or salt-water (Sharratt,
Chester Jones and Bellamy, 1964)—a sign of less depletion (p. 245).
According to Jacquot (1961) it is "frequently maintained" that the
flesh of female fish contains more protein than that of males, but he
went on to state that this is not a general phenomenon, and that female
fish are usually the more depleted.

We need not worry about these inconsistencies. It has already been
shown (p. 91) that larger fish, which are more depleted by spawning
than smaller fish, also tend to lay down greater reserves in preparation
for the next spawning. It is not unreasonable to suppose that female
fish do the same relative to males.

The patterns of hormones are not as specific to each sex as one might
suppose. Cholesterol is thought to be the steroid from which both
androgens (male hormones) and oestrogens (female hormones) are
derived, and since all of them are probably created along a common
metabolic pathway, it is possible to find most of them together in both
sexes, though not necessarily acting in opposite directions. As Hoar
(1965) says in his review "The mere presence of a gonadal steroid is no
evidence for its hormonal activity."

No oestrone or oestriol could be detected in the gonads of male
Gadus morhua by Gottfried, Hunt *et al.* (1962), but the concentration in

the mature gonads of the female was 0·48 μg% of oestradiol-17β and 0·1 μg% of oestrone; immature ova contained only traces of these compounds. However, in the blood of *male Conger conger, Muraena helena* and *Cyprinus carpio*, appreciable quantities of oestrone and oestradiol were reported by Cedard and Nomura (1961). The finding should be treated with some caution, since the method of analysis used was rather non-specific.

In *Raja radiata* and *Raja ocellata*, the plasma of the males contains much more testosterone (a male hormone) than does that of the females (Idler and Truscott, 1966), but in *Oncorhynchus nerka* the testosterone concentration is higher in the females at all stages of maturity (Schmidt and Idler, 1962). In the same species, the cortisol concentration in the blood is greater in the female than the male (Schmidt and Idler, 1962; Fagerlund, 1967), but in *Salmo salar* after spawning the relative concentrations in the two sexes are the other way round (Schmidt and Idler, 1962). These contradictions emphasize the common origin of the various hormones and show that the concentration of a given single hormone in the blood cannot usually be used to determine the sex of an individual unequivocally, although if the level is high it at least indicates that the fish is approaching maturity. Fish hormones are an interesting and as yet little-explored subject, and the reader is referred to Hoar (1965) for a fuller account; he concludes that there is "great diversity in the interplay of coordinating pituitary and gonadal hormones". We must leave the subject there.

The difference in concentration of blood calcium between males and females (Figs. 26 and 27, pp. 61 and 62) is probably great enough to enable the sexing of fish near the spawning time without killing them. Oestradiol is the hormone responsible for the effect.

Male and female fish have been shown to differ by a number of other criteria. Electrophoresis of the serum proteins has shown differences in the number or quantity of certain fractions in *Anguilla anguilla* (Drilhon, 1954), *Blennius pavo* (Lecal, 1958), *Cyprinus carpio* (Drilhon, 1954), *Petromyzon marinus* (Thomas and McCrimmon, 1964; Fine, Boffa and Drilhon, 1964) and *Salvelinus fontinalis* (Hunn, 1964), though as usual in this kind of work the physiological significance of the extra bands is not yet established. Differences in the levels of hormone synthesis probably explain the lower level of serum cholesterol (the 'parent' steroid, see p. 63) in male *Salmo trutta* (McCartney, 1965, 1966, 1967), and hormone activity of some sort was thought by Slicher (1961) to account for the higher haematocrit (red blood cell volume) found in male fish (*Carassius auratus*: Summerfelt, Lewis and Ulrich, 1967; *Fundulus heteroclitus*: Slicher, 1961; *Salmo trutta*: Snieszko,

TABLE XXV. SUBSTANCES REPORTED TO HAVE NO RELATIONSHIP WITH THE SEX OF THE FISH
('concentration' is meant unless stated otherwise)

Substance	Location	Species	Reference
Albumin	serum	*Acipenser sturio*	Magnin (1960)
Ash	muscle	*Clupea pallasii*	McBride, MacLeod and Idler (1959b)
Astaxanthin	muscle	5 *Oncorhynchus* spp	Kanemitsu and Aoe (1958)
Calcium	serum, liver and gonad	*Ophicephalus punctatus*	Siddiqui (1967)
Chloride	muscle	*Salmo trutta*	Gordon (1959)
Fatty acids	flesh lipids	*Gadus morhua*	Jangaard, Ackman and Sipos (1967)
Globulin	serum	*Acipenser sturio*	Magnin (1960)
Haemoglobin	blood	*Prosopium williamsoni*	McKnight (1966)
Haemoglobin*	blood	Freshwater teleosts	Callegarini (1966)
Haemoglobin*	blood	12 salmonid species	Yamanaka, Yamaguchi *et al.* (1967)
Lipid	muscle	*Clupea pallasii*	McBride, MacLeod and Idler (1959b)
		Gadus morhua	Dambergs (1963)
			Jangaard, Brockerhoff *et al.* (1967)
Myogen*		*Oncorhynchus* spp	Tsuyuki and Roberts (1966)
Phospholipid		*Gadus morhua*	Jangaard, Brockerhoff *et al.* (1967)
Phosphorus		*Salmo trutta*	Gordon (1959)
Potassium	muscle	*Oncorhynchus gorbuscha*	Thurston and Groninger (1959)
		Salmo trutta	Gordon (1959)
Protein		*Clupea pallasii*	McBride, MacLeod and Idler (1959b)
		Gadus morhua	Dambergs (1963)
	serum	*Acipenser sturio*	Magnin (1960)

Protein†	serum	*Salvelinus fontinalis*	Booke (1964a)
Protein*		*Salmo gairdnerii*	Meisner and Hickman (1962)
Sodium	muscle	*Oncorhynchus gorbuscha*	Thurston and Groninger (1959)
		Salmo trutta	Gordon (1959)
Sugar	blood	*Clarias lazera*	Al-Gauhari (1958)
Visual pigments‡	retina	*Belonesox belizanus*	Bridges (1965a)
		Cyprinodon variegatus	
Water	muscle	*Clupea pallasii*	McBride, MacLeod and Idler (1959b)
		Gadus morhua	Dambergs (1963)

* Electrophoretic analysis. † Only outside the spawning season; within spawning season the concentration in female blood was greater. ‡ Lambda maximum.

1961), because the difference between the sexes disappears after spawning (Slicher, 1961, confirmed by Poston, 1966a) and is progressively enhanced as spawning approaches (C. S. Wardle, personal communication: *Pleuronectes platessa*). The blood of female *Raja undulata* and *Scyllium canicula* is richer in mineral substances than that of the males (Pora, 1936b).

Testis is much poorer in vitamin C (ascorbic acid) than ovary (various authors, quoted by Higashi, 1961), so we might expect the remainder of the bodies of the females to become deficient in this vitamin during maturation, though no such demonstration has come to the attention of the writer so far.

The vitamin A aldehyde (retinal) content of the blood of maturing female *Gadus morhua* increases 5-fold during maturation, because of requirements by the eggs, and no change occurs in the males (Plack and Woodhead, 1966). Presumably for the same reason in skates and rays (*Raja* sp.) the vitamin A reserves in the livers of the females are almost always lower than those in the males (Fisher, 1964). However, these effects are dynamic, and there is usually so much variation in the vitamin A concentration from fish to fish that the determination of this substance in the blood of a fish is of little use in determining its sex or state of maturity.

Some differences have been observed in the lipid fractions of the two sexes during maturation because of differing requirements of the gonads. In *Salmo salar*, the concentration of palmitoleic acid in the lipid reserves drops steadily, while C_{22} acids show a marked rise in the male, little change in the female (Lovern, 1934a). In *Gadus morhua* it appears that the longer-chain mono-unsaturated fatty acids from the liver are preferentially utilized for the synthesis of particular lipids in the developing eggs (Ackman and Burgher, 1964b). Outside the breeding season it was found by Jangaard, Ackman and Sipos (1967) that liver oils in female fish contain increasing amounts of 20- and 22-carbon chain mono-unsaturated fatty acids as the lipid content of the liver increases. In males the seasonal trend is not as obvious and no other fatty acids behave in this way. The fatty acids of the flesh lipids behave independently of sex.

Sekiné (1921 and 1926, quoted by Geiger and Borgstrom, 1962) showed that in six species of fish the muscle protein of the male is richer in lysine and arginine but poorer in histidine than that of the female.

Finally, a number of substances have been stated as having no relation with the sex of the individual. These are summarized in Table XXV, but it should be remembered that any substances which change during the depletion of the animal are likely to show a difference between the sexes at certain times of the year.

7. Conclusion

We have seen that sexual maturation is accompanied by profound changes in the chemistry of the fish. Can any of these in fact be used to assess the state of maturity? At present, maturity is expressed in roman numerals from visual examination of the sex organs on what is known as the Hjort scale, which ranges from I (immature) to VII (spent) (see legend to Fig. 29, p. 63). This scale is insufficiently precise for some purposes, and an objective method would be useful. The limiting factors are the variability of the constituent decided upon and the time necessary for its determination, although the analysis of very many substances can be automated nowadays if the number of samples justifies it.

As we have seen, determinations of DNA are likely to show no advantage over measurements of total gonad weight, and the accumulation of vitamin A and glycogen in the ovary probably depends so much on initial reserves as to be unsuitable for this purpose. Little is known about the reproducibility of the increase in total free amino acids in the ovary, but if the increase were proportional to the size of the eggs, the estimation on a large scale following an ethanol extraction is not insuperably difficult.

Of blood constituents, the decrease in cholesterol and increase in cortisol and calcium all depend on the stage of maturity, but the cholesterol level may be governed largely by the (variable) initial level. The increase in calcium in the blood seems the most likely possibility here, since it is mobilized from large resources and can be determined with automated equipment if necessary. It could also be carried out without killing the fish.

On reflection, though, it appears that the decrease in glycine and proline in the gonad, or Korzhenko's glycine : alanine ratio (1966), would be the best guide to the state of maturity, since they depend on the 'dilution' of inert and presumably unchanging constituents with an increasing proportion of sex products.

So far no exhaustive systematic work has been done to correlate these amino acids with Hjort numbers, though Korzhenko's results are promising; the establishment of any of them to use as a substitute scale would involve thousands of determinations and careful consideration of all the variables, but this is not an impossible task.

E. Aging

The changes in fish corresponding with 'aging' as familiar in mammals have been little studied. In the common commercial European species, signs are uncommon or absent—one rarely sees blind or crippled fish, nor do the scales go grey.

In Fig. 45 (p. 91) it is shown that the once-yearly drain on the body proteins of *Gadus morhua* caused by reproduction become steadily more severe with each extra year of spawning, until recovery is no longer possible and the fish die. This had already been suggested as a mechanism of death by Orton in 1929, and it occurs in addition in *Clupea harengus, Gadus aeglefinus, Hippoglossoides platessoides* (Gerking, 1959) and *Pleuronectes platessa* (Beverton and Holt, 1959). Thus many species of fish in fact never reach a state of 'old age' anyway.

An important difference between fish and mammals is that fish never quite stop growing, although the annual increments in older fish such as Bear Island cod above about 12 years old (Trout, 1954) are very small. Furthermore, a few species are known to reach great ages, at which they still grow and appear vigorous, e.g. *Acipenser* and *Hippoglossus* species (Comfort, 1961). Taking all these facts into consideration, a number of writers have concluded that fish do not become senile, but maintain perpetual vigour by virtue of their continued growth and can be considered 'immortal', meeting their death only by accident, or by being eaten or caught.

We now know that this is not true, especially from the results of Robertson's experiment (1961) referred to earlier (p. 115): *Oncorhynchus nerka kennerlyi* which always die after reproducing for the first time were prevented from spawning by castration, and thus were enabled to live much longer than usual. The interesting point in the present context is that they did not live for ever, but after about 8 years, although they were still growing, they started to lose weight, their eyes acquired a sunken appearance and they eventually died.

Sterility also accompanies aging in some species, unlike the commercial species described above. *Astyanax mexicanus* in an aquarium gradually lose their reproductive powers, and concretions form in the sperm ducts analogous to those in the aging mammalian prostate gland (Rasquin and Hafter, 1951). The interstitial tissue of the gonads also increases in old fish, being laid down in the form of connective tissue. We would therefore expect an increase in the concentrations of proline and glycine in the gonads, although actual measurements have not been carried out. In very large hake, *Merluccius merluccius*, the seasonal weight decrease in liver and flesh becomes less pronounced, indicating a reduction of sexual activity here also (Hickling, 1930).

Guppies (*Lebistes reticulatus*) in an aquarium also die from what appears to be old age. In the kidney, numerous symptoms of degeneration appear, with loss of nephra, appearance of phagocytes, and the formation of a pigment and of calcareous nodules (Comfort, 1961). Fatty degeneration of the liver is also frequently observed, but this may be that degeneration common to fish kept under artificial conditions (p. 54). Sometimes sex reversal is seen: female fish tend to acquire spermatogenic areas in the ovary, and clumps of yellow cells occur in several organs with increasing frequency as the fish age. As in the castrated *Oncorhynchus nerka kennerlyi* (Robertson, 1961) the fish decrease in weight because of a striking loss of skeletal muscle, so if the general appearance of the fish is an insufficient indication of aging, it is probable that in species which exhibit aging the relative proportions of glycine and proline would increase and could again be used as a guide (p. 101).

In the same species, Woodhead and Ellett (1966) noted that the thyroid degenerates markedly with age, and that in the oldest fish the gland becomes completely inactive. The follicular (secretory) cells show a flattened appearance, similar to that in fish from which the pituitary has been removed. It is likely therefore that the pituitary also degenerates with age.

Longevity in fish is associated with slow growth in youth (Gerking, 1960), so fish living in warmer seas, which grow quickly, have a shorter life than those from colder seas (Alm, 1959).

Thus the few studies on aging in fish are physiological or anatomical, and chemical studies are almost absent, although chemical approaches to the field come at once to mind in the light of what we have already learned.

Several papers do appear to show a relationship between chemical constitution and the age of the fish. The melting point of fish lipids has been shown to rise with age (Privol'nev and Brizinova, 1964), and the serum globulin component 1 of *Coregonus clupeaformis* increases steadily, perhaps as an increase in globulin antibody as the fish is exposed to various diseases during life (Booke, 1965). Das (1965) reported many changes in the blood constituents of *Catla catla* with age, which have been recorded in Table XVIII (p. 95). However, while these reports describe chemical changes in relation to age, this is not the degeneration of old age leading to death, and they were thought to be classified more appropriately under growth.

Studies on the properties of collagen in mammalian tissue are now common in the literature relating to aging. For example, the content of *free* hydroxyproline decreases with age (Kobrle and Chvapil, 1962: rats), the tensile strength of collagen fibres increases (Brocas and Verzár, 1961: rats) as does the diameter (Fitton Jackson, 1957: birds). The collagen content of the skeletal muscle increases (Schaub, 1963: rats), the hexuronic acids of the collagen decrease (Nemeth-Csoka, 1965: man) and so do the proportions of soluble collagens (Nimmi, de Guia and Bavetta, 1965: rabbits). In spite of this, the levels of hydroxyproline and proline in the collagen appear to remain constant during the aging process (Pine and Holland, 1966: man).

There is thus a potentially fruitful field in the study of fish collagen in relation to aging; it is unfortunate that so little is known about the properties of this interesting protein in fish tissues.

CHAPTER 3

DIFFERENCES BETWEEN AND WITHIN SPECIES

A. General

Since fish have been found alive in the most unlikely habitats, such as hot springs and subterranean rivers, and since in general they differ greatly in their shapes and modes of life, it is to be expected that they will also show diversity in their composition. Baldwin (1948) assessed the situation thus:

"There exists a common, fundamental chemical ground-plan of composition and metabolism to which all animals, and very probably other living organisms also, conform, and . . . superimposed on these foundations there are numerous secondary, specific and adaptational variations, some of addition and others of omission."

However, the variations actually encountered are sometimes greater than this summing-up would suggest, and many of them are not obviously adaptational. *Salvelinus namaycush namaycush* and *Salvelinus namaycush siscowet*, for example, are closely related fish found in the same habitat, but while the lipid content of the former is not unusual, that of the latter is grotesquely high, averaging 67% in the fillets, and reaching 97% in the ventral part (Thurston, 1962). It is remarkable that a fish which is so nearly just a bladder of oil can swim.

Again, the Japanese lamprey, *Entosphenus japonicus*, has a very high content of vitamin A in the muscle, much higher than in any other species, for no reason that has struck anyone so far. Fish are found without eyes (*Anoptichthys jordani*, see Fig. 74, p. 186), so presumably with a reduced need for vitamin A, and *Chaenocephalus aceratus* (Fig. 68, p. 178) and related species from the Antarctic have no haemoglobin, so the 'blood' iron content is less than 1 mg% (Ruud, 1954).

Composition from one species of fish to another therefore often differs widely, and it is futile to tabulate the tissue constituents of 'man', 'cattle', 'dog' and then . . . 'fish', without even naming the species, though, strangely, papers of this sort do still appear from time to time, e.g. Tallan, (1962).

A few attempts to relate chemical composition to the place occupied by the fish on the evolutionary ladder are discussed in the following section, and later the differences between races or stocks of the same species are considered, with their potential for studying movements of fish populations.

The pattern of digestive enzymes varies to some extent according to the normal diet of the fish. Thus, *Tilapia mossambica*, a herbivore, digests carbohydrates more efficiently, and proteins less efficiently, than carnivorous fish such as *Perca fluviatilis* (Fish, 1960). Differences in dietary habits may possibly also cause the differences in the levels of stored fat-soluble vitamins, which can be extreme in that some species of shark store enormous quantities of vitamin A, others little or none (Cruickshank, 1962).

The pyridoxine (vitamin B_6) level in the liver also varies considerably between species, while showing constancy within a species (Yanase, 1958), ranging from 2 $\mu g/g$ in *Sebastiscus marmoratus* to 20 $\mu g/g$ in *Euthynnus pelamys*.

Formaldehyde occurs in *Gadus macrocephalus* muscle to the extent of 2·5—15 mg% (Harada, Shimonoseki College of Fisheries, Private Communication) and is found only in gadoid species, not in non-gadoids.

The ratios of the bases of testis DNA vary in different species of tuna. However, there is so much variation of the same sort within one species that inter-species identification is not possible by analysis of these constituents (Fujii, Mimoto and Higasa, 1960).

Analysis of the bound amino acids of the muscle proteins has shown that the proportions do not vary significantly between many species (Konosu, Katori *et al.*, 1956; Connell and Howgate, 1959b; Braekkan and Boge, 1962c), but there is a hint that the *free* amino acids show some differences. Cowey (1965) points out that the proportions and levels tend to be similar among related species and to differ from those of other species, but that variations within a species impair their usefulness in taxonomic studies—a familiar cry. Yur'eva and Mel'kova (1967) found that the sarcoplasmic proteins of *Lucioperca* lack arginine, those of *Esox* lack cysteine and those of *Acipenser* lack methionine. These patterns seem to be characteristic of the genera mentioned.

Other properties of whole proteins sometimes vary consistently enough to characterize fish at species level. The temperature at which heat denaturation of the actomyosin occurs differs according to species: a decrease in viscosity can be observed after keeping at 25° for 30 minutes in some species, but in others it may be as high as 35° (Ueda, Shimizu and Simidu, 1964). These authors suggest that the temperature of denaturation might depend on the temperature at which the fish normally live.

If fish are frozen and stored in the frozen state, the properties of the myofibrillar proteins gradually change, an uncoiling of the molecular helix leading to cross-linking between adjacent parallel molecules. One consequence of this is that the actomyosin complex becomes steadily less soluble in 5% sodium chloride solution after increasing time of storage, and the higher the temperature is (below the freezing point of the muscle), the more rapidly the actomyosin becomes inextractable. The rate of reaction at constant temperature is different for each species (Fig. 53). Numerous theories have been suggested to account for the

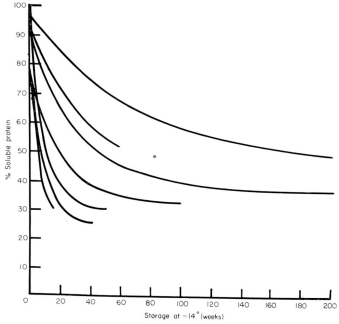

Fig. 53. Rates at which actomyosin in the muscle of different species becomes insoluble in 5% sodium chloride during storage at −14°. The curves, reading from top to bottom, relate to *Pleuronectes microcephalus*, *Gadus aeglefinus*, *Hippogossus hippoglossus*, *Squalus acanthias*, *Gadus virens*, *Gadus morhua*, *Gadus merlangus*. After Love and Olley (1965), reproduced by courtesy of Mr. Arthur J. Heighway.

differences (see review by Love, 1966) but none of them accounts satisfactorily for all the species. The most popular at the time of writing is that free fatty acids, liberated enzymatically in the frozen state, cause the proteins to become inextractable, but that if much neutral lipid is present at the same time it absorbs the free fatty acids and reduces their effectiveness (Anderson and Steinberg, 1964). However, although the lipid patterns of *Gadus morhua* and *Gadus aeglefinus* are almost identical, the rates of insolubilization are very different (Fig. 53). Also, elasmobranch (cartilaginous fish) muscle gradually becomes insoluble, like that of the teleosts (bony fish), but in at least three species no free fatty acids are liberated unless the pH rises—the optimum pHs for elasmobranch phospholipases are higher than for teleost phospholipases (Olley, Stephen *et al.*, 1967). Much more could be said, but this interesting subject is beyond the scope of the present work. Suffice at present that there are fundamental chemical differences between each species which influence the insolubilization reaction.

If myosin is extracted from various species of fish and allowed to stand at about 0°, it slowly aggregates, and the rate of aggregation, as studied with the ultra-centrifuge, again differs between species (Connell, 1961). Unfortunately, though, if the different fish are placed in order of rates of aggregation, the order of the species is not the same as that relating to extractability of actomyosin during storage in the frozen state (Fig. 53), so it is difficult to reach any satisfactory conclusion from such study. In any case, neither type of observation lends itself to the identification of unknown species of fish.

For this we must turn to electrophoresis, which makes use of the different speeds at which protein fractions travel under the influence of an electric field. Connell (1953) examined a considerable number of species by the original Tiselius technique, and showed that the patterns given by extracts of muscle made at low ionic strengths are sufficiently different to enable unknown species to be identified (Fig. 54). The proteins are 'myogens' of rather small molecular weight, the fibrillar proteins actin and myosin being unextracted by the dilute buffers used.

More recently, modified electrophoretic techniques have been applied to the characterization of further species, and successful results have been obtained by starch gel (Tsuyuki and Wold, 1964; Tsuyuki, Roberts and Kerr, 1967), disc (Mancuso, 1964; Thompson, 1967; Mackie, 1968), polyacetate strip (Lane, Hill and Learson, 1966) and polyacrylamide gel electrophoresis (Cowie, 1968). The differentiation of closely-related salmonid species by starch gel is illustrated in Fig. 55, which shows the complexity of the patterns obtained. The identity of the different bands is not known, but most of them are thought to be enzymes; it is curious that no two species have exactly the same pattern.

The same can be said of blood serum proteins, which have also been shown to differ between species. A number of papers are reviewed by

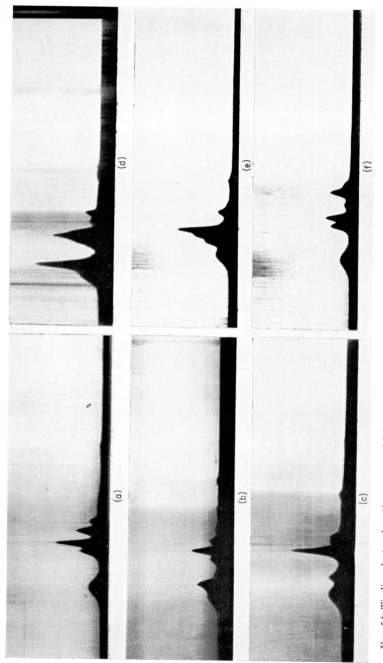

Fig. 54. Tiselius electrophoretic patterns of fish muscle extracts, selected from those of Connell (1953). Ascending limbs only, migration from left to right. (a) *Gadus morhua*; (b) *Gadus aeglefinus*; (c) *Gadus virens*; (d) *Pleuronectes microcephalus*; (e) *Pleuronectes platessa*; (f) *Pleuronectes cynoglossus*. Species within one genus do not resemble each other, differences being as great as between the two genera shown. Reproduced by courtesy of the author and the Biochemical Society.

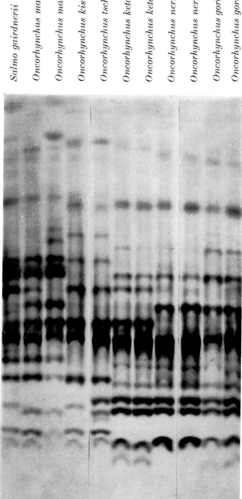

Salmo gairdnerii

Oncorhynchus masou

Oncorhynchus masou ishikawae

Oncorhynchus kisutch

Oncorhynchus tschawytscha

Oncorhynchus keta from British Columbia

Oncorhynchus keta from Asia

Oncorhynchus nerka from British Columbia

Oncorhynchus nerka from Asia

Oncorhynchus gorbuscha from British Columbia

Oncorhynchus gorbuscha from Asia

FIG. 55. Starch gel electropherograms of the muscle myogens of salmonid species from different localities. The anode is to the right of the picture. After Tsuyuki and Roberts (1966), reproduced by courtesy of Dr. H. Tsuyuki and the Fisheries Research Board of Canada.

Booke (1964b), who points out that the one conclusion lacking in them all was whether any similarities in the patterns followed the phylogenetic relationships of the fish.

Fish blood contains a globulin capable of binding iron (transferrin), and the electrophoretic mobility of transferrins, like the other proteins, has been shown to vary between species (Fine, Drilhon et al., 1965).

Patterns of the haemoglobins of various species have been shown to differ (Hashimoto and Matsuura, 1959, 1960a; Yamanaka, Yamaguchi and Matsuura, 1965; Wilkins and Iles, 1966; Tsuyuki, Uthe et al., 1966 and Yamanaka, Yamaguchi et al., 1967). Wilkins and Iles (1966) pointed out that while haemoglobin polymorphism (appearance in several forms) is common in fish, its inheritance is not governed in all cases by simple Mendelian mechanisms. Be that as it may, the way in which the proteins of the body are linked together seems to be as much a characteristic of each species as is the shape, structure and colour. This applies not only to the myogen and blood proteins, but also to the proteins of the slime (Barry and O'Rourke, 1959), egg-yolk (Jared and Wallace, 1968) and eye lenses (Bon, Swanborn et al., 1964; Rabaey, 1965), all of which yield electrophoretic patterns characteristic of each species. In addition, the purified myoglobins of different species can be distinguished from one another: small differences are found in the absorption spectra, and the thermal coagulation temperatures differ considerably (H. Tomita, Sendai University, private communication). However, from what we have seen in this section, electrophoresis seems to offer the best chance of success in species identification.

B. Phylogenetic considerations

Correlating the chemistry of a fish with its place in the evolutionary tree, or to see certain chemical features as being more 'primitive' than others is a process fraught with danger, but this has not lessened the interest which the topic holds for many investigators. The fundamental assumption is that those surviving groups of fish which evolved early in the history of vertebrates have retained up to the present the same mechanisms as they had at the beginning, rather than developing different systems with the passage of time within the same external shape. As we shall see, there does seem to be some justification for the assumption, but we should always remember that it *is* an assumption, and that the 'primitive' fish are modern descendents of ancient fish and not the ancient fish themselves. A fascinating series of studies awaits us if we are prepared to accept this basis.

Fish have a phylogenetic history at least three times as long as that of birds and mammals (Hoar, 1965), and since living examples of several very early genera are found today, a wide diversity of composition and function is to be expected. The earliest of all surviving fish are the cyclostomes ('round mouths'), the hagfish and lampreys (*Myxine, Eptatretus, Petromyzon = Lampetra* species, and a few others), whose circular mouths are considered primitive rather than a specific adaptation to their parasitic way of life. They arose in the Ordovician period, about 500 million years ago (Hoar, 1965). Following this come the cartilaginous fish (Elasmobranchs = Chondrichthyes), the sharks, skates and rays, which have survived since Devonian times (Gottfried, 1964). The line then branches into two, leading on one side to the holostei, older bony fish such as the sturgeons (*Acipenser*) and gar pike (*Lepidosteus*), and terminating in the teleosts, a relatively modern group which arose in the Jurassic period (Marshall, 1965), and which comprises most of the present-day commercial species of bony fish. Along the other branch after the sharks come the dipnoi (lung fish), for example *Protopterus*, and the coelacanth (*Latimeria*), discovered as recently as 1938 in the living state, which has primitive limbs. Later come the amphibia and the higher vertebrates, and it is noteworthy that the lung fish has chemical features in common with both fish and terrestrial animals (Dean and Chester Jones, 1959; Sawyer, 1966). Thus the amino acid composition of lung fish collagen is close to that of mammalian collagen, while a teleost (*Gadus morhua*) at the extremity of the opposite branch, farthest away from the mammals, shows collagen of a very different type (Harrington and von Hippel, 1961). The neurohypophysial hormones of lung fish also resemble those of amphibia rather than other bony fish, and from its position in the scheme we would expect the hormones of the coelacanth to do the same (Follett and Heller, 1964).

The organization of the original blood-forming organ, the spleen, also throws some light on evolutionary history (Jordan and Speidel, 1930). In the hagfish (most primitive) it is dispersed throughout the intestinal wall, while in the lamprey it is aggregated to some extent in the spiral valve. Lung fish spleens are more sharply segregated in the wall of the stomach, and of course in higher vertebrates the spleen is a separate organ. Haemoglobin is present in the blood of almost all teleosts and elasmobranchs, but the blood of the cyclostomes contains erythrocruorin, a pigment rich in iron, which is often present in invertebrates (Vinogradov, 1953). Cyclostome blood pigment lies intermediate in structure and properties between myoglobins and haemoglobins of higher animals, and so provides a clue as to the evolution of the whole group of proteins (Allison, Cecil *et al.*, 1960). The haemoglobin of *Latimeria*, the coelacanth, has also been stated (de Prailauné, 1955) to be primitive, although the basis of the conclusion was not made clear. Hall and Gray (1929) found that the concentration of iron in the blood of elasmobranchs was lower than that in "the majority of" teleosts, and Vinogradov (1953) concluded that in general the higher the organism rose in the evolutionary scale, the greater was the concentration of iron. Similarly, plasma proteins have been reported to increase during the progress of evolution, the primitive elasmobranchs, for example, lacking albumin (Gunter, Sulya and Box, 1961). The genesis of the red blood cells of elasmobranchs resembles that of the cyclostomes rather than that of the teleosts : the cells are continuously differentiated in the blood stream from primitive cells, and may also proliferate mitotically in the same place (Jordan and Speidel, 1930; Dawson, 1933).

The 'islet' tissue of cyclostomes has also been considered to be more primitive than that of any other vertebrate (Falkmer and Winbladh, 1964), but comparative studies on the structure of the insulin do not appear to have been carried out.

The kidney is most primitive in the cyclostomes. *Eptatretus*, for example, has a pronephros, the most rudimentary structure (Parker and Haswell, 1940), and in consequence the ion and water balance is accomplished by a very simple mechanism which "seems to be primitive by vertebrate standards" (Morris, 1965). Ionic regulation is less active in these fish, and the composition of blood is little different from that of the surrounding sea water. Table XXVI shows a comparison between

TABLE XXVI. Ionic Composition of the Serum of a Cyclostome, Myxine glutinosa, Compared with that of the Surrounding Sea Water
(after Bellamy and Chester Jones, 1961)

| Element | mM/kg water | |
	Sea water	Hagfish serum
K	12·2	11·1
Na	470	549
Cl	550	563
Ca	8·4	5·1
Mg	49·7	18·9

sea and serum in *Myxine glutinosa ;* the resemblance is marked. Similar results were obtained for *Myxine* by Robertson (1954), and the blood of another species of hagfish, *Polistotrema stoutii*, has also been shown to be isotonic with sea water (McFarland and Munz, 1958).

In this feature, cyclostomes resemble primitive invertebrates, such as coelenterates, which correspond osmotically with their environment and do not possess significant ability to change the ionic balance of their internal fluids (Nesterov and Skul'skii, 1965). With the changeover from invertebrates to vertebrates, the concentration of sodium in the extracellular fluid falls while that of potassium stays fairly constant. Similarly, intracellular lithium and sodium fall, and the potassium tends to rise as the animal ascends the evolutionary scale. Thus Burovina, Glazunov *et al.* (1964) suggested that the ratio of sodium : potassium in the muscles of aquatic organisms could be used as an additional character in biological classification.

In contrast to the cyclostomes, later forms of fish and land animals all have blood in which the concentration of inorganic substances is more dilute than that of sea water. The most likely reason for this is that the tissues function best in this particular environment (Baldwin, 1948), but earlier speculation ran along different lines. The fact that the salts of sodium, calcium and potassium existed in tissues in roughly the same proportions as in the sea prompted some writers to suggest that as a kind of inheritance we still carried diluted sea water in our blood, our ancestors being marine animals (Loeb, 1911). Macallum (1926, quoted by Marshall, 1965) supposed that the ionic composition of the blood reflected the composition of the oceans at the time that any particular group of fish had arisen: that moment in the history of the oceans had as it were been 'fossilized' for all time. Thus divergences in the composition of different groups of animals could be explained by changes in the ionic proportions of the oceans at different epochs. However, this theory is no longer accepted. Geochemical evidence indicates that the seas of Ordovician times were quite similar to those of today, and in any case there is a continual exchange of ions and fluid between the tissues of fish and their environment (Marshall, 1965). In addition, the salt concentration of teleost blood is extremely variable (Green and Hoffman, 1953), so could not be related to that of the primeval ocean anyway.

Having tissue salts at a concentration different from that of the surrounding medium poses problems for the fish, since marine fish will tend to become dehydrated and freshwater fish waterlogged. The process by which fish adjust themselves is known as osmoregulation, which is fully described by Conte (1969), so will not be considered at length here except insofar as it is of phylogenetic interest.

There is an idea that the armour plating of extinct fossil fish 'waterproofed' them against osmotic flooding or dehydration of their body tissues (Lagler, Bardach and Miller, 1962), but fish alive today employ other methods. Very early in the evolution of vertebrates it became possible for them to synthesize urea as the end product of nitrogenous excretion* (the end product in simple aquatic organisms is ammonia). This urea is retained in many tissues of the body by the elasmobranchs, both embryo and adult (Read, 1968: *Squalus suckleyi* and *Raja binoculata*), in a concentration often exceeding 2%, the remainder of the osmotic balance being achieved with high concentrations of sodium and chloride and by the presence of other organic substances of low molecular weight such as trimethylamine oxide and betaine (Smith, 1936, quoted by Robin, Murdaugh and Weiss, 1964). Smith (1929, 1931a,b) carried out extensive analyses of elasmobranch tissues, and attributed to Staedeler and Frerichs (1858) the discovery of large quantities of urea in the blood and tissues of this group of fish, and to Rodier (1899) the conclusion that its function was to preserve the osmotic balance. Freshwater elasmobranchs still contain urea in the blood, but in lower concentrations (Smith, 1931a). Primitive sharks re-invaded the seas from fresh water during the Devonian period, and this may have been possible only because they had retained the ability to synthesize urea (Brown, 1964).

Like the elasmobranchs, the coelacanth (*Latimeria chalumnae*) osmoregulates by means of elevated urea concentrations (Brown and Brown, 1967; Pickford and Grant, 1967) and the dipnoi and amphibia also possess the ability to synthesize this compound. However, the fish in the other branch of the evolutionary tree seem to have lost the requisite enzymes, so that both the modern teleosts and the descendants of their forbears, the holostei, do not produce urea (Brown and Brown, 1967). Instead they are thought to make up their water balance by ingesting sea water, salt and all, and then excreting the salt afterwards (Smith, 1931b). Thus the division of the evolutionary line into two branches subsequent to the elasmobranchs is confirmed by the separation into forms which have and which do not have a mechanism for synthesizing urea.

Lovern (1942) considered that as animals ascended the evolutionary scale the composition of the fatty acids of the 'depots' (lipid storage tissues) became simpler. The change took the form of a steady loss of all unsaturated acid groups other than those with 18 carbon atoms, leading finally to lipids in which the predominant constituents were palmitic and oleic acids. Traces of the primitive large range of fatty acids could still be found, but these decreased progressively with the evolution of more advanced animals. At the same time, this picture was sometimes obscured by the influence of the diet on the fatty acid pattern.

---

* Ammonia appears to be formed first whether the end product is ammonia or urea (Salvatore, Zappia and Costa, 1965).

Studies by Diplock and Haslewood (1967) have indicated that the possession of appreciable amounts of ubiquinone in the heart is usually a character of advanced vertebrates; that of *Myxine glutinosa* is almost insignificant, while that in the hearts of teleosts tends to be more concentrated, though considerable variation occurs between species.

Deoxyribose nucleic acid (DNA) carries the inheritance characteristics of each cell, so would be expected to reveal much information of evolutionary significance. However, systematic study has yielded little of interest. The quantity of DNA per cell in teleosts varies widely from species to species (Vendrely and Vendrely, 1950; Mirsky and Ris, 1951), but while no obvious evolutionary trend can be discerned between the surviving ancestors of the teleosts and the teleosts themselves, studies on the series lungfish—amphibia—reptiles—birds have suggested that during evolution there has been a decline in the amount of DNA per cell (Mirsky and Ris, 1951). The same authors concluded that the amount of DNA per cell was not proportional to the number of different genes, but may have related to the number of strands in the chromosomes.

A principal function of the special substances found in bile is to emulsify lipids from the food, to render them more easily digested. In a series of publications, Haslewood and his colleagues have studied the evolution of these bile salts, the findings being summed up in a monograph (Haslewood, 1967a). In fish, bile salts are either the sulphate esters of bile alcohols or taurine conjugates of bile acids. They were originally derived from cholesterol, and as found in cyclostomes ('myxinol') and the coelacanth ('latimerol') they resemble cholesterol in having 27 carbon atoms. The emulsifying properties depend partly on the number of hydroxyl groups, and myxinol, with four, has the smallest number of these of all C_{27} bile alcohols studied. All others have at least five, and it appears that since myxinol is thus not very effective as an emulsifier, the cyclostomes need large quantities of it during digestion (Haslewood, 1966).

The chimaeras are found among the holocephali, and may be survivors of a group whose ancestors were early elasmobranchs. Bridgwater, Haslewood and Watt (1963) elucidated the chemical nature of the bile alcohol of living elasmobranchs ('scymnol'), and also that from the chimaeras ('chimaerol') and found the structures sufficiently similar to support the phylogenetic relationship. Evolution of these substances results in a reduction of the number of carbon atoms from 27 to, finally, 24. The structural formulas of these various compounds are illustrated by Haslewood (1967b).

While the bile salt patterns do therefore indicate taxonomic relationships, Haslewood (1967a) concluded that the finer distinctions of evolution have been obliterated during the passage of time. For example, the bile of *Latimeria* contains small amounts of what are regarded as more 'modern' bile alcohols, although the functioning majority are 'primitive'. He pointed out the special interest of the fact that the 'newer' substances should exist in early genera in quantities too small to confer any selective advantage, but that nevertheless during evolution they have increased in proportion and finally come to dominate the bile of later animals, displacing the earlier substances.

It has already been demonstrated (p. 133) that the electrophoretic patterns of certain proteins are specific for each species of fish. A few workers have in addition studied the patterns in the context of phylogenetic relationships. Rabaey (1965) noticed a fundamental difference between the patterns of soluble lens proteins of elasmobranchs and those of teleosts, and Bon, Swanborn *et al.* (1964), who studied the lens proteins of 30 species, found that family and order relationships could be perceived in the patterns. Tsuyuki, Roberts and Vanstone (1965) examined 50 species of fish, and found that the interspecific and intergeneric similarities of muscle myogen patterns within any one family parallel the existing classification based on external shape, but that the same degree of relationship is not observable in the haemoglobin patterns. Tsuyuki and Roberts (1966) studied the interspecific relations within a number of genera, and observed that the degree of similarity of muscle myogen patterns appears to be related directly to the closeness in phylogenetic relationship as established by the usual taxonomic methods. A part of their findings has been illustrated already in Fig. 55 (p. 134). *Oncorhynchus masou* appears to be more closely related to *Salmo* than to the *Oncorhynchus kisutch—tschawytscha* group. Neave (1958) believed that *Oncorhynchus masou* was the first to evolve from *Salmo* and so of existing species is the most closely related to it. The muscle myogen patterns are reproducible, independent of sex and completely species specific, and, incidentally, Robertson, Love and Cowie (1967) showed that the myogen pattern of *Gadus morhua* is also uninfluenced by varying degrees of starvation*. In plasma protein electrophoresis, the species specificity is maintained, but is not nearly so self-evident as in the electrophoresis of the muscle myogens. Booke (1964b), in reviewing papers describing blood protein patterns, pointed out that no phylogenetic conclusions have emerged from such work.

The creation of a new species through the branching of the evolutionary line requires that a portion of the original common stock should

---

* Extreme starvation can cause the bands to fade or sometimes disappear (Love, 1969, unpublished).

become isolated so that interbreeding of the two forms is prevented. A potentially interesting case arises in *Oncorhynchus gorbuscha*, which matures and dies at exactly 2 years of age, so that for countless generations there has been complete segregation of 'even' and 'odd' year forms. However, study has so far revealed no morphological difference between them (Neave, 1958).

A further negative report relates to the size of the molecule of muscle lactate dehydrogenase, which had earlier been reported as changing during the evolution of more advanced species. Arnheim, Cocks and Wilson (1967) showed that it is no different in the cyclostome *Eptatretus* from that in higher vertebrates.

This brings to an end the descriptions of investigations specifically designed to shed light on phylogenetic relationships. In addition there are a few miscellaneous studies on the coelacanth and on the differences between elasmobranch and teleost fish, which are summarized below. The chemistry of the coelacanth is distributed among several papers listed in Part III.

The lipid composition of *Latimeria chalumnae* is unusual though not unique in that wax esters largely predominate and the presence of glycerides has not yet been established (Nevenzel, Rodegker *et al.*, 1966). It is thought that wax esters, which have a low specific gravity, are present in quantity in order to bring the buoyancy of the fish near to that of the surrounding water. Fox and Crozier (1965) showed that no carotenoids are present either in *Latimeria* or in the cyclostome *Eptatretus stoutii*, so that possibly the capacity to store these compounds evolved only later. Further up the scale, some elasmobranchs do possess carotenoids in their organs, but the mako shark, *Isurus glaucus*, does not.

Elasmobranchs differ from teleosts in that their skeleton is composed of cartilage, or ossified cartilage, rather than true bone. Vitamin D is essential for normal bone growth and calcification, and many animals suffer rickets (a deformation of the bones) if they are deprived of this vitamin. However, having no bony skeleton, the elasmobranchs are able to live satisfactorily without it. They are almost devoid of vitamin D (Lovern, 1958), storing less than 25 International Units per gramme of liver oil (papers quoted by Cruickshank, 1962).

The lipid of elasmobranchs tends to be unusual. Lovern (1937) stated that certain fatty acids are abnormally saturated or abnormally unsaturated, and the contents of saturated fatty acids and unsaturated acids with 18 carbon atoms have been said to be above the average for other marine animals (Jacquot, 1961). Also, while the stored ('depot') lipids in most fish species are in the form of triglycerides, those in elasmobranchs often occur at least partly as glyceryl ethers (Lovern,

1964). Elasmobranchs have no swim bladder, and if such a marine fish is to be weightless in water, then about 30% of its weight must be lipid. Certain deep-sea sharks contain as much as 90% of the hydrocarbon squalene in their livers, which may make up a quarter of the bulk of the fish. Squalene is lighter than, for example, cod liver oil, the specific gravities being respectively 0·86 and 0·93 (Marshall, 1965), and by this means these sharks are said to achieve buoyancy in sea water—though what happens during starvation has not been considered so far in this connection.

Muscle 'extractives' differ between teleosts and elasmobranchs, anserine and methyl histidine being found only in the former, and betaine and sarcosine in the latter (Shewan, 1953). Kutscher and Ackermann (1933) found that elasmobranch heart muscle usually contains less creatin than that of teleosts, and Velankar (1965) reported the presence of propionic acid in elasmobranch muscle, absent from that of teleosts or crustaceans. Trimethylamine oxide also occurs in greater concentration in elasmobranch muscle than in teleost muscle (see Table XXVIII, p. 146).

The plasma corticosteroid level is lower in elasmobranchs than in cyclostomes or teleosts (Chester Jones and Phillips, 1960). The implications of this finding are not at present clear, as with the zinc content of elasmobranch blood, which is also lower than that of teleosts (Vinogradov, 1953).

Isolated corneas from the eyes of teleosts swell when placed in salt solutions, so presumably need a stabilizing mechanism during life. Elasmobranch corneas do not swell in this way, and it is a puzzling aspect of evolution that these fish should have had a seemingly ideal and transparent cornea, which then evolved to a more complex one (Smelser, 1962). Maybe some additional advantages of the teleost cornea have not yet been realized.

C. Freshwater and saltwater fish

As we have already seen (p. 138), marine fish are constantly struggling against dehydration, while those from fresh water tend to become waterlogged, because of the difference in osmotic pressure between the body fluids and the environment. Thus freshwater teleosts produce in one day ten or more times the volume of urine of their marine counterparts (Marshall, 1965). We might expect that the total ash content of marine fish would be higher than that of freshwater fish, but this is not so. On the whole, the quantity of inorganic material in the solid tissues of the body is similar in both kinds of fish, although trace elements such as boron, bromide, iodine, lithium, strontium and copper are all more concentrated in marine fish (Vinogradov, 1953). Parks and Rose (1933) considered the copper contents of the two types of fish to be comparable.

Differences arise in the case of blood, the composition of which does to some extent reflect the nature of the environment. Robertson (1954) showed that the total ionic composition of the plasma of *Muraena helena*, a marine teleost, is about one third of that of the sea water, and differs from that of a freshwater fish which is less still (Table XXVII).

TABLE XXVII. IONIC COMPOSITION OF THE PLASMA OF A MARINE AND A
FRESHWATER TELEOST, COMPARED WITH THAT OF SEA WATER
(after Robertson, 1954)

	m-eq/kg Water								Total ions relative to sea water
	Na	*K*	*NH$_4$*	*Ca*	*Mg*	*Cl*	*SO$_4$*	*HCO$_3$*	
Sea water	564	12	—	24·8	128·7	659	68	2·8	100
Muraena helena (marine)	212	2	2·1	7·7	4·9	188	11·4	8	32
Coregonus clupeoides (freshwater)	141	4	0·3	5·3	3·4	117	4·6	10·6	25

Cholinesterase has been reported to occur in a number of tissues which transport sodium. Fleming, Scheffel and Linton (1962) examined the gill tissue of 9 species of cyprinodonts, and found that the enzyme occurs only in the gills of those species that enter or occupy habitats of varying salinity : it was not found in species which inhabited fresh water permanently. The gills are therefore indicated as excretory organs for sodium, in this species at least.

The osmotic pressure of the blood of freshwater elasmobranchs is typically much lower than that of marine elasmobranchs, but is somewhat higher than in freshwater teleosts. Their blood urea content is lower than in marine elasmobranchs, but still characteristically high when compared with teleosts from the same environment. Typical values of blood urea nitrogen are given by Smith (1931a) as 300 mg% for freshwater elasmobranchs, 1000 mg% for marine elasmobranchs* and 10 to 30 mg% for other animals. Table XXVII shows that there is less chloride in the blood of a freshwater teleost as compared with

* A value as high as 1326 mg% urea nitrogen was given by Kisch (1930) for *Trygon violacea*.

marine, and Smith (1931a) showed that the same applies to elasmo-branchs from the two habitats, which possess 604 and 816 mg%, respectively. He also observed that although urea permeates all tissues, it is typically lower in concentration in the pericardial fluid than in the serum or perivisceral fluid, and that this distribution characterizes both marine and freshwater elasmobranchs.

Hoppe-Seyler and Schmidt (1927, quoted by Kutscher and Ackermann, 1933) observed that trimethylamine oxide (TMO) occurs in marine fish but not freshwater fish, and concluded that it resembles urea in its non-poisonous nature, small molecular weight and neutral reaction, and in that it appears to help regulate osmotic pressure. Beatty (1939) confirmed the observation, and found the compound also present in *Pomolobus pseudoharengus*, a marine fish which migrates into fresh water to spawn. It is however absent from *Anguilla* during the freshwater period of its life. Cook (1931) showed that young *Oncorhynchus tschawytscha* in fresh water contains 0—4·5 mg% in the muscle tissue, whereas the same species at sea contains 50—60 mg%. On the other hand, when Benoit and Norris (1945) gradually increased the salinity of the fresh water in which this species lives up to that of sea water, no change occurred in the TMO level unless it had been added to the diet.

Lange and Fugelli (1965) showed that the sum of TMO and total free proteinaceous materials correlates well with the osmolarity of the blood, and so added evidence for the osmoregulatory role of this com-pound. However, its origin in fish is still obscure. Several studies point to a dietary source, while others indicate that synthesis takes place (Goldstein, Hartman and Forster, 1967).

Howbeit, the difference in concentration between fresh and salt-water fish is clear enough. A few examples are given in Table XXVIII, which shows the still higher values in marine elasmobranchs, where it presumably serves an osmoregulatory function like that of urea.

Freshwater and marine fish probably do not differ basically in their mechanisms for the deposition, synthesis and interconversion of fatty acids (Reiser, Stevenson *et al.*, 1963), but there are significant differ-ences in the fatty acid composition of the two groups. The C_{18} unsaturated acid group is consistently higher, and the C_{20} and C_{22} groups lower in freshwater fish compared with marine. Palmitoleic acid is a more important component of freshwater fish, the only marine species showing this characteristic being *Hippoglossus hippoglossus*. Apart from this, freshwater and marine fish oils are similar in that in each class the average unsaturation (number of double bonds) of the various groups is of the same order, and the general proportions of fatty acid mixtures is the same (Lovern, 1932a). Gruger, Nelson and

TABLE XXVIII. TRIMETHYLAMINE OXIDE IN MUSCLE OF FRESHWATER
TELEOSTS, MARINE TELEOSTS AND MARINE ELASMOBRANCHS

$mg\%$

*Freshwater teleosts**

Esox niger	58·9	Lepomis gibbosus	30·5
Lepomis macrochirus	91·5	Micropterus dolomieu	25·7
Morone americana	64·2	Pomoxis nigromaculatus	79·4

Marine teleosts[†]

Anarhichas lupus	255	Gadus aeglefinus	235
Gadus merlangus	213	Gadus morhua	330
Limander limander	180	Pleuronectes platessa	120

Marine elasmobranchs[‡]

Mustelus manozo	1462	Raja batis	1100
Raja hollandi	1359	Scyllium canicula	1080
Scyllium catulus	1430		

* Data from Anderson and Fellers (1952).
† Data from Shewan (1951).
‡ Data from Reay (1939); Suyama and Tokuhiro (1954b).

Stansby (1964) found the linoleic acid content to be greater in freshwater
fish, and were of the opinion that the differences between the two groups
are largely due to differences in diet. This conclusion was held also by
Kelly, Reiser and Hood (1958), who reported that at the same time
both groups seem to be able to synthesize some polyunsaturated fatty
acids from non-fatty precursors.

These separate phenomena had all been observed earlier by Lovern
(1935), who stated that although both types of fish possess lipids typical
of their environments, certain fish can modify their food lipids considerably. Thus the lipids of the parr stage (p. 80) of *Salmo salar* are
typical freshwater fish lipids, but after the parr changes to the smolt
form in the same environment the lipids change to the type peculiar to
adult salmon, though still retaining some characteristics of freshwater
fish lipids (Lovern, 1934b).

Sturgeon (*Acipenser* sp.) inhabit both environments at various stages
of their lives, but the lipids from a specimen caught in the North Sea
were like those of a freshwater fish; Lovern (1932b) pointed out that
sturgeons do most of their feeding in fresh water. Eels (*Anguilla anguilla*)
differ in their fatty acid composition according to whether they are

caught in fresh water or in the sea, and those from brackish estuarine waters have an intermediate type of lipid (Lovern, 1942), so diet does appear to be a crucial factor.

The most recent papers on this subject confirm and extend the earlier findings. Ackman, Eaton *et al.* (1967) showed that freshwater fish contain more linolenic, linoleic and arachidonic acids than do marine fish, and Ackman (1967) showed that the total C_{16} fatty acids are greater in freshwater species. Total C_{18} acids are also higher but probably less definitive as a means of distinguishing freshwater from marine triglyceride oils. Stansby (1967), reviewing several papers, stated that linoleic acid values for marine fish usually amount to 0·7—3%, while in freshwater fish a value of 6% can be expected. He reported that the lipids of the immature freshwater form of *Oncorhynchus kisutch* are typical freshwater fish lipids, but are more different from typical marine oils than are those of permanent freshwater fish. Further, the lipids of the marine adult form of the same species are more different from freshwater fish oils than those of typical marine species. Whether these extremes of change characterize other euryhaline (able to live in fresh or salt water) species remains to be found.

A few miscellaneous observations have no known explanation so far. Yudaev (1950) found that the muscle of freshwater fish contain a relatively high concentration of histidine and a low concentration of carnosine and anserine. Lukton and Olcott (1958) reported a higher concentration of carnosine in relation to anserine in freshwater fish than in marine fish. The hearts of freshwater teleosts contain about 50 mg% of N-acetyl histidine, but in marine teleosts this compound is either absent or present only in traces (Hanson, 1966).

The muscle of freshwater fish is poorer in some vitamins than is that of their marine counterparts. Less vitamin C (ascorbic acid) was found by Fomin, Romanjuk and Khvoynitskaya (1937) and less pyridoxine and niacin have been reported by Yanase (1956) and Braganca (1944), respectively.

D. Intrinsic activity

There is enormous variety in the habitual behaviour of different species of fish, ranging from perpetual movement in the pelagic species such as tuna (*Thunnus*), mackerel (*Scomber*) and herring (*Clupea*) species to long periods of complete inactivity. The fish usually studied especially because of its 'laziness' is the toadfish, *Opsanus tau* (Fig. 56).

The flat fish are more sluggish than the rounded ones, and from studies on the rupture of connective tissue after death (Love, Lavéty

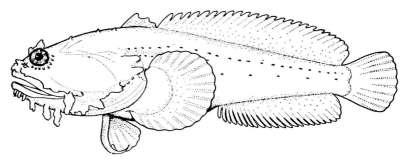

FIG. 56. The toadfish (*Opsanus tau*). After Robinson and Schwartz (1965), reproduced by courtesy of Dr. F. J. Schwartz and the Chesapeake Biological Laboratory.

and Steel, 1969) it appears that their muscular contraction is weaker as well.

Other anatomical features also correlate with activity. As the muscle segments pass inwards towards their attachments on the vertebral column, they form four series of nesting cones pointing towards the tail. The more active the fish is, the greater is the development (depth) of these conical "Chinese puzzles" (Marshall, 1965), the mackerels, sharks and tunas in particular showing very deep cones. The presence or absence of certain named muscles can also be correlated with the activity of the fish, or with its acceleration at the commencement of swimming (Ganguly and Nag, 1964).

It is obvious that the oxygen requirements will vary according to the activity of the fish, and a number of investigators have studied the capacity of the blood for carrying it. More active fish not only have larger gill areas, but the conditions for gaseous exchange are better than in sluggish forms, and the area is increased in such a way as to keep low the resistance to water flow by having an increased total filament length and a large number of secondary folds (Hughes, 1966). Inactive fish have more widely spaced lamellae of short filament length.

The blood of active fish contains more haemoglobin than that of sluggish fish (Hall and Gray, 1929; Root, 1931; Vernberg and Gray, 1953; Klawe, Barrett and Klawe, 1963; Engel and Davis, 1964; Hunn and Robinson, 1966), in order to increase its oxygen capacity. Hall and Gray (1929) measured haemoglobin as iron, and found 45 mg per 100 ml blood in *Sarda sarda* and 43 mg in *Scomber scombrus*, with similar values for other active species. At the bottom of the scale, among others, comes *Narcacion nobilianus*, with 8·8 mg and *Opsanus tau* with 13·5, while fish exhibiting a moderate amount of activity show intermediate values. Engel and Davis (1964) measured the blood cell volumes (haematocrit values) and haemoglobin concentrations in 4 active and 3 inactive species, and their results are presented in Table XXIX. *Opsanus tau* shows the lowest values in each case.

TABLE XXIX. HAEMOGLOBIN CONTENTS AND HAEMATOCRIT VALUES OF
THE BLOOD OF ACTIVE AND INACTIVE FISH
(after Engel and Davis, 1964)

	per cent Haemoglobin	Haematocrit
Active fish		
Pomatomus saltatrix	10·4	43·4
Roccus saxatilis	9·5	38·7
Scomberomorus cavalla	9·3	36·3
Scomberomorus maculatus	10·4	38·8
Inactive fish		
Micropogon undulatus	7·3	29·0
Opsanus tau	6·2	27·5
Paralichthys sp.	6·6	29·3

While the blood of active species possesses a greater number of red blood cells per unit volume, the oxygen capacity of the haemoglobin itself appears not to change, although earlier work had suggested that it might increase with the intrinsic activity of the fish (Black, 1940).

The quantity of haemoglobin in a single species can change if there is a change in activity: Shubnikov (1959) showed that in the blood of *Clupea harengus* it is greater during migration than in quiescent periods. Haemoglobin levels are particularly high in those fish which are both migrating and intensively feeding, and at a later date, when the rate of northward migration slackens, they begin to decrease again.

Although the blood of sluggish fish has a lower capacity for oxygen, it is able to remove the gas more efficiently from the water, so that such fish can live in water of low oxygen content, in contrast to the more active species (Hall, 1930; Root, 1931). If active fish are placed in an oxygen-poor environment, they are unable to complete their carbohydrate metabolism, and lactic acid accumulates in their tissues (Heath and Pritchard, 1965).

For some reason, the blood of the most active fish contains the greatest number of immature red blood cells, about 20% of the total in circulation. Less active fish have 3—6% of immature cells, while the blood cells of *Opsanus tau* and other inactive fish are virtually all mature. Possibly these figures reflect differences in the life spans of the red cells (Dawson, 1933). Thrombocyte and leucocyte (white blood cell) numbers do not appear to correlate with activity (Engel and Davis, 1964).

The muscle of energetic species of fish obviously needs a copious supply of oxygen. Vernberg and Gray (1953) showed that the excised brains also required more oxygen than those of less active species.

Certain Antarctic fish, such as *Chaenocephalus aceratus* (see Fig. 68, p. 178 for illustration) have no haemoglobin at all (Ruud, 1954), and, commenting on this, Munro Fox (1954) concluded that the tissues of many fish when swimming quietly can obtain all the oxygen they require from that dissolved in the blood plasma, requiring an additional supply, with the aid of haemoglobin, only when they are moving actively. While haemoglobin would therefore be a luxury for such fish, it is definitely not so in active species such as *Scomber scombrus*, which are not able even to respire properly unless they are for ever moving forwards—the ability of such species to achieve adequate ventilation in a stationary position has been practically lost (Hall, 1930).

We have seen earlier that changes in a constituent in liver or muscle are not necessarily mirrored in the blood, but the increased demands by active fish for energy in the form of carbohydrate are in fact clearly shown. Blood sugar as determined by Gray and Hall (1930) ranges from 90·7 mg% in *Pneumatophorus colias*, 79·4 mg% in *Poronotus triancanthus* and 75·2 mg% in *Brevoortia tyrannus*, all active fish, to 15·4 mg% in *Opsanus tau* and 5·6 in *Lophius piscatorius*, the angler fish, which spends nearly all of its adult existence partly buried on the sea bed just waiting for food to come to it. Other writers reporting higher blood sugar values in the more active species are McCay (1931), Vernberg and Gray (1953) and Fukuda (1958). Kiermeir (1939) found no clear relationship between activity and blood sugar level, but observations had been confined to some freshwater species. Gray and Hall (1930) stated that the normal blood sugar level of some sluggish fish is often lower than the sugar of more active species even after it has been reduced by insulin.

Less iodine (as thyroxine) circulates in the blood of sedentary fish (Jacquot, 1961), and since less energy is utilized, less food is consumed and the quantities of digestive enzymes secreted have been shown by Chesley (1934) to be less than those of active fish, especially in the case of trypsin. The activity of muscle adenosine triphosphatase, which releases chemical energy to be used in muscular contraction, is also lower in inactive fish (Noda and Tachino, 1965), as is the activity of those enzymes which are capable of breaking down the muscle itself (cathepsins). Bailey, Koran and Bradley (1942), who made this observation, believed that it revealed a mechanism for the sustenance of life through the mobilization of tissue proteins during periods of food scarcity. We shall have much more to say about this later (p. 231), but in the meantime it is interesting to find the rate of reaction to be enhanced in active fish.

Several of the vitamins play important roles in muscle metabolism, for example niacin (nicotinic acid) forms a part of the coenzymes DPN and TPN (di- and tri-phosphopyridine nucleotide). We might therefore expect greater concentrations in the muscle of active species, and this is in fact the case, although some exceptions make the relationship a little uncertain, presumably because vitamins have other functions as well. Thus niacin is more concentrated in the muscle of active species, and *Thunnus thynnus*, the most active species examined, shows the greatest concentration (Braekkan, 1959). However, *Gadus aeglefinus* also shows high values of this vitamin although it is not an especially active fish, and the concentrations in some flat fish species are higher than those of the gadoids.

In most cases the muscle of active fish also contains more vitamin B_{12} (Braekkan, 1959), pantothenic and folic acids (Higashi, 1961), pyridoxine (Yanase, 1956) and riboflavin, the latter in both white and dark muscle (Tomoda and Hotta, 1957), so a general correlation can be seen with substances involved in metabolism. Other compounds having functions which are less well understood also appear to relate to the activity of the fish, vigorous species possessing more copper (Vinogradov, 1953) and cholesterol (Hunn and Robinson, 1966) in the blood and trimethylamine oxide (Shewan, 1951) and free histidine (Shewan, 1955; Schaefer, 1962) in the muscle. The position of carnosine and anserine is not clear, since pelagic (active) species have been reported by Lukton and Olcott (1958) to contain large amounts, and by Shewan (1955) to contain little or none. A better knowledge of their function might clarify the issue.

E. Variations within a species
Genetic factors which distinguish between different populations
1. *Introduction*

Up to now we have considered only differences between species of fish. However, various features have from time to time been reported as characters of certain local populations of the same species. Nikolsky (1963), with his tidy outlook on adaptation, considered that these variations were designed to ensure that the greatest variety of habitats were occupied, and quoted several instances of fish species which could occur either as an elongated river form or as a high-bodied lake form.

The main section dealing with purely ecological factors follows the present one (p. 172) and should be read in conjunction with it. A certain untidiness of presentation seems inevitable, because some apparent characteristics of a local race are in fact the result of ecological influences, but in this section we will endeavour to find out whether any races differ from others by factors which are inherited, rather than those which would disappear with a change of surroundings.

Distinctions are not easy to make, and one obstacle has been described by Farris (1958):

"Students of animal ecology, population dynamics, and resource management have long been faced with the problem of describing the size and integrity of the populations with which they are working. This general problem is often confused, on the one hand, by the fact that morphological differences may only be a reflection of environmental differences and not of genetic differences and, on the other hand, by the fact that genetic differences are not always reflected morphologically."

2. *Meristic Characters*

A number of workers have investigated the small differences that occur in the anatomy of fish (known as "meristic characters") caught in various localities. The external appearance of *Clupea harengus* was studied by Heincke (1898), one of whose illustrations is shown in Fig. 57, in which a herring from Barra (West coast of Scotland) is compared with one caught off Iceland, and can be seen to differ in minor details of appearance.

The trouble is that systematic research along these lines is difficult, because no numerical scale can be used to investigate the consequences of artificially imposing ecological stresses one at a time, so that the individual contributions of ecology and genetics cannot be separated. Much more satisfactory are counts of the numbers of vertebrae or of the numbers of bony rays in various fins, which show small but significant variations between fish from different grounds when large numbers are averaged. Jordan (1892 and onwards, quoted by Tåning, 1952) showed that the number of vertebrae vary according to the place of catching, and that there is a correlation with the temperature of the ground. Schmidt (1917) found that the number of vertebrae in *Zoarces viviparus*

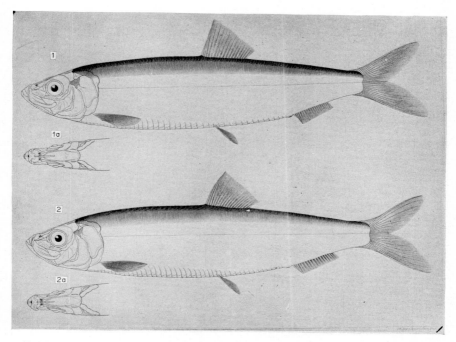

FIG. 57. The external appearance of *Clupea harengus* from two grounds. 1. From Barra, West coast of Scotland; 2. From Iceland. After Heincke (1898).

is always lower within the Scandinavian fjords than in the waters outside, and suggested that the fjords contain, or lack, certain unknown factors. He did not commit himself as to the possibility of the vertebral count being genetically controlled, and variations in the salinity of the water appear to be unimportant. In 1919, working with *Salmo trutta*, he concluded that while the numbers of fin-rays or vertebrae are influenced by the environment, the possible range is determined genetically. In a paper published in 1930, Schmidt reported the results of counting the vertebrae and the dorsal fin rays of no fewer than 20,000 *Gadus morhua* from different localities. He again found that fish from inshore or shallow water tend to have fewer vertebrae than those from the open sea, but now, taken in conjunction with his main findings (Fig. 58) it is clear that this was a temperature effect. The chart shows the numbers of vertebrae (his other chart on fin rays is not illustrated here) in cod from different parts of the Northern Hemisphere, and also the average surface temperatures: the counts increased from South to North, as the temperature decreased. Recently, Kubota and Ono (1965) followed the

7*

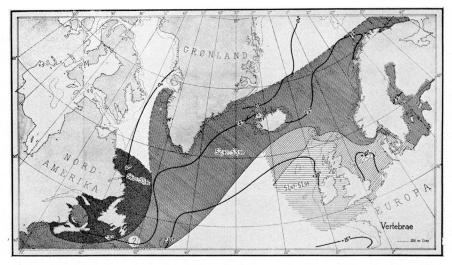

FIG. 58. Average numbers of vertebrae in *Gadus morhua* from different parts of the ocean. Isotherms at the surface of the sea are also shown. Note the increase in number with decrease in temperature. After Schmidt (1930).

scheme to its logical conclusion by plotting the number of vertebrae against the degrees of latitude where caught, and obtained an easily recognizable correlation (Fig. 59). Nikolsky (1963) regarded the changes in vertebral and fin-ray counts as adaptations to swimming in waters of different densities.

The numbers of vertebrae and fin rays are fixed very early in the life of the larvae, so one may envisage a certain 'sensitive' period of

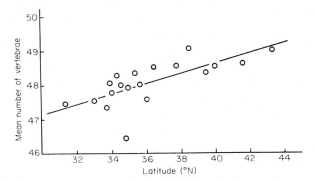

FIG. 59. Average numbers of vertebrae in *Misgurnus anguillicaudatus* caught at different degrees of latitude (locations on the globe). After Kubota and Ono (1965), reproduced by courtesy of Dr. Z. Kubota.

development during which the vertebral count is influenced by the environment. Beyond this, temperature fluctuation is unimportant. Schmidt (1930) concluded that the 'sensitive' phase for the number of fin rays occurs somewhat later than that governing vertebrae, hence his geographical charts for the two characters differ slightly. Hempel and Blaxter (1961) found a temperature-sensitive phase 6—7 days after fertilization in *Clupea harengus* incubated at 10°: at this point, transfer of the eggs to an environment at 4° for 24 hours result in an increased vertebral (and myotome) count.

The number of vertebrae of *Sardinella aurita* also varies according to the water temperature, and since this fish spawns more than once during the season, there is a progressive decrease in the number of vertebrae of larvae spawned later, because the sea becomes warmer as the summer progresses. Year-to-year variations are also possible, depending on the amount of sunshine (Ben-Tuvia, 1963a,b).

A considerable number of other investigators have studied the effects of various factors on meristic characters, usually vertebral count, and for a complete summing-up in tabular form see the reviews by Tåning (1952), Blaxter and Holliday (1963) and Garside (1966b).

Turning now to experiments in which the environment for the incubation of the fertilized eggs is altered artificially, we see that an

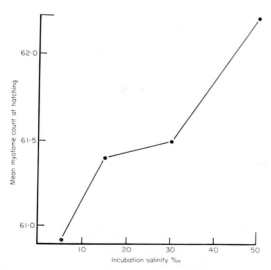

Fig. 60. The effect of the salinity of the environment on the mean myotome count of *Clupea harengus* larvae from Cuxhaven. After Hempel and Blaxter (1961), reproduced by courtesy of Mr. J. H. S. Blaxter and the International Council for the Exploration of the Sea.

increase in the time for which eggs are exposed to light during early development decreases the number of both vertebrae and anal fin rays (McHugh, 1954: *Leuresthes tenuis;* Lindsey, 1958: *Oncorhynchus nerka*) although Lindsey pointed out that the intensity of the light used is greater than that ever encountered under natural conditions. Tåning (1952: *Salmo trutta*) found the effect of salinity to be rather indefinite, but Hempel and Blaxter (1961: *Clupea harengus*) found that an increase during incubation leads to an increase in the vertebral count (Fig. 60).

Tåning (1952) showed that the greatest average number of dorsal and pectoral fin rays is obtained in *Salmo trutta* which have been incubated at 8—10°, lower or higher temperatures each leading to smaller numbers. The reverse is true of vertebrae: the lowest number appears at the intermediate temperature, 6°, while higher or lower temperatures lead to higher numbers. Hempel and Blaxter (1961) incubated the eggs of *Clupea harengus* at various temperatures and showed, like Tåning, that an increase above 7° causes a steady reduction in the number of vertebrae (Fig. 61). However, while herring from both the West of Scotland and from the German coast respond to a change of temperature in similar ways, the actual numbers of vertebrae at a given temperature are different according to the place of capture, indicating the presence of a genetic factor in the background. While, therefore, the sea temperature at the critical stage markedly affects the numbers of vertebrae in herrings, it is just possible that races could be identified by vertebral counts, since the lines in Fig. 61 do not overlap. In *Gadus morhua* the differences would appear to be too small for the technique to be useful (Fig. 58).

Differences in the body proportions of *Hippoglossus stenolepis* from different grounds were reported by Thompson and van Cleve (1936, quoted by Dunlop, 1955). Those of *Gadus morhua* were reported by Lundbeck (1953) to change markedly according to locality, the mean weight of 4- to 7-year-old fish ranging from 4·9 kg in the North Sea to only 1·4 kg in the "North East area". The differences were thought to be related to the growth rate, cod from Iceland being noteworthy in that those from the South grow quickly and resemble the plump North Sea cod, while those from the North coast have less flesh, presumably growing more slowly in the cold Arctic waters. Dannevig (1953) also concluded that the shape of the cod depends on the rate of growth, and reported that those from the fjords are more corpulent than those from the open sea.

In addition, Dannevig (1953) described variations in the colours of Norwegian cod. Three types of pigment cells (black, yellow and red) are

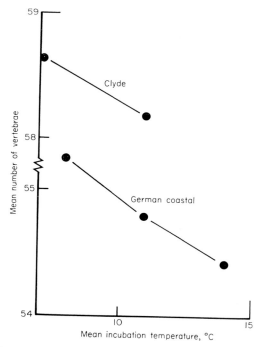

FIG. 61. The effect of temperature during the 'sensitive' phase of growth on the mean number of vertebrae in *Clupea harengus* from the Clyde (West Scotland) and the German coast. After Hempel and Blaxter (1961), reproduced by courtesy of Mr. J. H. S. Blaxter and the International Council for the Exploration of the Sea.

present in the skin, and while the fish can change their colour to some extent according to the colour of the background (by contracting or relaxing the pigment spots), there appears to be a genetic difference by which the deep-sea cod are completely lacking in red chromatophores, and so look a greenish-yellow. Norwegian cod from coastal waters are unusually rich in red pigment (see Fig. 62), so the contrast between the coastal and deep-water fish is considerable, though when cod from different sources are kept together in a pond they all expand their black chromatophores and appear dark. The reddish cod were found to eat mostly crustaceans, while the greenish lived on small fish, but diet is hardly likely to cause the presence or absence of pigment cells.

The writer's experience with the appearance of *Gadus morhua* from different grounds is summed up in Fig. 62. The fish were still alive when photographed, so no post-mortem changes had occurred. These are sometimes considerable, for example the dark Greenland cod in the

Fɪɢ. 62. The external appearance of *Gadus morhua* from different grounds (R. M. Love, 1965 and 1966 trips). Note that the South Faroe (Faroe Bank) fish is the stoutest and also the palest coloured, West Greenland the darkest, Bear Island the leanest and Norway the reddest.

Figure became much darker some hours after death. The lightest coloured and also the most thick-set come from South Faroe (Faroe Bank). Schmidt (1930) found, from the counts of fin-rays, that these fish are separate from the main Faroe stock. A convenient measure of the leanness or stoutness is the diameter of the caudal peduncle, the most posterior piece of body flesh just before the tail fin, as a percentage of the body length, and by this criterion, Faroe Bank fish, at 5·19%, are the stoutest and those from Bear Island the leanest at 4·35% (Love, unpublished, 1968 expedition). The most darkly pigmented fish come from West Greenland, and the reddest, as already noted, from the Norwegian coast.

These observations are potentially useful, but little of their actual relevance is known as yet, since chemical studies on the pigments of the skin have not been carried out. We have seen that certain fish lack chromatophores, presumably a genetic feature, but how much the colour of the background contributes to the light colour of Faroese cod or the darkness of Greenland cod is unknown : since most of the fish were caught at depths in excess of 100 metres, it seems unlikely that much light would have reached the bottom anyway. Perhaps the body proportions are governed by the water temperature, but for obvious reasons no experiments have been carried out on cod larvae transferred from one natural environment to grow up in another.

Geographical location also influences the date of the spawning period of many fish. For instance, cod caught off Aberdeen, Scotland, spawn during the first week in March, those off the Faroes at the beginning of April, while some Icelandic cod spawn in May. Fig. 45 (p. 91) shows how depletion at the spawning season causes the water content of cod muscle to rise, the extent depending on the size of the fish. Since fish from different grounds spawn at different times, it is to be expected that the position of the maximum will move. Redrawing the data of Dambergs (1964) and that of the medium-sized fish in Fig. 45 so that the maxima are of equal height, one obtains a striking demonstration of the difference between the cod populations from the Canadian and Scottish East coasts (Fig. 63). It could not, of course, be used for stock identification,

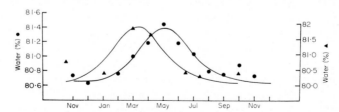

Fig. 63. Seasonal changes in the muscle water content of *Gadus morhua* caught off the coasts of Scotland (▲) and Canada (●), showing that the period of maximum depletion occurs later in Canadian fish. The data of Dambergs (1964) and Love (1960) have been redrawn to give curves of the same height.

and seems more likely to be controlled by water temperature than inheritance.

3. *The Evidence of Otoliths*

Within the ear cavities on either side of the brain lie two calcareous bodies, the otoliths ("ear stones"), which steadily increase in size during the life of the fish. Where the increase in body length is sporadic and affected by the seasons, the accretions vary in their appearance, so that if an otolith is broken across the middle it is seen to be built up of alternate light and dark zones, like those on the trunk of a tree. When the fish is in poor condition, the material laid down is mostly calcium carbonate (light zone), but during a season of plenty the deposit contains a greater proportion of organic matter (dark zone) which chars if the otolith is heated in a gas flame, giving a series of concentric black rings. The organic material is a protein, closely related to that in the shells of certain molluscs (Dannevig, 1955). Holden (1955), who studied *Tilapia* in a warm water environment, noted a threshold level of biological condition above which no light rings were formed, and below which ring formation was continuous, the width depending on the time for which the fish remained in this state. Mugiya (1965) removed with a tiny diamond disc samples of the different zones for analysis, and found in several species that there was in fact some protein present in the light zones as well, but that it was less than in the dark zones—for example, 0·16 and 0·24% nitrogen, respectively, in *Kareius bicoloratus*. Most of the calcium originates in the food, at least in *Cyprinus carpio*, a freshwater fish (Irie, Yokoyama and Yamada, 1967), the remainder being absorbed from the surrounding water.

The composition of the material being laid down does not follow the seasonal variations in plasma calcium (Woodhead, 1968) already described (p. 61) in relation to sexual maturity, but reflects changes in the fluid surrounding the otolith, which contains a characteristic albumin fraction which varies seasonally in some species (Mugiya, 1964). The same author showed that in *Salmo gairdnerii*, of which the otolith is homogeneously glassy, the albumin fraction in the otolith fluid does not change throughout the year.

Much may be learned of the history of a fish by a skilled examination of the otoliths. Thus, the bulge on the long side of the approximately triangular cross section becomes more pronounced if the fish is relatively big for its age, and since, at least in *Gadus morhua*, the colour of the rings changes subtly when the fish becomes mature, the number of times it has spawned during its life can also be ascertained.

These findings relate to the present chapter in that the stresses to which fish are subjected vary geographically, and these again are faithfully reflected in the otolith patterns. Thus the dark and light zones are defined more clearly in whiting (*Gadus merlangus*) caught in the North Sea than elsewhere (Gambell and Messtorff, 1964). Similarly, cod from fjords in south Norway possess distinct dark and light zones in the otoliths, while zones from the inner Oslofjord cod are diffuse and made difficult to read by the presence of many secondary zones, that is, rings not relating directly to winter and summer (Ruud, 1939, quoted by Otterbech, 1953).

Similarly, cod differ between local (coastal) and oceanic stocks (Trout, 1958). The differences appear very early in life : in oceanic forms, the nucleus (centre dark portion) is large, corresponding with a long period of active growth in the first summer when the little fish lives in the surface waters (pelagic phase). This period of 5—7 months contrasts with that of North Sea cod, which lives in the surface waters for only $2\frac{1}{2}$ months. Frequently in the Svalbard Bank area of the Barents Sea the first year also includes a very narrow opaque zone, known as the autumn zone, separated from the nucleus by a white ring corresponding to a check in growth, and assumed to be laid down in the new bottom habitat after the pelagic phase and before the next winter (light) ring.

Several of these differences are shown in Figs. 64 and 65, where the otoliths of cod of the same ages from the North Sea and Svalbard areas are compared. The bulge on the long (right-hand) side is more pronounced in the North Sea cod (Fig. 64), showing that the fish had grown more than its Arctic counterpart (Fig. 65), and the second summer (dark) zone is bigger, again as the result of greater growth. On the other hand, the nucleus of the Svalbard cod otolith is larger, on account of the extended pelagic phase already referred to.

How much of this fascinating picture is genetically controlled? Probably none of it : as far as can be seen, the otolith pattern is largely a history of the fish, and a change of habitat would probably produce a new pattern.

As the fish increase in length, an increase in diameter is also seen in the scales, which vary in their growth rates in the same way as otoliths. This results in an uneven accretion at the margin which can give information on the age of the fish. However, although the annual rings are easier to read than those of the otolith in *Clupea harengus* and some other species, they are less satisfactory in *Gadus morhua*, and Duff (1929) showed that the season of their maximum growth did not coincide with that of the maximum body growth of the fish.

4. *Serology*

It is well known that in man the serum from one individual may cause the red blood cells of another to clump together. Human plasma contains two types of 'agglutinins', which correspond with 'agglutinogens' in the red cells. The two types of agglutinogens are designated A and B : individuals with A or B agglutinogens in their blood cells are considered to belong to blood groups A or B, respectively, while those in group AB contain both agglutinogens, and those in group O have neither.

A person's blood group is determined genetically and cannot be altered, and the same appears to be true for fish. The early work on fish

Fig. 64. Cross section of otolith from *Gadus morhua*, viewed by transmitted light to show annual rings (dark = summer, light = winter). This fish was caught in the North Sea in April 1962, and was 7 years old, 106 cm long. Picture kindly supplied by Dr. R. W. Blacker.

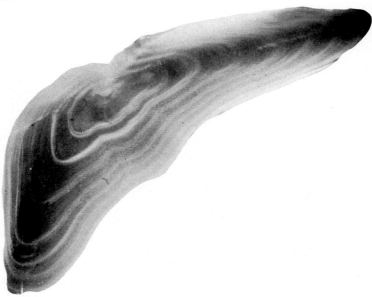

Fig. 65. As in Fig. 64. This fish was caught off Spitzbergen (Svalbard) in August 1961, and was also 7 years old, but a smaller size, 72 cm. Picture kindly supplied by Dr. R. W. Blacker.

blood has been reviewed by Lee (1962): much of it is negative, for example that of Jensen (1937), who found that the sera of individual cod does not agglutinate sera or cells of other cod. Similarly, Suehiro (1949, quoted by Lee, 1962) reacted sera from about thirty marine and freshwater species of fish with human cells of groups A and B, but obtained negative results.

However, in 1952 Cushing studied the precipitation reaction of human blood cells with sera from *Neothunnus macropterus* and *Katsuwonus pelamis*, and found that, according to the intensity of precipitation, the blood samples of the different fish can be separated into four groups. A corollary was found by Wilkins (1967a), who showed that variations occur in the agglutination of the cells of *Gadus morhua* by different types of human blood serum, and appear to characterize separate populations of this species. Ridgway, Cushing and Durall (1961) found that the cells of *Oncorhynchus nerka* will react with the sera of horse and pig, and consistent differences appear in the strengths of reaction (measured by diluting the serum more and more) of the cells of individual fish. The frequency of individuals displaying the various strengths of reaction differs significantly between the areas of origin of the salmon tested. Further observations along the same lines, which presumably depend on the geographical separation of groups of fish for long periods of time, were made by Ridgway and Klontz (1961). Authors obtaining positive results with other species have been listed by Lee (1962).

Diversity also exists in the antigenic activity of blood. Patterson and Hutton (1965) pooled red cells from individual *Oncorhynchus tschawytscha* of a reference population spawning in one place, and injected them into rabbits, which then formed antibodies to them. The resulting rabbit serum was tested for antibody activity against more of the same cells, and against those of a different population of the same species. It was found that the serum agglutinates cells of the reference population but fails to do so with the second group.

There is room for further work here. The present brief account shows that reactions of serum and cells could be a powerful tool for studying sub-populations. Readers requiring more detailed information on this technique are referred to the review recently written by de Ligny (1969).

5. *Electrophoresis*

(a) *Serum proteins and muscle myogens*

Tsuyuki and Roberts (1966) carried out many electrophoretic analyses of fish muscle myogens, and concluded that the patterns are virtually unaffected by factors other than genetic, so the technique at least bears potential for distinguishing races of fish regardless of environment. However, in studying the myogens of different species of *Oncorhynchus*, they found no outstanding differences between those from North America and those from Hokkaido, Japan (a part of their findings has already been illustrated in Fig. 55, p. 134). On the other hand, Dessauer and Fox (1956) had found variations in the electro-phoretic patterns of the blood sera of amphibia and reptiles according to geographical location, so the possibility remained. Nyman (1965) showed that the serum proteins of two hundred specimens of *Salmo salar* from the Indal river (Sweden) were remarkably constant among themselves, 5 major bands invariably being present, but differed from those of Canadian salmon of the same species.* Mairs and Sindermann (1960) had also found geographical differences in the serum patterns of *Clupea harengus*. Uthe, Roberts *et al.* (1966) studied the myogen patterns of several families, but of these only *Stizostedion vitreum*, of the family Percidae, showed geographical variation.

Thus the successful 'typing' of sub-populations in this way has not been of universal application, and in his review of the causes of variation in fish serum proteins, Booke (1964b) mentions only one instance of intraspecific variation in fish from different grounds.

Where a hybrid species has been reared, no new protein bands are formed (Tsuyuki and Roberts, 1965), but the hybrid gives electro-phoretic patterns characteristic of *one* of the parental types (Sanders, 1964).

(b) Haemoglobins

Much more profitable has been the study of haemoglobins, which are electrophoretically separable into several bands, this phenomenon being know as polymorphism ("many forms").

The pioneer in this work was Sick (1961), who found differences in the electrophoretic patterns of the haemoglobins of *Gadus morhua* which were not correlated with the sex or size of the fish. The band nearest the origin, called HbII, is common to all electropherograms, but HbI, which migrates further, can exist in two forms, HbI1 or HbI2, which migrates different distances in the same period. Thus there are three possible patterns, showing bands of HbI1, HbI2, or both, together with HbII in each case. A diagrammatic representation is shown in Fig. 66. Sick postulated the presence of two co-dominant allelic genes HbI^1 and HbI^2 which give rise to the haemoglobin components HbI1 and HbI2, respectively.

---

* This is not the only difference between European and Canadian *Salmo salar*—see footnote to p. 112.

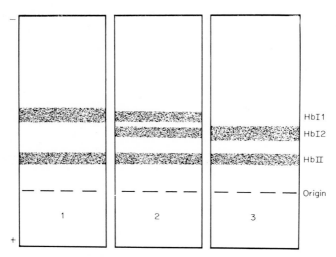

Fig. 66. Diagrammatic representation of the three possible electrophoretic patterns of fish blood, which contains the HbII band together with HbI1 or HbI2 or both. The diagram is analogous to an original of *Gadus merlangus* published by Sick (1961). The separation of bands in *Gadus morhua* was not so clear.

Now the frequency with which these two alleles occur varies according to the place where the fish are caught, and preliminary results have indicated variations in the haemoglobin patterns of *Solea solea* and *Zoarces viviparus* as well.

Haemoglobin polymorphism is a comparatively new study, and as yet little is known of the stability of the patterns of the population of a given ground. However, Frydenberg, Nielsen and Sick (1967) have been able to show that in the cod population of Sejerö Bay the frequency of the occurrence of the HbI[1] allele of haemoglobin did not change between the years 1961 and 1966, inclusive : no single year's estimate deviated as much as its own standard error from the total frequency.

Studying geographic variations in the same allele, Møller, Naevdal and Valen (1966) found clear differences between the Norwegian coastal cod and the 'skrei'—spawners invading from the Barents Sea. The frequencies in cod from the North Sea, Skagerak, Kattegat, Danish Belt Sea and Western Baltic were the same at about 0·62 (Sick, 1965, quoted by Frydenberg, Nielsen and Sick, 1967), but they decreased continuously along the Norwegian coast, reaching a value of only 0·1 in the Barents Sea, with even lower figures off the coast of Faroe (0·06) and Iceland (0·01). A slow increase was seen as one moved southwards along the American coast, reaching 0·07 to 0·08 off the coast of Maine.

The astonishingly regular decrease in HbI1 frequency with north-ward position of coastal cod is shown in Fig. 67. Frydenberg, Møller *et al.* (1965) were unable to state whether the frequency decline was continuous or not, but no distinct discontinuity has been observed. Indications of the same trend along the American coast suggest that water temperature might be involved, but supporting evidence is lacking at present.

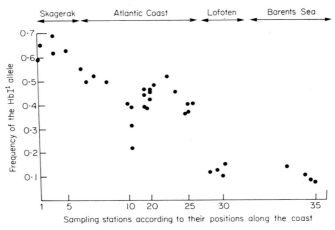

FIG. 67. Frequency with which one electrophoretic form of haemoglobin is to be found in the blood of *Gadus morhua*, according to the fishing ground (a figure of 1·0 would mean that nothing but this form was present). The sampling stations are spaced on the abscissae in proportion to their distances along the coast. After Frydenberg, Møller *et al.* (1965), reproduced by courtesy of Professor O. Frydenberg and the Editor of *Hereditas*.

No significant heterogeneity has been observed between cod from the Moray Firth (Scotland) and from the North Sea near Aberdeen and Arbroath (Wilkins, 1967a), nor between the haemoglobins of *Salmo salar* from Scotland or Scandinavia (Koch, Wilkins *et al.*, 1967). However, whatever its underlying mechanism, variations in the haemoglobin patterns are obviously valuable in the study of populations, and there is a possibility of further development with other species—for example, Rumen and Love (1963) found no fewer than six different haemoglobins in the blood of *Petromyzon marinus*, which are potentially useful for investigating intraspecific variation.

Studying the haemoglobin of eels, Sick, Westergaard and Frydenberg (1962) discovered that the electrophoretic patterns of the American eel and European eel (*Anguilla rostrata* and *Anguilla anguilla*, respectively) are the same, while that of the Japanese eel (*Anguilla japonica*) differs. On the strength of this evidence they suggested that the first "two species" are in fact the same.

(c) *Eye lens proteins*

Rabaey (1965) found that the electrophoretic patterns of lens proteins are species specific and that similarities can be detected in the patterns of closely related species. Differences within a species were not observed, but when the proteins of the nuclei of the eye lenses of *Caulolatilus princeps* were subjected to electrophoresis, there were found to be differences between the patterns of two Californian populations from grounds 500 miles apart (Smith and Goldstein, 1967).

(d) *Enzymes*

Odense, Allen and Leung (1966) showed that lactic dehydrogenase and aspartate amino transferase in *Clupea harengus* can occur in different forms that are identifiable by electrophoresis. The patterns appear to be genetically controlled, and are unaffected by physiological or environmental factors. The frequency of the alleles differed between catches of fish, so it was postulated that herring populations might be characterized by a study of the electrophoretic patterns of the enzymes. No systematic appraisal of the characteristics from different grounds appears to have been carried out so far.

(e) *Transferrins*

Fish blood contains a globulin known as transferrin, which is capable of fixing iron. Fine, Drilhon *et al.* (1965) noted that the electrophoretic mobility varied within a species, thus offering the possibility of studying different forms in each. Diversity of transferrins was also studied by Jamieson (1967) in West Greenland cod, and it was concluded that genetically separate stocks were present.

6. *DNA*

While the concentrations of DNA (deoxyribose nucleic acid) in different fish are not useful for distinguishing species or races, there is a possibility that the proportions of the bases in the molecule can be used in this way. As stated earlier, the DNA molecule consists of a base (four possible compounds with purine or pyrimidine structure), sugar and phosphate, and the proportions of compounds in the base moiety vary. Fujii (1965) studied the ratio of adenine + thymine : guanine + cytosine in testis DNA, and found differences between tuna species. He observed that the ratio varies little among a group of fish caught on the same day and at the same place in the sea, but that changes occur if different grounds are fished at different seasons. It appeared that the variations are the result of mixtures of sub-populations of fish, since the DNA is not influenced by environmental factors. Clearly much more work is needed to establish the usefulness of this approach.

7. Conclusion

In this section we have seen a variety of phenomena which change according to the locality where the fish were caught. When we survey the evidence, the important point seems to be whether or not a character of a sub-population persists throughout adulthood regardless of migration, rather than whether it is determined genetically or not. For instance, the shape, colour and number of bones or spines are probably governed by the temperature early in the development of the fish, but this is not necessarily a disadvantage to the biologist who wishes to see what stocks of fish have been visiting his favourite ground during the year, since the pattern is fixed after the early stage has been passed.

As we have seen, the range of vertebral numbers which can be affected by temperature is genetically determined according to the sub-population, but this does not confer any noticeable advantage. Meristic characters of this sort need to be averaged over a considerable number of specimens, as do the haemoglobin types where one is studying the proportion of a particular allele. However, otoliths can be used in the study of single fish—a migrating Svalbard cod can readily be spotted among a batch of local Norwegian coastal fish. Also, it is often possible for a single fish from different stocks to be identified by means of shape or colour. Buyers in the fish market have no difficulty in identifying Faroese or Bear Island cod mixed in with others. Off the coast of Norway, too, different populations of cod are distinguished by differences in body proportions and colour. While these differences may be caused by water temperature or diet rather than genetic mutations, this may not invalidate their use for distinguishing stocks, because, like bone counts, they persist.

CHAPTER 4

THE INFLUENCE OF THE ENVIRONMENT

A. "Seasonal variation"

It has to be admitted that the title of this sub-section 'A' was chosen deliberately for the sake of those who would turn to it for guidance, believing it to be a factor with a specific effect. Many writers have indeed recorded the effects of "seasonal variation" on the levels of chemical constituents in fish and yet, truth to tell, it is a virtually hopeless task to attempt a systematic appraisal of "seasonal variation", since the effects embrace not only all of the environmental influences but also those of maturity and spawning—to quote Jacquot (1961):

"The significance of the seasonal variations is complex, and it is almost impossible to distinguish surely between the effect of the many factors which play a part."

Thus to classify a chemical inconsistency in this way is to admit ignorance of the specific underlying cause. Indeed, the mechanisms of a number of variations are still completely unknown, so that at present the phenomena can only be described.

Castell, Dale and Greenough (1959) noticed a seasonal variation in the rate of spoilage of gadoid species after death, perhaps resulting from the combined influence of several factors. The concentrations of vitamin C (ascorbic acid) in various tissues of freshwater and marine fish are highest in summer (Fomin, Romanjuk and Khvoynitskaya, 1937) while those of sugar in the blood increase during the winter (Schuh and Nace, 1961 : *Opsanus tau*) and muscle trimethylamine oxide (Ronold and Jakobsen, 1947; Hughes 1959a : *Clupea harengus*) and whole-body collagen (McBride, MacLeod and Idler, 1959a, 1960 : *Clupea pallasii*) increase steadily from June to January. The appropriate mechanisms are in all cases unknown.

Whereas seasonal variation in the protein content of the muscle of *Gadus morhua* (Anon., 1966a) would seem to be the result of depletion, the regular increase in ash seen every January in *Sarda sarda* (Herrera

169

and Muñoz, 1957) is puzzling at first sight. These authors ascribed it to a build-up preceding the season of vigorous growth, but as it occurs at the period of spawning it may be the result of impaired osmoregulation following the shedding of sex products, or, more probably, the result of depletion of substances other than ash, the increase in which is therefore relative.

The diet of fish, for example *Gadus morhua* (Rae, 1967a), differs qualitatively at different times of the year and is therefore likely to cause variations in some body constituents. The rapid ingestion of much highly unsaturated lipid during the month of June has in fact been shown (Lovern, 1938a) to change temporarily the degree of hydrogenation of herring (*Clupea harengus*) body lipid; slight variations in the proportion of 20 : 1 fatty acid have been reported in summer-caught *Gadus morhua*, relative to the proportion present in those caught at other times (Jangaard, Ackman and Sipos, 1967). Seasonal variation in the food intake also affects the quantity of digestive enzymes secreted by the alimentary canal (Ananichev, 1959: various freshwater species), which probably accounts for the fact, well-known amongst fishermen, that 'feedy' (gorged) fish keep less well on the boat on their way to market, since more of the gastric and intestinal enzymes are spilled on to the flesh during gutting, causing softening or break-up. In addition, the number of leucocytes in the blood follows the amount of food eaten (Smirnova, 1962: various freshwater species), though the reason here is unknown.

There is an anthropomorphic echo in Popova's remark (quoted by Dambergs, 1964) that unlike the cod from European waters, the North American cod does not have to suffer from a lack of variety or quantity of food at any time of the year. Whether we feel that this is fair or not, it means that "seasonal variation" from dietary causes can vary geographically. Further observations on the influence of diet are given on p. 198.

It is unsatisfactory, though, to make the present section merely a repository for unexplained phenomena. Can anything definite be said, apart from conclusions about depletion or maturity which have been covered elsewhere in the book? To some extent it can. The key to understanding certain seasonal variations seems to lie in the concept of a biological 'clock', an inner rhythm which persists in the absence of outside stimulus.

Figure 45 (p. 91) shows that the depletion suffered by spawning *Gadus morhua* occurs to a modified extent in sexually immature fish during the same period. While feeding is normal in February, it declines in March and April in the immature fish (Rae, 1967a) and it was suggested by Rae (1967b) that the fish are affected by some factor other than spawning. One is reminded of the "dummy run" of immature Svalbard cod, which migrate for part of the journey to the spawning grounds alongside the mature fish (Trout, 1957). Graham (1924) also noticed an unexplained loss of condition, as measured by the ratio of weight to length, in immature cod at the breeding season, and Hickling (1934) observed that in at least four species of marine fish the seasonal changes which characterize the somatic tissue of the adult fish are also foreshadowed in the immature fish, even though no crop of eggs or spermatozoa is being produced. He also found seasonal changes in the size of the ovaries of undoubtedly immature hake (*Merluccius merluccius*) which corresponded in time with those of the mature fish, and finally concluded that the loss of condition in the summer time of immature and adolescent fish cannot adequately be explained in terms of nutrition, but must result from an inbuilt rhythm.

The periodicity seen in the growth of fish from cold-water habitats is probably the combined effect of spawning and of fluctuation in water temperature. In fish from tropical waters where the temperature is less variable the seasonal fluctuation in growth does not occur; hence it is not possible to age them by counting rings on the otoliths or scales (Bridges, 1964a). However, the resistance of *Carassius auratus* to temperature stress varies seasonally even in fish maintained at a constant temperature and fed on a uniform diet. Hoar (1955), who observed this phenomenon, suggests that changes in the endocrine physiology, controlled by differences in the length of daylight throughout the year, are responsible. The cholinesterase activity of the brain of *Fundulus heteroclitus* also varies seasonally, and this was shown by Baslow and Nigrelli (1964) to occur even under conditions of constant temperature. The count of red blood corpuscles in *Eupomotis gibbosus* decreases during the winter months, a phenomenon that could be attributed to a slowing of metabolism or to starvation. The latter is unlikely, because the red cell count of fish in an aquarium, presumably under constant conditions, which decreases during the winter, shows its customary increase the following spring, although no food is given throughout the experiment (Schaefer, 1925).

It seems probable that all phenomena acting apparently under the influence of an internal 'clock' are controlled by the endocrine system. Hoar (1965) described the seasonal appearance in the testes of certain cells which were presumed to have an endocrine function, and the pituitary, the master endocrine gland, changes seasonally in its histological appearance (Lagios, 1965: *Embiotoca jacksoni*). Arginine vasotocin and an oxytocin-like principle, 4-serine, 8-isoleucine oxytocin, have both been identified in extracts from the pituitary of *Fundulus heteroclitus* and shown to vary seasonally, differently according to the sexes (Sawyer and Pickford, 1963). An increase in growth-promoting hormone occurs in April in *Perca fluviatilis*, followed by a maximum in June, a decline in July and near-disappearance in August. The maximum accumulation of growth hormone in the pituitary precedes the estimated natural growth peak of the fish by 4—6 weeks, but no such lag occurs in respect of the gonads, where the peak of maturity in April coincides with the peak of gonadotrophin in the pituitary. The thyrotropic activity of the pituitary of this species follows a similar cycle. These observations were all made by Swift and Pickford (1965).

The instances quoted of seasonal changes which continue even under constant conditions seem to show the existence of an internal rhythm. Other variations which appear at certain times of the year are almost certainly the result of environmental influences and are dealt with elsewhere.

B. Ecology

1. *Introduction*

Little systematic work has been done to show the individual contributions made by factors such as light, temperature and abundance of food to the state of a fish when they are all acting together. The most detailed paper to come to the writer's attention is by J. D. Thomas (1964), who compared trout (*Salmo trutta*) from four contrasting habitats in three river systems in Wales, and worked out that the factors best favouring growth are a pH of 7 or more, high calcium and other ionic constituents, low susceptibility to sudden flooding, favourable temperature range (specified), rich growth of algae and a wide variety and high density of other animals. How one could wish for similar studies on marine fish, where so often the conclusions have been reached indirectly or by studying only one parameter.

As already pointed out, maturity and the annual date of spawning occur later in more northerly latitudes—presumably a temperature effect—but not all differences between North and South are caused by temperature. The level of vitamin A in the liver of *Hippoglossus hippoglossus*, for example, is often higher if the fish are caught in more northerly waters (Lovern, Edisbury and Morton, 1933); in this species there is a tendency for the larger fish to migrate northwards, and since more vitamin A occurs in a given weight of liver from larger fish, the effect is most probably due to size. More specifically, the vitamin A level is governed by the age of the fish rather than by size as such. MacPherson (1937) found that Newfoundland cod have higher concentrations of liver vitamin A than those of like size from Europe. The explanation is that although the sizes are the same, the ages are not; Newfoundland cod grow more slowly than those from the North Sea, so for comparable sizes they are older.

We have seen that the date of spawning is affected by the location of the environment, but the duration of spawning can also be modified. For some reason, cod from the Baltic Sea (*Gadus callarias*—for Latin name in this locality see Svetovidov, 1948, p. 169) have a greatly prolonged spawning season, and the chemical consequence of this can be seen in the water content of the flesh, which is raised during the whole period from May to September (Bogucki and Trzesinski, 1950).

Variations in the diet might account for differing growth rates between *Gadus morhua* from the Faroe plateau and from Faroe Bank (Jones, 1966) and for the differences in the plasma vitamin A levels of cod from Faroe and the Barents Sea (Plack and Woodhead, 1966), but these could equally well be caused by temperature and age, respectively. The higher protein nitrogen reported in cod from Iceland and Faroe compared with those from more distant waters (Anon., 1966a), or its corollary, that cod caught near Greenland are softer in consistency than those caught elsewhere (Rakow, 1963) could be meaningful, but only if the timing of the yearly cycle from each ground is known, since the differences may again be caused by the spawning cycles being out of step.

The differing yields of food on different grounds can influence the composition of the fish in a striking way. Karrick, Clegg and Stansby (1956) studying the lipid content of *Aplodinotus grunniens*, found that it was possible to be seriously misled by taking specimens from only one habitat. Sixteen fish from Clearwater Lake, Minnesota, showed an average oil content of 1·04% (ranging from 0·72—1·67%) so that if they had been considered representative of all specimens bearing this name it would have been concluded that they were non-fatty fish. From Kegonsa Lake in Wisconsin the oil content of the same species averaged 4·9% (2—8·8%), so these fish would have been classed as slightly oily. The average oil content of a further 16 caught in the Mississippi River, 8·8% (3·6—14·2%), would give the impression that *Aplodinotus grunniens* was an oily species. The lesson to be drawn from these observations is obvious where one is trying to establish 'typical' values for a given species.

2. Motion of the Sea

One of the most puzzling effects has been that of the degree of movement of water on the condition of the fish. A relationship has been thought to exist for a long time. Venner, in his "Via recta ad vitam longam" (1650, quoted by Mitchell, 1883) stated, " . . . of sea-fish the best swimmeth in a pure sea, and is tossed and hoist with wind and surges; for by reason of continual agitation it becometh of purer and less slimey (*sic*) substance. And for the same cause, the fish that is taken near a shore that is neither earthy or slimey, is of a harder digestion, and of a more slimey and excremental substance." It is a common tradition among fishermen of the North-East of Scotland that where the water is 'tidal', or running, the fish are firmer and more lively than those from still water, the theory being that they "get more exercise" and so are fitter! It could equally well be argued that only the fit and lively ones would in fact be able to swim against the tidal race, the weaker ones retiring to stationary waters.

In bays and coastal inlets there is often more food available than in the open sea, so fish tend to be better nourished (Jacquot, 1961), but the growth rate of Norwegian coastal cod, which varies from fjord to fjord according to food supply, was stated by Dannevig (1953) to be lowest in the most stagnant water masses.

In an investigation into 'condition', Love (1962b) found that *Gadus morhua* caught in 45 metres of water, East of Aberdeen, Scotland, were good, while a further batch, caught the same week in a deeper pool (100 metres) in the vicinity were very poor, thus apparently lending further support to the tradition. However, later experiments showed that starving cod in an aquarium reproduced exactly the symptoms of poor condition, so this parameter appears to reflect nutritional status only. In such a case, the finding of good and poor fish in relatively shallow and deep habitats, respectively, makes sense in the light of Trout's observation (1957) that after spawning the cod enters shallow water to feed and recover. Presumably any from deep water had not yet started to recover from spawning. There is room for further work here: Hickling (1930), for example, stated that the recovery of hake (*Merluccius merluccius*) after spawning follows a return to *deeper* water, so the 'tidal' tradition should work in reverse with this species.

In the case of freshwater fish, it appears that the concentrations of the principal body constituents do not differ between those caught in running streams and those caught in lakes where the water is stationary (Phillips, Lovelace *et al.*, 1956, p. 46: *Salvelinus fontinalis*) but, predictably, the blood sugar levels of fish from ponds or gently moving streams are lower than in those from rushing torrents (Fukuda, 1958) owing to the smaller energy demands of the former group. A further aspect of river-water movement is that fish in cold, fast-running streams are usually supplied with all the oxygen they need, while those from ponds may be subjected to a wide range of concentrations. Pond fish have therefore adapted and are more efficient at taking up oxygen at low concentrations. Heath and Pritchard (1965) showed that if *Salmo clarkii*, which are adapted to life in running streams with high oxygen content, are placed together with *Lepomis macrochirus*, a pond fish, into water of which the oxygen level is progressively reduced, it is the *Salmo clarkii* which first lose consciousness. Similarly, J. A. Lovern (private communication, 1968) found that when a small freshwater pond becomes completely sealed with ice in winter time, any *Carassius auratus* present die, but *Tinca tinca*, which tolerate low oxygen levels, all survive.

3. Condition of Cod on 'Hard' and 'Soft' Grounds

A further tradition among local fishermen is that the 'feel' of the flesh of a fish, an aspect of its biological condition, is related to the physical nature of the ground. Cod from Bell Rock, near Dundee (East Scotland), where the sea-bed is stony, are almost always in good condition (firm flesh), while those from the Moray Firth, which has a soft, sandy or muddy bottom, are soft themselves and spoil rapidly on their way to market. So strong is this traditional belief that fishermen from the little ports along the Moray Firth trawl as closely as possible to the stony ground, that is, very near the edge of the sandy area, although they risk damaging their nets if they actually reach the stones.

The experience of freshwater fishermen runs along similar lines. In the English Lakes, *Esox lucius* (pike) from Esthwaite Water, a muddy-bottomed lake, are soft and have a poor flavour, while those from Loughrigg or Blelam tarns, both of which have stony bottoms, are firmer and sweeter-tasting (C. D. Hayward, personal communication, 1968), and I have heard from a coastal pilot of the behaviour of Norwegian freshwater fish in almost identical terms.

It is hard to know what to make of this concept. Certainly, in my own experience, the cod from Faroe are in excellent condition, the sea-bottom being hard (gravel and shells). If we accept Love's thesis (1962b) that all aspects of condition reflect the nutritional status of the fish and nothing else, then the food on the sandy bottom is either insufficient or unsuitable.

Tradition can be faulty. After the great depletion caused by spawning in the spring, cod gorge themselves with food as soon as it becomes available. It takes time, though, to reverse the poor condition, so that most 'feedy' fish are still very soft—and the fisherman concludes wrongly that overeating softens the flesh. Similarly, it is common for cod at this time to feed heavily on herring larvae or sand eels (*Ammodytes* sp.), both of which have a high lipid content which gives their flesh a slimy feel. The cod flesh is very soft owing to lack of protein and the sensations when touching the cut surface of the fish flesh and that of its food are somewhat similar, although the reason is the wateriness and definitely not because of an elevated lipid content. However, fishermen do not carry out lipid analysis, and it is assumed that the fatty food gives rise to a slimy fish, cod caught in this condition being known locally as 'greasers'.

4. *Oxygen Concentration*

It has already been pointed out (p. 45) that sudden asphyxia causes an increase in blood sugar, and that the growth of the egg (p. 69) is retarded by a low oxygen concentration, as, incidentally, is that of the fish itself (Stewart, Shumway and Doudoroff, 1967: *Micropterus salmoides*; Whitworth, 1968: *Salvelinus fontinalis*).

The swimming speed is affected if the oxygen falls below a certain concentration. Dahlberg, Shumway and Doudoroff (1968) found that it is markedly reduced below 5 or 6 mg of oxygen per litre at 25° (*Micropterus salmoides*), but that above this value it is virtually independent of concentration. The effect varies between species: in *Oncorhynchus kisutch* at 20° a reduction in oxygen level below 9 mg per litre is enough to cause a falling-off in swimming speed.

Three species of fish examined by Bouck and Ball (1965) ceased feeding during periods of low oxygen concentration, and also showed a change in the proportions of proteins (as revealed by electrophoresis) in the serum. Perhaps the two observations are related.

Since the blood becomes diluted when migratory fish enter fresh water from the sea (p. 188), the number of red cells per unit volume, and so the oxygen capacity, decreases (Benditt, Morrison and Irving 1941). This is probably not harmful to the fish, since the oxygen concentration of river water is high. In the reverse situation, when young *Oncorhynchus* species enter the ocean from the river, they appear to synthesize a haemoglobin with a higher affinity for oxygen than that of the juvenile form. Vanstone, Roberts and Tsuyuki (1964) pointed out that the presence of the two classes of haemoglobin with different physical properties would be of distinct advantage to an adult salmon, ensuring adequate oxygen transport and unloading over a wider range of environmental conditions than if only one class were present.

Where a marked annual cycle of oxygen concentrations occurs, it is possible for the fish to adapt by varying the concentration of red blood cells in circulation. Smirnova (1962) found that the concentration of haemoglobin in the blood of freshwater species from the Rybinsk reservoir is highest in January, when the concentration of oxygen is lowest, and decreases under the more favourable summer conditions. Whether the effect is achieved by varying the water content or by bringing extra cells in from the spleen was not stated.

van Dam and Scholander (1953) related the amount of iron in the blood, as a measure of haemoglobin, to the depth at which the fish are caught, to see whether those from deeper water develop a higher oxygen capacity to facilitate the secretion of gas into the swim bladder against higher pressures. The average figure from 11 species of deep-sea fish was 19·6 mg%, very similar to the average from 14 species of shallow-water fish (22·3%) determined by Hall and Gray (1929), so depth is probably unimportant in this respect.

More oxygen dissolves in cold water than in warm, so that at lower temperatures fish have less need for haemoglobin. Platner (1950) noticed that the blood of *Carassius auratus* exposed to near-freezing temperatures in aerated water becomes diluted, so that the haematocrit (blood cell volume) goes down. This may merely represent a breakdown in the osmoregulatory mechanism, but in the light of the following observations it may be an adaptive decrease in the oxygen-carrying capacity of the blood.

Scholander and van Dam (1957) showed that the iron content of the blood of two cold-water Arctic species, out of four examined, was low. A general relationship between temperature and haemoglobin content was, however, clouded by the effect of intrinsic activity, so that some fish from warmer waters showed similar low values. Much more striking was the report by Ruud (1954) that certain species of Antarctic fish possess no haemoglobin at all. These fish are well known among Antarctic fishermen as 'ice-fish' or "white crocodile fish", the most noticeable characteristic being the white colour of the gills. Figure 68 shows a specimen of *Chaenocephalus aceratus*, and in Fig. 69 a bottle of blood from this fish is compared with that of an ordinary fish, showing a remarkable difference. The fish are not especially sluggish, and in fact some species are pelagic and exhibit shoaling behaviour (Ruud, 1958). To assist the exchange of gases, the gill

FIG. 68. An 'ice-fish' or "white crocodile fish" (*Chaenocephalus aceratus*) which has only blood plasma in its circulatory system, and no haemoglobin. Photograph kindly supplied by Professor J. T. Ruud.

FIG. 69. The colourless 'blood' of an ice-fish (*left*), which contains no haemoglobin, compared with that of an ordinary fish. Reproduced by courtesy of Professor J. T. Ruud and Academic Press.

surfaces are large, and Ruud (1958) suggested that skin respiration might be important also.

Although the blood of these fish possesses no red cells, it clots in two or three minutes in the usual way. The iron content is less than 1 mg%, and it can be regarded as a blood plasma with a moderate content of white blood cells (leucocytes). It holds about 0·7% oxygen by volume, compared with about 6% in two red-blooded species from the same area (Ruud, 1954). Munro Fox (1954), commenting on Ruud's paper, concluded from other work that many fish when swimming gently obtain enough oxygen for their needs in solution in the blood plasma, haemoglobin being the emergency precaution which 'ice-fish' do without. Other Antarctic species which do possess haemoglobin, but in quantities less than usual, are reviewed on p. 220.

The fact that fish are so well supported by the medium in which they swim has enabled fundamental differences to develop between them and terrestrial vertebrates. We have already seen (p. 34) that the white muscle of fish, which makes up the bulk of the motive power, is superfluous for most of the time and is brought into play only during emergency or unusual activity. It now appears that much of the haemoglobin is not really necessary either.

5. *Depth and Illumination*

As already noted, the depth of the habitat can affect the degree of ossification of the bones (reviewed by Vinogradov, 1953), perhaps because of the solubility of calcium salts at the high partial pressure of carbon dioxide in deep water.

Lipid composition also changes with depth. Lewis (1967) showed that saturated fatty acids of medium chain-length, and also long-chain poly-unsaturated acids decrease with species that live in increasingly deep water, while oleic acid increases. The presence of the latter was thought to indicate the presence of large amounts of wax esters which (see also p. 142) probably serve to achieve neutral buoyancy. From what has been stated elsewhere about lipids, however (pp. 146, 170), it is equally likely that the changes encountered with depth have a dietary origin.

The effect of depth that has attracted most interest is that of the change in illumination. The size of the eye of a fish is often related to the depth of its habitat (Rass, 1964). In species living in the upper layers of the ocean, the eyes are fairly small (19—29% of the head length). Those of species living down to 1500 metres' depth are much bigger, sometimes as much as 1/3 of the head length, presumably so that they can utilize the last minute traces of light filtering down. Below this depth the size decreases again until in species living at 6100—7579 metres it is only 9% of the head length. No light penetrates to this depth from the surface, but when prey are luminous they are presumably easy to see.

A great deal of interest centres on the retinal pigments, which are continuously being broken down in the eye of the living fish by the action of light, the breakdown stimulating the nerves of the pigment cells so that the animal sees. The pigments can be extracted in the dark with emulsifiers such as digitonin, and the wavelength at which light is maximally absorbed can be measured in a spectrophotometer without too much decomposition. It is not proposed here to dwell at length on the extensive earlier literature, which has been adequately reviewed by Dartnall (1962). Suffice to say that the pigment from most marine fish (and, incidentally, mammals, birds and reptiles) is of a rose-pink colour and is known as visual purple or rhodopsin, while that from many freshwater fish is of a violet hue and known as visual violet or porphyropsin (Wald, 1938), the wavelengths of maximum absorption of light (λ_{max}) being at about 500 mμ and 540 mμ, respectively. Retinal pigments from deep-sea fish are golden in colour, λ_{max} being below 500 mμ, and Denton and Warren (1956) proposed the name chrysopsin for them. The pigments are composed of vitamin A aldehyde ('retinal') attached to a protein. Vitamin A_1 forms the basis of rhodopsin and chrysopsin, while vitamin A_2, identical save for the presence of an extra conjugated double bond, forms porphyropsin.

Wald (1947) suggested that there is a correlation with the habitat in that the pigment of marine fish is based on vitamin A_1, that of euryhaline fish (migratory from salt water to fresh or vice versa) is a mixture of A_1 and A_2, while freshwater fish uses solely A_2. This scheme is too simple and is not now accepted. There are numerous exceptions to it, for example the euryhaline alewife (*Pomolobus pseudoharengus*) and the permanently marine wrasses (*Labridae*) have pure porphyropsin systems, and (Schwanzara, 1967) vitamin A_1 pigments are just as common as vitamin A_2 pigments among true freshwater species. As we shall see in a moment, there does appear to be a correlation with habitat, but not on the basis of salinity as proposed by Wald.

With improvements in the technique for measuring the λ_{max} of one visual pigment in a mixture, it soon became obvious that this wavelength is not confined to 500 or 540 mμ according to the vitamin involved, but can have a whole range of values according to species. These values are not evenly distributed throughout the spectrum but tend to form groups at certain wavelengths, roughly 6 mμ apart for vitamin A_1 pigments and 10 mμ apart for vitamin A_2 pigments (Bridges, 1965a; Dartnall and Lythgoe, 1965).

The link between the vitamin A and the protein* is thought to be a N-C link, but in view of the multiplicity of pigments it seems that

---

* It has become customary to refer to the proteins involved in visual pigments as 'opsins', but as this is merely the use of the second half of the word 'rhodopsin', the etymology is less than satisfactory.

either a variety of proteins is involved or that there are variations in the linkages between protein and vitamin additional to the main N-C bond (Dartnall and Lythgoe, 1965). Thus a considerable number of combinations is possible, since each protein or protein link can involve either vitamin A_1 or A_2. Pairs of pigments for the same protein or protein-link are shown in Fig. 70, based on data from fish possessing two pigments and both vitamins at the same time. Additional data

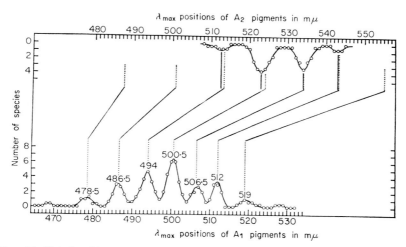

Fig. 70. Relationship between the wavelengths of maximum absorption (λ_{max}) of pairs of visual pigments, having the same protein but being based on different vitamins (A_1 and A_2). After Dartnall and Lythgoe (1965), reproduced by courtesy of the authors and Pergamon Press.

have been published by Bridges (1965a). It will be seen that three possible vitamin A_2 pigments have not yet been observed in fish, although the corresponding A_1 pigments are known. Much still remains to be learned: some pigments can be seen to fall exactly half way between two preferred positions, but the present state of knowledge of pigment structure in relation to the light absorption properties is too rudimentary to comment further (Bridges, 1965a).

Attempts to correlate the λ_{max} of fish rhodopsins according to the phylogenetic relationships have showed no clear trends except that *closely* related species often have very similar pigments (Munz, 1964).

The correlation with habitat has been much more successful. Wald, Brown and Brown (1957) plotted the λ_{max} of the pigments of different species against the depth at which the fish are usually caught in the summer time, and obtained a steady shift towards the blue with

greater depth (Fig. 71), thus realizing the prediction of Clark (1936,
quoted by Wald, Brown and Brown, 1957) that since the light
penetrating to deeper waters becomes increasingly blue, it is likely that
the eyes of deepwater fish will become more sensitive to light
belonging to this region of the spectrum. The light penetrating to deep
waters was characterized by Jerlov (1947, quoted by Denton and
Warren, 1957) as having a narrow band of wavelengths around 475 mμ,

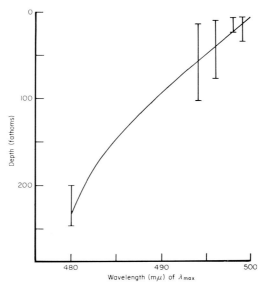

Fig. 71. Absorption maxima of visual pigments of different species of fish according
to the depth where usually caught in the summer time. After Wald, Brown and Brown
(1957), reproduced by courtesy of Professor G. Wald and MacMillan (Journals) Ltd.

so it can be seen that λ_{max} of the pigments of deepwater fish, that is,
the wavelength at which the pigments are most susceptible to bleaching,
is close to the predominant wavelength of the light which is there, so
that such fish can make the most use of whatever illumination is
available.

Denton and Warren (1956) were the first to describe the golden-
coloured pigments to be found in deep-sea fish, but since, like
rhodopsin, such pigments are based on vitamin A_1, it is probably not
justifiable to give them the special name of chrysopsin (Munz, 1957).
Munz (1958) extracted the pigments from further species of such fish,
and confirmed that the λ_{max} occurs near to 480 mμ. In contrast, those
from fish that inhabit muddy coastal waters occur well above 500 mμ,

for example in *Gillichthys mirabilis*, which lives in a turbid environment, λ_{max} is 512 mμ, based on vitamin A_1 (Munz, 1959). Thus there is a series of marine environments distinguished by the spectral maximum of available light, and the spectral sensitivities of the retinal pigments of marine fish appear to correlate with them (Munz, 1964). It is therefore the quality of the transmitted light, and not the depth of the water as such, which determines the nature of the visual pigments.

McFarland and Munz (1965) reported that the λ_{max} of the vitamin A_1 pigments of *Salvelinus fontinalis* and *Salvelinus namaycush* are respectively at 503 and 512 mμ. The retinas of the first generation of hybrids from these two species were found to contain *both* parental pigments. Second generation crosses have one or other of the individual pigments present, or a mixture of the two, so neither is genetically dominant.

While the presence of pigments based on both vitamins A_1 and A_2 is an inherited character of a species, the specific proportion of each is not, but depends on the illumination of the environment and can change during the life of the fish: Dartnall, Lander and Munz (1961) found that the combined λ_{max} of the mixed pigments of *Scardinius erythroph-thalmus* changes from 531 mμ in February to 515 mμ in March, owing to a decrease in the proportion of the vitamin A_2-based pigment ($\lambda_{max} = 543$ mμ) and an increase in the vitamin A_1-based pigment ($\lambda_{max} = 510$ mμ). When these fish are kept in an aquarium in total darkness, the proportion of the A_2-based pigment increases, while light causes the A_1 pigment to increase. There were found to be limits, probably determined genetically, in that the proportion of the pigment derived from vitamin A_1 never drops below 15% of the total, or rises above 85%.

Bridges (1964b) also demonstrated a seasonal change in the proportions of visual pigments, his results with *Belonesox belizanus* being illustrated in Fig. 72. He noted that the turbidity of the water had not changed during the period of observation so could not influence the pigment make-up, but in a later paper (Bridges, 1965c) he confirmed that fish exposed to longer periods of daylight acquire a higher proportion of pigment based on vitamin A_1.

Since, no matter what proportions of the two pigments are present, the total amount does not change much (Dartnall, Lander and Munz, 1961), it is not impossible that one pigment could be converted into the other, depending on the light conditions. Naito and Wilt (1962: *Lepomis* sp.) showed, using tritiated vitamin A_1, that this vitamin can act as the precursor of either pigment, the conversion taking place in

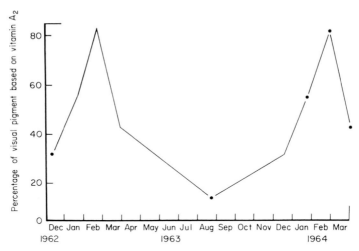

Fig. 72. Seasonal variation in the proportions of visual pigments based on vitamins A_1 and A_2 in *Belonesox belizanus*. After Bridges (1964b), reproduced by courtesy of the author and MacMillan (Journals) Ltd.

the isolated eye. The liver when removed from the fish is unable to convert much vitamin A_1 into vitamin A_2, but some striking work by Beatty (1966) has shown that an increase in the proportion of the vitamin A_2-based pigment in the eye of adult *Oncorhynchus* sp. as it migrates upstream coincides with an increase in the proportion of vitamin A_2 in the liver, though the relationship is not a simple one. His results are shown in Fig. 73, which also shows the change in pigment pattern as the fish changes its habitat from ocean to tidewater and, later, river spawning ground.

It is possible that the vitamin-protein relationship of a single pigment can also alter during or perhaps preceding a change of habitat. Carlisle and Denton (1959) found that the retinas of immature *Anguilla anguilla* in fresh water are purplish coloured, while on reaching maturity, when the eye enlarges and the fish enters the ocean, they become golden coloured, λ_{max} shifting 33 mμ towards the blue.

Though the proportions of the pigments in the eyes of several fish clearly vary seasonally (for example in Fig. 72), there can also be considerable variation between individual fish caught at the same season from the same place. Bridges (1964a) observed that in extreme cases the proportions of the vitamin A_1 and A_2 pigments in *Notemigonus crysoleucas boscii* can be 44% apart, although no significant difference

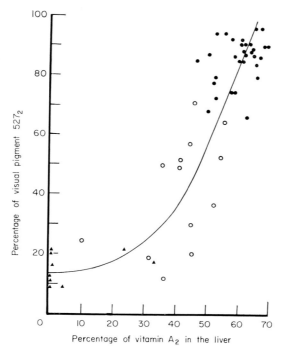

F$_{IG}$. 73. A correlation between the percentage of visual pigment 527_{A2} in the retina and the percentage of vitamin A_2 in the liver of individual adult *Oncorhynchus kisutch*. ▲ Fish caught in the ocean; ○ Tidewater group I; ● Tidewater groups II and III, and fish taken from the spawning site. After Beatty (1966), reproduced by courtesy of the author and the National Research Council of Canada.

between the two eyes of a single fish has been found. He suggested that variations between the spectral sensitivities of different individuals are related to schooling behaviour in this species, and might serve to sharpen the visual acuity of the school over a greater range of the spectrum. Paired pigments (both vitamin A_1 and A_2) are in fact generally found in schooling *Cyprinidae*, whereas species with a single pigment show only sporadic schooling or live alone (Bridges, 1964a, 1965b).

The possession of paired pigments confers on a fish the ability to vary its maximum visual sensitivity, and it is probably no coincidence that the facility occurs mostly in species occupying variable aquatic habitats. The spectral quality of the light in such habitats as rivers and marine coastal localities is often changed by turbidity and dissolved products of vegetable decay. Fish with paired pigments are well adapted to deal with such changes, which often occur at different times of the year (Bridges, 1965b). It should be borne in mind, however, that many fish with just one pigment can live successfully in the same environments.

Colour vision has been found in 15 species of fish. These have been listed by Protasov (1964), who in addition has named fish having monochromatic and dichromatic vision. He also notes the limits of light intensity below which the visual function is performed by rods instead of cones.

The role of vitamin A in the visual pigments is the only function of this vitamin that can be explained at the molecular level (Pitt, 1964), though belief in generalized effects of deficiency such as lack of growth and decreased resistance to infection in mammals is widely held (corresponding symptoms in *Salmo gairdnerii* are given in Table XXXII, p. 208). Several species of fish have lost the ability to see because of degeneration of the eyes, for example the hagfish (*Myxine glutinosa*), the deepsea ray (*Benthobatis*) and certain fish which inhabit caves and underground streams, such as *Anoptichthys jordani*. Specimens of the latter are shown in Fig. 74, where it may be seen that scales have grown over the place where eyes are usually found. This recession through non-use poses an interesting question: do such fish require vitamin A at all? So far as the writer is aware, no one has attempted to answer this, although it is known that while vitamin A may not be necessary for *growth* in *Salvelinus fontinalis* (Phillips, Lovelace

Fig. 74. Eyeless fish, *Anoptichthys jordani*, from caves or underground streams. The fish are 'albino', but a pigment (melanin) spot can sometimes be seen in the region where the eye should be. The body scales appear to grow normally over the optic area (author's picture).

et al., 1955), lack of it in *Salmo gairdnerii* produces a number of deficiency symptoms and high mortality (Kitamura, Suwa *et al.*, 1967). Both of these species are, of course, normally sighted.

6. *Salinity*

Some fundamental differences in composition between permanently marine and permanently freshwater species have already been described (p. 143). We shall now consider the effects of a change in salinity on species which can live in either habitat (euryhaline species).

A marine fish must keep drinking sea water and then excreting the salt afterwards if it is not to become dehydrated by the hypertonic environment. On the other hand, a freshwater fish must not drink, but excrete water if it is not to become waterlogged—as Baldwin said in a lecture (Baldwin, 1951), if you say of an acquaintance that he "drinks like a fish", it is important to specify whether you mean a marine or a freshwater species. . . . *

A few fish can survive transfer from the sea to fresh water by ceasing to ingest water, but others such as *Pleuronectes platessa* are unable to change their habits and so swell up and die in water of reduced salinity (Henschel, 1936). *Sebastiscus marmoratus* protects its tissues from changes in the surrounding salinity, increased or decreased, by secreting a transparent mucous film over its entire body surface when the salinity changes from that to which the fish is accustomed (Yamashita, 1967). In addition, the swimming activity of this species is much reduced under these conditions. Motais, Romeu and Maetz (1965) observed that when *Platichthys flesus* are transferred from sea water to fresh, there is an immediate reduction (about 85%) in the elimination of sodium and chloride by a mechanism located in the gills. *Serranus scriba*, which dies if the salinity is changed (stenohaline), does not possess this mechanism.

The specific gravity of the blood of euryhaline fish correlates positively with the salinity of the environment, presumably because of changes in its water content (Yamashita, 1967). The specific gravity has been found to depend on the amount of protein in the blood, and Lecal (1958) showed that the protein itself changes with a change in salinity : the electrophoretic pattern of the serum proteins of *Blennius pavo* is considerably modified within an hour of transfer from salt to fresh water, but after a day it has almost completely reverted to its original pattern, as adaptation to the new environment is completed.

* This remark did not appear in the printed version.

The role of *free* amino acids is equivocal, but there are indications that they can contribute to the osmoregulatory system of the fish. Duchâteau, Florkin and Jeuniaux (1959) and Florkin and Schoffeniels (1965) reported that the muscle and blood of crabs, lobsters and other inshore invertebrates become enriched with *free* amino acids when the animals are transferred from brackish water to full marine concentration, or from fresh to brackish, and vice versa. No information was given on fish, but it has been found that when *Fundulus heteroclitus* are placed in water free from potassium ions, the total *free* amino acids of the muscle increase from up to 330 mg% in the controls to up to 620 mg% in the experimental animals. The difference in the concentrations of lysine is more striking: 3·3 mg% in the controls and 38·0 mg% during potassium deficiency (Hanlon, 1960). The results could indicate a restoration of ionic balance, but perhaps they show just a failure in protein synthesis. Jones (1959a) suggested that, both in *Pleuronectes microcephalus* and *Gadus morhua*, the variations in the *free* amino acids and more particularly in the taurine of the muscle might be governed by the salinity of the water, but no evidence to support this concept has emerged from the work of Cowey, Daisley and Parry (1962) on the blood of *Salmo salar*: the sum of all the *free* amino acids (without proline) in this species in sea water is 669 μ-moles/100 ml, while that in fresh water is 710 μ-moles/100 ml— a shift opposite to that expected. Cowey (1965) concluded that there is no satisfactory evidence to show that the *free* amino acids of the tissues normally play a significant role in regulating the osmotic balance of fish tissues. Work on additional species is obviously required here.

The dilution of blood when fish migrate from the sea to fresh water was observed by Greene as long ago as 1904 in the form of an elevation of the freezing point from $-0\cdot76°$ to $-0\cdot63°$ in *Oncorhynchus tschawytscha*, and Benditt, Morrison and Irving (1941) found corresponding values of $-0\cdot79°$ and $-0\cdot64°$ in *Salmo salar*, noting also a decrease in the proportion of red cells, which reduces the oxygen capacity from 12·3 to 8·8 volumes %, respectively, in the two environments. On the other hand, in *Fundulus heteroclitus* which had lived for several months in fresh water the red cell count was observed by Slicher (1961) to be greater than in those kept in salt water. This discrepancy has not so far been explained.

Calcium ions play an important part in osmoregulation. Ringer (1883) noted that while unfed fish live for weeks in tap water, they soon die if placed in distilled water, perhaps because of a loss of calcium, which is necessary for muscular contraction, through the gills. Loss of sufficient sodium, potassium and other ions will, of course, also lead to death. The role of calcium in survival in fresh water is still uncertain (Pickford, Pang et al., 1966). The ion has an inhibitory effect on the diffusion of water across biological membranes, and Hulet, Masel et al. (1967), found that, in the presence of a high concentration of calcium (about 40 mg%) permanently marine fish were able to thrive in a much diluted medium. These workers had already noted that a number of marine teleost species habitually invade the freshwater streams and lakes of South Florida, which are rich in calcium ions. Phillips, Podoliak et al. (1963), found that *Salvelinus fontinalis* are not distressed by the presence of several toxic substances, such as copper ions, provided that calcium is present in the water as well; heavy mortalities occur when the fish are exposed to these substances, at a mere quarter of their original concentrations, if the water is calcium-free. Podoliak (1965) found that the same species habituated to 50 parts per million of calcium can survive a certain degree of handling and of osmotic and temperature stress, but die if the same stresses are applied in a calcium concentration below about 3 parts per million. *Salmo trutta* are more euryhaline, and always survive abrupt transfer to a different temperature or salinity.

Survival in salt water after migration from fresh appears to require increased metabolic activity in the liver. Isolated hepatic tissue from *Tinca tinca* and *Anguilla anguilla* was shown by Pequignot and Serfaty (1965) to consume more oxygen after the fish have been transferred from fresh to salt water. It is also noteworthy that changes in salinity cause a rise in the spinal lactic dehydrogenase activity of some elasmobranch species (Rasmussen and Rasmussen, 1967), indicating increased metabolic activity here also. The greater consumption of energy may be connected with acquiring water and secreting salt, but a migration to salt water must sometimes be undertaken, in spite of the extra energy required, if the fish is to survive. When *Anguilla anguilla* begin to mature in European rivers, they suffer a loss of minerals from the body which gives rise to muscular debility. They drift passively downstream, and achieve renewed liveliness only when they reach the sea and increase their mineral content. Failure to migrate leads to increasing mineral imbalance and finally death (Tucker, 1959).

In *Salmo salar*, the ability to osmoregulate is not possessed at all stages of life. It will be remembered that the young 'parr' changes to the 'smolt' in the river, and then migrates to the sea. If parr on their way downstream are caught and abruptly transferred to full-strength sea water, the sodium content of the blood increases uncontrollably and they all die within a day. Wild smolts, among which are presumably some newly metamorphosed from parrs, usually survive, but show a concentration of blood sodium which increases for the first three days and then drops to normal. Cultivated smolts two years old, which are ready to migrate to the sea, are completely adaptable and show no change (see Fig. 75).

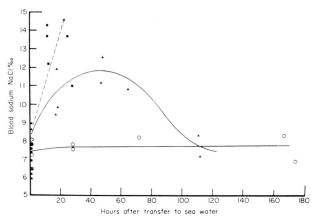

FIG. 75. Changes in the sodium content of the blood of parrs and smolts (*Salmo salar*) as a result of their being transferred suddenly from fresh water to full strength sea water, both at 6·3°. ■ 2-year parrs; ○ 2-year smolts (cultivated); ▲ Wild smolts. After Koch, Evans and Bergström (1959), reproduced by courtesy of Dr H. J. A. Koch and MacMillan (Journals) Ltd.

Under natural conditions, smolts spend a week or two at the river mouth in order to become adjusted to the salt water. Like the eels, most of them die if they are prevented from reaching the sea, though according to Parry (1961) there is no evidence of demineralization of the blood to stimulate a sea-going urge.

The effect of change of salinity on the inorganic constituents of fish has been studied by a number of workers. Lange and Fugelli (1965) found that the difference in sodium and chloride between *Pleuronectes flesus* adapted to fresh or to salt water adequately accounts for the difference in osmolarity of the serum, but that in the muscle the ionic composition is almost unaffected by the change of environment and appears to be maintained to a large extent by organic molecules comprising ninhydrin-positive substances and trimethylamine oxide. This conclusion does not seem to be valid for all species as we shall see in a moment.

Since there is a considerable bulk of literature describing changes in the levels of various inorganic substances with marine or freshwater adaptation, the findings are most conveniently summarized in tabular form (Table XXX).

The difference between the ionic compositions of the urines of fish from the two environments is striking. The volume of urine from *Fundulus kansae* was found to be 304 ml/kg/day in fresh water and only 31·3 ml/kg/day in sea water (Stanley and Fleming, 1967). Freshwater fish are unable to produce a salt-free urine, even when starvation prevents them from acquiring salts from their food, but they are thought to be able to acquire chloride from the surrounding medium by means of a mechanism in the gills, even if the ambient concentration of chloride is low (Krogh, 1937).

The advantage of compiling Table XXX will now be apparent, since we are shown that sodium and chloride, the principal extracellular ions, are not the only ions to alter with the environment, neither is blood the only tissue to change its composition. Among the examples given, the blood chloride and muscle sodium were both more concentrated in adult *Salmo salar* when the fish were in fresh water, but since spawning was taking place at the time these results are probably not comparable with the others. The fact that blood calcium in this species was also slightly higher during the freshwater stage is therefore probably not significant. Of the remaining four comparisons of blood calcium, three showed an increase when the fish migrated to salt water. Both comparisons of blood magnesium, all the sodium and 7/9 of the chloride comparisons (excluding spawning *Salmo salar*) showed an increase after the fish entered the sea. The increases in blood potassium were rather small, but were positive in seven out of nine cases, so probably real. Calcium, potassium and sodium all increased in kidneys and liver of fish which had migrated to a marine environment, and there are sufficient increases in the ions of the skeletal muscle to suggest a positive correlation with the habitat, most of the exceptions again being in the spawning *Salmo salar*.

The two examples of muscle water showed a decrease after transfer from fresh to salt water.

The study by Chester Jones' group of various named muscles of mature and immature eels showed that all ions increased in a marine environment (two individual exceptions), and since there was only one exception to this among eight potassium comparisons, it now seems certain that, in contrast to Lange and Fugelli's assertion (1965), this ion does increase in muscle tissue when the fish enters salt water.

While sodium is one of the ions most affected by a change of environment, the efforts of the fish to maintain a constant internal level are

TABLE XXX. IONIC COMPOSITION OF THE TISSUES OF EURYHALINE FISH ADAPTED TO FRESH OR SALT WATER

A. BLOOD
(Plasma, mg/100 ml, unless stated otherwise)

Species	In fresh water	In sea water	Reference
CALCIUM			
Anguilla anguilla (immature)	9·2	11·0 (serum)	Chan, Chester Jones et al. (1967)
(mature)	9·2	9·5 (serum)	
Fundulus kansae	10·6	10·4 (serum)	Stanley and Fleming (1967)
Platichthys flesus	10·7	13·4	Lahlou (1967)
Salmo salar (mg/100 g)	13·8 (spawning)	13·7	Parry (1961)
CHLORIDE			
Anguilla anguilla (immature)	248	525	Sharratt, Chester Jones and Bellamy (1964)
(mature)	373	550	
	313	496 (serum)	Chan, Chester Jones et al. (1967)
Fundulus heteroclitus	683	804	Harris, 1959, quoted by Sindermann and Mairs (1961)
Platichthys flesus	568	554	Motais, Romeu and Maetz (1966)
	468	596	Lahlou (1967)
	405	589	Lange and Fugelli (1965)
Salmo salar, smolt (mg/100 g)	650	589	Parry (1961)
adult (mg/100 g)	610 (spawning)	557	
Salvelinus alpinus	532	678	Gordon (1957)
MAGNESIUM			
Anguilla anguilla (immature)	7·4	10·2 (serum)	Chan, Chester Jones et al. (1967)
(mature)	5·2	9·1 (serum)	

POTASSIUM

Anguilla anguilla (immature)	13·3	10·9	Sharratt, Chester Jones and Bellamy (1964)
(mature)	10·9	12·1	
(immature)	8·8	13·1 (serum)	Chan, Chester Jones *et al.* (1967)
(mature)	6·8	12·6 (serum)	
Fundulus kansae	14·9	9·0 (serum)	Stanley and Fleming (1967)
Platichthys flesus	11·4	13·3	Lahlou, 1967
	19·9	21·1	Lange and Fugelli (1965)
Salmo salar, smolt (mg/100 g)	11·9	14·2	Parry, 1961
adult (mg/100 g)	11·9	12·3	

SODIUM

Anguilla anguilla (immature)	329	416	Sharratt, Chester Jones and Bellamy (1964)
(mature)	347	405	
(immature)	329	377 (serum)	Chan, Chester Jones *et al.* (1967)
(mature)	345	421 (serum)	
Fundulus kansae	361	386 (serum)	Stanley and Fleming (1967)
Platichthys flesus	322	386	Motais, Romeu and Maetz (1966)
	285	326	Lahlou (1967)
	361	446	Lange and Fugelli (1965)
Salmo salar, smolt (mg/100 g)	301	366	Parry (1961)
adult (mg/100 g)	405	488	

B. KIDNEY
(mg/100 g)

CALCIUM

Anguilla anguilla (immature)	13	20	Pequignot and Serfaty (1966)
(mature)	17	21	

POTASSIUM

Anguilla anguilla (immature)	310	320	
(mature)	300	320	

TABLE XXX—*continued*

Species	In fresh water	In sea water	Reference
SODIUM			
Anguilla anguilla (immature)	85	116	Pequignot and Serfaty (1966)
(mature)	78	119	

C. *LIVER*
(*mg/100 g*)

CALCIUM			
Anguilla anguilla (immature)	12	18	
(mature)	15	19	
POTASSIUM			
Anguilla anguilla (immature)	280	350	
(mature)	300	370	
SODIUM			
Anguilla anguilla (immature)	55	80	
(mature)	50	105	

D. *BODY MUSCLE*
(*mg/100 g tissue water*)

CALCIUM			
Salmo salar, smolt	12·6	14·2	Parry (1961)
adult	11·4	11·4	
	(spawning)		
spent	8·9	7·8	

C.B.F.

CHLORIDE			
Platichthys flesus	10·7	14·7	Lange and Fugelli (1965)
POTASSIUM			
Platichthys flesus	612	616	
Salmo salar, smolt	822	723	Parry (1961)
adult	1020	806	
spent	(spawning) 778	930	
SODIUM			
Platichthys flesus	23·5	33·8	Lange and Fugelli (1965)
Salmo salar, smolt	37·5	76·6	Parry (1961)
adult	153	64·6	
spent	(spawning) 105	84·4	
WATER			
Gasterosteus aculeatus	82·01%	80·25%	Lange and Fugelli (1965)
Platichthys flesus	81·24%	80·57%	

E. MOUTH MUSCLE
(mg/100 g tissue water)

POTASSIUM			
Anguilla anguilla (immature)	463	514	Sharratt, Chester Jones and Bellamy (1964)
(mature)	446	487	
SODIUM			
Anguilla anguilla (immature)	52	86	
(mature)	88	105	

9

TABLE XXX—continued

F. PARIETAL MUSCLE
(mg/100 g tissue water)

Species	In fresh water	In sea water	Reference
CALCIUM			
Anguilla anguilla (immature)	33·1	47·0	Chan, Chester Jones et al. (1967)
(mature)	47·6	43·6	
CHLORIDE			
Anguilla anguilla (mature)	57·2	90·6	
MAGNESIUM			
Anguilla anguilla (immature)	69·6	72·2	
(mature)	57·0	66·9	
POTASSIUM			
Anguilla anguilla (immature)	488	484	
(mature)	408	502	Sharratt, Chester Jones and Bellamy (1964)
(immature)	521	550	
(mature)	451	502	
SODIUM			
Anguilla anguilla (immature)	62·6	99·4	Chan, Chester Jones et al. (1967)
(mature)	84·1	91·0	
(immature)	41·2	62·3	Sharratt, Chester Jones and Bellamy (1964)
(mature)	62·5	75·7	

G. TONGUE MUSCLE
(mg/100 g tissue water)

	In fresh water	In sea water	Reference
CALCIUM			
Anguilla anguilla (immature)	10·4	12·2	Chan, Chester Jones et al. (1967)
(mature)	11·0	19·7	

CHLORIDE

Anguilla anguilla (mature)	82·3	143	Chan, Chester Jones et al. (1967).

MAGNESIUM

| Anguilla anguilla (immature) | 61·0 | 64·6 | |
| (mature) | 50·9 | 71·7 | |

POTASSIUM

| Anguilla anguilla (immature) | 453 | 474 | |
| (mature) | 397 | 484 | |

SODIUM

| Anguilla anguilla (immature) | 66·4 | 120 | |
| (mature) | 99·4 | 106 | |

H. URINE
(mg/100 ml)

CALCIUM

| Fundulus kansae | 0·90 | 16·2 | Stanley and Fleming (1967) |
| Platichthys flesus | 9·8 | 38·0 | Lahlou (1967) |

CHLORIDE

| Platichthys flesus | 57·8 | 365 | Stanley and Fleming (1967) |
| | | | Lahlou (1967) |

SODIUM

| Fundulus kansae | 29·9 | 109 | Stanley and Fleming (1967) |
| Platichthys flesus | 69·9 | 137 | Lahlou (1967) |

POTASSIUM

| Fundulus kansae | 1·92 | 4·85 | Stanley and Fleming (1967) |
| Platichthys flesus | 4·73 | 9·93 | Lahlou (1967) |

Authors have invariably expressed the ionic composition of muscle as units per given weight of tissue water, rather than of tissue itself, and as the water content of muscle changes with change of environment (see above), this mode of expression probably gives a more realistic portrayal.

remarkable. An extreme case is to be found in *Tilapia mossambica*, which can survive over a very wide range of salinities. Potts, Foster *et al.* (1967), showed that although the ambient sodium varies by a factor of 2500, the total body sodium is only 30% higher in double-strength sea water than in fresh water.

7. *Diet*

(a) *The fate of various foods*

Is it possible to acquire a different composition through a change of diet? One is reminded of the old Yorkshire song in which the singer tells his friend that he will catch his death of cold through going out without a hat, be buried and eaten up by the worms, which in turn would be eaten by the ducks of the neighbourhood. When the singer and his friends ate the ducks, then they "should all have eaten him! ' The cannibals of primitive societies believed that in eating their erstwhile enemies they were acquiring some of their strength and courage, but—does it really make any difference?

In this section we shall try to discover what changes in the chemistry of the fish can be traced back to dietary origins.

It has already been stated (Geiger and Borgstrom, 1962) that information on the subject is extremely scanty, but it is worth while exploring the present limits of knowledge to try to find anything that can be used. It would be so very convenient to be able to distinguish a cod that had been feeding regularly on herring larvae from one with a predilection for crustacea, but most published observations have up to now related to the state of depletion of the fish rather than to an unusual imposed chemical composition.

The enormous diversity of food eaten by fish, and some of the food chains involved, have been described by Marshall (1965). Seasonal changes in the diet of *Gadus morhua* were studied by Rae (1967a), who reported that *Nephrops* reaches its greatest importance as food from March to June and is of least significance from July to October. *Crangon* is eaten most frequently from October to March, while predation on *Pandalus* is a fairly uniform activity throughout the year. In the same area, the fish species most commonly eaten between the months of April and June is *Lumpenus*, while clupeoids (small *Clupea harengus* and *Sprattus sprattus*) are taken from December to April. Sand eels (*Ammodytes*) are most important in the diet in June and July, flat fish from October to April. We have seen a great deal in the present account on the subject of seasonal variation: here, surely, is a factor of importance.

The diet may also change according to the locality. Rae (1967a) found that Ophiuroids (brittle star-fish) are eaten by only about 4% of the cod on most grounds, but that on one particular region of Western Scotland some 20% of the fish are to be found feeding on them.

Sometimes the diet differs between the sexes: female *Abramis brama* from the Sea of Azov, for instance, feed mainly on *Hypaniola kovalevskii*, while males prefer *Nereis succinea* (Nikolsky, 1963).

A change of diet can markedly affect the life history of the fish. As stated earlier (p. 51), Algonquin Park lake trout (*Salvelinus namaycush*) may feed on plankton or on fish depending on the availability of the food in the summer months. Those feeding on plankton grow more slowly and do not reach as great an age as fish-feeders, maturing at a smaller size and younger age. Trout transferred from a plankton-feeding to a fish-feeding environment grow at a faster rate and extend their life-span (Martin, 1966).

What is the chance of being able to identify the diet from the composition of the predator? It is likely to be slim, but as we shall see there are a few pointers. Naturally, a constituent which differs between foods but which is broken down to common building units during digestion yields no information. Thus the amino acid composition of both 'wild' and cultivated *Salvelinus fontinalis* was shown by Block (1959) to vary only slightly under the influence of different natural and artificial diets (some of his results have been quoted already in Table IX, p. 54). To maintain a constant composition, however, the fish must consume an adequate amount of protein. *Sardinops caerulea* fed only on carbohydrates show a measurable appreciation of free aspartic acid in the tissues, but this is because the diet lacks nitrogen, causing the fish to mobilize tissue proteins. The concentration therefore declines if the diet is improved by increasing the protein (Farris, 1958).

The herring (*Clupea harengus*) becomes rich in lipids through the intake of large quantities of plankton; its flavour is pleasant if the diet was mainly crustaceans of the copepod family such as *Calanus finmarchicus*, but the flesh tastes bitter if the fish fed on certain larvae, for example those of *Mytilus* (Lücke, 1954, quoted by Rakow, 1963). The so-called 'blackberry' marine invertebrate confers an unpleasant smell on the flesh of *Gadus morhua* which have eaten a lot of them (Sipos and Ackman, 1964). The smelly substance has been identified as dimethyl sulphide, which is found at a concentration of 0·0001% in the stomachs of fish that have fed on this organism. In addition, the flesh of a few fish is toxic to man. This is probably caused by the absorption of poisonous materials from the food because, while some species are always toxic, others may be consumed safely hundreds of times before suddenly causing grave illness or death when eaten again. Ichthyo-sarcotoxin is thought to come from certain marine plants, and to be conveyed to man in the body of the fish which ate them, probably after an increase in concentration (Lagler, Bardach and Miller, 1962).

The exceptionally high zinc content of the tissues of some fish is thought to originate in a diet of molluscs, many of which are rich in this element (Vinogradov, 1953). The total content of trace elements (Cu, Mn, Fe, Co, Ni, Ag, Mo and Cr) is highest in plankton-eating fish (Petkovich, 1967a).

The vitamins of fish seem to be mostly or even entirely derived from the food consumed. Unlike mammals and birds, fish do not seem to have resident intestinal microflora which synthesize additional vitamins (Braekkan, 1959). Ackman and Cormier (1967) stated that the tocopherols (vitamins E) present in fish and shellfish originate in the phytoplankton and in multicellular algae.

Since vitamin A is concentrated in the liver, fish that feed on other fish receive an abundant supply—it has indeed been found that fish-eaters from the Red Sea (Abdallah and Salah, 1961) and Germany (Karst, 1965) contain more vitamin A than either herbivores or coral eaters, the latter being poorest in this vitamin (Abdallah and Salah, 1961). Diet is not, however, the sole governor of vitamin A concentration since, for example, *Hippoglossus hippoglossus* accumulates much more of it than most other species on a similar diet (Cruickshank, 1962). Plack and Woodhead (1966) reported that the levels of plasma vitamin A in *Gadus morhua* caught off the Faroe Islands were almost always higher than in those from the Barents Sea, but it is not known whether this represents a difference in the diet or a genetic difference in the stock.

Fish are also able to convert dietary carotene into vitamin A (Neilands, 1947: *Gadus morhua*). This precursor acts equally well as a precursor of vitamin A_1 or A_2 (which has an additional double bond), according to the balance of enzymes present in the fish (Morton and Creed, 1939: *Perca fluviatilis, Leuciscus leuciscus*; Gross and Budowski, 1966: *Lebistes* sp.; M. Hata, Sendai University, private communication 1967: *Channa argus, Carassius carassius*). Derivatives of carotene containing oxygen, such as astaxanthin, can also be converted into vitamin A (Gross and Budowski, 1966).

Like other animals, fish are unable to synthesize carotenoids, but they can alter those in the diet by oxidation and then store the resulting products (Sumner and Fox, 1935b: *Fundulus parvipinnis*; Katayama,

Ikeda and Harada, 1965; *Chrysophrys major*). According to Steven (1948), *Salmo trutta* appear not to be able to convert one type of carotenoid into another, so that all such pigments must have originated in the diet. The source of the pigments laid down in the skin during the larval period is the yolk, in which carotenoids were deposited by the parent fish (Steven, 1949). Peterson, Jäger *et al.* (1966), have reviewed other papers which show that the xanthophylls, which are responsible for the pigmentation of *Salmo trutta*, originated in the diet. The colour of *Carassius auratus* is due to astaxanthin, and captive fish on a carotenoid-free diet become pale. Wild fish feed on green algae which contain lutein, not astaxanthin, so this carotenoid is therefore a precursor for the pigment in the skin (T. Tomiyama, Kyushu University, private communication, 1967).

There is little to add to what has already been stated regarding the fate of dietary lipids; the salient points will be repeated briefly. Both marine and freshwater fish appear to be able to synthesize polyunsaturated fatty acids from non-fatty precursors, but the difference between the fatty acid composition of the body lipids of fish from the two environments is largely the result of differences in the diet (Kelly, Reiser and Hood, 1958). The lipids of the food are usually similar to the lipids subsequently stored by the fish themselves (Lovern, 1935). This conclusion is now amply confirmed (DeWitt, 1963; Gruger, Nelson and Stansby, 1964; Malins, Wekell and Houle, 1965; Kaneko, Takeuchi *et al.*, 1967a), although it is clear that in *Gadus morhua* and *Salvelinus fontinalis* the larger part of the ingested lipid has been broken down completely before being 'reassembled' in the storage depots (Brockerhoff and Hoyle, 1967). *Anguilla anguilla* from the sea or from fresh water differ in their fatty acid composition, and those from brackish estuarine waters have lipids of an intermediate type (Lovern, 1942). However, when they are kept in captivity on the same diet in fresh or salt water, no difference can be detected in the composition, and if they are kept in one environment but fed the food typical of the other, the stored lipid composition follows that of the diet and not of the salinity (Lovern, 1938b). Similarly, a sturgeon (*Acipenser* sp.) caught in the North Sea showed a lipid composition typical of a freshwater fish, but, as Lovern (1932b) pointed out, most of the feeding had been done in fresh water. Thus diet is the over-riding factor.

In addition, certain fish can modify the ingested lipid considerably (Lovern, 1935). The process is probably best illustrated in the young *Salmo salar*. The body lipid of the 'parr' form (early freshwater) is like the lipid that they ingested, but the 'smolt' (later freshwater) lipid is more like that of the adult (marine) form, though there has been no change of diet or environment (Lovern, 1942).

The concentration of trimethylamine oxide is much lower in freshwater fish than in marine fish (see Table XXVIII, p. 146), and it has been suggested that the difference originates in the diet (Beatty, 1939; Reay, 1939; Benoit and Norris, 1945; Anderson and Fellers, 1952). The muscle of *Salmo trutta* raised in a hatchery was found to be free from this compound for the first eight months of life, the fish being fed a diet free from trimethylamine oxide, but later the diet was changed to one containing pieces of herring flesh, which contained trimethylamine oxide, and the flesh of the young fish then began to accumulate it. The concentration increases with age, $1 \cdot 7$ mg% at 2 years increasing to $18 \cdot 5$ mg% at 5 (Anderson and Fellers, 1952). Beatty (1939) found that the muscle of *Anguilla rostrata* taken from the sea contains a little trimethylamine oxide, but that that from the same species captured in fresh water is free from it, again indicating a dietary source. Reay (1939) showed that some mixed freshwater zooplankton contains only a trace, but that a sample of marine zooplankton contains 248 mg%. The evidence for a dietary origin for trimethylamine oxide is therefore strong.

The position of carbohydrates in this discussion is doubtful, since diets rich in such compounds are not eaten by the fish, with the possible exception of some herbivores, in the natural state. Thus while Kiermeir (1939) noted that the feeding of freshwater fish had but little influence on the level of blood sugar, which showed just a slight increase after 4—5 hours, the diet was in fact horse flesh, so the result is hardly surprising. The rise in blood sugar of *Clarias lazera* some 20 hours after feeding, illustrated in Fig. 25 (p. 50), followed a diet of bread and earthworms—again not the sort of diet to be found in a natural environment!

However, it can definitely be stated that an increase in the carbohydrate content of the diet causes a rise in that of the tissues of the fish. Miller, Sinclair and Hochachka (1959) found that in *Salmo gairdnerii* fed an artificial mixed diet, the muscle was richer in glycogen than that of fish fed only beef liver. Tunison, Phillips *et al.* (1940), fed various forms of carbohydrate, such as cellulose, sucrose and starch, to *Salvelinus fontinalis*, and showed that a diet containing cooked starch gives rise to the highest concentration of liver glycogen in the fish. Phillips, Podoliak *et al.* (1958), found that a high level of dietary carbohydrate increases the level of blood glucose, but that lack of carbohydrates has no effect, presumably because the blood glucose level is being maintained from reserves in the liver. Glycogen in the muscle of *Salmo gairdnerii* was shown to rise eight- or nine-fold under the influence of heavy feeding of carbohydrates (Hochachka and Sinclair, 1962), and Phillips, Livingston and Poston (1966) were the first to show that carbohydrates can definitely be used as a source of energy, but that the fish, *Salvelinus fontinalis*, is a relatively inefficient metabolizer of high levels of these substances. It is clear that studies of this kind are of more interest to fish breeders than to those examining fish from a natural environment.

To sum up, the diet chosen by the fish cannot be identified later from the amino acid composition of the predator, but dimethyl sulphide, certain toxins, zinc, trimethylamine oxide and the vitamins are stored unchanged and can in certain instances indicate a high concentration in the diet. Lipids and carotenoids also reflect those of the diet, but may be modified by the fish before deposition.

In spite of the tendency to modify ingested lipids, fish that normally feed in fresh water may be distinguished from eaters of marine diets by their lipid constitution, and those eating fish may be distinguished from herbivores by their high content of vitamin A. It may also be possible to distinguish fish fed an artificial diet from natural feeders, since the livers and muscles of the former are sometimes richer in carbohydrate than those of the latter.

Thus the information on the eating habits of the fish to be gained by studying the body of the eater, within the framework outlined at the beginning of this section, is very limited, but this is still an incompletely explored field of research, and further possible approaches remain.

(b) Influence of diet on the intestine and its secretions

The intestines of fish, as in mammals, are longer in herbivores than in carnivores (Lagler, Bardach and Miller, 1962; Nagase, 1964) and their shape and structure may be modified by the nature of the diet, according to papers listed by Gohar and Latif (1961a). Further, the intestines are bigger if the fish are well fed than if they have been starved (Lühmann and Mann, 1957; *Cyprinus carpio*).

Pavlov (1902) stated that the proportions of the different digestive enzymes of the dog alter according to the composition of the diet consumed, but very little is known of this phenomenon in fish.* Barrington (1957) reviewed several papers showing that the enzymes produced correlate with the habitual diets of individual species, but was unable to give an opinion as to whether they are modified in a

* The influence of the diet on the anatomy and secretions of the digestive tracts of mammals has been reviewed by J. E. Thomas (1964).

single fish if the diet is changed. Fish (1960) showed that the digestion of carbohydrates is more efficient in *Tilapia mossambica*, a herbivore, than in *Perca fluviatilis*, a carnivore, and vice versa with the proteins. Work by Kashiwada (1952) indicated that the secretion of proteolytic enzymes by a single species is not constant: in the pyloric caecae of *Katsuwonus vagans* it increases in the spring time and falls in summer.

The most definite evidence of modification in a single species in relation to diet has been presented by Nagase (1964), working with *Tilapia mossambica*, here described as omnivorous and possessing a full complement of enzymes. Separate groups of fish were fed on rabbit muscle (protein diet), bread (carbohydrate diet) and fatty beef (fat diet), and the production of enzymes was measured. Pepsin and

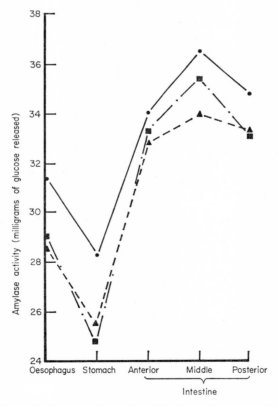

Fig. 76. Amylase activity of various parts of the alimentary canal of *Tilapia mossambica* on different diets. ●————● Carbohydrate-rich diet; ▥—.—▥ Fat-rich diet; ▲————▲ Protein-rich diet. After Nagase (1964), reproduced by courtesy of the author and Springer-Verlag, Berlin.

lipase activities appeared not to be affected by the diet, but trypsin and amylase showed a positive correlation. The results for amylase, which digests carbohydrates, are shown in Fig. 76. It can be seen that the activity was greatest on a carbohydrate-rich diet in all parts of the alimentary canal. More work is needed in this field, however, since work by Schlottke (1939, quoted by Barrington, 1957; *Cyprinus carpio*) seems to show that amylolytic and proteolytic activity does not depend on the composition of the food.

Other studies of a semi-quantitative nature carried out on intestinal carbohydrases (Gohar and Latif, 1961b), lipases (Gohar and Latif, 1961c) and proteases (Gohar and Latif, 1963), in fish from the Red Sea have confirmed the existence of differences between species, presumably corresponding with different diets.

(c) *Absorption of nutrients from the environment*

Fish are not completely dependent for their nourishment on food taken by mouth. A few substances, most inorganic, are absorbed directly from the surrounding water, presumably by way of the gills.

In contrast to their action in promoting growth in agriculture, the action of nitrogenous compounds on the growth of fish after they have been added to ponds is negligible, since they are rapidly broken down by bacteria (Mann, 1961). However, glucose is absorbed, and raises the level of blood glucose significantly (Schuster-Woldon, 1936, quoted by Phillips, Lovelace *et al.*, 1953: *Cyprinus carpio*). In experiments with *Salvelinus fontinalis*, Phillips, Lovelace *et al.* (1953), found that fish placed in a glucose solution show higher blood glucose values than those placed in plain water, allowing for the increase in glucose caused by handling alone. The difference between the two groups shows a steady increase with time after placing in 0·5% glucose solution, reaching a maximum after 48 hours (Fig. 77). If a weaker solution is used, the maximum occurs after 12 hours. The value of this work is somewhat theoretical, since glucose is not found in the natural environment, but it does show that a compound which supplies energy can be absorbed from the surrounding medium. This is the only example known to the writer, however, and it is unlikely that a fish could subsist indefinitely without eating*. The following diversion, surely the father and mother of exaggerated "fisherman's stories", is therefore almost certainly without foundation, although it makes entertaining reading nowadays:

"Fishes, though for ever hungry and prowling, can endure the want of food for a long time. A pike, one of the most gluttonous of fishes,

---

* In fact, Sterne, Hirsch and Pele (1968) have shown that *Carassius auratus* maintained in a glucose solution develop enlarged livers and an unusual form of diabetes.

will live, and even thrive, where there is none but itself. Rondeletius mentions one that was kept at his house in this manner for three years, which grew to such a size that the vase could scarcely contain it, nor could it be brought out by the same passage by which it was introduced into the vessel. It would appear, therefore, that, in certain situations, fishes are as remarkable for abstinence as, in others, they are distinguished for voracity, and that nature, in compassion to the

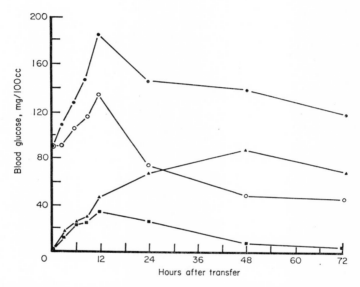

FIG. 77. The effect of placing *Salvelinus fontinalis* into glucose solutions on the level of blood glucose. ● Fish placed in 0·5% glucose; ○ Controls placed in plain water, showing effect of handling; △ Difference between experimental fish and control, showing glucose actually absorbed; ■ Difference between experimental fish, when 0·0625% glucose was used, and control, showing smaller amount of glucose absorbed. After Phillips, Lovelace *et al.* (1953), reproduced by courtesy of Professor A. M. Phillips.

want which they must often suffer, has indulged them with a power of accommodating their appetite to scarcity of fish, as well as to abundance." (Encyclopedia Londiniensis, 1801.)

Among inorganic constituents which can traverse the gills, calcium is but little absorbed unless phosphate is present as well, so that it can be deposited as calcium phosphate in the body of the fish (Phillips, Lovelace *et al.*, 1955; Phillips, Podoliak *et al.*, 1957a: *Salvelinus fontinalis*). In a similar way, the absorption of cobalt by the same species is assisted by the presence of a mixture of trace minerals (Phillips, Podoliak *et al.*, 1957a).

Published work on the absorption of inorganic substances from the surrounding water is summarized in Table XXXI. Workers from the Cortland Hatchery (New York) predominate in this field, as in so many others.

TABLE XXXI. INORGANIC SUBSTANCES SHOWN TO HAVE BEEN ABSORBED BY FISH OR LARVAE DIRECTLY FROM THE SURROUNDING WATER

Substance	Species	Reference
Ca	Salvelinus fontinalis	McCay, Tunison et al., 1936
		Phillips, Lovelace et al., 1955
Cl	(Several species)	Papers quoted by Hunn and Fromm, 1966
Co	Salvelinus fontinalis	Phillips, Lovelace et al., 1956
		Phillips, Podoliak et al., 1957a
I	Salmo gairdnerii	Hunn and Reineke, 1964
	Salvelinus fontinalis	Papers quoted by Hunn and Fromm, 1966
Sr		Podoliak and McCormick, 1967
SO$_4$		Phillips, Podoliak et al., 1960

(d) Nutritional requirements

Accurate measurements of the minimum requirements of water-soluble nutrients is difficult in fish, since one cannot be certain that some material does not diffuse out of the mouth again after ingestion, and unconsumed food is soon dispersed in the water and cannot be weighed. Considerable ingenuity must therefore be used in feeding the fish. In spite of this, a number of workers have been able to show that fish, like mammals, depend on certain substances being present in the diet for normal growth and health.

It is not intended to deal fully here with the nutritional requirements of fish, since a comprehensive account of the subject was in preparation at the time the present work was being written, and the reader is referred to it for further information (Halver, in press).

The protein requirements of fish are two to four times higher than those of birds and mammals, and the optimum protein level depends on the temperature of the water. In Oncorhynchus tschawytscha it is 40% of the dry diet at 8° and 55% at 14° (DeLong, Halver and Mertz, 1958).

Some amino acids can be synthesized, but others must be present in the diet if the fish is to grow at all. The 10 'essential' amino acids are arginine, histidine, isoleucine, leucine, lysine, methionine, phenylalanine, threonine, tryptophan and valine, while those that can be omitted from the diet without harm are alanine, aspartic acid, cysteine,

glutamic acid, glycine, hydroxyproline, proline, serine and tyrosine
(Halver, DeLong and Mertz, 1957: *Oncorhynchus tschawytscha*; Shanks
and Halver, 1960: *Oncorhynchus nerka* and *Salmo gairdnerii*). The
first group of amino acids is also essential to the rat and pig (Halver,
DeLong and Mertz, 1957).

The requirement of isoleucine was influenced by the amount of
leucine present, being 0·9% of the dry diet in the presence of 1·5%
leucine, 1·0% with 3·7% and 1·1% with 6% leucine (Chance, Mertz
and Halver, 1964: *Oncorhynchus tschawytscha*).

Cephalin in the diet appears to stimulate growth (Phillips, Lovelace
et al., 1955: *Salvelinus fontinalis*), and choline (Phillips, Lovelace
et al., 1956: *Salmo trutta*) and iodine (Woodall and LaRoche, 1964:
Oncorhynchus tschawytscha) are essential.

Fish appear to need most of the vitamins if they are to survive,
although vitamins A and D have been reported as unnecessary for
Salvelinus fontinalis (Phillips, Lovelace *et al.*, 1955), B_{12} (cyanoco-

TABLE XXXII. VITAMIN DEFICIENCY SYMPTOMS IN SALMO GAIRDNERII
(after Kitamura, Suwa *et al.*, 1967)

Vitamin	Symptoms
Vitamin A (retinol, axerophthol)	Poor growth, anaemia, high mortality, light coloured body, haemorrhagic skin and eye, bent operculum, poor appetite.
Vitamin B_1 (aneurin, thiamine)	Poor growth, high mortality, poor appetite, sluggish swimming, extended operculum, loss of equilibrium.
Vitamin B_2 (riboflavin)	Poor growth, high mortality, necrosis of gill operculum and front of fin, poor appetite, sluggish swimming.
Vitamin B_6 (pyridoxine)	Poor growth, high mortality and rapid death, normal appetite, violent and spiral swimming.
Nicotinic acid (niacin)	No symptoms.
Pantothenic acid	Poor growth, high mortality, poor apetite, abnormal swimming, pin head, extended gills.
Inositol	High mortality, fragile fins, loss of tail fin, white-coloured liver, poor appetite.
Biotin	No symptoms.
Folic acid	High mortality, anaemia, loss of tail fin, sluggish swimming.
Vitamin B_{12} (cyano-cobalamin)	No symptoms.
Vitamin C (ascorbic acid)	Deformity of vertebrae and operculum, haemorrhagic skin, liver, kidney, intestine and muscle.
Vitamin D (calciferol)	Slightly increased blood cell count.
Vitamin K	Anaemia.

balamin) unnecessary for *Oncorhynchus tschawytscha* (Halver, 1957) and vitamin C (ascorbic acid) and para-amino benzoic acid unnecessary for *Oncorhynchus kisutch** (Coates and Halver, 1958). It will be noticed also in Table **XXXII** that lack of niacin, biotin or vitamin B_{12} produces no symptoms in *Salmo gairdnerii*.

Completing this short account, Table **XXXII** shows the principal symptoms of vitamin deficiency in *Salmo gairdnerii*. Vitamin A has also been shown to be essential in *Salmo salar* (Chudova, 1961).

8. *Temperature*

(a) *Introduction*

Fish are to be found in habitats which range from below zero to over 50°, and in this section we shall compare the properties of tissues from species accustomed to high and to low temperatures, and note also any effects of a change of temperature. No one species can survive over the full range stated above, but by slow acclimatization the temperatures of indefinite survival can be considerably extended. On the other hand, sudden transfer to water of a different temperature, even within the tolerated range, will often kill the fish as every aquarium owner knows.

Given a choice of temperature, fish usually select that near the middle of their physiological range (Woodhead and Woodhead, 1959: *Gadus morhua*), though starvation can alter their choice. *Salmo salar* prefer a higher temperature than usual within a day after the cessation of feeding, while *Salmo gairdnerii* and *Salvelinus fontinalis* prefer to be cooler (Javaid and Anderson, 1967). *Neothunnus macropterus* and *Thunnus obesus* choose their surrounding water to be as close as possible to 28°, and their depth in the ocean corresponds with the depth of the 28° layer (Nakagome, 1965). While this temperature is relatively high for fish, the tissues of tuna species in general seem to function best in a warm environment, and the fish use an exchange system in their gills to retain some of their metabolic heat and maintain an internal temperature warmer than that of the surrounding water (Carey and Teal, 1966).

Brett (1956) and Fry (1964) have compiled tables showing the upper and lower lethal temperatures of numerous species as determined by various workers. Species able to live at temperatures below 0° are found at the bottoms of fjords around Alaska and the two polar regions. The fish that tolerates the highest temperature of all, 52°, is *Cyprinodon macularius* (Nikolsky, 1963), while among common species the most tolerant is *Carassius auratus* with an upper limit of 40°.

* See Note in Proof (p. 257).

(b) Temperature-rate relationships

As we should expect, a rise in temperature brings about an increase in metabolic rate which is seen in the accelerated growth of both eggs and fish. Embody (1934) reported a logarithmic increase in the rate of hatching and development of the eggs of *Salmo trutta* with arithmetic increase in temperature, but according to Forrester and Alderdice (1966) the eggs of *Gadus macrocephalus* develop at a speed directly related to the temperature. Those of *Cyprinodon macularius* develop more slowly if the salinity is increased, and more quickly in a higher concentration of oxygen; both the retardation and acceleration have been found to become increasingly accentuated as the temperature is raised (Kinne and Kinne, 1962).

The velocity of development of *Salvelinus fontinalis* and *Salmo gairdnerii* embryos increases with increasing water temperature (Garside, 1966a,b), while in livebearing fish the period of gestation is reduced (Marshall, 1965, p. 256).

The relationship between water temperature and growth rate is demonstrated for adult *Perca fluviatilis* in Fig. 78. A similar situation exists in *Gadus* species, where it has been shown that the size of a generation increases in a season of unusually high temperature (Moiseev, 1955). Jonsson (1953) and Coble (1966) have reported an increase in the growth rates of *Gadus morhua* and *Perca flavescens*,

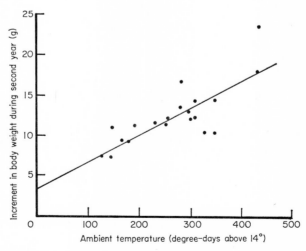

FIG. 78. The influence of temperature on the growth rate of *Perca fluviatilis*. After Le Cren (1958), reproduced by courtesy of the author, the British Ecological Society and Blackwell Scientific Publications.

respectively, at higher temperatures, but pointed out that other factors could also influence the growth and blur the general relationship —for example, overcrowding of young fish in some areas would retard it.

The faster metabolic rate of fish living in a warm environment has been given as the probable cause of their shorter lives compared with the same species from colder water (Alm, 1959). An example is to be found in *Cynolebias adloffi*, the "annual fish", which lives for about a year at its usual temperature of 22°, but which can be made to live much longer if kept at 16° (Liu and Walford, 1966). *Gadus morhua* rarely lives for more than eight years in the North Sea, while in the Barents Sea and Svalbard regions it is known to live for considerably more than 20 years. In *Cyprinus carpio* the regeneration of the severed cardiac parasympathetic nerve is speeded up at higher temperatures (Gas-Baby, Laffont and Labat, 1967), so the healing of tissue evidently follows the same temperature relationship as growth.

Turning now to other metabolic phenomena, we find that the digestion of food in *Perca flavescens* is three times as rapid in summer as in winter (Pearse and Achtenberg, 1917), while the gastric secretion itself has been shown to increase at higher temperatures (Smit, 1967: *Ictalurus nebulosus*). Phillips, Podoliak *et al.* (1957a: *Salvelinus fontinalis*), observed that a capsule of food containing a red dye moved more rapidly along the intestine in warmer water, so peristaltic movement appears to be affected as well. Direct absorption of nutrients from the water is increased (Phillips, Lovelace *et al.*, 1956: cobalt in *Salvelinus fontinalis*; Phillips, Podoliak *et al.*, 1960: sulphate and calcium in *Salvelinus fontinalis*) though for some reason *Cristivomer namaycush* absorbs more cobalt at lower temperatures (Phillips, Podoliak *et al.*, 1957a).

Depletion in the absence of food is enhanced at higher temperatures. Love (1958c) found that *Gadus morhua* kept at about 14° without food reached the point of death in 78 days, but that if the aquarium was maintained at 9°, the fish were only moderately depleted after 98 days (Love, Robertson and Strachan, 1968). Similarly, *Salvelinus fontinalis* kept at 14° for 84 days lost 31% of their weight, but at 8° lost only 20% over the same period (Phillips, Podoliak *et al.*, 1960).

When pellets containing cortisol were implanted in *Salmo gairdnerii* so that the hormone was released continuously, death from post-spawning symptoms (loss of weight, skin infections and so on, see Fig. 51, p. 113) occurred in five to nine weeks at 13°, but the fish died much sooner and with smaller doses of the corticoid when the water temperature was raised to 17° (Robertson, Hane *et al.*, 1963).

Increased metabolic rate and blood flow at high temperatures appear to account for the smaller concentration of lactic acid in the blood of *Ictalurus melas, Lepomis macrochirus, Pomoxis annularis* and *Micropterus salmoides* after exercise at 20° as compared with 5° (Dean, 1962). Presumably the same amount is formed for the same energy output, but it is more quickly swept away and oxidized at the higher temperature.

Another manifestation of increased metabolic rate is seen in the activity of the enzymes of the liver. Vellas (1965) found that uricase, allantoicase and allantoinase activities all increased in the livers of *Cyprinus carpio* kept at 20° compared with those kept at 8°.

(c) *Metabolic adaptation to different temperatures*

While a change of temperature usually alters the rate of metabolism in fish, an internal adjustment may take place to minimize the effect and keep the metabolism as near normal as possible. Stroganov (1956) noted that *Gambusia holbrooki* which have adapted to low temperatures consume more oxygen than warm-adapted fish do when both groups are brought to an intermediate temperature. Scholander, Flagg *et al.* (1953), showed that the oxygen consumption of Arctic fish *at their usual environmental temperature* is only 4 to 10 times lower than that of tropical species at *their* normal temperature; if one extrapolates the values for the tropical forms down to 0°, it is clear that if the fish survived there would be a 30- to 40-fold decrease, so the Arctic fish must modify their metabolic system. Wohlschlag (1963) showed that *Rhigophila dearborni*, an Antarctic species from deep waters of the McMurdo Sound, has a higher oxygen uptake at low temperatures than would be expected from studies in warmer water, and Winberg (1961) observed that fish habitually living at about 30° have an unexpectedly *low* rate of metabolism. In spite of these modifications, fish in warmer water do require more oxygen, and since less is available in solution, the oxygen capacity of the blood is improved by increasing the number of red cells per unit volume, and also the amount of haemoglobin in each cell (DeWilde and Houston, 1967: *Salmo gairdnerii*).

Dissecting brain tissue from Polar cod (*Boreogadus saida*) and a temperate species (*Huro salmoides*) and measuring the respiratory quotient of the isolated material, Field and Peiss (1949) showed that at every temperature studied, the oxygen consumption of the Arctic species is the greater of the two, and that below 10° the rate of consumption in the temperate fish shows an additional retardation, that is, the curve becomes steeper, while that of the Polar fish shows a constant slope from 25° right down to 0°. Both features in the Polar cod would be advantageous in a cold environment.

Jankowski and Korn (1965) found that the oxygen uptake of a muscle homogenate from *Idus idus* at a given temperature is higher in fish adapted to 8° than in those adapted to 22°. Muscle from fish adapted to lower temperatures was seen to contain a greater number of mitochondria, and those bodies, which contain many of the enzymes of the cell, are enlarged. Enzymes of the tricarboxylic acid cycle show an increased activity with falling adaptation temperature, and the activity of cytochrome oxidase was shown by Freed (1965) to increase in the muscle of *Carassius auratus* during cold acclimatization. Cholinesterase in the brain of *Fundulus heteroclitus* changes in such a way that the optimum level of activity is maintained regardless of the ambient temperature (Baslow and Nigrelli, 1964). Studies with the isolated enzyme seem to show that warmer-water species have a more heat-stable enzyme as well, although work by Siebert, Schmidt *et al.* (1960), has shown that the thermal stabilities of eight different enzymes from the muscle of *Gadus morhua* do not differ appreciably from those of the same enzymes from mammals, 50% destruction occurring only at temperatures above 30°.

Earlier reports of metabolic adjustments which compensate for temperature change have been reviewed by Fry (1957).

Metabolic activity in mammals is governed to a large extent by the activity of the thyroid gland. In some fish, the thyroid seems to act as a temperature-compensator, since the follicular cell height, usually accepted as a measure of hormone output, increases at lower temperatures (Swift, 1959, 1960, quoted by A. D. Woodhead and P. M. J. Woodhead, 1965: *Salmo trutta*; Drury and Eales, 1968: *Salvelinus fontinalis*). However, the phenomenon does not seem to be universal, since no relationship between water temperature and thyroid activity has been found in *Carassius auratus* (Klicka, 1965) or *Gadus morhua* (A. D. Woodhead and P. M. J. Woodhead, 1965).

As stated in the introduction to this section, the upper and lower temperatures which narcotize or kill a fish can be changed by acclimatization. Tsukuda (1960) found that *Lebistes reticulatus* shows a rise in both the heat- and cold-coma temperatures of 2·2° for a 10° rise in acclimatization temperature. The lower lethal temperature of *Carassius auratus* was found by Roots and Prosser (1962) to be 10°, 5° or 1°, after acclimatization to, respectively, 35°, 25° and 15°. Both groups of authors believed that acclimatization involves some modification to the nervous system, and as usual there are differences between species in the amount of acclimatization possible (Tsukuda, 1961).

The temperature tolerance of *Carassius auratus* can be extended by the addition of cholesterol or phospholipid to the diet, but their effectiveness varies with the season (Irvine, Newman and Hoar, 1957). The mechanism is unknown.

Workers quoted by Roots and Prosser (1962) have shown that acclimatization to high temperatures takes place relatively rapidly, over a period of about a day, while complete adjustment to lower temperatures may take as many as 20 days. Once acquired, high temperature tolerance is remarkably persistent. Loeb and Wasteneys (1912) showed that the resistance against damage at 35° acquired by keeping *Fundulus* sp. for two days at 27° is not lost or even weakened if they are then kept for 33 subsequent days at 10 to 14°, or for 14 days at 0·4°.

The behaviour of a fish in response to a change in temperature may vary according to its biological condition. For example, the autumnal drop in the temperature of the Aral Sea causes *Abramis brama* to cease feeding and commence the winter migration—but only if they are well fed. Undernourished individuals continue to feed and remain on the feeding grounds (Nikolsky, 1963).

(d) Proteins

Up to now we have considered in general terms the responses of fish to different temperatures. Specific observations on chemical constituents are not numerous, but where they reveal changes in the stability of various molecules they are of considerable interest.

'Structural' proteins (actin and myosin) when extracted from the muscle of cold-water fish such as *Gadus morhua* alter from the native state and aggregate within an hour at room temperature. It is therefore surprising that these proteins in the living bodies of warm water species are able to exist indefinitely at the same temperature without harm. Ueda, Shimizu and Simidu (1964) studied the phenomenon and concluded that the temperature of the water in which the fish usually live controls the thermal denaturation temperature of the isolated protein. *Eopsetta grigorjewi*, *Gadus macrocephalus* and *Argentina semifasciata* prefer an environmental temperature of 2° to 3°, and their actomyosins show a change of viscosity after 30 minutes at 25°. *Trachurus japonicus* and *Cypselurus agoo* normally inhabit water at 14° to 17°, and their actomyosins change after 30 minutes at 30°, while the same proteins of *Histiophorus orientalis*, which lives at 19° to 21°, require a temperature of 35° to alter their state within the same period. Ohsawa and Tsukuda (1964) concluded that adaptation to a change in temperature does not concern a few isolated systems, but is fundamental to all tissues and cells of the organism. They took as a working hypothesis that the properties of tissue proteins are governed by the environmental temperature at which they have been synthesized.

Only in connective tissue protein is it possible to link thermal changes with actual chemical constitution. The first sign of a thermal change in collagen is that it suddenly shrinks, as for instance when skin, which is rich in collagen, is slowly heated. Gustavson (1953) was the first to show that warm-water fish have a higher skin shrinkage temperature than fish from cold water, and used data by Åqvist to show that there is actually more of the amino acid hydroxyproline present in the collagen of the warm-water fish, while that of cattle contains more still. The unique properties of collagen—its mechanical toughness and inelasticity and its chemical stability—are due to the presence of hydroxyproline, which occurs only in traces in ordinary muscle tissue. Takahashi and Yokoyama (1954b) demonstrated that there is a direct proportion between the hydroxyproline content of a collagen and its shrinkage temperature. Their results are shown in Fig. 79, each point relating to a different species; the lowest shrinkage temperature is shown by *Theragra chalcogramma* and the highest by *Cyprinus*

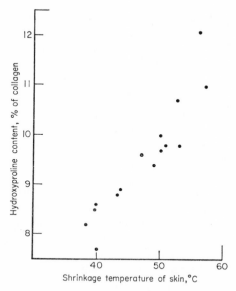

FIG. 79. Relationship between the shrinkage temperature of the skin of different species of fish and the hydroxyproline content of the collagen. Redrawn from the data of Takahashi and Yokoyama (1954b), reproduced by courtesy of Professor T. Takahashi and the Japanese Society of Scientific Fisheries.

carpio. Rigby (1968) showed that the lowest shrinkage temperature, coupled with the lowest hydroxyproline, proline and glycine contents are found in the skin of *Chionodraco kathleenae*, an 'ice-fish' (see p. 177) from the Antarctic, where the ambient temperature does not rise above 3°. It remains to be seen whether a cold-water fish habituated to a higher temperature than usual will gradually incorporate more hydroxyproline into its collagen.

When mammals age, the intermolecular cross-linking progressively increases in the collagen, which therefore becomes more stable. The collagen of fish has not been investigated in this respect, but Nakagome, Tsuchiya *et al.* (1965a,b), found that as various species of tuna aged, they seemed to prefer higher water temperatures. This observation is consistent with greater stability of the collagen—again, further work is needed.

(e) *Lipids*

Lovern (1938b) showed that lower temperatures result in greater unsaturation (more double bonds) in the body lipids of *Anguilla anguilla*, and vice versa. He pointed out (Lovern, 1950) that at higher temperatures the bodily activity increases and requires a correspondingly greater expenditure of energy, so that less dietary lipid will be available for storage. However, this is not the only factor involved.

It will have become clear by now that most changes in the lipids of fish have their origin in the diet, and the present factor seems to be no exception. The fatty acid composition of a blue-green alga was investigated by Holton, Blecker and Onore (1964), and found to change with the environmental temperature. Farkas and Herodek (1964) showed that the unsaturation of the lipids of crustacean plankton in Lake Balaton increases as the temperature drops, and decreases again in the summer time (Fig. 80). The effect of this on the lipid of the plankton, and so presumably of the predator fish, is to keep the melting point below that of the water temperature, and so maintain flexibility and motility. The fatty acid composition of the plankton changes more during the year in a small lake than in a large one, since the temperature fluctuation is greater.

J. G. Hunter (unpublished, quoted by Hoar and Cottle, 1952b) reported an average change in iodine value (a measure of unsaturation) of 0·5 unit per 1° change in acclimatization temperature in the body lipids of *Carassius auratus*, and Hoar and Cottle (1952b) found a change of similar magnitude in the same species. Other authors who related an increased unsaturation or decreased melting point of the

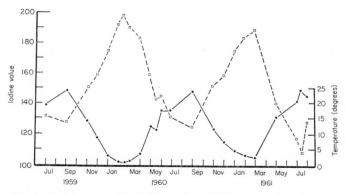

FIG. 80. Seasonal changes in the iodine values of the lipids of crustacean plankton (broken line) and water temperature (continuous line) in Lake Balaton, 1959-1961. After Farkas and Herodek (1964), reproduced by courtesy of Dr T. Farkas and the Rockefeller Press.

body lipids to lower water temperatures are Lewis (1962), Privol'nev and Brizinova (1964: fish in general) and Knipprath and Mead (1965, 1968: *Salmo gairdnerii* and *Carassius auratus*, respectively). Johnston and Roots (1964: *Carassius auratus*) showed a similar change in the lipids of the brain.

Hoar and Cottle (1952a) could discern no relationship between the tolerance of *Carassius auratus* to cold and the degree of unsaturation of the body lipids, but found that the resistance to both low and high temperatures can be modified by feeding diets containing high concentrations of certain fatty acids. Reiser, Stevenson *et al.* (1963), also reported no significant influence of low or high temperature on the unsaturation of the lipids of both marine and freshwater fish, but noted that lauric and myristic acids (saturated) are absorbed from the diet at 23° but not at 13°.

While the picture is not therefore completely clear, it seems likely that temperature does affect the lipid composition of fish, at least partly through the diet. The change is of benefit, since at higher temperatures the protein-lipid-calcium complex which forms the various cellular membranes will be more stable (Hoar and Cottle, 1952a,b; Johnston and Roots, 1964). According to Heilbrunn (quoted by Hoar and Cottle, 1952b), the essential feature of thermal death is the disorganization of the membrane structure, though Lewis's view (1962) is that many of the life processes can continue only if the cell lipids have a suitable viscosity, which is changed, of course, by a change of temperature.

(f) Minerals and resistance to freezing

The maintenance of various inorganic substances at certain levels within the fish obviously requires a delicately balanced mechanism, where concentrations in the surrounding water differ from those in the body. The mechanism requires energy and is known to place some strain upon the fish, because a normally fatal stress may not cause death if the ions in the water are similar to the concentrations in the tissues (Phillips, Podoliak *et al.*, 1964: *Salmo trutta*). A change of temperature may stress the fish sufficiently to upset the ionic balance. For example, a sudden cooling causes the muscle cells to lose potassium and gain sodium, perhaps by depressing the "sodium pump" mechanism, which normally extrudes sodium from the cell (Eliassen, Leivestad and Møller, 1960).

When *Cyprinus carpio* are acclimatized to various temperatures between 4° and 33°, the concentrations of plasma chloride and calcium increase steadily with rise of temperature, and sodium rises to a maximum at 27°. Potassium and magnesium concentrations show no consistency of behaviour (Houston and Madden, 1968). The interpretation of these observations is uncertain. Platner (1950) reported that the serum magnesium rises when *Carassius auratus* are exposed to low temperatures. At the same time the blood is diluted by an influx of water (a similar dilution was reported by Phillips, Podoliak *et al.*, 1964, when *Salmo trutta* were suddenly cooled), and Platner considered that the magnesium has been 'washed' from the red blood cells by the more dilute suspending medium. In *Petromyzon fluviatilis*, a reduction in temperature reduces the daily urine output and so presumably the permeability of the fish to fresh water. The capacity of the kidneys to reabsorb ions in order to retain them in the body is also reduced at lower temperatures, but the chloride concentration of the urine is about the same because of the smaller daily volume (Wikgren, 1953).

Considerable interest attaches to the osmotic behaviour of marine fish at very low temperatures, since there is evidence of an influx of ions which can prevent them from being killed by freezing in polar waters. The blood of most fish freezes at about $-0.8°$, but sea-water at the bottom of some fjords may be as cold as $-1.7°$ or even less. If fish swimming in water at $-1.7°$ are touched with an ice-cube, they go into convulsions, stiffen, and gradually become white as the ice propagates, although the surrounding water is not affected (Scholander, van Dam *et al.*, 1957: *Lycodes turneri, Liparis koefoedi, Icelus spatula*). These workers found that fish which usually inhabit the bottoms of cold fjords are supercooled, but are in little danger of freezing because the floating ice never reaches them. On the other hand, the plasma of *Myoxocephalus scorpius*, shallow-water fish from the same region, will not freeze until a temperature of $-1\cdot5°$ or $-1\cdot6°$ has been reached, so that where there is a danger of the fish coming into direct contact with the ice, the plasma freezing point is depressed almost to that of the sea. The plasma of *Gadus ogac* from the same region freezes at $-1\cdot47°$ in the winter time when ice is about, but in the summer the plasma freezing point of both species rises to $-0\cdot8°$. At the onset of winter, when the freezing point drops, there is little change in the concentration of chloride, and Scholander, van Dam *et al.* (1957), suggested that non-protein nitrogen might help to prevent freezing in sub-zero sea-water.

Eliassen, Leivestad and Møller (1960) found that lowering the water temperature from $10°$ to $-1\cdot5°$ causes a rise both in the total osmolarity and the chloride concentration of the plasma, both in natural surroundings and in aquaria (*Cyclopterus lumpus, Anarrhichas minor, Drepanopsetta platessoides*). When *Myoxocephalus scorpius* are cooled in this way over a period of 8 weeks, the freezing point drops from $-0\cdot6°$ to about $-0\cdot9°$, so that in this species acclimatization does not bring full protection to the fish, which are supercooled below $-0\cdot9°$ and so are in danger of being 'seeded' by accidental contact with ice. Most, but not all, of the depression of the freezing point of the plasma can be explained on the basis of increased chloride concentration.

Umminger (1968) acclimatized *Fundulus heteroclitus* to $20°$, $10°$, $2°$ and $-1°$, and found that after a time at $2°$ there is a 41% increase in the serum nitrogen, 44% in calcium, 73% in cholesterol, and the glucose, well known as an 'anti-freeze' agent, shows no less than a 119% increase. The supercooled fish at $-1°$ show a 51% increase in bicarbonate and a further increase in the glucose. Altogether, the glucose increases by 440% from $85\,\text{mg}\%$ in the serum at $20°$ to $458\,\text{mg}\%$ at $-1°$, so an adaptive resistance to freezing obviously occurs in this species.

Much work has been done by the Woodheads on the response of *Gadus morhua* to low temperatures (Woodhead and Woodhead, 1959, 1964; P. M. J. Woodhead and A. D. Woodhead, 1965). During the winter months, temperatures between $5°$ and $10°$ are preferred, and the fish usually avoid water at $2°$ or below. However, in the summer, they were observed to enter colder water without, apparently, showing any alteration in their plasma ion concentrations. If they enter such water in the winter time, the plasma sodium, potassium and chloride increase by up to 25%. Since there is considerable evidence that *Gadus morhua* are killed by low temperatures as such, without actually being frozen, the Woodheads regarded the rise in salt concentrations not as an adaptation to low temperatures but as a breakdown in control of the internal milieu which is bound, sooner or later, to end in death. In the winter of 1963, temperatures fell to exceptionally low values in the North Sea, and dead fish were reported over wide areas. Survivors at the time were found to have high serum sodium values, sometimes twice the normal, and it seemed therefore as though the osmoregulatory mechanism had begun to fail.

The difference between summer and winter fish has not so far been explained, neither is it certain whether the increase in plasma ions is adaptational or a change presaging death. The observations, however, seem clear : there is no difference between the plasma salt concentrations of fish caught at 5°, 4°, or 2°, but where the temperature is below 2° the values rise.

For a full account of osmoregulation in fish the reader is referred to "Fish Physiology", at present in preparation (Academic Press, London and New York).

(g) *Miscellany*

Reference has already been made to the various 'ice-fish' (p. 177, Figs. 68 and 69), which live in the Antarctic, where the high level of oxygen in the water renders blood haemoglobin less vital. These species transport all the oxygen their tissues need by means of plasma only (Ruud, 1954), so one might expect a series of species carrying progressively less haemoglobin as the temperature of the normal habitat fell. Tyler (1960) has in fact shown that *Trematomus borchgrevinki* and *Notothenia larsoni*, both Antarctic species, have red blood cell counts of 0·71 and 0·39 millions per cubic mm, respectively, while among the usual higher fish counts of less than 1 million are uncommon—teleosts usually have counts of between 1 and 2 millions. The haemoglobin contents of the two species are respectively 3·6 and 3·5 g/100 ml, the temperate teleost level being 7 to 12 g/100 ml, so that there do seem to be grounds for believing that there is an intermediate stage between the true 'bloodless' fish and normal.

Kooyman (1963) examined four species of *Trematomus* from the Antarctic, and found red blood cell counts ranging from 0·74 to 1·19 millions per cubic mm and haemoglobin contents of 2·5 to 5·3% —again rather low values. Determinations of red blood cells and haemoglobin in several other Antarctic fish by Everson and Ralph (1968) show nothing remarkable apart from one species, *Parachaenichthys georgianus*, which yields values of only 0·212 millions and 0·8% respectively. This species is therefore a truly intermediate form, and the Chaenichthidae may be regarded as the extreme forms of a series with diminishing haemoglobin contents.

Low haemoglobin values are not found in all polar fish, but Scholander and van Dam (1957) analysed the blood from four Arctic species and found low iron concentrations in two of them.

The blood sugar may be affected by the temperature. That of *Opsanus tau* is inversely related, either under natural conditions (Schuh and Nace, 1961) or in an aquarium (Nace and Schuh, 1961). While one may envisage a decrease in the requirements of sugar at low temperature, so that less is taken from the blood stream by the tissues, the blood sugar level in these fish kept at low temperatures often drops to normal in the summer season without change of temperature, so other factors are involved as well (Nace, Moule and Schuh, 1964).

The mechanisms or purposes of some other changes cannot even be guessed at. Macleod and Simpson (1927) referred to a rapid change-over in the livers of dogfish, which are laden with oil while the fish live in cold water, but which become filled with glycogen when they pass into warm water. V. S. Black (unpublished, quoted by Hoar and Cottle, 1952b) noticed that the water content of muscle in *Carassius auratus* is 80% if the fish are habituated to temperatures between 2° and 11°, but 82% at temperatures above this range. Parvatheswararao (1967) found increases in the water contents of brain, liver and muscle on warm acclimatization of *Etroplus maculatus*.

Free amino acids in fish muscle extracts were studied by Schaefer (1962), using paper chromatography. Large concentrations of beta-alanine and hydroxyproline are found in fish from the Iceland-Greenland area, and nearly all fish rich in beta-alanine have been caught in cold waters. The trimethylamine oxide contents of eight species of fish are higher if the fish have been caught in Arctic waters rather than in the North Sea (Shewan, 1951). Similarly, *Gadus morhua* from northern areas contain more thiamine and riboflavin than specimens from warmer areas (Novikova, 1952, quoted by Higashi, 1961).

Parvatheswararao (1967) found that the ascorbic acid content of *Etroplus maculatus* increases by 89% on cold acclimatization and decreases by 28% in a warmer environment, and regarded this as temperature compensation which raised or lowered the metabolic rate by decreasing or increasing the susceptibility of the cells to fatigue. It is perhaps worth pointing out that rats habituated to a cold environment also increase their synthesis and storage of ascorbic acid (Dugal and Thérien, 1947), although here, of course, the temperature of the tissues does not actually change.

CHAPTER 5

DEPLETION

A. General

Unlike most terrestrial animals, the majority of fish experience severe depletion for a part of every year of their lives. They are therefore unusually well adapted to mobilizing their body constituents as fuel for survival, and Siebert, Schmitt and Bottke (1964) have concluded that the large quantities of catheptic (autolytic) enzymes present in fish muscle are there in readiness for such periods of depletion.

We have already seen (p. 33) that the physical support obtained from their environment enables fish to conduct their daily affairs without much recourse to their white muscle, which is used only in pursuit or escape, and without so much need of haemoglobin, since their basal energy consumption is low. For the same reason, they are able to withstand astonishingly long periods of total abstention from food, although this period is reduced at higher ambient temperatures. Love (1958c) found that *Gadus morhua* survived for 78 days at 14° without food, but were much less depleted after 100 days at 9° (Love, Robertson and Strachan, 1968) and in fact could survive more than 195 days at this temperature (Love, 1969, unpublished). *Clupea harengus* survived for 129 days at 6° to 12° (Wilkins, 1967b), and *Amia calva* managed to survive for 20 months without food (Smallwood, 1916). *Anguilla anguilla* started to die only after they had been starved for 3 years (Boëtius and Boëtius, 1967), and *Protopterus*, the lung fish, which slows down its metabolic rate to a low level during aestivation, when it is buried in the mud of dried-up ponds, were able to live in this state for even longer—three and a half years, according to the work of Smith (1935). The record so far is held by a male silver eel (*Anguilla anguilla*) which survived for 1515 days (over 4 years) at 15° without food, during which time it lost no less than 76% of its weight (J. Boëtius, personal communication, 1968). No doubt at a lower temperature it could have held out for even longer.

Different organs are not depleted at the same rate. While liver and muscle are affected soon after the cessation of feeding, some organs

222

do not show measurable changes even up to the point of death. For example, the brain of *Gadus morhua,* which contains 8·8% lipid, shows no reduction in this figure even when the fish are dying of starvation, although the lipids of the liver have fallen from about 40% right down to 2% (Love, 1958c). During the starvation of *Clarias lazera,* Yanni (1962) observed that the quantities of lipid in the heart and gills, as well as in the brain, do not change either. Measuring the weight loss of various organs of *Cyprinus carpio* during starvation, Creach and Cournède (1965) found that during the first two months the exploitation of the organs occurs in the following order: intestine, liver, kidneys, spleen, muscle and heart. After eight months the liver and kidneys are most affected, spleen and intestine less, and heart hardly at all.

Thus the brain and heart are allowed to retain virtually all of their constituents, so that their function is unimpaired. It is interesting to note that the same occurs in a species of desert lizard which is also subjected to depletion during its life: in this case, all tissues show a noticeable loss of protein and lipid during starvation apart from the brain, spinal cord, lungs and heart (Khalil and Abdel-Messeih, 1959).

Immature *Salmo gairdnerii* starved for 3 months show some atrophy of the adrenocortical tissue, and the thymus and spleen become involuted. The stomachs show marked atrophy (noted also in spawning *Salmo salar* by Gulland, 1898) with degeneration of the epithelium, which could presumably be used for nourishment. In addition, the liver degenerates to some extent, but the thyroid, kidney, heart and vascular system show no change (Robertson, Hane *et al.,* 1963).

While testes lose weight during starvation, maturing ovaries are able to increase in size during the first few months in which food is withheld from *Cyprinus carpio* (Creach and Cournède, 1965), but the developing eggs of *Salmo gairdnerii* are resorbed in numbers proportional to the severity of the starvation (Scott, 1962). Although partial depletion influences the number of eggs reaching maturity, it does not influence their size, which is normal.

Another gross manifestation of starvation is to be seen in the gall bladder, which becomes greatly enlarged (Love, 1958c: *Gadus morhua*). Presumably it discharges its contents only under the stimulus of food, lacking which the bile continues to accumulate. Gohar and Latif (1959, quoted by Gohar and Latif, 1961a) reported likewise that it becomes progressively denser. At the same time, *free* amino acids and proteins precipitable by trichloroacetic acid disappear from the bile

during the course of starvation (Creach, 1964: *Cyprinus carpio,
Leuciscus erythrophthalmus* and *Tinca tinca*).

Depletion of oil from the livers makes them appear small and red or
mottled, and in a non-fatty species like *Gadus morhua* the depletion of
protein from the muscle gives the flesh a soft, watery consistency,
while the usual bluish translucence gives place to a white opacity
which can be measured (Fig. 81). It is proportional to the degree of
starvation (Love, 1962b). Physical weakness is apparent in severely
starved fish, and a considerable amount of fluid is to be found within
the body cavity (Creach and Serfaty, 1965: *Cyprinus carpio*; Love,
unpublished: *Gadus morhua*).

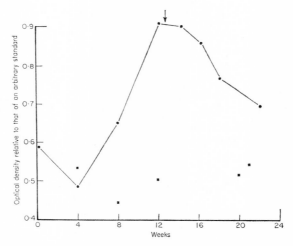

Fig. 81. Effect of starvation and subsequent feeding on the opacity of the muscle of
Gadus morhua. Starvation was begun at 0 weeks, and feeding was recommenced at the
point indicated by the arrow. The figures illustrated by square points relate to fish taken
from the same fishing ground as the starved captive fish at various times during the
experiment (controls). After Love (1962b), reproduced by courtesy of the International
Council for the Exploration of the Sea.

The weight loss in starving *Anguilla japonica* was shown by Inui
and Ohshima (1966) to be rectilinear over a period of 95 days, apart
from a sharp initial loss shown by eels caught in the summer, presumably due to the emptying of full stomachs. On the other hand,
Creach and Serfaty (1965) found that the weight of *Cyprinus carpio*
decreases asymptotically to 53% of the original value.

B. Inter-Relationships of Main Constituents

While we shall consider water, protein, lipid and minerals individually under separate headings, it is useful at the outset to study their relationships with one another during starvation. A familiar snare for the unwary appears again, and one must be quite sure whether constituents are expressed as total gain or loss per animal, or as a concentration in the tissue. Thus, Phillips, Livingston and Dumas (1960) reported an increase in the ash of *Salvelinus fontinalis* during starvation, which appeared because the whole fish had been analysed, and the proportion of flesh and viscera had decreased in relation to bones. However, if bone- and skin-free muscle is analysed, it is found that the proportion of ash in fact declines (Love, 1958c: *Gadus morhua*).

The inter-relationships of the main constituents of the flesh vary between species according to where the reserve lipid is stored. 'Fatty' fish such as *Clupea harengus* store most of it in the muscle, and great changes in the concentration occur there during the year. 'Non-fatty' fish like the Gadidae store it in the liver, so the situation in the muscle is different as we shall see in a moment.

Taking the muscle tissue of fatty fish first, there is a striking relationship between lipid and water, an increase in the proportion of one leading to a decrease in the other, so that the sum is approximately constant. The relationship was noted as long ago as 1888 (Atwater, 1888, quoted by Jacquot, 1961) in species of *Alosa* and *Scomber*. In more recent times, further work has been done by Brandes and Dietrich, who showed "fat water lines" for *Clupea harengus* (1953b), *Sebastes marinus* (1956) and two species of *Anarhichas* (1958); Fig. 82 illustrates lines for all three genera. The proportions of lipid and water are similarly related in the flesh of *Scomber scombrus* (Anon., 1966c). Black and Schwartz (1950) noted that the sum of the two remained 'fairly' constant in *Sardinia ocellata*, and in *Scomber scombrus* it was shown to vary by no more than $\pm$ 1·8% (Coppini, 1967). Idler and Bitners (1959) found that the water content of *Oncorhynchus nerka* (whole body) increased from 60% to 77%, approximately, during the spawning migration, but that the sum of lipid plus water was still about 80%. Herrera and Muñoz (1957) plotted monthly values of water and lipid over a three-year period in *Sardina pilchardus*, the graphs revealing an obvious inverse relationship, water being maximal and lipid minimal in January or February of each year. The protein did not appear to change in this species, perhaps because the depletion was not severe enough, but it is clear that in some species it is consumed

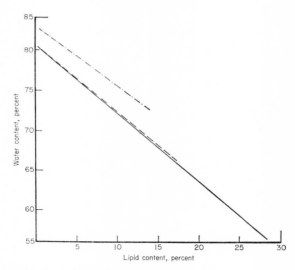

FIG. 82. Fat-water lines for various species of fish. —·—·—· *Anarhichas* (average of *A. minor* and *A. lupus*); ——— *Sebastes marinus*; ——— *Clupea harengus*. After Brandes and Dietrich (1958), reproduced by courtesy of Dr. C. H. Brandes.

after the lipid has dropped below a critical level. Greene (1919) found that the water in the muscle of *Oncorhynchus tschawytscha* migrating upstream increases from 63·2% to 79·7%, and the protein decreases, but only in the final stage, from 17% to 13·7%. Parker and Vanstone (1966) showed that *Oncorhynchus gorbuscha* lose lipid at first during a period of restricted food supply, and that protein is consumed later on. With moderate starvation and lipid loss, the body weight is maintained through the uptake of water.

A good fat-water line is given by Takahashi and Shiokawa (1953) for the *skin* tissue of various fish species.

A loss of protein occurring at the extremity of depletion in *Trachurus trachurus*, and a steady loss of lipid preceding this is clearly shown in Fig. 83, which illustrates also the inverse lipid-water relationship. The proportion of ash seems not to change here.

While the lipid and water together make up *about* 80% of the constituents, the sum is not in fact constant, but rises as the lipid rises. Iles and Wood (1965) took figures from the data of two other authors to illustrate the relationship in *Clupea harengus*, and the figures are reproduced in Table XXXIII. The proportion of protein plus ash declines as the lipid increases in this species, and similar behaviour is revealed in a graph by F. Villmark (unpublished, 1964, quoted by Braekkan, 1965: *Scomber scombrus*).

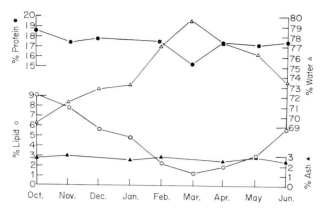

Fig. 83. Seasonal variation in the four principal constituents of *Trachurus trachurus*. Note how the protein decreases only at the extremity of starvation. After Arevalo (1948), reproduced by courtesy of the Instituto Español de Oceanografia.

TABLE XXXIII. THE CONTENT OF "LIPID PLUS WATER" IN THE MUSCLE OF CLUPEA HARENGUS IN RELATION TO THE LIPID CONTENT (after Iles and Wood, 1965).

	Per cent	
	Lipid plus water	
Lipid	A	B
0	80·3	79·4
10	81·8	80·6
20	83·3	81·8
30	84·8	83·0

A: data of Brandes and Dietrich. B: data of Wood.

The sum of the protein and ash may change according to the lipid content, but the proportions of the two do not vary, according to the work of Phillips, Podoliak *et al.* (1963), who showed that in *Salvelinus fontinalis* and *Cristivomer namaycush* the dry lipid-free residue consisted of 86·5% protein and 13·5% ash, no matter what the water and lipid contents had been.

The muscle of non-fatty fish behaves differently in that there is a time-lag before the gross effects of depletion appear. Figure 45 (p. 91) shows that the water content of *Gadus morhua* increases during a period of natural depletion, but if well-fed fish are starved artificially in an aquarium the water content does not in fact rise until several weeks have elapsed (Fig. 84). This is presumably because the fish at first consumes lipid from the liver, and starts to mobilize muscle protein only when this source of energy has been nearly used up. After that, as protein is utilized, water moves in to take its place.

No mention of a "protein-water line" for the muscle of non-fatty fish, comparable with Brandes and Dietrich's "fat-water line" for fatty fish (Fig. 82, p. 226) has been mentioned in the literature, but such a

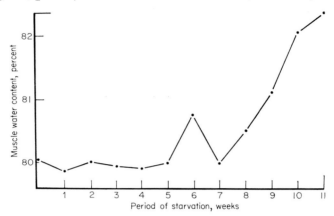

FIG. 84. Muscle water content of *Gadus morhua* during an extended period of starvation in an aquarium at 9°. Note the lag period during which the fish is presumed to be using carbohydrate and liver lipid, before the water content starts to rise. After Love (unpublished).

relationship does exist and is now presented (Fig. 85). It illustrates once again the validity of water determinations in assessing the condition of fish, but the delay during which liver lipid is being used should always be borne in mind.

In severe starvation the water content of this species may rise to as much as 88%* (Love, 1958c) with a corresponding fall in protein. The lipid content of the muscle, even in fish which have been well fed, is only about 1%, so changes in this constituent can be virtually discounted. Nonetheless, a measurable seasonal cycle has been discovered in the lipid of *Gadus morhua* by Dambergs (1964), even though the values traverse a total range of only about 0·1% (Fig. 86). There is no question here of being able to detect a "fat-water line", since the protein-water effect predominates.

Although one may therefore think of a fat-water line in fatty fish and a protein-water line in non-fatty fish, the two groups resemble one another in that a bulk of lipid, whether in the flesh or the liver, is

* See footnote on p. 230.

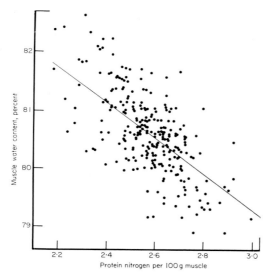

FIG. 85. "Protein-water line" for 275 specimens of *Gadus morhua*. The correlation is highly significant at the 0·01% level. Correlation coefficient = −0·632. After Love (unpublished: Greenland expedition, 1966).

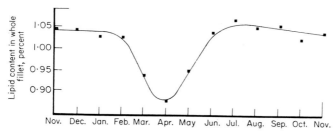

FIG. 86. Seasonal variation in the muscle lipid of *Gadus morhua*. After Dambergs (1964), reproduced by courtesy of the author and the Fisheries Research Board of Canada.

used up first and protein is drawn upon afterwards. It seems likely, though no evidence has yet been produced, that fish would tend to draw upon their protein reserves more readily when building up gonads than during simple depletion.

Two anomalies should be mentioned. Gras, Reynaud *et al.* (1967a), published a graph showing the levels of protein and water in the muscle of *Salmo gairdnerii* over a six-month period which included the spawning season. Predictably, the protein values dropped sharply for 4 weeks—but during this time the water content did not change.

Further work is needed to explain this. Even stranger is the behaviour of immature *Anguilla anguilla* kept in captivity, which lose weight as a result of loss of protein only and not lipid (Lovern, 1939). The lipid concentration therefore appears to rise as the creatures are starved— an unusual response. The reason why these eels should hold on to their lipid reserves with such tenacity is a mystery. Once again we are unable to generalize completely about a phenomenon, because it is not universal to all species.

C. Individual Constituents

1. *Water*

An increase in tissue water during starvation is common to animals in general, and has, for example, been observed in cockroaches (Wharton, Wharton and Lola, 1965), mice (Goldspink, 1966) and man, the latter either as a result of experiment (Keys, Brozek *et al.*, 1947) or of confinement in a prison camp (Mollison, 1946). In the case of rats, however, there seems to be a slight decrease in body water when food is withheld for 168 hours, the animals having an unrestricted supply of water (Annegers, 1954).

In *Oncorhynchus nerka* migrating upstream the water content of the whole body was observed by Idler and Bitners (1959) to rise from 60% to 77%, but this was a 'fat-water' relationship, and the sum of the two constituents remained at about 80%. In this species the water content never seems to rise above 80% as it would do in non-fatty species.

Values of 86% and 88% water have been measured in the muscle of starved *Gadus morhua* by Sutton (1968) and Love (1958c), respectively*, and Sorvachev (1957) increased the water content of *Cyprinus carpio* muscle to 88% by starving them for 3 months in an aquarium at 12° to 15°. After 8 months at 20° the water content of this species had risen from 78·9% to 91% (Creach and Cournède, 1965), and that of *Carassius carassius* rose from 78·9% to up to 93·3% after 105 days at 27° (Borek, 1958). The record appears to be held by *Hippoglossoides platessoides* depleted naturally (Templeman and Andrews, 1956). These fish, found in the Grand Bank area in water at −1° to 0°, become progressively more depleted as the size increases, and the muscle of

---

* The high value of 93·4% has been obtained in the same species in the writer's laboratory (1969, unpublished) by starving a large male during the period of gonad development.

the most 'jellied' specimen investigated was found to consist of 2·83% protein, 0·06% lipid and the astounding value of 96·18% water. The ability of such a fish to swim is a source of wonder.

2. *Proteins and Amino Acids*

As we might expect, the impact of starvation is felt sooner in active than in sluggish fish. Thus the electrophoretic pattern of the blood proteins of *Salmo trutta* is seen to change after starvation for 30 days, while a period of 6 months is needed to bring about the same change in *Cyprinus carpio* (Drilhon, 1954). Further, a considerable reduction in the concentration of blood serum protein was found in *Scyllium canicula* after starvation for only 15 days, which is not long enough to affect such fish as *Anguilla anguilla* (Cordier, Barnoud and Brandon, 1957).

Since mobilization of the protein of fast-swimming fish is correspondingly more rapid, the activity of catheptic enzymes is greater, and more rapid autolysis of the muscle of such species as *Scomber scombrus*, as compared with *Cyprinus carpio* or *Gadus morhua* was observed by Bailey, Koran and Bradley (1942).

As mentioned above, the electrophoretic pattern of *Salmo trutta* serum changes during starvation (Drilhon, 1954), and differences have also been demonstrated in *Astroconger myriaster* (Fujiya, 1961), *Cyprinus carpio* (Sorvachev, 1957), *Gadus aeglefinus*, *Gadus morhua* and *Gadus virens* (Khailov, 1962), *Petromyzon marinus* (Thomas and McCrimmon, 1964) and, incidentally, in amphibia and reptiles also (Dessauer and Fox, 1956).

The changes show that certain fractions are utilized preferentially. Sorvachev (1957) studied the protein fractions of the blood of *Cyprinus carpio* during a fast of 6 months, and found that the total protein concentration dropped from 3·9 to 2·8%. The decrease occurred in the first instance at the expense of the albumins, and later at the expense of the α- and β-globulins. The γ-globulins were not utilized in this way, and showed an increase in absolute values, which suggests that either the blood volume decreased or that γ-globulin entered the blood stream as a result of protein breakdown in other tissues. The changes in the various fractions are shown in Fig. 87.

Khailov (1962) observed a similar increase in γ-globulin and a decrease in all the other fractions in the serum of *Gadus aeglefinus*, *Gadus morhua* and *Gadus virens* caught in the winter, when compared with summer-caught fish. He believed that the cycle of changes in blood proteins results from the historical reactions of the fish to typical annual changes in the environment, and that they will repeat

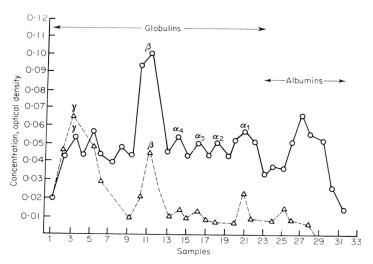

Fig. 87. Protein fractions in the serum of *Cyprinus carpio* (○———○) after 6 months of feeding and (△———△) after 6 months of starvation. Note how the γ-globulin is the only fraction which does not decrease during starvation. After Sorvachev (1957).

themselves to a large extent independently of the actual availability of food at the time. Kosmina (1966) found a decrease in the blood serum albumin of starving *Lota lota* after an initial rise (Fig. 91, p. 235), but a steady increase in the *relative* content of globulin. This phenomenon therefore is clearly established, with albumin the principal victim of starvation. It is interesting to note that when starved rats are allowed to re-commence feeding, a substantial proportion of protein newly synthesized in the liver is albumin (Wilson, Hill and Hoagland, 1967).

The seasonal reduction in the serum protein of *Limanda herzensteini* and *Salmo gairdnerii* is reflected in a reduction of the protein of the fluid which bathes the otoliths. It is this factor which probably causes winter accretions to the otoliths (see p. 159) to embody less protein than summer accretions, giving rise to the alternating light and dark rings when a section of the otolith is viewed (Mugiya, 1964).

Turning now to the solid tissues of the body, we find that, in common with mammals, fish break down contractile proteins more readily than connective tissue proteins during depletion. Collagen, the principal connective tissue protein, has a stable molecule, and since it is but little mobilized, the relative quantity increases during the starvation of chickens (Fisher and Griminger, 1963) and sheep (Holmes, 1965). Some collagen appears to be mobilized from the skin of mice during starvation (Harkness, Harkness and James, 1958; Sobel, Hewlett *et al.*, 1967), and atrophy of the epidermal layers of *Salmo gairdnerii* was observed by Robertson, Hane *et al.* (1963), but such mobilization is always less than that of other proteins. The *relative* changes in the proteins of *Pomolobus pseudoharengus* are strikingly illustrated in Figs. 88 and 89 by the use of amino acid analysis. Whole fish were analysed, and Fig. 88 shows the decline in aspartic acid and valine corresponding with the depletion of contractile and other proteins at the spawning season. In contrast, Fig. 89 shows the relative increase in hydroxyproline and hydroxylysine, both of which are found in the stable collagen and not in the other proteins.

As already described, there seems also to be an increase in the *absolute* quantity of skin collagen laid down during the spawning season of *Clupea harengus* and *Clupea pallasii*, but nothing is known about the mechanisms involved, and it is not possible to add anything to the earlier account (p. 102).

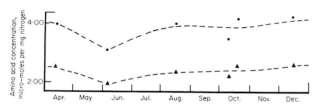

Fig. 88. Seasonal variation in (●) aspartic acid and (▲) valine in whole *Pomolobus pseudoharengus*. After Thompson and Farragut (1965), reproduced by courtesy of Dr. R. N. Farragut and the United States Bureau of Commercial Fisheries.

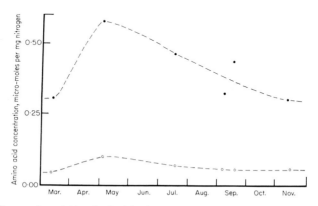

Fig. 89. Seasonal variation in (●) hydroxyproline and (○) hydroxylysine in whole *Pomolobus pseudoharengus*. The increase at the spawning season is relative, caused by the mobilization of other amino acids. After Thompson and Farragut (1965), reproduced by courtesy of Dr. R. N. Farragut and the United States Bureau of Commercial Fisheries.

A curious phenomenon came to light during studies on the depletion of the muscle proteins of *Gadus morhua*, which were kept for increasing periods at 9° without food. Whatever might have been the re-arrangement of different protein fractions during starvation, it was to be expected that the total protein would remain steady for a while and then start to decline once the liver lipid reserves had fallen below a certain value (p. 227). In actual fact, in all experiments carried out the muscle protein *increased* during the early stages of starvation before the decline set in, though no obvious change was occurring in the water content at the same time. In four experiments, maximum protein levels were observed 3 weeks after the beginning of starvation, and in the other two they occurred at around 4 weeks (Fig. 90).

The serum albumin of *Lota lota* has been shown by Kosmina (1966) to follow a similar course, with a maximum occurring about 3 weeks from the start (Fig. 91). Unless the maximum is the result of a change in blood volume, it seems likely that the additional protein comes from the liver. If liver lipid and carbohydrate are heavily drawn upon in starvation, it is not unreasonable to suppose that some of the

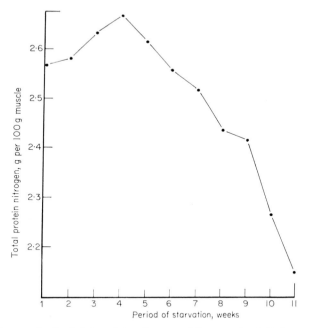

Fig. 90. Changes in the total protein nitrogen of the muscle of *Gadus morhua* during starvation at 9°. Note the increase during the first 4 weeks. After Robertson, Love and Cowie (1967), reproduced by courtesy of the Society of Chemical Industry.

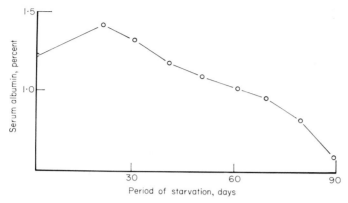

Fig. 91. Changes in the concentration of albumin in the serum of *Lota lota* during starvation. Note again the increase during the early stages. After Kosmina (1966), by whose courtesy the Figure is reproduced.

cellular material that contained them would become degraded and be transported elsewhere, though actual proof of this would be difficult.

Starvation of *Anguilla japonica* results in a slight rise in serum protein (Sano, 1962a), but since the non-protein nitrogen and haematocrit values increase as well (Sano, 1962b) the observation seems to reflect only a change in the water content of the blood. Also, as it occurs 3—5 days after the commencement of starvation, it is probably not related to the phenomena illustrated in Figs. 90 and 91.

A further effect, which may be part of the same mechanism of mobilization, has been observed at the same time. If the muscle of *Gadus morhua* (dissected free from myocommata) is homogenized in ice-cold 5% sodium chloride and centrifuged, then about 2·5 g of the protein nitrogen are found to dissolve in the salt solution and about 0·1 g to be insoluble, per 100 g of fresh muscle. If the fish are starved, the absolute quantity of insoluble protein nitrogen rises in a sharp peak to about 0·6 g per 100 g, during the first 2—4 weeks after the commencement of starvation. It then drops just as sharply. Over a 2-year period it was found that the phenomenon appears only if the fish are well fed and have recovered from spawning before the artificial starvation is imposed. If artificial starvation begins soon after the finish of the natural depletion due to spawning in the spring time of the year, then no peak appears. The phenomenon in spring and autumn is shown in Fig. 92.

If the appearance of this small insoluble fraction in the muscle corresponds with the mobilization of liver resources, the seasonal

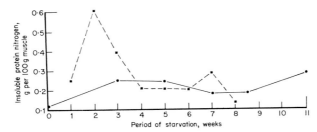

FIG. 92. Changes in the fraction of muscle protein (nitrogen) *in*soluble in chilled 5% NaCl during starvation of *Gadus morhua* at 9°. ■———■ Captured and starved from October onwards; ●———● Captured and starved from May onwards. After Love and Robertson (1967), reproduced by courtesy of the Society of Chemical Industry.

difference of Fig. 92 is to be expected, because very little carbohydrate or lipid reserves would remain in the liver in the spring, so mobilization, and further breakdown of the protein 'container', would not occur.

The appearance of the insoluble fraction is not the result of shock caused by the capture of the fish. Ironside and Love (1958) showed that it appears naturally in fish caught in late autumn and the beginning of winter (Table XXXIV). *Gadus morhua* become sexually mature on reaching about 75 cm in length, and it was noticed that those above this length acquire the insoluble protein fraction sooner and to a greater extent than the immature fish, which are less depleted (Fig. 45, p. 91). The insolubility is not a relative effect caused by the depletion of soluble protein, because the total protein changes little until maturation is well advanced (March). The results of starvation

TABLE XXXIV. SEASONAL CHANGES IN THE SALT-INSOLUBLE AND TOTAL PROTEIN NITROGEN IN TWO SIZE-GROUPS OF GADUS MORHUA (after Ironside and Love, 1958).

| | | g nitrogen/100 g tissue | |
	Size (cm)	Insoluble protein-N	Total protein-N
November	under 75	0·144	2·550
	over 75	0·450	2·577
January	under 75	0·255	2·456
	over 75	0·479	2·428
March	under 75	0·136	2·558
	over 75	0·392	2·308
April	all sizes	0·096	2·468
August	all sizes	0·104	2·585

imposed at a time when the gonads were inactive (Fig. 92) show that the phenomenon is caused by depletion, and is not brought on by hormones at the time of maturation.

A further peak of insoluble nitrogen appeared later during starvation. A small one is seen in Fig. 92, seven weeks after the commencement of starvation, and another example is illustrated in Fig. 93 (after 10 weeks) to show its reality and sharpness. Its presence is unexplained.

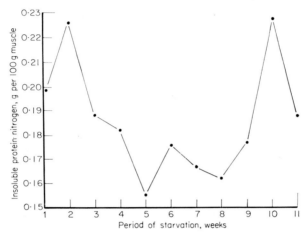

Fig. 93. Changes in the fraction of muscle protein (nitrogen) *insoluble* in chilled 5% NaCl, during starvation of *Gadus morhua* at 9° (from September onwards), showing the second peak (unexplained) at 10 weeks. After Robertson, Love and Cowie (1967), reproduced by courtesy of the Society of Chemical Industry.

Electrophoresis of muscle myogens (water-soluble proteins) shows nothing of interest during starvation, though occasionally one band has been seen to increase in intensity while another becomes paler (Dingle, Hines and Neelin, 1962: *Gadus morhua*). Robertson, Love and Cowie (1967) found nothing significant between the patterns of the myogens of the same species over a 10-week starvation period, and Uthe and Tsuyuki (1967) found no differences between young, adult and spawning lampreys, even when the latter were in poor condition and presumably depleted (*Ichthyomyzon unicuspis, Petromyzon marinus* and *Lampetra lamottei*).

The previous section gives some idea of the range of water contents resulting from extremes of depletion in different species, and Fig. 45 shows the range occurring in *Gadus morhua* from one ground under natural conditions. The range of total protein to be found in the latter species has been unusually well documented, six independent laboratories collaborating to analyse fish from different grounds at different times of the year. The combined reports are illustrated in Fig. 94, which shows an impressive range of values with an average of 2·871 g of protein nitrogen per 100 g of muscle. If we multiply the figures for protein nitrogen by 6*, to convert them into weights of actual protein, it appears that the protein content can extend from about 13% to 19% under natural conditions. The protein content of the muscle of the most severely starved *Hippoglossoides platessoides* reached the very low figure of 2·83% (Templeman and Andrews, 1956).

Most of the studies on combined amino acids relate to depletion at the spawning time, and show the selection of material for building up the gonads. Tables XX–XXII (pp. 100 and 101) showed that proline and glycine, which are present in high concentrations in the inert connective tissues of the body, decrease in the gonads as they grow in size, owing to their 'dilution' with egg or spermatic material, and increase in the muscle, as other more labile proteins are transported away. Straightforward depletion of the muscle at a time when the gonads of the fish are inactive would presumably do the same.

Apart from the papers by Creach and Serfaty (see below), published work on the *free* amino acids of fish during depletion also refers only to the depletion of maturation. Thus Jones (1954b) found that *free* lysine in *Gadus morhua* muscle reaches a seasonal maximum just before the spawning period, while the level of taurine becomes reduced. *Free* glutamic acid and glycine were also shown to be maximal at the spawning period (Jones, 1959a: *Pleuronectes microcephalus*). Cowey, Daisley and Parry (1962) found that the size of the *free* amino acid fraction as a whole, and the proportions of its constituents, do not alter markedly at any stage of the spawning migration of *Salmo salar*. Cowey (1965) commented that the result is unexpected, and indeed the experience with *Cyprinus carpio* kept in an aquarium without food has been quite different, considerable changes developing in the patterns of the plasma and the muscle.

Creach and Serfaty (1964) found that when *Cyprinus carpio* are kept in running water without food for 8 months, the *free* valine, leucine and isoleucine in the blood increases, while other *free* amino acids remain unchanged or diminished, the greatest decreases being shown by alanine, aspartic acid, glycine and serine.

Table XXXV shows the changes in the *free* amino acids in the blood of this species (Creach and Serfaty, 1965). It was noted in the same

---

* Bailey (1937) and Nottingham (1952) concluded that a nitrogen-protein conversion factor of 6·025 is more appropriate for fish muscle than the traditional 6·25.

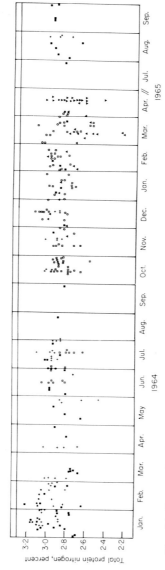

FIG. 94. Range of values for total protein nitrogen in *Gadus morhua* from different areas throughout the year. Six laboratories collaborated in the survey, accounting for six of the different symbols, while two extra symbols (▲ and ▼) denote especially-thin medium-sized fish and distant-water fish, respectively, both investigated by Laboratory no. 2. Anonymous (1966a), reproduced by courtesy of the Society for Analytical Chemistry.

TABLE XXXV. CHANGES IN THE FREE AMINO ACIDS OF THE BLOOD OF
CYPRINUS CARPIO AFTER STARVATION FOR 8 MONTHS
(after Creach and Serfaty, 1965)

	Increase or decrease, per cent
Alanine	− 50·3
Arginine	+ 4·6
Aspartic acid	− 63·4
Cystine	absent
Glutamic acid	− 21·3
Glycine	− 30·3
Histidine	− 30·7
Isoleucine	+ 29·5
Leucine	+ 45·0
Lysine	− 7·3
Methionine	− 17·0
Phenylalanine	− 9·1
Proline	+ 2·0
Serine	− 27·4
Threonine	+ 18·5
Tyrosine	− 47·3
Valine	+ 39·5

paper that the fish lose weight asymptotically, reaching the low level of 53% of their original weight after 13 months at 20°. Changes in the *free* amino acids of the blood have also been recorded by Chance (1962: *Oncorhynchus tschawytscha*), but starvation here was only of 24 hours' duration, so his results are not comparable with the others.

In 1966, Creach published tables showing the changes in the *free* amino acids of other organs of *Cyprinus carpio* after starvation for 8 months, and these are reproduced in Table XXXVI, apart from the results for cystine and ornithine, which were present, with one exception, only in traces.

It will be seen that the total *free* amino acids of muscle decrease to about 1/6 of their normal values, and most of the individual amino acids decrease also, especially glycine and histidine. In addition, the intestine shows decreases in most of the *free* amino acids and their total, iso-leucine being the exception in showing a large increase. On the other hand, many of the *free* amino acids of liver, kidney and spleen increase during starvation, especially leucine which increases in every organ investigated apart from the intestine.

Little can be learned in physiological terms from these figures, but the tremendous fall in *free* glycine in the muscle may relate to the non-synthesis or non-breakdown of collagen under these conditions. The behaviour of combined glycine was more informative (p. 101).

TABLE XXXVI. CHANGES IN THE FREE AMINO ACIDS OF VARIOUS ORGANS OF CYPRINUS CARPIO AFTER STARVATION FOR 8 MONTHS

(after Creach, 1966)

	Muscle		Liver		Kidney		Spleen		Intestine	
	A	B	A	B	A	B	A	B	A	B
Alanine	15·03	11·76	9·03	12·37	13·33	25·69	10·05	7·01	16·36	12·18
Arginine	2·34	tr	2·32	4·62	2·79	9·23	2·24	8·63	7·73	4·86
Aspartic acid	tr	tr	tr	tr	4·12	4·39	3·71	tr	2·83	3·29
Glutamic acid	5·18	2·99	37·73	17·10	20·73	19·38	17·16	3·12	16·74	13·23
Glycine	145·01	12·43	4·66	4·96	11·03	16·00	7·87	4·87	10·75	7·55
Histidine	96·10	2·01	tr	3·06	tr	3·51	tr	2·90	2·90	tr
Isoleucine	3·49	3·78	tr	2·67	2·85	8·27	2·05	8·41	4·31	16·26
Leucine	5·30	6·52	2·44	9·74	5·33	16·00	4·16	17·84	9·59	7·62
Lysine	15·03	6·64	3·81	9·49	5·64	19·38	4·16	16·62	11·27	7·10
Methionine	tr	tr	tr	tr	tr	3·11	tr	4·69	tr	tr
Phenylalanine	tr	tr	tr	3·23	tr	9·41	tr	8·46	6·63	3·36
Proline	tr	tr	4·35	5·56	tr	6·40	tr	9·76	tr	tr
Serine	4·08	2·19	2·92	3·29	5·33	10·15	4·74	tr	6·44	5·98
Threonine	6·29	2·13	6·06	3·06	6·85	9·23	6·40	tr	5·99	4·48
Tyrosine	tr	tr	tr	2·51	tr	4·84	2·37	5·50	3·22	2·32
Valine	3·73	4·63	tr	4·62	3·88	11·70	3·27	9·50	6·57	5·01
Total	301·58	55·08	75·45	86·28	81·88	176·69	68·18	107·01	111·33	93·24

A = control. B = after starvation for 8 months. Tr = present only in traces.

3. *Lipids*

While a steady depletion of lipid characterizes subsistence without food in almost all cases, the lipid content cannot necessarily be taken as a reliable index of the nutritional status of the fish. Lovern (1938b) showed that there was a direct relationship between the size of *Anguilla anguilla* and their lipid content, so an assessment of the status of this species would be difficult, as would that of *Trachurus trachurus*, which behaves similarly (Arevalo, 1948: Fig. 46, p. 92). However, the transport of lipids during mobilization may be seen in the *free* fatty acid content of the blood, which rises during starvation and maintains the raised level for a considerable period (Bilinski and Gardner, 1968: *Salmo gairdnerii*).

The selectivity of the fish in utilizing its lipid stores is more interesting, although information is scanty. Lovern (1934a) noticed that there is a drop in the proportions of the remaining C_{14} and C_{16} acids as the lipid stores of *Salmo salar* are drained off. This selectivity was considerably more marked in the males than in the females. *Clupea harengus* select the more highly unsaturated lipids when stores are being utilized (Lovern, 1938a) and the same would appear to be true of *Gadus morhua*, in which the iodine value (a measure of unsaturation) of the liver oil falls at the time of maximum depletion. The distribution of saturated fatty acids, however, changes little during the annual cycle (DeWitt, 1963). This arrangement does not apply to all species: the proportion of highly unsaturated fatty acids in the muscle of *Salmo gairdnerii* increases during starvation, presumably indicating utilization of the saturated acids (Kaneko, Takeuchi *et al.*, 1967b).

In mammals it appears that phospholipids form part of the structure of the body tissues, for example cell walls, and so cannot be utilized when food is scarce, although triglycerides can be drawn upon in this way (Masoro, 1967: rats). However, starvation of *Oncorhynchus tschawytscha* and *Gadus morhua* causes a fall in the phospholipid as a proportion of the total lipid (Greene, 1919; J. Olley, 1965, unpublished, quoted by Wilkins, 1967b, respectively). Wilkins (1967b) showed that a reduction in the proportion of phospholipid in *Clupea harengus* during starvation coincides with a reduction in certain protein fractions, indicating that a breakdown in body tissues is in fact occurring. It may be that the greater facility of fish for utilizing proteins during starvation enables them to utilize phospholipid at the same time, whereas in higher vertebrates the same degree of cellular disorganization would be disastrous. Fish seem able to undergo considerable degeneration in the cells of their body musculature (see Fig. 99, p. 248), and survive, as yet another perquisite of their aquatic mode of life, whereby the tissues receive support from the environment.

4. *Inorganic Substances and Extracellular Space*

Only recently has the relationship between inorganic substances and depletion become clear. The confusion of some of the earlier work probably arose because (a) definite changes in the ionic composition occur only after much of the lipid has gone, when the muscle proteins begin to be utilized, and some of the earlier studies were made on fatty fish. (b) Some species become depleted after migrating to fresh water, which complicates the issue as regards ionic balance and (c) the total ash increases during starvation if the whole fish is analysed, but decreases in bone-free muscle tissue.

Phillips, Livingston and Dumas (1960) realized, in observing that the total ash in *Salvelinus fontinalis* increased during starvation, that one component was increasing because others were decreasing, but Herrera and Muñoz (1957), who observed a seasonal rise in the ash of *Sardina pilchardus*, thought that it corresponded with the period of maximum growth, which it preceded. Their graph shows, however, that the ash maximum was corresponding with the water maximum, so it is clear that depletion is at its greatest and the phenomenon is the same as that reported by Phillips, Livingston and Dumas (1960). Bone is not the only tissue to increase in relative proportion during starvation. Skin also is probably not mobilized, and may even increase in absolute thickness (p. 102), so here is another source of an increase in whole-body ash during starvation, since the ash content of skin exceeds that of muscle (3·6% as compared with 1·3% in *Gadus morhua*: Young and Lorimer, 1960).

Insufficient depletion of a rather fatty fish probably accounts for Greene's observation (1919) that the ash content of *Oncorhynchus tschawytscha* was not affected by depletion, but in fact it is now completely established that the total ash of muscle *decreases* if the fish are starved (Tilik, 1932: *Salmo salar*; Kordyl, 1951: *Gadus callarias*; Love, 1958c, Love, Robertson and Strachan, 1968: *Gadus morhua*). Data from the latter two papers have been combined in Fig. 95, which shows that as the water content of the muscle rises above about 83%, the ash content begins to fall steadily. As we shall see later, the proportion of extracellular fluid increases, accounting for at least some of the change. In any case, the proper functioning of muscle depends on a correct balance of water, protein and ionic constituents, so it is logical

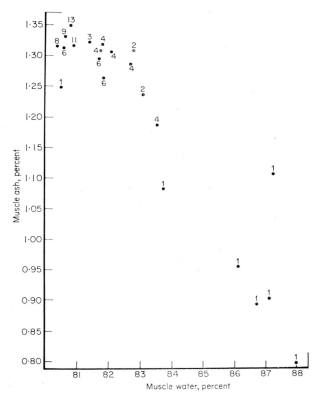

FIG. 95. Relationship between ash and water in the muscle of *Gadus morhua* of various degrees of depletion. Small figures denote numbers of fish pooled for combined results. Data from Love (1958c) and Love, Robertson and Strachan (1968), reproduced by courtesy of the Society of Chemical Industry.

to expect a readjustment of the inorganic substances when the proportions of water and proteins alter.

Figure 96 shows the increase in muscle ash content that occurs when starving *Gadus morhua* are allowed to eat again, confirming the relationship between depletion and inorganic substances.

Love, Robertson and Strachan (1968) showed also that the ash in the blood plasma decreases during starvation in the same species and rises again when feeding is allowed.

Of individual ions, sodium and potassium have been studied almost exclusively in the present context. Seasonal variations were observed by McBride and MacLeod (1956b) in *Oncorhynchus* species, but with too many variations of other sorts to permit a clear conclusion to be

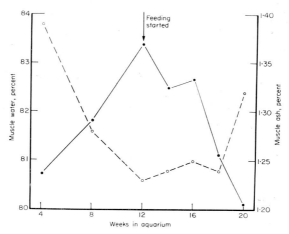

Fig. 96. Relationship between ash (○) and water (●) in the muscle of *Gadus morhua* during starvation at 9°, followed by a resumption of feeding. Starvation began at 0 weeks and feeding was allowed beyond 12 weeks (arrow). After Love, Robertson and Strachan (1968), reproduced by courtesy of the Society of Chemical Industry.

drawn. MacLeod, Jonas and McBride (1958) also studied the variations in several *Oncorhynchus* species, and observed that in general a decrease in sodium is accompanied by a rise in potassium, and vice versa. The highest sodium and lowest potassium values are found in fish taken on the spawning ground, which are presumably the most depleted. For example, compared with immature fish caught in the sea, the sodium concentration rises from 44·9 to 72·6 mg%, while potassium values fall from 469 to 368 mg% (*Oncorhynchus nerka*). The same conclusion was reached by Thurston (1958a : *Oncorhynchus gorbuscha*) but expressed differently as a high sodium value being associated with a low content of ash, while a high potassium content goes hand-in-hand with high protein levels. Thurston (1961c) reported muscle sodium and potassium values in a number of species, and found that one, *Microstomus pacificus*, had as much as 195 mg% sodium and as little as 210 mg% potassium in the extreme cases. Some of this particular species were noted as 'jellied' as described by Templeman and Andrews (1956), that is, extremely depleted. Tomlinson, McBride and Geiger (1967) showed that the muscle sodium of *Oncorhynchus nerka*, which is 24 mg% in fish taken at the beginning of migration, rises to 61 mg% in fish recently spawned, while potassium values fall from 500 to 363 mg%, respectively.

Meyer, Westfall and Platner (1956) showed that starvation of *Carassius auratus* in an aquarium causes a rise in sodium and fall in potassium (whole fish without guts), the (inverse) relationship showing a high degree of correlation. They calculated that every milli-equivalent of potassium lost results in the gain of 1·2 milli-equivalents of sodium.

Love, Robertson and Strachan (1968) starved *Gadus morhua* in an aquarium, and showed that the effect is reversed when the starving fish are fed (Fig. 97). Since the experiment was carried out at a season when the gonads of the fish were inactive, it is clear that the changes in sodium and potassium were caused by starvation alone, and not mediated by hormones, as had been tentatively suggested by MacLeod, Jonas and McBride (1958: *Oncorhynchus* sp.).

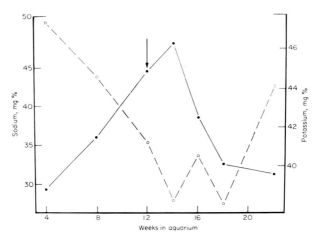

Fig. 97. Changes in the concentration of sodium (●) and potassium (○) in the muscle of *Gadus morhua* during starvation at 9°. Starvation began at 0 weeks and feeding was resumed at the point indicated by the arrow. After Love, Robertson and Strachan (1968), reproduced by courtesy of the Society of Chemical Industry.

The concentrations of these two ions in the blood plasma of *Gadus morhua* both decrease during starvation and rise again when feeding is resumed (Fig. 98).

Sutton (1968) measured the concentrations of several ions during the artificial starvation of *Gadus morhua*, and found that sodium and chloride, which are extracellular, increase, and the predominantly intracellular potassium, magnesium and phosphorus decrease. Calcium shows no definite trend. Apart from phosphorus and magnesium, which show a steady decline throughout the experiment, the ions change markedly in concentration only when the water content of the muscle

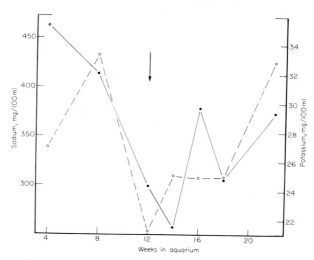

Fig. 98. Legend as for Fig. 97, but constituents here are in the blood plasma.

increases above about 83%, and Sutton considered that beyond this point there is an increase in the extracellular fraction and a decrease in the intracellular fraction of the muscle.

The extracellular space of rats has been stated to increase during starvation, as measured by 'chloride space' (Dicker, 1949), and 'thiocyanate space' (Hegsted, Milner et al., 1953). Goldspink (1965) showed that the mean cell diameter of the muscle tissue in mice decreases during starvation, so Sutton's conclusion is well grounded.

Love, Robertson and Strachan (1968) demonstrated the phenomenon histologically (Fig. 99), and the figures show that a definite increase in the extracellular space is visible by the time the water content has reached 82·3%, but that a significant rise in sodium and fall in potassium can be perceived only when it has exceeded 83% (see following table).

Picture	Period of starvation (weeks)	Water content %	Sodium mg %	Potassium mg %
a	1	80·3	56	514
b	5	81·2	60	486
c	11	82·3	52	491
d	14	83·3	74	438

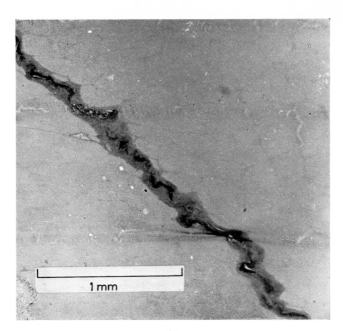

(a)

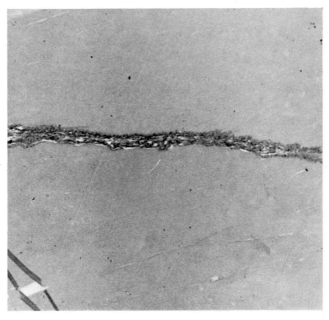

(b)

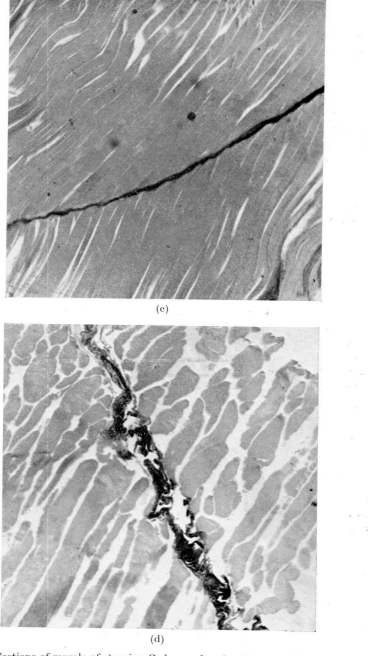

(c)

(d)

Fig. 99. Sections of muscle of starving *Gadus morhua* fixed immediately after death. The dark line across each picture is a myocomma. After Love, Robertson and Strachan (1968), reproduced by courtesy of the Society of Chemical Industry. See Table on p. 247 for details.

The extracellular space of *Hippoglossoides platessoides* which had been severely starved ('jellied') naturally was shown by the same technique to have increased considerably (Templeman and Andrews, 1956).

Thus when fish are starved, the lipid reserves, wherever situated, decrease to a certain point beyond which the muscle protein is mobilized. As the protein decreases, the water increases, and this change is mainly brought about by shrinkage of the cells and a corresponding increase in the fluid between them. Since most of the sodium is extracellular, the increase in extracellular fluid brings about a net increase in muscle sodium, and there is also a decrease in (intracellular) potassium corresponding with the decrease in the average cell diameters.

5. *Carbohydrates*

Carbohydrates are stored in the liver as glycogen, a polysaccharide built of glucose units. When required, for example to supply the energy for muscular contraction, the glycogen is broken down and transported to the muscle as glucose. On arrival, it may be used at once or reconverted into glycogen. Thus glucose and glycogen may both be determined in the muscle, but only glucose is found in the blood.

Of all the energy reserves, the carbohydrates are the most readily utilized, and the first to be affected by depletion. In the case of the barnacle (*Balanus* sp.), whenever carbohydrate reserves are substantial they are first utilized to the exclusion of other materials, but after they have fallen to 10% of the body weight, protein and lipid are broken down also (Barnes, Barnes and Finlayson, 1963). In *Anguilla japonica* it has been shown that of the three energy reserves (glycogen, lipid and protein), the glycogen shows the most rapid decrease during starvation (Inui and Ohshima, 1966). When *Opsanus tau* were fasted for 1—3 months, the liver glycogen fell from 12·7% to 4·1%, but the liver lipid showed only a slight fall during this period, from 5·3% to 4·4% (Tashima and Cahill, 1965).

Nearly all the energy used by salmon during spawning migration originates in lipid reserves, but a change in the carbohydrates has also been detected. The livers of adult *Salmo salar* commencing spawning migration contain about 2% of glycogen, while spent females returning to the sea have only about one tenth of this value (Fontaine and Hatey, 1953). Bellamy (1968) found that the liver glycogen of *Rooseveltiella nattereri* is rapidly mobilized during starvation, falling from 10·3% (wet weight basis) to 0·5% after only 8 days.

Figure 100 shows that mobilization is slower in *Gadus morhua* maintained at 9°, but in spite of the scatter it is clear that depletion is a steady continuous process right from the start of the experiment.

In contrast, the glucose in the *blood* of several species is maintained at a steady level during long periods of depletion. That of *Salvelinus fontinalis* decreases during the first 3 days, but remains steady thereafter (Phillips, Lovelace *et al.*, 1953), and similarly the blood glucose

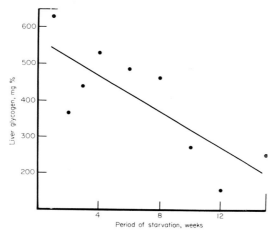

Fig. 100. Glycogen in the liver of *Gadus morhua* starved at 9° for increasing periods. After Love (unpublished).

of *Gadus morhua* declines from 108 mg% to 72 mg% in the first 37 days, but remains at this level after 51 days of fasting at 6·5° (Kamra, 1966). A decrease in liver glycogen without any corresponding change in blood glucose has been observed in *Salmo gairdnerii* after starvation for 14 days (Hochachka and Sinclair, 1962) and *Lampetra fluviatilis* starved for 5 months maintain the muscle glycogen level constant throughout the whole period (Bentley and Follett, 1965) although the blood glucose decreases somewhat. *Myxine glutinosa* was shown by Falkmer and Matty (1966) to maintain a constant level of blood glucose during starvation for 3 weeks.

The muscle glycogen does decrease in *Anguilla japonica* during starvation, but the rate is slower than that in the liver (Inui and Ohshima, 1966). It also decreases in *Cyprinus carpio* after fasting for 3 months (Sorvachev, 1957).

Kiermeier (1939), who studied several species of fish, observed that during long periods of starvation the blood glucose levels remain almost unchanged, and while lively fish show a very gradual decrease, sluggish ones show a remarkable constancy. The blood glucose of *Clarias lazera* shows no change at all during starvation for 4 months, but is reduced to 60% of its former level after 7 months, according to Hanna (1962). However, Al-Gauhari (1958) found no change in this constituent in the same species during the same period; almost identical levels of total blood sugar were shown after 4, 5, 6 and 7 months. During this period, a steady reduction had been taking place in the total lipid.

The effect of spawning migration on the blood sugar of *Oncorhynchus tschawytscha* seems to depend on the time the fish spend in the river. Robertson, Krupp, Favour *et al.* (1961), found that on the autumn run, the level is 214 mg% during migration when the fish have been 1—2 months in the river, and this is reduced, probably not significantly, to 198 mg% at the time of spawning, after 2—3 months in the river. On the other hand, during the spring run after 2—3 months in the river the average value is 210 mg%, while at spawning it shows a definite drop to 129 mg%. Considering, though, that the fish have by this time been 5–6 months without feeding, the decrease is remarkably small. It is likely that glucose is created from lipid precursors during migration, and this effectively obscures the consequences of depletion of carbohydrate reserves.

During the recovery of the liver with feeding after starvation, there is an enormous though transient increase in the glycogen, 10 or 20 mg% increasing to 702 mg%, which is thought to be derived from carbohydrate in the diet (Kamra, 1966: *Gadus morhua*).

6. *Vitamins*

It seems almost certain that vitamin A is not utilized to any great extent during starvation, and therefore the effect of depleting the lipid reserves, in which the vitamin is soluble, is to increase its concentration (Zilva, Drummond and Graham, 1924: *Gadus morhua*; Shorland, 1953: *Polyprion oxygeneios*; Higashi, Hirao *et al.*, 1958: *Entosphenus japonicus*). On the other hand, Plack and Woodhead (1966: *Gadus morhua*) noted that there is a steady decline in the vitamin A esters and alcohol in the blood during the winter, which they attributed to starvation.

Alpha tocopherol (vitamin E), which is also lipid-soluble, was found by Ackman and Cormier (1967) to be reduced by about half in the muscle of *Gadus morhua* starved for 3 months.

Starvation of *Salvelinus fontinalis* for about the same period results in a reduction in riboflavin, pantothenic acid and biotin in the liver, but an increase in the niacin (nicotinic acid) content from about 3·5 mg% to 5 mg% (Phillips, Lovelace *et al.*, 1953). Since the liver becomes smaller during starvation, this is probably only a relative increase. These authors also noted that the depletion of vitamins from the livers of starved fish occurs at a much slower rate than from the livers of fish kept on a vitamin-deficient diet. This is probably a manifestation of the well-known fact that vitamin requirements depend on the amount of food eaten, so that food deficient in vitamins probably causes the reserves of vitamins to be used up.

D. Studies on Enzymes

Metabolic cycles involve complex sequences of reactions mediated by enzymes. It is therefore logical to expect that if the first event, the arrival of metabolites via the bloodstream from the gut, is stopped, some reaction sequences will be arrested altogether and the enzymes will not be needed, at any rate for a while. The enzymic activities of some tissues might therefore be expected to decline during starvation, and so it turns out. In rats, Stielau, Freedland and Meyer (1965) showed that changes in enzyme activity in the liver can be used to assess nutritional status as regards the B vitamins, since, for example, pyridoxine or thiamine deficiency results in a lowering of the activities of enzymes that require these vitamins as co-factors. The response of almost all the relevant liver enzymes to fasting is the same as to a vitamin-free diet. Schimke (1962) studied those enzymes in the livers of rats which are involved in urea synthesis, such as ornithine trans-carbamylase and arginase. Both starvation and maintenance on a protein-free diet causes a great loss of liver protein, but whereas the latter treatment causes a decrease in enzyme activity and urea output, starvation causes an increase in both. The reason for this is not known. Freedland (1967) showed that starvation decreases the activity of a number of rat liver enzymes, especially those associated with lipogenesis such as glucose-6-phosphate dehydrogenase and malic enzyme. The enzymes involved in gluconeogenesis, however, appear to be unaffected.

In fish, the lysolecithinase was found by Yurkowsky and Brockerhoff (1965 : *Gadus morhua*) to decline in some cases of mild starvation, while the activities of uricase, allantoicase and allantoinase decrease in the liver of *Cyprinus carpio* starved for 9 months at 20°, the latter two enzymes after an initial rise in activity (Vellas, 1965).

Figure 101 shows the changes in alkaline phosphatase activity in different organs of *Salmo gairdnerii* after various periods of depletion. In the kidney and intestine there is a sharp fall at the beginning of starvation, followed by a steady level of activity. The alkaline phosphatases of kidney, intestine, stomach and spleen all show increases when feeding is resumed.

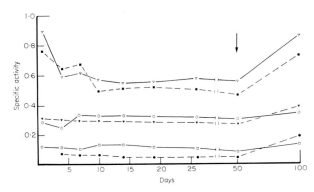

FIG. 101. Alkaline phosphatase activity in various organs of *Salmo gairdnerii* during starvation. The point at which feeding was recommenced is indicated by the arrow. ▽ Kidney; ■ Intestine; ▼ Stomach; ○ Pyloric caecae; ● Spleen; □ Liver. After Noda (1967c), reproduced by permission of the author and the Faculty of Fisheries, Mie University.

A few snatches of rather equivocal information exist on the influence of starvation on the enzymes of the digestive tract. The pepsin activity was found to be less in *Salmo salar* caught in the upper reaches of the river than in those taken nearer the sea (Gillespie, 1898), though the results were very variable. Activity of pepsin, trypsin and lipase was found by Ananichev (1959) to be maximal during periods of intense food intake in three species of freshwater fish, but that of amylase was in each case maximal during starvation. Gastric digestive activity was observed to be reduced in starving *Tilapia mossambica* (Fish, 1960), but much of this finding was merely the result of a deficiency of chloride, for which *Tilapia* relies heavily on its food. Further work would be profitable in this field.

Fish are in general well adapted to withstand long periods of depletion and, as already mentioned, this is probably why the muscle is rich in proteolytic enzymes which can mobilize the body tissues for fuel when required (Siebert, 1962; Siebert and Schmitt, 1965; Siebert, Schmitt and Bottke, 1964; Schmitt, Siebert and Bottke, 1966).

E. Haematology

Starvation causes a reduction in the populations of different cells floating in the blood plasma. Smallwood (1916) observed that the red blood cell count of *Amia calva* dropped from 1,640,000 per cubic mm to 400,000 after starvation for 20 months. The specific gravity of the blood was recorded as 1·03, as compared with 1·04 for a fish feeding normally. We may compare this with Murachi's finding (1959: *Cyprinus carpio*) that the red cell sedimentation rate was greatly increased after starvation for 7 weeks at 16° to 22°. In each case the blood plasma would almost certainly have lost much of its protein, which would affect its specific gravity in the first case and its viscosity in the second, the drop in viscosity allowing the cells to sediment more quickly. In addition, Murachi (1959) found a decrease in red cell volume (haematocrit) from 50% to 33%, and a corresponding reduction in haemoglobin from 11 to 7 g per 100 ml. Higginbotham and Meyer (1948: *Ictalurus lacustris punctatus*) have also observed a reduced red cell volume, haemoglobin content and blood specific gravity when fish were in poor condition (emaciated).

Smirnova (1962) found that the number of white blood cells (leucocytes) was reduced during the starvation of freshwater fish. In a later paper (1965: *Lota lota*) the reduction was confirmed, but the decline in red cell numbers was shown to be preceded by an increase

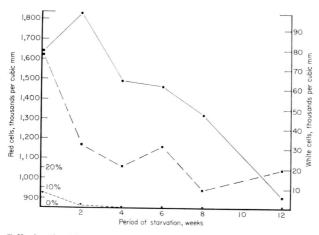

Fig. 102. Cells in the blood of *Salmo gairdnerii* during starvation. ●——● Red; ■———■ White; ▼-----▼ Immature. After Kawatsu (1966), through whose courtesy the Figure is reproduced.

during the first 60 days of fasting, an effect which was thought to result from a decrease in the total blood volume. The restoration of feeding in this case led to a further decline in red cell numbers.

The changes in red and white blood cells and in immature cells was investigated in *Salmo gairdnerii* by Kawatsu (1966). His results (Fig. 102) also show that the decline in red cell count is preceded by an increase, agreeing with Smirnova (1965). White cells decline steadily, but perhaps the most interesting curve in the Figure is the small one at the bottom, which shows that the number of immature cells vanishes after starvation for about 4 weeks. This may explain the decline in mature cell numbers, and is presumed to mean that the fish is unable to manufacture new blood cells under conditions of starvation. The numbers in circulation therefore decline at a rate related to their life-span.

F. Excretion

The excretion of nitrogen soon declines if mammals are given a diet free from protein, and after a while it reaches a steady level known as the "endogenous nitrogen excretion" (Folin, 1905, quoted by Wessels and Fisher, 1965). At first sight, excretion in fish appears to follow a similar path. Pora and Precoop (1960) found that *Cyprinus carpio* starved for 90 days excreted less organic nitrogen per day than fed ones, and Sano (1962b), who measured the urea output of *Anguilla japonica* during starvation, found that it dropped sharply during the first 5 days and then remained steady up to the 90th day when the experiment was concluded.

The nitrogen excretion of the same species according to Inui and Ohshima (1966) is illustrated in Fig. 103, which shows the results in fish starved for 60 days during the winter time. The asymptotic level in summer-caught fish was higher than that shown, presumably because of the higher temperature and metabolic rate.

When *Cyprinus carpio* were starved by Vellas and Serfaty (1967), the excretion of urea, via both gills and urine, was observed to decrease at first, but when starvation had been continued for 5 months it increased again, especially in the urine. This observation is unique up to now, and at first sight it is difficult to explain, but it will be remembered that the first phase of starvation always involves the mobilization of carbohydrates and lipids, rather than proteins. It seems likely, therefore, that the preliminary drop in nitrogen excretion marks

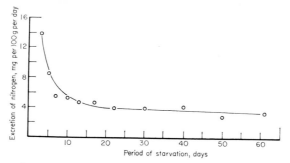

Fig. 103. Excretion of nitrogen by *Anguilla japonica* during starvation in the winter time. After Inui and Ohshima (1966), reproduced by courtesy of the authors and the Japanese Society of Scientific Fisheries.

the end of ingested nitrogen circulating in the blood, while the secondary rise is brought about by the rapid mobilization of structural protein after the other reserves have been utilized. This should be considered distinct from the normal basic catabolism of protein, which is going on all the time, and the phenomenon may be different in fish from that in mammals. The interpretation of urine nitrogen levels in relation to starvation is therefore likely to be complicated.

Note added in proof (to p. 209)

Recent work has shown that vitamin C is in fact essential for *Oncorhynchus kisutch*, *Salmo gairdnerii* and *Salvelinus fontinalis* (Halver, Ashley and Smith, *Trans. Am. Fish Soc.* in press). Deficiency results in a delay in wound healing, degeneration of the gill filaments and spinal curvature. Scurvy-like symptoms have also been observed by Kitamura, Ohara, Suwa and Nakagawa (*Bull. Jap. Soc. scient. Fish.* **31**, 818–824, 1965) in *Salmo gairdnerii* fed a diet deficient in this vitamin.

INDEX OF CHEMICAL SUBSTANCES

Introduction

This index lists papers in the bibliography which give the concentrations of substances in various organs. It is realized that ideally such a compilation should list actual values so that no further consultation would be needed, but previous experience has shown that this is not a practical proposition. An earlier publication, now out of print (Love, Lovern and Jones, 1959), performed just this service, converting various units to a common series and listing values that appeared to be meaningful, having regard to the method of analysis and the preparation of the sample. Compilation took 7 months with a bibliography of 183 references. Since that time, interest in fish tissue chemistry has increased considerably, so that the present index, which includes all the papers of the earlier report, now comprises nearly 750 papers, and conversion and compilation is simply more than one person's work if the finished product is not to be hopelessly out of date before publication. I have therefore followed the precedent of a still earlier review (Love, 1957) and simply shown where to find the information, in the hopes that this still fulfils a need.

Nomenclature

The steroid hormones have been identified both in the text and in this section by their common names. The corresponding systematic names, which give a clue to structure, have been listed by Gottfried (1964).

Although vitamins apart from those of the B group are given as vitamin A, D, etc., the word 'vitamin' appears to be passing from general usage, so the alternative recommended names (Anon., 1960) are given as well.

Descriptive Matter

Extra information is supplied on many of the substances in addition to the bibliographical references. The notes refer specifically to the roles played in fish tissue, so for a more general account the reader is referred to a standard textbook of biochemistry. Where an author reference is given, the material is 'new', but otherwise it has been summarized from the text (Part I).

Page Index

Numbers in italics refer to pages in the text where the substance has been mentioned; those not italic are reference numbers.

Blood Chemistry

Originally it was planned to differentiate between papers showing constituents in whole blood, in serum or in plasma, but several papers had not made it clear which blood fraction was being analysed and so it was decided to list all fractions together as 'blood'. Readers seeking further information on the chemistry of fish blood are referred to the compilation by Hunn (1967), who lists over 850 references on this subject alone.

Amino Acids

Where an author has listed the concentrations of 5 or more amino acids in a tissue, they are given here under 'amino acids', either free or combined. Where 4 or fewer are given, they are listed under their individual names.

Gonads

The male gonad is given as 'testis', the female as 'ovary'. They are listed as 'gonad' where the sex of the fish was not made clear in the paper.

Inorganic Substances

The great classical work on inorganic substances in fish and other aquatic organisms was written by Vinogradov (1953), who listed actual values. It seemed superfluous to quote the same work again here, so the original should be consulted for papers up to about 1946. Flame photometry came into being as an accurate research tool only after about 1950, and the papers listed in this section date from then. There is therefore a slight gap between the end of Vinogradov's work and the beginning of the present section, but it is not likely to be serious. Readers wishing to obtain further detailed information on inorganic constituents are referred to the review by Causeret (1962).

"Proximate Analysis"

The analysis of the four main tissue constituents, protein, water, lipid and ash is sometimes described as "proximate analysis". The etymology of the word is uncertain, but the accuracy of the determinations is presumably not in doubt.

Although many papers show the concentrations of these four constituents, it was decided not to list them for a number of reasons. Many lipid analyses have been invalidated by the use of petroleum or ether for extraction, which results in very low and variable extraction of phospholipid (Olley, Pirie and Watson, 1962). Furthermore, total lipid is a mixture of so many substances that the biological significance of the collective figure is sometimes questionable. Figures for total ash likewise give no indication of the proportion of intracellular and extracellular ions, nor the proportion available for osmotic balance in the tissue. The same sort of criticism applies also to total protein, although one may assess depletion in a fish to some extent from a study of any one of these figures.

While some species of fish appear not to show any seasonal variation in the four substances (Muñoz, 1961: *Merluccius merluccius* and *Merluccius senegalensis*), the most useful papers take into account the variation throughout at least one year. Such a paper is that by Sohn, Carver and Mangan (1961: 5 species) and there are a few others.

However, for those who wish to see a large number of values of this kind, Vinogradov (1953) lists ash, protein and water, while protein and lipid values are given by Jacquot and Creac'h (1950). A list of papers which show the total protein in fish muscle is to be found in the review by Geiger and Borgstrom (1962). *Note:* Page references to the text (Part I) for the four constituents are given in the General Index (p. 543).

Protein

As already discussed in Chapter 5, the total protein of both blood and muscle declines during starvation, after a curious initial increase of which we can only guess the mechanism. In the muscle also it is found that the fraction which is insoluble in 5% NaCl shows a sharp increase about 3 weeks after the beginning of starvation, followed by an equally sharp decline, and a further peak may appear after 7—10 weeks. The different fractions of protein in the blood decrease during starvation, with the sole exception of gamma globulin, which shows a relative increase. Busson, Postel and Giraud (1953, quoted by Geiger and Borgstrom, 1962) stated that tuna caught off the Cape Verde Islands held the highest protein figures for all foods of animal origin, 22·5%. Other papers quoted by the same authors show that as much as 25% protein is possible. Since ingested proteins are broken down to individual amino acids before being absorbed, the proteins of the body do not, as far as is known, reflect in any way those of the diet.

Lipid

Body lipids, on the other hand, are markedly influenced by the diet. While the fish to some extent imposes a fatty acid pattern characteristic of itself, most ecological and other effects on the lipid composition can be explained as differences in the diet.

With one exception, starvation causes a progressive reduction in lipid reserves, which must reach a critical low value before proteins begin to be utilized. The most fatty fish on record is *Salvelinus namaycush siscowet*, with an average of 67% lipid in the musculature.

The ways in which lipid can be distributed in the bodies of different species have been beautifully illustrated by Yamada (1964), using differential staining techniques.

Ash

Ash in the muscle declines steadily during the starvation of non-fatty fish once the water content has increased above a critical value. For this reason, the observations by Fujii (1954) and Herrera and Muñoz (1957), that ash declines during and after spawning, probably reflect depletion only, the phenomenon not being connected with maturation as such. The relative proportions of the different ions do not change greatly according to circumstances. Baldwin (1948) has summarized the situation thus, that there is ". . . a common, and probably fundamental, chemical ground-plan to which the blood and tissue fluids of all animals must conform. They conform, not because they will, but because they must, for appreciable departures from the normal, relative balance of ions are not tolerated for long by any of the many kinds of cells and tissues that have been studied. The *relative* ionic composition of the bloods of different animals is always essentially the same, whether they inhabit the sea, the fresh waters or the dry land, but the *total* ionic composition, as reflected in the osmotic pressure, varies over a wide range, being far lower in freshwater and terrestrial animals than it is in marine forms."

The total ash content of different organs does not appear to vary greatly. Braekkan (1958a) gives values for *Gadus morhua* which were presumably not starving, as follows: Gonads, male and female: 1·4%; stomach: 1·2%; pyloric caecae, muscle, spleen and kidney: 1·1%; heart: 1·0% and gill: 0·9%. Scales of course are much richer in ash, and Qudrat-i-khuda, Rahman and Khan (1964) give values of 31 and 36% on a dry weight basis for *Hilsa ilisha* and *Barbus puntius*, respectively.

Water

The water content shows an inverse relationship with the lipid in the muscle of fatty fish, and with the protein in non-fatty fish. Analysis can therefore give information on the nutritional state of the fish. The highest value for tissue water to have been measured in a starving fish is 96·18% in *Hippoglossoides platessoides*. The water content also increases slightly when euryhaline fish are transferred from sea water to fresh. Among the organs of *Gadus morhua* with muscle containing 80·4% of water, that is, of well-nourished fish, the female gonad contains least water (74%) and the gills and male gonad most (83·3% and 84·5%, respectively: Braekkan, 1958a). The optic 'humours' naturally contain much more, aqueous and vitreous having 98·85 and 98·9%, respectively (Edelhauser, Hoffert and Fromm, 1965: *Salmo gairdnerii*). The eye lenses of fish are hard compared with mammalian lenses, and contain the least water of the body tissues (Lavagna, 1954: many species, ranging from 38·5 to 56·3%; Love, 1954: *Gadus morhua*: 51%; Edelhauser, Hoffert and Fromm, 1965: *Salmo gairdnerii*: 51·1%).

Enzymes

Papers referred to in the following list give the activities (weight of substrate changed per unit time) of fish tissue enzymes. Papers reporting merely the presence or absence of enzymes have been omitted. The list is probably incomplete, but will serve, it is hoped, as a basis for further reading. Numbers in italics refer to pages in the text; those not in italics are references in the Bibliography.

ACETYL CHOLINESTERASE 522, 1058, 1310, *74, 75*
ACID PHOSPHATASE 934, 935
ADENOSINE TRIPHOSPHATASE 934, *150*
ALDOLASE 238, 720, 1164
ALKALINE PHOSPHATASE 411, 644, 934, 935, 1058, *254*
ALLANTOICASE 408, 880, *50, 212, 253*
ALLANTOINASE 880, *50, 212, 253*
AMINE OXIDASE 1167
AMINO ACID DECARBOXYLASE 1167
D-AMINO ACID OXIDASE 1167
AMYLASE 24, 189, 218, 345, 644, 676, 870, 900, 1164, 1165, 1313, *95, 204, 205, 254*
ANSERINASE 1108
ARGINASE 234, 598, 843, *19, 20, 253*
ARGINO-SUCCINATE LYASE 598
ARGINO-SUCCINATE SYNTHETASE 598
ASPARAGINASE 1167
CATHEPSIN 1164, 1167, *151*
CYTOCHROME OXIDASE 367, *213*
DIPEPTIDASES (VARIOUS) 1125
ENDOPEPTIDASE 260
ENOLASE 1164
ENTEROKINASE 644
ESTERASE 644, 870, *24*

Other Substances

*Numbers in italics refer to paqes in the text; those not italic are references in the
Bibliography.*

ACETIC ACID
Muscle 543

ACETONE
Blood 608

ACETYL CHOLINE
Electric organ 873

N-ACETYL HISTIDINE   *147*
The role of this compound is still unknown, but it may function as a donor
of acetyl groups in acetylation (Hanson, 1966). The hearts of freshwater
teleosts contain about 50 mg%, but it is virtually absent from marine teleosts.
Brain 456; Eye lens 81, 456; Heart 456; Ocular fluid 81

AMINO ACIDS, COMBINED (hydroxyproline is listed separately)   *16, 17, 18, 20, 25, 26, 54, 58, 66, 75-7, 83, 94, 97, 99, 100, 101, 102, 106, 125, 130, 136, 199, 207, 238*

Beach, Munks and Robinson (1943) considered that the amino acid pattern was almost constant throughout the animal kingdom, and Konosu, Katori *et al.* (1956), who investigated fish, concluded that no distinction could be made between species, even when sharks were included. Carlson (1961) found a similarity in the amino acids of different species of lamprey, but noted that fish in general had higher levels of leucine, isoleucine and lysine than other animals. Lampreys had less glutamic acid than most other fish. A list of reviews of amino acid composition in fish muscle is given by Geiger and Borgstrom (1962). There is no appreciable difference between white and superficial dark muscle, but deep-seated dark muscle shows some small differences from white. The 10 'essential' amino acids, which must be present in the diet if the fish is to grow, are arginine, histidine, isoleucine, leucine, lysine, methionine, phenylalanine, threonine, tryptophan and valine. The others may be omitted from the diet.

Actin 239, 240, 528; Blood 663; Brain 25, 26; Collagen (muscle) 309; Collagen (skin) 715, 1013, 1390; Collagen (swim bladder) 48, 309, 1014, 1015; Dark muscle 41, 847; Egg 205, 1221, 1222, 1223; Enamel (tooth) 738; Enolase 247; Erythrocytes 1322; Ferritin 657; Fry (young fish) 1221; Gelatin (bone) 309; Gelatin (scale) 125, 1015, 1193; Gelatin (skin) 309, 1014, 1015; Haemoglobin 16, 313, 695, 831, 1039; Ichthylepidin 125; Insulin 548; Kidney 257; Liver 25, 26, 124, 257, 928; Muscle 2, 23, 25, 26, 34, 41, 80, 83, 141, 154, 198, 205, 240, 249, 257, 281, 305, 306, 318, 583, 629, 696, 723, 725, 750, 827, 838, 847, 924, 990, 1035, 1042, 1110, 1131, 1214, 1324, 1341; Myoglobin 695; Myosin 195, 239, 240; Ovary 249, 257, 281, 701, 990, 1135, 1136; Pyloric caecae 639; Scales 125, 183, 928, 1189; Shell (egg) 1388, 1391; Slime 323; Spleen 257; Testis 205, 257, 281, 701, 990; Tropomyosin 528, 713, 1094

AMINO ACIDS (FREE)   *65, 82, 96, 99, 125, 130, 188, 221, 223, 238, 240*

Steadily increase in the gonad during maturation, but not in the muscle or blood. Proportions of individual acids in the gonad also change during maturation. Total *free* amino acids may assist the fish to osmoregulate in a hypertonic environment, but this is not certain. Various changes occur also during starvation, the pattern differing in different organs.

Bile 253; Blood 249, 256, 985; Brain 956; Gill 985; Kidney 985; Liver 985; Muscle 42, 249, 250, 269, 299, 542, 615, 620, 678, 917, 1101, 1129, 1139

AMINO ACIDS (FREE: total figure, individuals grouped together)
Dark muscle 42; Liver 220; Muscle 220

AMMONIA   *49, 139, 144*

Blood 790, 1182, 1183, 1224; Dark muscle 42, 364; Gastric fluid 1183; Kidney 790; Liver 790, 1224; Muscle 19, 42, 201, 364, 366, 540, 645, 1224; Pericardial fluid 1182, 1183; Perivisceral fluid 1182, 1183; Urine 1183

ANDROSTENE DIONE
Semen 1170; Testis 221

BIOTIN   *20, 56, 67, 68, 208, 209, 252*
More concentrated in dark than in ordinary muscle. Not essential for health, at least in *Salmo gairdnerii*.
Egg 892; Gills 155; Heart 155; Intestines 155; Kidney 155; Liver 155; Muscle 155, 217, 750, 751; Ovary 148, 153, 155, 751; Pyloric caecae 155, 636; Spleen 155; Stomach 155; Testis 155

BROMINE   *144*
Bone 251; Kidney 251; Liver 251; Muscle 251; Pancreas 251; Scale 251; Stomach 251; Testicular fat body 251

n-BUTYRIC ACID
Muscle 543

γ-AMINO BUTYRIC ACID
Brain 949

CADMIUM
Eyeball 1201; 'Gonads' 1201; Heart 1201; Liver 1201; Muscle 987, 1201; Skin + Scales 1201

CAESIUM
Brain 186; Extracellular fluid 926; Muscle 184, 185, 186; Muscle (intracellular) 926

CALCIUM   *7, 25, 55, 56, 61, 62, 67, 73, 74, 77, 79, 84, 95, 106, 120, 121, 122, 125, 137, 138, 144, 160, 172, 179, 188, 189, 191, 192, 193, 194, 196, 197, 206, 207, 211, 217, 218, 246*
As maturity proceeds, serum calcium increases in the female though not in the male (egg-laying species). Vitellin, a serum protein, has calcium linked to it, and both the protein and the calcium are probably used in the developing eggs (Bailey, 1957). The phenomenon is hormonally controlled, and may be induced outside the breeding season by injecting oestradiol (Oguri and Takada, 1966, 1967). Calcium can be absorbed directly from the surrounding water, especially if phosphate is present as well, and seems to be important in regulating the metabolic rate. Similarly, the calcium content of various tissues increases when euryhaline fish go from fresh water to the sea. In the muscle it is largely bound to protein. It increases in the skin as some fish increase in size, probably owing to scale growth. Unlike several other ions, calcium in the muscle shows no definite trend during starvation.
Aqueous humour 293; Bile 1182; Blood 64, 92, 136, 212, 293, 315, 341, 356, 535, 538, 724, 858, 874, 951, 952, 953, 971, 992, 998, 1010, 1011, 1075, 1076, 1077, 1104, 1109, 1144, 1162, 1182, 1198, 1199; Bone 251; Cerebrospinal fluid 1182; Dark muscle 377; Egg 892, 947, 1376; Eyeball 1201; Gill 315, 995; 'Gonad' 1162, 1201; Heart 1201; Intestine 995; Kidney 251, 984; Liver 92, 220, 251, 315, 984, 1162, 1201, 1234; Muscle (body) 108, 220, 251, 377, 592, 652, 712, 918, 919, 966, 971, 1061, 1076, 1109, 1201, 1234, 1317, 1327, 1370; Muscle (parietal) 212, 1077; Muscle (tongue) 92, 212; Ovary 1234; Pancreas 251; Pericardial fluid 1182; Perivisceral fluid 1182; Pyloric caecae 531; Scales 55, 251, 1047, 1241; Skin 55, 995; Skin + Scales 1201; Stomach 251; Testicular fat body 251; Urine 724, 874, 950, 951, 952, 1183, 1184, 1198, 1199

11*

CANTHAXANTHIN
Muscle 1257

CARBON DIOXIDE *47*
Aqueous humour 832; Blood 116, 453, 832, 971; Cerebrospinal fluid 832; Muscle 453

CARDIOLIPID
Liver 692; Muscle 692

CARNITINE
Brain 949; Electric organ 361; Liver 361; Muscle 361; Testis 361

CARNOSINE *24, 147, 151*
The role of this compound has not been clearly established, but it may act as a buffer (Lukton and Olcott, 1958). There is a higher concentration, in relation to anserine, in freshwater fish than in marine fish.
Dark muscle 42, 783; Muscle 42, 532, 698, 783, 1392

CAROTENE *67, 200*
Carotene in the diet can be converted by fish equally well to vitamin A_1 or vitamin A_2.
Blood 341; Egg 414, 461, 1205; Liver 1204; Ovary 1204

CAROTENOIDS *67, 142, 200, 201, 203*
Derived from the diet and found widely distributed in skin. The compounds may serve only for colouring or camouflaging the fish, since no biochemical role has been found for them in the skin (Bellamy, 1966). Neither the type nor the concentration of carotenoid seem to have any bearing on the amount of vitamin A in the skin (Higashi, 1961). Deposited in the ovary during maturation, perhaps as vitamin A precursors. Very primitive fish do not store carotenoids, but the significance of this is not yet clear.
Egg 360, 461; Liver 360, 347; Muscle 420; Scales 360; Skin 360, 1293, 1294

CEPHALIN *208*
Cephalin in the diet appears to stimulate growth.
Cerebrum 658; Dark muscle 576; Egg 1400; Muscle 576, 1158

CEREBROSIDE *20*
More concentrated in dark than in ordinary muscle.
Brain 805; Cerebrum 658; Dark muscle 654, 655, 1296, 1396; Heart 655, 1396; Intestine 655, 1396; Kidney 655, 1396; Liver 654, 655, 1396; Muscle 654, 655, 1296, 1396; Ovary 654, 1396; Pyloric caecae 655, 1396; Spinal cord 806; Spleen 655, 1396; Stomach 655, 1396; Testis 654, 1396

CHLORIDE *3, 12, 81, 88, 89, 95, 106, 122, 137, 139, 144, 187, 190, 191, 192, 195, 196, 197, 207, 218, 219, 246, 254*
Extracellular. Concentration increases in organs during starvation and when euryhaline fish migrate to the sea.
Aqueous humour 293, 832; Bile 1182, 1183; Blood 92, 121, 193, 212, 293, 315, 321, 341, 356, 415, 534, 535, 538, 553, 724, 727, 807, 832, 858, 874, 877, 878,

895, 971, 992, 998, 1011, 1075, 1076, 1077, 1083, 1109, 1143, 1144, 1173, 1182, 1183, 1184, 1215; Bone 251; Brain 1083; Cranial fluid 321, 832, 895, 1182; Egg 853; Endolymph 321, 895; Endolymph from sacculus 321; Endolymph from semi-circular canal 321; Erythrocytes 1083; Gastric fluid 1183; Gelatin (skeleton) 392; Gelatin (skin) 392; Gill 1001; Jelly from ampullae of Lorenzini 895; Kidney 251; Liver 92, 220, 251; Marshall's gland 1182; Muscle (body) 121, 193, 220, 251, 727, 971, 1076; Muscle (parietal) 212, 1077; Muscle (tongue) 92, 212; Ovary 853; Pancreas 251; Pericardial fluid 1182, 1183; Perilymph 321, 895; Perivisceral fluid 1182, 1183; Pyloric caecae 531; Scales 251; Semen 121; Stomach 251; Testicular fat body 251; Urine 322, 724, 874, 1183, 1184, 1342

CHOLESTEROL   *18, 20, 24, 29, 36, 54, 63, 64, 65, 95, 96, 110, 120, 121, 125, 140, 151, 214, 219*
The cholesterol content of fish meat is largely independent of the lipid content, so does not vary much between species (Wurtziger and Hensel, 1967). Usually, however, it is more concentrated in dark muscle than in ordinary muscle. In serum it is minimal at times of greatest sexual activity, presumably because of its conversion to sex hormones. It is more concentrated in the blood of active than sluggish species.
Bile 553; Blood 341, 553, 729, 799, 800, 872, 991, 999, 1080, 1081, 1144, 1215, 1246; Brain 25, 630, 805, 946; Bulbus arteriosus 1228; Cerebrum 658; Dark muscle 122, 574, 654, 655, 915, 1396; Gall bladder 1228; 'Gonad' 1161; Heart 655, 1228, 1396; Intestine 1396; Kidney 655, 1396; Liver 25, 559, 654, 655, 1154, 1161, 1228, 1343, 1396; Muscle 11, 25, 122, 385, 573, 630, 654, 655, 822, 915, 958, 1153, 1154, 1161, 1369, 1396; Ovary 559, 654, 1154, 1396; Pyloric caecae 655, 1396; Spinal cord 806; Spleen 655, 1228, 1396; Stomach 655, 1396; Testis 559, 654, 1154, 1396

CHOLINE   *19, 20, 208*
Occurs both free and as a component of lecithin (phosphatidyl choline). Richer in dark muscle than in white, and in deep-seated dark muscle than in superficial dark muscle. An essential component of the diet.
Dark muscle 869, 1236, 1297; Intestine 1236; Liver 1236; Muscle 609, 869, 1109, 1236, 1297; Pyloric caecae 1236; Spleen 1401; Stomach 1236

CHROMIUM   *200*
Bone 251, 989; Eyeball 1201; 'Gonads' 1201; Heart 1201; Kidney 251; Liver 251, 1201; Muscle 251, 987, 1201; Pancreas 251; Scale 251; Skin + Scales 1201; Stomach 251; Testicular fat body 251

COBALT   *200, 206, 207, 211*
Bone 251; Eyeball 1201; 'Gonads' 1201; Heart 864, 1201; Kidney 251; Liver 251, 333, 864, 1201; Muscle 251, 987, 1201; Ovary 120, 864; Pancreas 251; Scale 251; Skin + Scales 1201; Stomach 251; Testicular fat body 251

COENZYME A
Adrenal 719; Blood cells 719; Brain 719; Electric organ 719; Heart 719; Intestine 719; Kidney 719; Liver 719; Muscle 719; Testis 719; Thymus 719

CYANOCOBALAMIN (Vitamin B_{12})   *23, 28, 56, 67, 74, 95, 96, 151, 208, 209*

The kidney and liver are usually recognized as the organs richest in vitamin B_{12}, but in fish the heart is often richest, a value of 425 $\mu g\%$ being found in *Gadus pollachius* (Braekkan, 1958c). However, fish liver does contain far more of the vitamin than the flesh, and dark muscle contains more than ordinary muscle. Fatty fish of the herring type have a higher concentration in their flesh than do non-fatty teleosts or elasmobranchs (Yanase, 1953). This vitamin occurs in appreciable concentrations in sea water, which may be a source for the fish. In most cases the muscle of active fish contains more vitamin B_{12} than that of sluggish fish. It is not essential for health, at least in *Salmo gairdnerii*.
Brain 25, 466; Dark muscle 146, 156, 466, 867, 868, 1380; Egg 892, 1380; Gill 147, 156; 'Gonad' 646; Heart 147, 149, 156, 466, 646, 683, 1380; Intestine 147, 156, 157, 466, 646, 1382; Kidney 147, 149, 156, 466, 646, 893, 1380; Liver 25, 146, 147, 149, 156, 157, 466, 497, 498, 646, 683, 868, 893, 1234, 1380, 1381, 1382; Muscle 25, 71, 72, 146, 147, 149, 150, 156, 157, 412, 466, 497, 498, 506, 526, 527, 592, 683, 867, 891, 893, 1234, 1251, 1380, 1381; Ovary 147, 148, 153, 156, 157, 466, 497, 498, 683, 893, 1234, 1251; Pyloric caecae 147, 156, 466, 635, 646, 1380; Skin 497, 498; Spleen 147, 156, 646, 1380; Stomach 147, 156, 466, 646; Stomach + Intestine 466, 683, 1380; Testis 147, 156, 157, 466, 497, 498, 683, 893

CYSTINE   *58, 130, 207*
Muscle 22, 592, 1090

CYTIDINE MONOPHOSPHATE
Eye lens 679

CYTIDINE TRIPHOSPHATE
Blood 425; Brain 425; Eye lens 679; Gill 425; 'Gonads' 425; Heart 425; Intestine 425; Kidney 425; Liver 425; Muscle 425; Pyloric caecae 425; Spleen 425; Stomach 425

CYTOCHROME C   *19, 20*
Richer in dark muscle than in ordinary muscle, and in deep-seated dark muscle than in superficial dark muscle.
Dark muscle 844; Muscle 844

CYTOSINE
DNA from muscle 127; DNA from testis 375

DEHYDRO-*EPI*-ANDROSTERONE
Semen 1170

11-DEOXYCORTICOSTERONE
Semen 1170, 1172; Seminal plasma 1172; Sperm cells 1172

DEOXYRIBOSE NUCLEIC ACID (DNA)   *3, 6, 7, 67, 74, 86, 87, 107, 108, 109, 125, 130, 140, 167, 168*
Occurs in constant amount in each cell nucleus. The *concentration* in muscle tissue therefore depends on the sizes of the cells, in gadoids being high at each

end of the fillet and lower in the middle. For a similar reason, as the fish grow there is a tendency for the DNA concentration in muscle to fall. Myocommata are rich in DNA. Commercially, herring sperm are often used as the raw material for preparing DNA. As eggs develop, the DNA increases at the expense of the ribose nucleic acid (RNA), the sum of the two nucleic acids being roughly constant.

Alimentary tract 258, 1111; Brain 25; Dark muscle 102, 1111; Diploid nuclei 1323; Egg 12; Erythrocytes 375, 862; Eye 1404; Heart 258; Kidney 258, 1111; Liver 25, 258, 1111; Muscle 25, 102, 127, 258, 755, 1111, 1281; Oocytes 1155; Ovary 258; Pyloric caecae 530; Spleen 258; Testis 258, 375

20 β-DIHYDROCORTISONE
Blood 567

20 β DIHYDRO 17α HYDROXY PROGESTERONE
Blood 1124

DIHYDROXYACETONE PHOSPHATE   *41*
Muscle 191

17α 20 β DIHYDROXY-PREGN-4-ENE-3-ONE
Blood 560

DIMETHYLAMINE
Gall bladder 21; Liver 21; Muscle 21; Ovary 21; Pyloric caecae 21; Skin 21; Spleen 21; Stomach 21; Testis 21

DIPHOSPHOPYRIDINE NUCLEOTIDE (Nicotinamide adenine dinucleotide)   *24, 41, 151*
Concentration in the muscle increases during exercise.
Blood 425; Brain 425; Gill 425; 'Gonad' 425; Heart 425; Intestine 425; Kidney 425; Lens 679; Liver 425; Muscle 425, 622, 623, 624, 625, 653, 894, 1249; Pyloric caecae 425; Spleen 425; Stomach 425

ELASTIN   *38*
Skin 1242, 1390; Swim bladder 1390

EPIOESTRIOL   *111*
Blood 316

ERYTHROCYTES (red blood cells)   *93*
Blood 475, 487, 504

FATTY ACIDS (combined, individual)   *55, 65, 75, 76, 77, 78, 95, 122, 124, 142, 145, 146, 217*
The fatty acids in the lipids of aquatic animals as a whole are a complex mixture compared with those of land animals. The biological significance of this is not certain (Lovern, 1942). Tables of the fatty acid compositions of the *oils* of many species of fish, both marine and freshwater, are given by Lovern (1942) and Tsuchiya (1961).

Brain 25, 607; Cephalin (muscle) 685; Cephalin (spleen) 1401; Cholesterol esters (liver) 472; Dark muscle 122, 473; Egg 31, 577; Ethanolamine (muscle) 11; Heart 1397, 1398; Lecithin (egg) 578, 1400; Lecithin (heart) 1399; Lecithin (muscle) 685, 1089, 1244; Lecithin (spleen) 1401; Liver 7, 11, 173, 595, 767, 927, 975, 1154, 1347; Muscle 6, 7, 10, 11, 122, 173, 472, 473, 572, 595, 667, 685, 822, 975, 1153, 1154; Ovary 7, 595, 1154; Pancreas 767; Phosphatidyl choline 11; Phosphatidyl ethanolamine 1089, 1244; Phosphatidyl serine 11, 1244; Phospholipid 685; Sphingomyelin (muscle) 685; Sphingomyelin (spleen) 685; Testis 595, 789, 1154; Triglycerides (liver) 472; Triglycerides (muscle) 11, 685, 1089; Triglycerides (spleen) 1401; Vitamin A ester (liver) 472; Vitamin A ester (muscle) 1089

FATTY ACIDS (combined, total)
Myosin 237

FREE FATTY ACIDS (total)   *131, 132, 242*
Blood 105, 729; Dark muscle 105; Muscle 105, 365, 609, 822, 959, 960; Skin 960; Spleen 927

FIBRINOGEN
Blood 991, 999, 1010, 1098

FLUORINE
Body 251; Kidney 251; Liver 251; Muscle 251; Pancreas 251; Scales 251; Stomach 251; Testicular fat body 251

FOLIC ACID (Pteroylmonoglutamic acid)   *56, 151, 208*
The muscle of active fish is richer in folic acid than that of more sluggish fish.
Blood 638; Dark muscle 503, 637; Egg 892; 'Gonad' 637, 638; Heart 498, 503, 637, 638; Intestine 503; Kidney 498, 503, 507, 637, 638, 893; Liver 498, 503, 637, 638, 893; Muscle **73**, 217, 498, 503, 506, **637**, 638, 751, 893; Ovary **498**, 503, 751, 893; Pyloric caecae 503, 636, 637; Skin 498; Spleen 503; Stomach 503; Testis 498, 503, 893

FORMALDEHYDE   *130*
Gall bladder 20, 21; Liver 20, 21; Muscle 20, 21; Ovary 20, 21; Pyloric caecae 20, 21; Skin 21; Spleen 21; Stomach 20, 21; Testis 20, 21

FORMIC ACID
Muscle 543

FRUCTOSE
Seminal plasma 434

FRUCTOSE DIPHOSPHATE   *7, 41*
Values are reduced during physical exertion.
Muscle 188, 901, 1249

GLUTAMINE
  Blood 1407; Gill 1407; Kidney 1407; Muscle 1407

GLUTATHIONE   *20*
  More concentrated in dark than in ordinary muscle.
  Dark muscle 955, 1311; Liver 955; Muscle 955; Ovary 955; Testis 955

GLYCEROL
  Lecithin (dark and white muscle) 1297; Lecithin (spleen) 1401; Muscle
  (parietal) 1077

L-α-GLYCEROPHOSPHATE   *41*
  Muscle 191

GLYCERYLPHOSPHORYL CHOLINE
  Muscle 609

FREE GLYCINE   *238, 240*
  This amino acid is found (in combination) in high concentrations in connective tissue, so that the concentration of gonad glycine progressively declines
  during maturation, as sex products accumulate and 'dilute' the connective
  tissue.
  Dark muscle 955; Heart 1311; Kidney 1311; Liver 1311; Muscle 1148, 1311

GLYCOGEN   *7, 18, 20, 24, 25, 30, 31, 40, 41, 43, 45, 49, 98, 99, 114, 119, 120,
  125, 202, 250, 251, 252*
  Levels in the muscle and liver of fish are low in comparison with those for
  the corresponding mammalian tissues, except for heart muscle, where levels
  may be considerably higher (Cordier, 1959). The glycogen reserve of adult
  salmon entering rivers is very small, so the energy for migration is probably
  derived from the breakdown of lipids (Fontaine and Hatey, 1953). A review
  of glycogen concentrations in muscle in relation to the effect of exercise is
  given by Tomlinson and Geiger (1962). Glycogen is the chief fuel for white
  muscle contraction, as distinct from dark muscle which uses mostly lipid. It
  accumulates in the ovary of fish during maturation, and is the first energy
  reserve to be utilized during starvation (before lipid or protein). Exercise for
  about 15 minutes reduces the concentration in dark and ordinary muscle, but
  does not affect that in the liver unless it is continued for about a day.
  Brain 25, 357, 455, 1025, 1385, 1387; Dark muscle 135, 364, 1352; Egg 357;
  Gill 455, 1385; Heart 245, 357, 455, 520, 672, 912, 978, 1385, 1387; Kidney 455,
  1385, 1387; Liver 25, 96, 115, 117, 215, 280, 357, 455, 479, 640, 672, 780, 813,
  859, 901, 912, 933, 978, 1142, 1219, 1224, 1250, 1277, 1352, 1385, 1387; Muscle
  19, 25, 85, 96, 114, 115, 117, 135, 280, 357, 364, 427, 455, 479, 520, 672, 797,
  798, 813, 817, 859, 901, 912, 933, 978, 979, 1195, 1224, 1352, 1385, 1387;
  Ovary 357, 455, 1385, 1387; Saccus vasculosus 1219; Skin 455, 1385, 1387;
  Sperm 357; Spleen 455, 1385, 1387; Stomach 455, 1385, 1387; Testis 357, 455,
  1385

GOLD
  Muscle 380

GUANINE   *80, 109*
Forms the basis of the silvery substance in the skin, and increases when salmon parr metamorphose.
DNA (muscle) 127; DNA (testis) 375

GUANOSINE DIPHOSPHATE
Lens 679

GUANOSINE MONOPHOSPHATE
Lens 679

GUANOSINE TRIPHOSPHATE   *42*
Level falls in the muscle during exertion.
Blood 425; Brain 425; Gill 425; 'Gonads' 425; Heart 425; Intestine 425; Kidney 425; Lens 679; Liver 425; Muscle 425, 623; Pyloric caecae 425; Spleen 425; Stomach 425

HAEMATOCRIT (blood cell volume) *93, 121, 149, 171, 176, 177, 188, 212, 220, 235, 255, 256*
Increases with the length of the fish, and correlates with intrinsic activity.
Blood 320, 328, 332, 341, 475, 504, 604, 640, 737, 802, 812, 858, 890, 1038, 1040, 1097, 1104, 1186, 1246, 1261; Lymph 604; Sinus fluid 604

HAEMOGLOBIN   *19, 20, 47, 80, 82, 83, 93, 94, 95, 104, 122, 135, 136, 137, 141, 148, 149, 150, 164, 165, 166, 168, 176, 177, 178, 179, 212, 220, 221, 222, 255*
Differs from mammalian haemoglobin in having isoleucine, high tryptophan and low histidine content (Eguchi, Hashimoto and Matsuura, 1960: *Oncorhynchus keta*). The quantity increases in the blood during migration (Shubnikov, 1959: *Clupea harengus*). Haemoglobin is not absolutely essential for fish, and certain Antarctic species manage without it. An eel which lived an active life without haemoglobin has also been described (Steen and Berg, 1966). It is more concentrated in dark than in ordinary muscle, and in deep-seated dark muscle than in superficial dark muscle. Electropherograms change in metamorphosis and during straightforward growth, also according to the state of maturity of various species and the ground where they were caught. The haemoglobin concentration increases with body length, and also with the intrinsic activity of the fish.
Blood 77, 111, 114, 115, 116, 117, 320, 328, 341, 475, 504, 553, 678, 812, 890, 1005, 1038, 1040, 1080, 1097, 1173, 1215, 1306; Dark muscle 179, 844, 845; Muscle 179, 844, 845

HEPARIN
Brain 25; Liver 25; Muscle 25

HEXOSAMINES (glucosamine and galactosamine are given separately elsewhere)
Cartilage 295; Slime 133, 1336

'HEXOSE'   *25*
Liver 901; Muscle 901

HEXOSE DIPHOSPHATE
  Blood 1224; Muscle 1224

HEXURONIC ACID
  Slime 324

HISTIDINE   *18, 20, 24, 124, 147, 151, 207, 240*
  An important free amino acid of *Clupea harengus*. Large quantities seem to be a character general to fatty fish. Non-fatty fish contain little or none of this substance in the free state, although it is still a major component of the muscle proteins (Hughes, 1959b). For some reason the muscle of freshwater fish contains more than that of marine fish, and that of active more than of sluggish species.
  Alimentary tract 1360; Dark muscle 546, 783; Haemoglobin 1039; Heart 1360; Kidney 1360; Lens 81; Liver 1360; Muscle 532, 546, 783, 1359, 1360, 1392; Ocular fluid (mixed) 81; Ovary 1360; Spleen 1360; Testis 1360

HYDROCORTISONE
  Blood 735, 1007

7-HYDROXYBIOPTERIN
  Skin 842

β-HYDROXYBUTYRATE
  Blood 608

17-HYDROXYCORTICOSTEROID
  Blood 452, 735, 1081

17α-HYDROXYPROGESTERONE
  Blood 560, 1124

HYDROXYPROLINE   *8, 10, 54, 101, 128, 208, 215, 216, 221, 233*
  Present in fish collagen in smaller amounts than in mammalian collagen.
  Collagen (scale) 1193; Collagen (skeleton) 392; Collagen (skin) 294, 392, 545, 1014, 1238, 1239, 1243; Collagen (swim bladder) 225, 1014, 1015; Scales 58; Skin 58;

17-HYDROXYSTEROIDS
  Blood 1080

HYPOXANTHINE   *20, 80*
  Increases in the skin during the metamorphosis of salmon parr. More concentrated in dark than in ordinary muscle (*Salmo gairdnerii*).
  Dark muscle 1099; White muscle 302, 653, 1099, 1101, 1109, 1280

ICHTHYLEPIDIN (scales minus minerals and gelatin)
  Scales 1193

INOSINE
  Muscle 653, 1280

Blood 266, 341, 443, 487, 802, 992, 998, 1109, 1126, 1144; Bone 251, 487, 989; Dark muscle 14, 377; Egg 892, 947, 1376; Eyeball 1201; 'Gonads' 1201; Heart 1201; Kidney 251, 487; Liver 251, 487, 1201; Muscle 251, 377, 487, 585, 592, 652, 918, 919, 987, 1109, 1201, 1234, 1317, 1327, 1370; Ovary 120, 1234; Pancreas 251; Pyloric caecae 531; Scales 251, 1047, 1189; Skin + Scales 1201; Spleen 487; Stomach 251; Testicular fat body 251

11-KETOTESTOSTERONE
Blood 562, 566, 1124

LACTIC ACID   7, 24, 25, 29, 31, 40, 41, 42, 43, 44, 45, 46, 47, 48, 51, 93, 149, 212
Increases greatly in blood and muscle during stress, and may kill the fish if the blood concentration rises above a certain level.
Blood 85, 110, 111, 114, 115, 116, 117, 199, 280, 479, 734, 859, 916, 991, 999, 1077, 1137, 1224; Brain 70; Dark muscle 364; Liver 115, 901, 1142, 1224; Muscle (body) 19, 70, 85, 114, 115, 191, 364, 734, 798, 817, 901, 979, 1224, 1279, 1283; Muscle (parietal) 1077

LEAD
Bone 251, 855, 989; Eyeball 1201; 'Gonads' 1201; Heart 1201; Kidney 251; Liver 251, 1201; Muscle 251, 855, 987, 1201, 1406; Pancreas 251; Scales 251; Skin + Scales 1201; Stomach 251; Testicular fat body 251

LECITHIN (Phosphatidyl choline)   21, 38, 76
Most concentrated in dark muscle, less in the belly and least in the white muscle (Sardinia melanosticta).
Actomyosin 1235; Blood 729; Brain 630, 805, 841; Cerebrum 658; Dark muscle 122, 576, 654, 655, 841, 1396; Egg 1400; Gall bladder 841; Heart 655, 841, 1396; Intestine 655, 1396; Intestine + Pyloric caecae 841; Kidney 655, 1396; Liver 654, 655, 692, 841, 1396; Muscle 11, 122, 575, 630, 654, 655, 692, 841, 958, 1158, 1396; Ovary 654, 1396; Pyloric caecae 655, 1396; Spinal cord 806; Spleen 655, 1396; Stomach 655, 841, 1396; Testis 654, 1396

FREE LEUCINE   238
Kidney 1311; Muscle 1148

LEUCOCYTES (white blood cells)   170, 178, 255, 256
Blood 487

LITHIUM   138, 144
Bone 989; Extracellular fluid 926; Eyeball 1201; 'Gonads' 1201; Heart 1201; Liver 1201; Muscle 182, 185, 987, 1201; Muscle (intracellular) 926; Scales 1189; Skin + Scales 1201

LUTEIN   50, 67, 201
Egg 461, 1205; Skin 1205

LYMPHOCYTES
Blood 487

LYSINE   *24, 124, 188, 207, 238*
Muscle 592

LYSO-PHOSPHATIDYL CHOLINE
Liver 692; Muscle 692

MAGNESIUM   *7, 42, 62, 79, 106, 137, 144, 191, 192, 196, 197, 218, 246*
In muscle mostly in a bound form. Cold shock increases the serum magnesium of *Carassius auratus*, as does anoxia. It was considered by Platner (1950) to have come from the red blood cells under these circumstances. Serum magnesium has also been reported to rise during sexual activity. It decreases in muscle during starvation owing to a decrease in the intracellular phase. Increases in tissues when euryhaline fish migrate to the sea.
Aqueous humour 293, 1011; Bile 1182; Blood 92, 212, 293, 341, 535, 858, 874, 953, 992, 998, 1011, 1024, 1075, 1076, 1077, 1109, 1182; Bone 251; Cerebrospinal fluid 1182; Egg 947; Eyeball 1201; Gill 315, 995; 'Gonads' 1201; Heart 1201; Intestine 995; Kidney 251; Liver 92, 220, 251, 315, 1201; Muscle (body) 108, 196, 220, 251, 652, 712, 1061, 1076, 1109, 1201, 1283, 1317, 1370; Muscle (parietal) 212, 1077; Muscle (tongue) 92, 212; Pancreas 251; Pericardial fluid 1182; Perivisceral fluid 1182; Pyloric caecae 531; Scales 251, 1189; Skin 995; Skin + Scales 1201; Stomach 251; Testicular fat body 251; Urine 874, 950, 1183, 1184

MANGANESE   *200*
Is an activator of alkaline phosphatase, and is found in appreciable quantities in the ovary, more so in the liver (Vinogradov, 1953). In general, bones contain the highest amount (Petkovich, 1967a).
Blood 341; Bone 251, 989; Dark muscle 987; Eyeball 1201; 'Gonads' 1201; Heart 1201; Kidney 251; Liver 251, 1201; Muscle 251, 987, 1201, 1229; Ovary 1229; Pancreas 251; Scales 251; Skin + Scales 1201; Stomach 251; Testicular fat body 251

MANNOSE
Brain 25; Liver 25; Muscle 25

MERCURY
Much more concentrated in fish tissues than in either fresh or salt water (Vinogradov, 1953).
Muscle 1337

METHIONINE   *21, 58, 130, 207*
Dark muscle 846; Muscle 592, 846

METHYL GUANIDINE
Muscle 645, 1109

1-METHYL HISTIDINE   *99, 143*
Found only in teleosts, not elasmobranchs.
Dark muscle 783; Muscle 615, 783, 1148, 1329

MOLYBDENUM   *200*
> Eyeball 1201; 'Gonads' 1201; Heart 1201; Liver 1201; Muscle 987, 1201; Skin + Scales 1201

MUCOPOLYSACCHARIDES
> Skin 1390; Swim bladder 1390

MYOGLOBIN   *19, 21*
> More concentrated in dark muscle than in ordinary muscle, and in deep-seated dark muscle than in superficial dark muscle.
> Dark muscle 179, 180, 844, 845; Muscle 179, 180, 844, 845

NIACIN (Nicotinic acid)   *18, 22, 24, 25, 28, 96, 147, 151, 208, 209, 253*
> Exists in tissues in combination as coenzymes, so is directly involved in energy metabolism. Thus a very active fish would be expected to have much of it in the muscle. While Braekkan (1959) found that this was so, *Thunnus thynnus thynnus*, the most active fish tested, having the greatest concentration of muscle niacin, there were exceptions among other species, so that other factors may be involved. There is less niacin in the muscle of freshwater fish than in that of marine fish. It is not essential for health, at any rate in *Salmo gairdnerii*.
> Blood 341; Dark muscle 146, 156, 494, 867; Gill 147, 156; Heart 147, 156, 494, 646, 683; Intestine 147, 156, 157, 494, 646; Kidney 147, 156, 494; Liver 146, 156, 157, 494, 631, 646, 670, 683, 707, 708; Muscle 69, 146, 147, 150, 156, 157, 158, 192, 217, 420, 494, 527, 583, 585, 592, 670, 681, 683, 690, 750, 785, 810, 867, 919, 1096, 1234, 1251; Ovary 69, 147, 148, 156, 157, 631, 681, 683, 690, 707, 708, 785, 1234, 1251; Pyloric caecae 147, 156, 636; Skin 494; Spleen 147, 156, 646; Stomach 147, 156, 646; Stomach + Intestine 494, 683; Testis 147, 156, 157, 494, 683, 708

NICKEL   *200*
> Bone 251, 989; Eyeball 1201; 'Gonads' 1201; Heart 1201; Kidney 251; Liver 251, 1201; Muscle 251, 987, 1201; Pancreas 251; Scales 251; Skin + Scales 1201; Stomach 251; Testicular fat body 251

NICOTINAMIDE
> Liver 429; Muscle 526

NICOTINAMIDE ADENINE DINUCLEOTIDE (*see* Diphosphopyridine nucleotide).

NICOTINAMIDE ADENINE DINUCLEOTIDE PHOSPHATE (*see* Triphosphopyridine nucleotide).

NORADRENALINE   *40*
> Increases in blood and kidney during exertion.
> Blood 912; Brain 327, 603; Chromaffin cell groups in sympathetic chain 327; Heart 327, 603, 912; Intestine 327; Kidney 327, 912; Liver 912; Muscle 327, 912; Spleen 327; Swim bladder muscle 327; Various parts of swim bladder 330; Whole swim bladder 330; Vagus nerve 327

OESTRADIOL   *61, 111, 112, 121*
Blood 210, 211, 316, 1171; Eggs 419; Ovarian sac 419; Ovary 142, 222, 419, 1171, 1368; Testis 221, 419

OESTRIOL   *111, 120*
Blood 210, 211, 316; Ovary 222; Testis 221

OESTRONE   *111, 112, 120, 121*
Blood 210, 211, 316, 1171; Egg 419; Ovarian sac 419; Ovary 419, 1171; Testis 221, 419

OPHIDIN
Muscle 1295

ORNITHINE
Dark muscle 42; Muscle 42, 1329

OXYGEN   *46, 47*
Blood 116

OXYTOCIN   *171*
Pituitary 354

PANTOTHENIC ACID   *22, 28, 56, 68, 96, 151, 208, 252*
Few data show the physiological function of this substance in fish (Higashi, 1961). It is usually not present in the free form, but mostly bound as co-enzyme A (Novelli, Kaplan and Lippmann, 1949, quoted by Braekkan, 1959). The gonad is richest in pantothenic acid, with dark flesh and liver next in order. Ordinary muscle is poor in it, but active fish have more than inactive fish (Higashi, Murayama *et al.*, 1959a). The amount in the ovaries declines during maturation (Braekkan, 1955). There is a much higher concentration in eggs from a hatchery than in 'wild' eggs—other vitamins are lower.
Blood 341; Dark muscle 146, 156, 502; Egg 892; Gill 147, 156; Heart 147, 156, 498, 502; Intestine 147, 156, 157, 502; Kidney 147, 156, 498, 502, 507, 893; Liver 146, 147, 156, 157, 498, 502, 893, 1234; Muscle 146, 147, 150, 156, 157, 217, 498, 502, 506, 526, 527, 751, 893, 1234; Ovary 145, 147, 148, 156, 157, 498, 502, 751, 893, 1234; Pyloric caecae 147, 156, 502, 636; Skin 498, 502; Spleen 147, 156, 502; Stomach 147, 156, 502; Testis 147, 156, 157, 498, 502, 893

PARA-AMINO BENZOIC ACID   *209*
Pyloric caecae 634

'PENTOSE'   *24*
Liver 901; Muscle 901

PHOSPHATIDYL CHOLINE (*see* Lecithin)

PHOSPHATIDYL ETHANOLAMINE
Blood 729; Dark muscle 122, 655, 1396; Heart 655, 1396; Intestine 655, 1396; Kidney 655, 1396; Liver 655, 692, 1396; Muscle 11, 122, 655, 692, 1396; Ovary 1396; Pyloric caecae 655, 1396; Spleen 655, 1396; Stomach 655, 1396; Testis 1396

PHOSPHATIDYL INOSITOL
  Liver 692; Muscle 692

PHOSPHATIDYL SERINE
  Blood 729; Dark muscle 655, 1396; Heart 655, 1396; Intestine 655, 1396;
  Kidney 655, 1396; Liver 655, 692, 1396; Muscle 11, 655, 692, 1396; Ovary
  1396; Pyloric caecae 655, 1396; Spleen 655, 1396; Stomach 655, 1396; Testis
  1396

PHOSPHOETHANOLAMINE
  Brain 956

3-PHOSPHOGLYCERIC ACID   42
  Blood 1224; Muscle 191, 1224

PHOSPHOINOSITIDE
  Muscle 1158

PHOSPHOLIPID   22, 36, 57, 62, 64, 122, 214, 242
  Blood 729, 872; Brain 25, 630, 805, 946; Cerebrum 658; Dark muscle 655,
  1396; Head and body 5; Heart 655, 1396; Intestine 655, 1396; Kidney 655,
  1396; Liver 5, 25, 655, 692, 1396; Muscle 25, 385, 609, 630, 655, 692, 822, 958,
  960, 1158, 1396; Ovary 1396; Pyloric caecae 655, 1396; Skin 960; Spinal cord
  806; Spleen 655, 1396; Stomach 5, 655, 1396; Testis 1396

PHOSPHOPYRUVIC ACID
  Blood 1224; Muscle 1224

POTASSIUM   3, 6, 7, 12, 24, 42, 43, 79, 84, 87, 88, 106, 114, 122, 137, 138, 144, 188,
  189, 191, 193, 194, 195, 196, 197, 218, 219, 244, 245, 246, 247, 248
  The main intracellular ion. Tends to decrease when marine fish migrate to
  fresh water, and vice versa. Often decreases in the muscle from head to tail,
  probably a reflection of the decrease in cell size towards the tail and the
  increase in the proportion of connective tissue, which is poor in potassium.
  Sudden cooling (thermal shock) causes fish muscle to lose potassium. Decreases
  in both muscle and serum during starvation, in the former because of a decrease
  in the intracellular phase.
  Aqueous humour 293, 310, 832; Bile 1182; Blood 92, 193, 212, 262, 293, 315,
  321, 341, 535, 538, 553, 664, 724, 727, 815, 832, 858, 874, 895, 971, 992, 998,
  1011, 1075, 1076, 1077, 1080, 1081, 1083, 1109, 1143, 1144, 1182, 1198, 1199,
  1215; Bone 197, 251; Brain 70, 186, 736, 1083; Cerebrospinal fluid 262, 832,
  1182; Cornea 310; Cranial fluid 321, 895; Dark muscle 649, 1271; Egg 947;
  Endolymph 321, 601, 895; Endolymph (sacculus) 321; Endolymph (semi-
  circular canal) 321; Erythrocytes 1083; Extracellular fluid 926; Extradural
  fluid 262; Gill 315; Heart 736; Jelly from the ampulla of Lorenzini 895;
  Kidney 251, 984; Lens 81, 310; Liver 92, 220, 251, 315, 736, 984; Marshall's
  gland 1182; Muscle (body) 70, 108, 175, 184, 185, 186, 192, 193, 197, 202, 206,
  220, 251, 462, 649, 652, 712, 727, 736, 792, 793, 814, 871, 919, 948, 971, 1061,
  1076, 1083, 1109, 1258, 1262, 1263, 1266, 1267, 1268, 1269, 1270, 1271, 1274,
  1283, 1284, 1317, 1327, 1370; Muscle (mouth) 1143; Muscle (parietal) 212,

RIBOFLAVIN (vitamin B_2) *22, 28, 38, 69, 96, 151, 208, 221, 252*

In general, skin has a higher content of riboflavin than muscle, that in liver and gonad being intermediate (Hoar and Barberie, 1945). Riboflavin is slightly more concentrated in eggs of high hatching rate than in those of low hatching rate (Hirao, Yamada and Kikuchi, 1955b). In flat fish, it is more concentrated in the upper flesh than the lower. It is also more concentrated in the muscle of active than of sluggish fish, and in *Gadus morhua* from the Arctic than in those from warmer waters. Dark muscle is richer than white muscle.

Bile 1152; Blood 341; Brain 25; Dark muscle 146, 156, 867, 1285; Egg 511, 584, 892, 932; Gall bladder 932; Gill 147, 156; Heart 147, 156, 489, 646, 683; Intestine 147, 156, 157, 646; Kidney 147, 156, 489, 507, 893, 1151; Liver 25, 146, 147, 156, 157, 429, 489, 497, 498, 501, 517, 631, 646, 683, 707, 785, 786, 787, 891, 893, 1113, 1151, 1234; Muscle 25, 52, 146, 147, 150, 156, 157, 192, 217, 420, 497, 498, 506, 517, 526, 527, 583, 585, 592, 683, 750, 785, 787, 867, 919, 1113, 1129, 1234, 1251, 1285; Ovary 147, 148, 156, 157, 497, 498, 517, 631, 683, 707, 785, 786, 787, 893, 932, 1113, 1129, 1234, 1251; Pyloric caecae 147, 156, 634, 891; Skin 497, 498, 517; Slime 497, 498; Spleen 147, 156, 646, 932; Stomach 147, 156, 646; Stomach + Intestine 683; Testis 147, 156, 157, 497, 498, 683, 785, 787, 893, 932, 1113

RIBOFLAVIN ADENINE DINUCLEOTIDE
Dark muscle 1285; Muscle 1285

RIBOFLAVIN MONONUCLEOTIDE
Dark muscle 1285; Muscle 1285

RIBOSE *42*
Muscle 188, 314, 616, 617, 618, 1248, 1280; Slime 326

RIBOSE NUCLEIC ACID *38, 48, 67, 74, 107, 108, 109*
Alimentary tract 258, 1111; Brain 25; Dark muscle 102, 1111; Egg 12; Eye 1404; Heart 258; Kidney 258, 1111; Liver 25, 258, 1111; Mauthner axon 312, 593; Mauthner axon sheath 593; Muscle 25, 102, 127, 258, 1111, 1280, 1281; Ovary 258; Pyloric caecae 530; Spleen 258; Testis 258

RIBOSE PHOSPHATE *42*
Blood 1224; Muscle 188, 1224, 1249

RUBIDIUM
Bone 251; Brain 186; Extracellular fluid 926; Kidney 251; Liver 251; Muscle 184, 185, 186, 251; Muscle (intracellular) 926; Pancreas 251; Scales 251; Stomach 251; Testicular fat body 251

SARCOSINE *143*
Found in elasmobranchs but not in teleosts.
Muscle 1329

SELENIUM
Bone 251; Kidney 251; Liver 251; Muscle 251, 448; Pancreas 251; Scales 251; Stomach 251; Testicular fat body 251

SERINE ETHANOLAMINE PHOSPHATE
'Gonad' 1088; Kidney 1088; Liver 1088; Muscle 1088

SIALIC ACID
Cartilage 325; Slime 133, 325

SILICON   *79*
Bone 251; Egg 947; Kidney 251; Liver 251; Muscle 251; Pancreas 251; Scales 251, 1189; Stomach 251; Testicular fat body 251

SILVER   *200*
Bone 989; Eyeball 1201; 'Gonads' 1201; Heart 1201; Liver 1201; Muscle 987, 1201; Skin + Scales 1201

SODIUM   *3, 4, 6, 7, 12, 13, 14, 22, 42, 43, 79, 83, 84, 86, 87, 88, 89, 106, 114, 120, 123, 137, 138, 139, 144, 187, 189, 190, 191, 193-8, 218, 219, 220, 244, 245, 246, 247, 250*
The principal extracellular ion, so comparatively concentrated in connective tissue and also brain. Tends to increase in the muscle from head to tail, probably through the decrease in cell size and increase in the proportion of connective tissue. Rises in muscle during starvation because of a relative increase in extracellular space, but falls in blood plasma. Rises in the muscle of eels on metamorphosis. Decreases in the muscle of *Gadus morhua* with increase in body length, provided the fish are not depleted. A sudden cooling (thermal shock) causes the muscle to gain sodium, perhaps by depressing the "sodium pump" mechanism. Dark muscle is richer than white muscle (*Hippoglossus hippoglossus*). The concentration increases markedly when euryhaline fish enter the sea, and vice versa.
Aqueous humour 293, 310, 832; Bile 1182; Blood 92, 121, 193, 212, 293, 315, 321, 341, 535, 538, 553, 664, 724, 727, 807, 815, 832, 858, 874, 877, 878, 895, 971, 992, 998, 1011, 1075, 1076, 1077, 1081, 1083, 1109, 1143, 1144, 1182, 1198, 1199, 1215; Bone 251; Brain 70, 186, 736, 1083; Cerebrospinal fluid 832, 895, 1182; Cornea 310; Cranial fluid 321; Dark muscle 649, 1271; Egg 947; Endolymph 321, 601, 895; Endolymph (sacculus) 321; Endolymph (semi-circular canal) 321; Erythrocytes 1083; Extracellular fluid 926; Gill 315; Heart 736; Jelly from the ampulla of Lorenzini 895; Kidney 251, 984; Lens 81, 310; Liver 92, 220, 251, 315, 736, 984; Marshall's gland 1182; Muscle (body) 70, 108, 121, 175, 184, 185, 186, 193, 202, 206, 220, 251, 649, 712, 727, 736, 792, 793, 814, 919, 948, 971, 1061, 1076, 1083, 1109, 1258, 1262, 1263, 1266, 1267, 1268, 1269, 1270, 1271, 1273, 1274, 1283, 1284; Muscle (intracellular) 926, 1083; Muscle (mouth) 1143; Muscle (parietal) 212, 1077, 1143; Muscle (tongue) 92, 212; Ocular fluid (mixed) 81; Ovary 736; Pancreas 251; Pericardial fluid 1182; Perilymph 321, 601, 895; Perivisceral fluid 1182; Pyloric caecae 531; Scales 251, 1189; Semen 121; Stomach 251; Testicular fat body 251; Testis 736; Urine 322, 724, 874, 950, 1198, 1199; Vitreous humour 310

SPHINGOMYELIN   *22*
Richer in dark than in ordinary muscle.
Blood 729; Brain 630, 805; Cerebrum 658; Dark muscle 654, 655, 1296, 1396; Egg 1400; Heart 655, 1396; Intestine 655, 1396; Kidney 655, 1396; Liver 654,

655, 1396; Muscle 630, 654, 655, 1158, 1296, 1396; Ovary 654, 1396; Pyloric caecae 655, 1396; Spinal cord 806; Spleen 655, 1396; Stomach 655, 1396; Testis 654, 1396

SQUALENE   *143*
Usually found only in elasmobranch livers, but has recently been found in a teleost, *Thaleichthys pacificus* (Ackman, Addison and Eaton, 1968).
Head + Body 5; Liver 5; Stomach 5

STRONTIUM   *144, 207*
Bone 251, 989; Eyeball 1201; 'Gonads' 1201; Heart 1201; Kidney 251; Liver 251, 1201; Muscle 251, 987, 1201; Pancreas 251; Scales 251, 1189; Skin + Scales 1201; Stomach 251; Testicular fat body 251

'SUGAR' (mostly glucose)   *45, 46, 92, 99, 123, 150, 169, 174, 176, 202, 221, 252*
Rises in the blood during asphyxia and exercise, and is higher in the blood of active than of sluggish species.
Blood 428, 671, 731, 802, 897, 898, 950, 978, 995, 1104, 1132; Urine 950

SULPHATE   *22, 58, 144, 207, 211*
Most sulphate is intracellular, not in the inorganic form but largely as part of the amino acids methionine and cysteine.
Aqueous humour 293; Bile 1182; Blood 293, 341, 874, 998, 1076, 1077, 1182; Bone 251; Cerebrospinal fluid 1182; Dark muscle 377; Kidney 251; Liver 251; Marshall's gland 1182; Muscle 251, 377, 1076, 1109; Pancreas 251; Pericardial fluid 1182; Perivisceral fluid 1182; Pyloric caecae 531; Scales 251; Stomach 251; Testicular fat body 251; Urine 874, 1183, 1184

TAURINE   *22, 82, 99, 140, 188, 238*
Decreases in the muscle of *Salmo salar* when they change from parr to smolt. Richer in dark than in white muscle (*Engraulis japonicus*).
Blood 663; Brain 956; Dark muscle 42; Muscle 42, 249, 250, 614, 615, 698, 1101, 1109, 1148

TESTOSTERONE   *112, 121*
Blood 422, 423, 568, 1124; Testis 221, 423, 571

THALLIUM
Muscle 448

THIAMINE   *22, 28, 208, 221, 253*
Within one species, individual variations in the concentration of thiamine are less than in fat-soluble vitamins, perhaps because tissues use only what they need and do not accumulate any excess (Higashi, 1961). Eyeballs contain about 60 times as much thiamine as does muscle tissue, and the retina contains most of all (Fukuda and Hirami, 1955). The highest value quoted by these authors was 27·7 mg% dry weight. *Gadus morhua* from arctic waters contains more than those from warmer waters. Dark muscle is richer than ordinary muscle.

Brain 25; Dark muscle 146, 156, 839, 867; Egg 932; Eyeball 382; Gall bladder 932; Gill 156; Heart 156; Intestine 156, 1044; Kidney 156; Liver 25, 146, 156, 429, 497, 498, 631, 707, 742, 785, 786, 787, 1112, 1234; Muscle 25, 146, 156, 192, 217, 382, 405, 420, 497, 498, 526, 527, 583, 585, 592, 682, 725, 742, 750, 785, 787, 839, 867, 919, 966, 1044, 1112, 1234; Ovary 156, 497, 498, 631, 707, 742, 785, 786, 787, 1112, 1234; Pancreas 1044; Pyloric caecae 156, 636, 891; Skin 497, 498; Spleen 156, 932; Stomach 156; Testis 156, 497, 498, 785, 787, 1112

THREONINE ETHANOLAMINE PHOSPHATE
'Gonad' 1088; Kidney 1088; Liver 1088; Muscle 1088

THYMINE
DNA (testis) 375

TIN
Bone 989; Muscle 987, 1406

TITANIUM
Bone 251, 989; Kidney 251; Liver 251; Muscle 251, 987; Pancreas 251; Scales 251; Stomach 251; Testicular fat body 251

TRIGLYCERIDE   *242*
Blood 729; Dark muscle 122; Head + Body 5; Liver 5; Muscle 11, 122, 822; Ovary 789; Stomach 5

TRIMETHYLAMINE
Values increase soon after death in most fish species, owing to formation of this compound by bacterial reduction of trimethylamine oxide.
Dark muscle 1236; Gall bladder 21; Intestine 1236; Liver 21, 1236; Muscle 21, 365, 540, 631, 645, 919, 971, 979, 1085, 1236, 1237, 1253, 1359; Ovary 21; Pyloric caecae 21, 1236; Skin 21; Spleen 21; Stomach 21, 1236; Testis 21

TRIMETHYLAMINE OXIDE   *23, 38, 95, 139, 143, 145, 146, 151, 169, 190, 202, 203, 221*
Hoppe-Seyler and Schmidt (1927, quoted by Kutscher and Ackermann, 1933) found TMO in all sea fish but not in freshwater fish. They concluded that the compound was related to urea, which it resembles by virtue of its non-poisonous nature, small molecular weight and almost neutral reaction. Several workers have tried to show an osmoregulatory function for TMO, with greater or lesser success. Lange and Fugelli (1965) showed that the sum of the TMO and total free ninhydrin-positive substances correlated well with the osmolarity of the blood. At present it is uncertain if TMO arises from dietary origins or is synthesized in the fish (Bilinski, 1964; Goldstein, Hartman and Forster, 1967); there is some evidence on either side. Young fish have a very low level, which increases if the food contains TMO (Benoit and Norris, 1945), but it is hard to explain the winter upsurge of TMO in herrings on the basis of diet (Simidu, 1961). Increases in concentration can be found in some species as one passes from head to tail. The blood of active species contains more than that of sluggish species, and there is more in fish caught in Arctic waters than

in the same species from warmer localities. Dark muscle is richer than ordinary muscle (*Thunnus albacares*). Freshwater teleosts possess a little in the muscle, marine teleosts more and marine elasmobranchs most (see Table XXVIII). Aqueous humour 293; Blood 321, 293, 727; Brain 1227; Dark muscle 42, 1236, 1373; Eye fluid 1227; Gall bladder 21; Intestine 1236; Kidney 1227; Liver 21, 92, 220, 1227, 1236; Muscle 21, 28, 42, 220, 243, 250, 307, 365, 541, 631, 645, 691, 727, 1065, 1085, 1101, 1148, 1227, 1236, 1237, 1253, 1319, 1359, 1373; Foetal muscle 1227; Muscle (parietal) 1077; Muscle (tongue) 92; Ovary 21, 243; Pancreas 1227; Pyloric caecae 21, 1236; Shell gland 1227; Skin 21; Spleen 21, 1227; Stomach 21, 1236; Testis 21, 243

TRIOSE PHOSPHATE
Blood 1224; Muscle 1224

TRIPHOSPHOPYRIDINE NUCLEOTIDE (Nicotinamide adenine dinucleotide phosphate) *42, 151*
Muscle 623, 1249

TRYPTOPHAN *207*
Haemoglobin 1039; Muscle 22, 592, 697, 1036, 1090

TUNAXANTHIN
Skin 1293

TUNGSTEN
Muscle 380

TYROSINE *208*
Collagen (skeleton) 392; Collagen (skin) 392; Haemoglobin 1039; Muscle 22, 1090

UBIQUINONE *140*
Ascent of the evolutionary tree corresponds in many cases with an increase of ubiquinone in the heart, so cyclostomes contain less than elasmobranchs, which in turn contain less than teleosts.
Heart 292, 920, 982; Intestine 292; Liver 292, 920; Muscle 920, 982

URACIL
DNA (muscle) 127

URANIUM
The average figure for fish muscle is $2 \cdot 1 \times 10^{-5}$ mg/g.
Muscle 1327

UREA *139, 144, 145, 253, 256*
Particularly rich in elasmobranch blood, where it helps the fish to osmoregulate. No other vertebrate or invertebrate contains as much, apart from the aestivating lung-fish in which nitrogen excretion has ceased (Smith, 1931a). Unlike trimethylamine oxide, which may serve a similar purpose, the urea concentration in each organ is proportional to its water content (Suyama and

Tokuhiro, 1954b). The concentration in pericardial fluid is less than in peri-visceral fluid or serum.

Aqueous humour 293, 674, 1011; Bile 674, 1182, 1183, 1227; Blood 293, 341, 674, 895, 991, 999, 1011, 1080, 1104, 1182, 1183, 1184, 1227; Brain 1227; Cerebrospinal fluid 674, 895, 1182; Ear fluid 674; Electric organ 674; Embryo 1226; Endolymph 895; Erythrocytes 1182; Eye 1227; Eye fluid 1227; Gastric juice 1182, 1183; Heart 674, 1227; Intestine 1182; Jelly from the ampullae of Lorenzini 895; Kidney 1227; Liver 177, 1130, 1182, 1227; Marshall's gland 1182; Muscle 201, 631, 674, 938, 1148, 1182, 1226, 1227, 1329; Foetal muscle 1227; Muscle (parietal) 1077; Ovary 1182; Pancreas 1227; Pericardial fluid 674, 1182, 1183; Perilymph 895; Perivisceral fluid 674, 1182, 1183; Shell gland 1227; Skin 1182; Spleen 1182, 1227; Stomach 1227; Testis 1227; Urine 674, 1183; Uterus 1227; Yolk 1227

URIC ACID   23

More concentrated in dark muscle than in ordinary muscle.

Blood 341, 991, 999, 1144

URIDINE DIPHOSPHATE

Blood 425; Brain 425; Gill 425; 'Gonads' 425; Heart 425; Intestine 425; Kidney 425; Liver 425; Muscle 425; Pyloric caecae 425; Spleen 425; Stomach 425

URIDINE DIPHOSPHOGALACTOSE

Lens 679

URIDINE TRIPHOSPHATE   42

Muscle level falls during exertion.

Blood 425; Brain 425; Gill 425; 'Gonads' 425; Heart 425; Intestine 425; Kidney 425; Lens 679; Liver 425; Muscle 425; Pyloric caecae 425; Spleen 425

URONIC ACID

Cartilage 295

FREE VALINE   238

Kidney 1311; Muscle 1148

VANADIUM

Bone 989, 1194; Eyeball 1201; 'Gonads' 1201; Heart 1201; Liver 1201; Muscle 987, 1201; Skin + Scales 1201

VITAMIN A_1 (retinol)   23, 25, 38, 39, 67, 74, 95, 96, 105, 124, 125, 129, 130, 172, 173, 180-6, 200, 203, 208, 209, 252

Obtained ready-made in the food of fish, or from carotenoid precursors. Liver tissue may contain as much as 99·95% of the vitamin A of the fish (Higashi, Hirao et al. 1953a). The possible range of values is enormous, one review, for example, quoting values from 179—9,819,000 Units per 100 g (Fixsen and Roscoe, 1940). There are great variations according to the age of the fish and the ground, as well as the sex of the fish and the season. Papers quoting liver vitamin A values are not listed below because of the variability of the results, but collections of data by Lovern, Edisbury and Morton (1933) and Fisher (1964) are useful. Concentrations in many samples of liver *oil*, without reference to the original tissue, are given by Bailey, Carter and Swain (1952) and Cruickshank (1962). Miwa and Kinoshita (1956, quoted by Mega, 1965) reported that much of the liver vitamin A was used up in the recovery period after spawning. This may not be a true interpretation, since starvation usually causes an apparent *increase* in concentration of the vitamin, the oil in which it is soluble being utilized, while the vitamin is not. There are great variations in the concentrations as between different parts of one liver, or of one fillet. In flat fish there is more in the flesh and skin from the upper than from the lower side. The highest concentration ever found in muscle is that in *Entosphenus japonicus*.

The aldehyde ('retinal') accumulates in the ovary during maturation, reaching the highest concentrations just before spawning. The blood level of retinal increases at the time of maturation in the female, but not in the male.

The vitamin A concentration in the liver increases with the *age* of the fish, so slower-growing specimens have a higher concentration, size-for-size. In most teleosts there is more in the dark muscle than the white, but the relationship is reversed in elasmobranchs.

Blood 341, 1022; Brain 25; Dark muscle 156, 508, 509; Egg 495, 496, 511, 932, 1019, 1020, 1021, 1376; Embryo 495, 496; Eye 311; Gall bladder 496; 'Gonad' 1156; Heart 496, 982; Intestine 157, 311, 497; Kidney 156, 495, 496, 497, 498, 499; Muscle 25, 156, 495, 497, 498, 499, 508, 509, 510, 511, 512, 513, 750, 982, 1371, 1374; Ovary 496, 497, 498, 1020, 1023; Pancreas 495, 496; Pyloric caecae 50, 156, 311, 509; Skin 497, 498, 511, 512, 1374; Slime 497, 498; Spleen 311, 495, 496; Stomach 311; Testis 157, 497, 498; Yolk 496

VITAMIN A$_2$ (dehydroretinol) *180, 183, 184, 185, 200*

Occurs in the eyes and livers of some freshwater fish or fish living in certain light-environments. Carotenoids can be precursors of vitamins A$_1$ or A$_2$ with equal facility, and no precursors specifically for vitamin A$_2$ have been found (Gross and Budowski, 1966).

Egg 1019, 1020; Ovary 1020

VITAMIN B

(*See under* Thiamine (B$_1$), Riboflavin (B$_2$), Pyridoxine (B$_6$), Cyanocobalamin (B$_{12}$). Nicotinamide, Biotin, Para-amino benzoic acid, Niacin, Pantothenic acid, Folic acid, Inositol and Choline also come under this heading.)

VITAMIN C (ascorbic acid) *25, 74, 124, 147, 169, 208, 209, 221*

Little is known about metabolic reactions which require vitamin C, but it is said to be involved in oxidation-reduction systems, maybe as catalyst or coenzyme (Bai and Kalyani, 1960c), and is considered a fatigue retardant, enzyme catalyst and anti-oxidant (Parvatheswararao, 1967). It may be necessary for the production of connective tissue and the healing of wounds (papers quoted by Bai and Kalyani, 1960b; Siddiqui, 1967), and the concentration has been noticed to rise in summer and fall in winter (Fomin, Romanjuk and Khvoynitskaya, 1937; Shanta and Motelica, 1962; Siddiqui, 1967). There is much more vitamin C in the brain than in other tissues (Bai and Kalyani, 1960c), and it has a characteristic level in other organs as well (Giroud, Leblond *et al.*, 1938), being, for instance, richer in testis than in ovary. Shanta and Motelica (1962) considered that the concentration in the tissues depended on the physiological state of the fish, rather than on the amount of the vitamin available, and the concentration rises during cold acclimatization. There is less vitamin C in the muscle of freshwater fish than marine fish.

Aqueous humour 293; Blood 57, 293, 341; Brain 57, 355, 579, 781, 1141; Dark muscle 965; Egg 861, 932; Eye 579, 1141; Gall bladder + Bile 579; Gill 1044, 1141; "Gonad" 1141; Heart 579, 781, 965, 1044, 1141; Intestine 1044, 1141; Kidney 57, 355, 579, 781, 965, 1141; Lens 781, 965; Liver 57, 355, 399, 471, 556, 579, 781, 840, 965, 1044, 1095; Muscle 56, 355, 399, 420, 471, 556, 579, 717, 781, 840, 965, 1044, 1095, 1141; Ovary 355, 471, 556, 579, 781, 840, 932, 965; Pancreas 1044; Skin 56; Spleen 579, 781, 965; Testis 471, 579, 781, 785, 965

VITAMIN D (calciferol, now to be known as ergocalciferol—Anon., 1960) *142, 208*

Absent from many fish. The highest amounts are present in the lipid of *Cyprinus carpio* and *Abramis brama* (Bukin and Erofeeva, 1951, quoted by Higashi, 1961). The low concentrations in elasmobranchs contrast with the abundance of vitamin A in many of them, showing that there is no inter-relationship between vitamins A and D (Cruickshank, 1962). Elasmobranchs presumably do not need vitamin D because they have no true bony structures, so do not suffer from rickets in its absence.

Heart 1374; Intestine 1053, 1056, 1057, 1374; Kidney 1374; Liver 47, 707, 785, 1052, 1053, 1054, 1055, 1056, 1057, 1374; Muscle 47, 60, 785, 1374; Ovary 707, 785, 1374; Pyloric caecae 1374; Skin 1374; Stomach 1374; Swim bladder 1374; Testis 1374

VITAMIN E (tocopherol) *23, 200, 252*

The tocopherols present in fish originate in the phytoplankton (algae). The principal type is α-tocopherol (Ackman, 1967a; Ackman and Cormier, 1967). Of the various organs, the heart contains most (Ikeda and Taguchi, 1966). The vitamin is present in relatively large amounts in the gonads (Mega, 1965) and becomes largely depleted during spawning (Mori, Naito and Mejika, 1957, quoted by Higashi, 1961). There is a tendency for the vitamin E content to be lower in organs with a high oil content, and vice versa (Mega, 1965). Some decrease in the muscle occurs during starvation.

Dark muscle 8; 'Gonad' 1213; Heart 581, 850, 920, 982, 1213; Kidney 581, 850, 1213; Liver 8, 581, 850, 920, 1213; Muscle 8, 581, 850, 919, 920, 982; Ovary 707, 850; Pyloric caecae 850, 1213; Stomach 850; Testis 850

WAX ESTERS *142*

Adipose tissue 927; Muscle 927; Ovary 789

XANTHOPHYLLS *50, 201*

Form the basis of much of the pigmentation of the fish, and many species need large quantities in the diet to keep a normal colouring. Specimens in captivity often fade for this reason.

Egg 414; Liver 1204; Muscle 1204; Ovary 1204; Skin 1204

XANTHOPTERIN

Skin 842

ZEAXANTHIN
  Liver 360

ZINC   *23, 95, 143, 200, 203*
    In general, zinc is concentrated in the same organs which concentrate iron
(liver and spleen): Vinogradov (1953). When taken up by eggs, about 70%
becomes bound to the chorion and 26% enters the perivitelline fluid. Little
reaches the yolk or embryo (Wedemeyer, 1968: *Oncorhynchus kisutch*). Lower
concentrations are found in elasmobranch blood than teleost blood. High concentrations in the tissues of some fish have been shown to have originated in a
diet of molluscs.
    Bone 251; Eyeball 1201; Gill 315; 'Gonads' 1201; Heart 1201; Kidney 251;
Liver 251, 315, 1201; Muscle 251, 344, 987, 1201; Pancreas 251, 344; Pyloric
caecae 531; Scales 251; Skin + Scales 1201; Stomach 251; Testicular fat
body 251

INDEX OF FISH NAMES

Many systematic names of fish have been mis-spelt in chemical papers, and indeed more than one author quoted a number of fish names, every one of which was wrong. A modest attempt has therefore been made to check the list, and give notes on the distribution and habitat of the species concerned; the following authorities have been used for the purpose, spellings being modified where necessary. These references do not occur in the main bibliography, since the checking was done after the latter was complete.

Anonymous (1960). "Catalogue of the names of fishes of commercial importance in the Mediterranean." FAO, Rome.

Cabo, F. L. (1965). "Official Spanish nomenclature of marine animals of interest to fishing." Madrid.

Clemens, W. A. and Wilby, G. V. (1967). "Fishes of the Pacific Coast of Canada." Fisheries Research Board of Canada, Bull. no. 68, 2nd ed., Ottawa. **278**

Chute, W. H. and others (1947). "A list of common and scientific names of the better-known fishes of the United States and Canada." American Fisheries Soc. Spec. Publ. no. 1, 44 pp. Reprinted in *Trans. Am. Fish. Soc.* (1948), **75**, for the year 1945, 355–97.

Day, F. (1876). "The fishes of India." 2 vols. Bernard Quaritch, London.

Gibbs, R. H. and Collette, B. B. (1967). "Comparative anatomy and systematics of the tunas, genus *Thunnus.*" U.S. Dept. of Interior, Fish and Wildlife Service, *Fishery Bull.* **66**, 65–130.

Grant, E. M. (1965). "Guide to fishes." (Queensland). Dept. of harbours and marine, Queensland.

Jordan, D. S. (1963). "A classification of fishes." Stanford University Press, California.

Jordan, D. S., Evermann, B. W. and Clark, H. W. (1930). "Checklist of the fishes and fishlike vertebrates of North and middle America north of the northern boundary of Venezuela and Colombia." Reprinted 1955. U.S. Fish and Wildlife Service, Washington.

Leim, A. H. and Scott, W. B. (1966). "Fishes of the Atlantic Coast of Canada." Fisheries Research Board of Canada, Bull. no. 155, Ottawa.

Munro, I. S. R. (1955). "The marine and freshwater fishes of Ceylon." Dept. of external affairs, Canberra.

Norman, J. R. (1935). *In* "List of British Vertebrates," pp. 40–66. British Museum, London.

Okada, Y. (1955). "Fishes of Japan." Maruzen Co. Ltd., Tokyo.

Perlmutter, A. (1961). "Guide to Marine fishes". Bramhall House, New York.

Roughley, T. C. (1966). "Fish and fisheries of Australia." Angus and Robertson, Sydney.

Schindler, O. (1957). "Freshwater fishes." Translated by P. A. Orkin. Thames and Hudson, London and New York.

"The South African Fishing Industry Handbook and buyers' guide." 1964/5, 7th Ed. South African Shipping News and Fishing Industry Review, Cape Town.

Weber, M. and de Beaufort, L. F. "The fishes of the Indo-Australian archipelago."
11 volumes issued between 1913 and 1962 (continuing). Volume 11 with
Briggs, J. C.   E. J. Brill Ltd., Leiden.
Wheeler, A. (1969). "The fishes of the British Isles and North-West Europe."
Macmillian, London.

A number of species were not mentioned in any of the books consulted, and
for these we must rely hopefully on the spellings as originally quoted. In such
cases the only information on the locality where the fish may be found is quoted
from the original paper, and is usually incomplete. Generalized descriptions such
as 'Europe' or 'America' generally fall into this category.

It is almost certain that some fish will appear in the list under more than one
name. For any resulting confusion I would plead for the reader's indulgence: the
task of sorting out the correct designations has not been easy because of the
steady rejection of names over the years and their substitution by new ones.
I would be most grateful if duplications were pointed out to me for the sake of
any future editions.

The inclusion of synonyms without chemical values, thus: "*Stromateus
niger*—see *Parastromateus niger*" shows that the first name has been quoted in
a chemical paper, but the bibliographical information has been added to that
given under the second name.

It seemed better not to include the name of the classifier with each Latin
name, as in, for example, "*Ictalurus ictalurus* Rafinesque". Only about half of
the chemical papers, perhaps not even that proportion, gave them, and it was
felt better to omit them altogether than provide an incomplete list.

The common names, limited to those in the English language, are arranged
alphabetically in Appendix B with their systematic equivalents. Again the list
is far from exhaustive, as common names vary from region to region and there
are probably several times this number in existence.

The systematic family relationships of fish named in the text are shown in
Appendix A. In the present list, groups that seem likely to differ chemically have
been distinguished by their manner of presentation, as follows.

*Fish living exclusively in fresh water are marked †, and elasmobranch fish ‡. The few
fresh water elasmobranchs are marked thus ¶, and cyclostomes §. Fish marked * are euryhaline and may spend part of their lives in fresh water, part in sea. No more should be read
into it than this—marine fish so marked can tolerate fresh water, but do not necessarily spawn
there. The names of all bony marine fish, and fish of which I have been unable to discover
the nature are without any distinguishing symbol. Numbers in italics refer to pages in the
text; those not italic are reference numbers.*

N.B. 100 *metres* = 55 *fathoms.*

ABRAMIS BRAMA† (Bream, Bronze bream, Carp bream)   *97, 199, 214*
Central, N. and E. Europe in lakes, slow streams and brackish environments.
N-Acetyl histidine 456; Amino acids 25, 26; Cholesterol 25; Copper 1406;
Cyanocobalamin 25; DNA 25; Fatty acids 25; Galactose 25; Glucose 25, 664;
Glycogen 25; Heparin 25; Lead 1406; Mannose 25; Phospholipid 25; Potas-
sium 462, 664; Riboflavin 25; RNA 25; Sodium 664; Thiamine 25; Tin 1406;
Ubiquinone 292; Vitamin A 25

ABRAMIS FARENUS†
    Europe
    Potassium 462

ABRAMIS VIMBA†
    Europe: Danube Basin, Eastern Baltic and tributaries. Keeps near the bottom.
    Vitamin C 781

ACANTHISTIUS SERRATUS (Wirrah)
    Seas of the Southern Hemisphere, Australia, on weedy foreshores of coasts and estuaries
    Cholesterol 872; Phospholipid 872

ACANTHOCYBIUM SOLANDRI
    Warmer parts of the Pacific
    Haemoglobin 77; Vitamin A 513

ACANTHOGOBIUS FLAVIMANUS* (Genuine goby)
    Japan. Estuarine, can ascend rivers.
    Cholesterol 1153; Cyanocobalamin 1380; Fatty acids 1153; Folic acid 503; Lecithin 1235; Pantothenic acid 502; Riboflavin 584; Vitamin A 513

ACANTHOPAGRUS SCHLEGELI
    Japan.
    Vitamin C 579

ACANTHURUS BLEEKERI (Bleeker's lined surgeon-fish)
    Red Sea, India, Philippines, Java.
    Iron 585; Niacin 585; Riboflavin 585; Thiamine 585

ACANTHURUS HEPATUS (Common surgeon, Doctor fish, Lancet fish)
    N. America: West Indies to Woods Hole.
    DNA 862

ACENTROGOBIUS VIRIDIPUNCTATUS (Green-spotted goby)
    Seas of India, common Bombay and Madras, on coastal reefs.
    Hydroxyproline 58; Proline 58

ACHOERODUS GOULDII (Blue groper)
    S. half of Australian coast, along shores and reefs.
    Cholesterol 872; Phospholipid 872

ACIPENSER GÜLDENSTÄDTI*   71, 94
    DNA 1155

ACIPENSER HUSO*
    N. America, Europe, Black and Caspian Seas, basin of Amur River.
    Amino acids 309

ACIPENSER RUTHENUS* (Sterlet)
    Russia.
    Anserine 1392; Carnosine 1392; FREE histidine 1392

ACIPENSER STELLATUS*   71

ACIPENSER STURIO* (Sturgeon)   *122, 146*
Atlantic Ocean, North, Baltic and Mediterranean Seas. Rivers. Winters in deep water with muddy bottom.
FREE Amino acids 1139; Creatin + Creatinine 1139; DNA 862; Fatty acids 767

AILIA COILA†
Rivers of India.
Calcium 1327; Copper 1327; Iron 1327; Potassium 1327; Uranium 1327

ALBURNUS LUCIDUS† (Bleak)
Europe, in slowly flowing and still waters, sometimes brackish. Pelagic.
"Sugar" 671

ALLOMYCTERUS JACULIFERUS
Australia.
Cholesterol 872; Phospholipid 872

ALOPIAS PELAGICUS‡ (Fox shark, Thresher, Whip-tail shark)
Warmer waters of S. Japan. Viviparous.
Urea 1226

ALOPIAS PROFUNDUS‡ (Thresher shark)
Japan.
Hydroxyproline 1239, 1243

ALOSA KESSLERI PONTICA
Russia.
Aluminium 987, 989; Barium 987; Beryllium 987; Cadmium 987; Chromium 987, 989; Cobalt 987; Copper 989; Gadolineum 987; Iron 987, 989; Lead 987, 989; Lithium 987, 989; Manganese 989; Molybdenum 987; Nickel 987, 989; Silver 987, 989; Strontium 987, 989; Tin 987, 989; Titanium 987, 989; Vanadium 987, 989; Zinc 987

ALOSA PSEUDOHARENGUS* (Alewife, Glut herring)   *104, 106*
N. America: Newfoundland to N. Carolina. Landlocked in Great Lakes.
Amino acids 34; Chloride 1173; Haemoglobin 1173; Trimethylamine 243

ALOSA SAPIDISSIMA* (American shad, Common shad)
N. America: Gulf of St. Lawrence to Florida. Introduced to Pacific Coast. Coastal waters and coastal rivers. Spawns in both fresh and brackish waters.
Amino acids 723, 1035; Anserine 783; Carnosine 783; Histidine 783; 1-Methyl histidine 783; Niacin 192; Potassium 192, 1263; Riboflavin 192, 517; Sodium 192, 1263; Thiamine 192; Trimethylamine 365; Trimethylamine oxide 307, 365

ALOSA SARDINA
Europe.
Potassium 871

ALOSA SP.
DNA 862

AMBLYPHARYNGODON MOLA†
India, Ceylon and Burma.
Niacin 1096; Vitamin C 1095

AMEIURUS CATUS†
N. America.
Amino acids 1035

AMEIURUS MELAS MELAS† (Black bullhead, Small catfish) *40*
N. America.
Lactic acid 110

AMEIURUS NEBULOSUS† = ICTALURUS NEBULOSUS (Brown bullhead, Common
bull-head, Horned pout, Small catfish) *29, 211*
N. America: Great Lakes, southward to Texas and Florida. Shallow lakes and
rivers. Introduced to Europe.
DNA 862; Erythrocytes 475; Haematocrit 475, 802; Haemoglobin 475;
Iron 802; 'Sugar' 671, 802

AMEIURUS SP.†
Trimethylamine 28; Trimethylamine oxide 28

AMIA CALVA† (Bowfin, Lawyer, Mudfish) *222, 255*
N. America: Great Lakes to Florida. Lakes and sluggish streams.
Cerebroside 805, 806; Cholesterol 805, 806; Lecithin 805, 806; Phospholipid
805, 806; Sphingomyelin 805, 806

AMIA SP.†
DNA 862

AMMODYTES TOBIANUS (Arctic sandlance, Lesser sandeel)
N. America: South California to Bering Sea. Newfoundland. W. Europe
including Iceland. Sandy shores from mid-tide level down to 30 m. Shoals.
Carotene 414; Xanthophylls 414

ANABAS SCANDENS† = ANABAS TESTUDINEUS† (Climbing perch)
India, Burma, Malaya, Philippines, China. Estuaries and fresh waters.
Cyanocobalamin 71, 72; Cystine 1090; Folic acid 73; Iron 585; Niacin 585;
Riboflavin 585; Thiamine 585; Tryptophan 1090; Tyrosine 1090; Vitamin C
1095

ANABAS TESTUDINEUS† (*see* A. SCANDENS)

ANAGO ANAGO (Silvery conger)
Japan.
Vitamin A 513

ANARHICHAS LATIFRONS (Broadheaded catfish)
Both sides of N. Atlantic, mostly north of Arctic Circle.
Trimethylamine oxide 307

ANARHICHAS LUPUS (Atlantic wolf fish, Catfish, Striped wolf fish) *146, 219, 225,
226*
Both sides of Atlantic, Spitzbergen, Murman Coast, W. France, Davis Strait
to New Jersey. Shallow, cool waters down to more than 150 m. Solitary.
Amino acids 154; Calcium 1061, 1234; Cyanocobalamin 150, 1234; FREE

Fatty acids 365; Iodine 1234; Iron 1234; Magnesium 1061; Niacin 150, 1234; Pantothenic acid 150, 1234; Potassium 1061; Riboflavin 150, 787, 1234; Sodium 1061; Thiamine 742, 787, 1234; Trimethylamine 365; Trimethylamine oxide 307, 365

ANARHICHAS MINOR (Leopard fish, Lesser catfish, Spotted catfish, Spotted wolf fish) *225, 226*
Both side of Atlantic (further north than *A. lupus*), Grand Bank, Greenland, Spitzbergen, White Sea. Deep water, down to 460 m, on muddy or fine sandy bottoms.

ANGELICHTHYS ISABELITA (Angel fish)
West Indies to Florida.
Niacin 413; Riboflavin 413; Thiamine 413

ANGUILLA ANGUILLA* = A. VULGARIS (Eel) *83, 91, 105, 120, 121, 145, 146, 166, 184, 189, 191, 192–7, 201, 216, 222, 230, 231, 242*
All Europe, including Iceland. From electrophoretic data this fish may be the same as the American ANGUILLA ROSTRATA (Sick, Westergaard and Frydenberg, 1962). Coasts, ascending rivers.
N-Acetyl histidine 456; Amino acids 663; Betaine 529; Calcium 212, 984, 1234; Chloride 212, 1143; Cyanocobalamin 1234; DNA 1323; Fucose 1336; Glucose 664; Glutamine 1407; Glycogen 245; Hexosamines 133, 1336; Iodine 1234; Iron 1234; Magnesium 212; Niacin 1234; Oestradiol 211; Oestriol 211; Oestrone 211; Pantothenic acid 1234; Potassium 212, 664, 871, 984, 1143; Riboflavin 1234; Sialic acid 133; Sodium 212, 664, 984, 1143; 'Sugar' 671; Taurine 663; Thiamine 1234; Ubiquinone 982; Vitamin A 982; Vitamin E 982.

ANGUILLA BOSTONIENSIS* (American eel)
N. America.
Trimethylamine oxide 307

ANGUILLA JAPONICA* (Japanese eel) *166, 224, 235, 250, 251, 256, 257*
Japan.
Amino acids 323; FREE Amino acids 698; Carnosine 532, 698; Cyanocobalamin 1380; Fatty acids 472; Folic acid 503; Fucose 326; Galactose 326; Glucose 326; Glucosamine 324; Hexuronic acid 324; Hydroxyproline 1238, 1239, 1243; Manganese 1229; Pantothenic acid 502; Pyridoxine 1384; Renin 1192; Riboflavin 489, 501, 932; Ribose 326; Taurine 698; Thiamine 932; Vitamin A 512, 513, 1374; Vitamin C 579, 840, 932; Vitamin D 1374

ANGUILLA ROSTRATA* (American eel, Silver eel) *166, 202*
N. America: Labrador to West Indies. May be the same as A. anguilla.*
Ammonia 790; Chloride 193; Glutamate 790; Iron 443; Potassium 193; Riboflavin 517; Sodium 193; 'Sugar' 428

ANISOTREMUS INTERRUPTUS (Mojarron)
Pacific coast of America: Magdalena Bay to Panama and the Galapagos.
Niacin 413; Riboflavin 413; Thiamine 413

ANODONTOSTOMA CHACUNDA (Gizzard shad)
India, Thailand, Philippines, Java, Borneo.
Iron 585; Niacin 585; Riboflavin 585; Thiamine 585

ARGYROPS SPINIFER
   Japan.
   Inositol 1149

ARGYROSOMUS ARGENTATUS
   Japan, muddy bottom of shore.
   Actin 1309; Creatin 1100; Creatinine 1100; Vitamin A 513

ARIUS ARIUS*
   India to China, in sea, estuaries and rivers.
   Niacin 1096; Vitamin C 1095

ARIUS LEIOTETOCEPHALUS*
   Philippines, Java, Singapore, Malacca. Seas and estuaries.
   Iron 585; Niacin 585; Riboflavin 585; Thiamine 585

ARIUS MANILLENSIS (Manila sea catfish)
   Philippines.
   Iron 585; Niacin 585; Riboflavin 585; Thiamine 585

ARIUS SERRATUS† (Catfish, Saw-edged catfish)
   India: Sind.
   Fatty acids 667

ARIUS SONA* (Dusky catfish)
   India, Singapore. Seas, entering estuaries and tidal rivers.
   Cholesterol 630; Lecithin 630; Niacin 631; Phospholipid 630; Riboflavin 631;
   Sphingomyelin 630; Thiamine 631; Trimethylamine oxide 1319

ARRIPIS GEORGIANUS (Ruff, Tommy rough, Sea herring)
   Seas of Australia, New Zealand and neighbouring islands.
   Copper 88

ARRIPIS TRUTTA (Salmon trout)
   S. Australian coast.
   Copper 88

ASPIUS ASPIUS† (Asp)
   Sweden and E. Europe to Russia. Rivers, lakes and brackish water.
   Calcium 1317; Iron 1317; Magnesium 1317; Potassium 1317

ASTROCONGER MYRIASTER (Common Japanese conger)   *231*
   Japan, coastal.
   Amino acids 323; Cholesterol 1153; Fatty acids 1153; Trimethylamine 1237;
   Trimethylamine oxide 1237; Vitamin A 513, 1374; Vitamin D 1374

ASTYANAX MEXICANUS†   *126*
   N. America: Rio Balsas to tributaries of the Mississippi.

ATHERESTHES EVERMANNI
   Japan.
   Cyanocobalamin 1381; FREE Amino acids 917

ATHERESTHES STOMIAS (Arrowtooth flounder, Long-jaw flounder, Turbot)
N. America: N. California to Bering Sea. Coastal.
Potassium 1268; Riboflavin 1113; Sodium 1268; Thiamine 1112

ATHERINOPSIS CALIFORNIENSIS (California blue smelt)
California coast.
Anserine 783; Carnosine 783; Histidine 783; l-Methyl histidine 783

ATHLENNES HIANS
Red Sea, India, Pacific, Japan. Atlantic, N. Carolina to Brazil.
Trimethylamine oxide 1319

AULOSTOMUS MACULATUS (Trumpet fish)
N. America: S. Florida, Caribbean Sea.
DNA 862

AUSTROGLOSSUS PECTORALIS (Agulhas sole)
S. Africa.
Amino acids: 1341

AUXIS HIRA
Japan.
Vitamin A 510

AUXIS MARU
Japan.
Vitamin A 510

AUXIS ROCHEI (Frigate mackerel, Plain bonito)
America, Europe. Perhaps the same as A. THAZARD.
Haemoglobin 77, 678

AUXIS TAPEINOSOMA (Frigate mackerel)   7
Japan. Shoals far from coast.
Adenosine triphosphate 378; Ammonia 19; Glycogen 19; Lactic acid 19;
Phosphocreatin 378

AUXIS THAZARD (Frigate mackerel, Plain bonito)
Oceanic in warm parts of Atlantic and Pacific, also Mediterranean and occa-
sionally around Britain.
Cyanocobalamin 891, 1380; Iron 585; Niacin 585; Pyridoxine 1383, 1384;
Riboflavin 501, 585, 891; Thiamine 585; Tryptophan 697; Vitamin A 513

BAGRE MARINUS (Gafftopsail, Sea catfish)
N. America: Cape Cod to Panama. Fertilised eggs carried in the mouth of the
male until they hatch.
Chloride 1215; Cholesterol 1215; Haemoglobin 1215; Potassium 1215; Sodium
1215

BALISTES CAPRISCUS (File fish, Grey triggerfish)
Tropical Atlantic, both sides; south of Ireland and S.W. England; Mediter-
ranean. A feeble swimmer.
DNA 862

BALISTES HIPPOCREPIS
  Australia.
  Cholesterol 872; Phospholipid 872

BARBUS CARNATICUS†
  India: rivers in Madras and W. coast.
  Calcium 918; Iron 918

BARBUS CHRYSOPOMA† = B. SARANA† (Olive barb)
  India: coasts of Deccan, Madras and Darjeeling. Streams, rivers, ponds and
  lakes.
  Calcium 918, 1327; Cholesterol 1161; Copper 1327; Cystine 1090; Iron 918,
  1327; Potassium 1327; Tryptophan 1090; Tyrosine 1090; Vitamin C 1095

BARBUS DUBIUS†
  India: Bowany River in Madras.
  Calcium 918; Iron 918

BARBUS FLUVIATILIS†
  Germany.
  'Sugar' 671

BARBUS HEXAGONOLEPIS†
  India: Assam.
  Calcium 918; Iron 918

BARBUS KOLUS†
  India: Deccan, Kistna River.
  Calcium 1327; Copper 1327; Iron 1327; Potassium 1327

BARBUS PUNTIUS† *262*
  Bengal and Burma.
  Calcium 1047; Copper 1047; Iron 1047; Potassium 1047

BARBUS PUTITORA†
  India.
  Cholesterol 1161

BARBUS SARANA† (*see* B. CHRYSOPOMA†)

BARBUS SP.†
  India.
  Calcium 1327; Copper 1327; Iron 1327; Potassium 1327

BARBUS STIGMA†
  India and Burma.
  Cholesterol 1161

BARBUS TOR†
  Throughout India. Rapids, hill streams.
  Calcium 918; Iron 918

BELONE BELONE (Garfish, Garpike)
All Europe, Mediterranean and Black Seas. Oceanic near the surface, also inshore.
N-Acetyl histidine 456; FREE Amino acids 1139; Creatin + Creatinine 1139; Lithium 926; Potassium 736, 871, 926; Sodium 736, 926; Trimethylamine 1253; Trimethylamine oxide 1253

BELONESOX BELIZANUS† *123, 183, 184*
S. Mexico, Honduras, Guatemala.

BENTHOBATIS SP. *186*

BERYX SPLENDENS (Alfoncino)
Japan, American coast. Among rocks, 300–400 metres depth.
Cyanocobalamin 1381; Potassium 871; Riboflavin 501; Vitamin A 508, 513

BLENNIUS PAVO (Peacock blenny) *121, 187*

BLENNIUS SANGUINOLENTUS (Red-speckled blenny)
Europe.
Calcium 712; Magnesium 712; Potassium 712; Sodium 712

BLEPSIAS DRACISCUS
Vitamin E 850

BOLEOPHTHALMUS BODDAERTII
India, coast of Burma to Malaya. Muddy bottom.
Calcium 55; Hydroxyproline 58; Proline 58; Vitamin C 56, 57

BOREOGADUS SAIDA* (Arctic cod, Polar cod) *212*
Circumpolar, observed further north than any other species.
FREE Amino acids 1139; Anserine 1139; Creatin + Creatinine 1139

BOX BOOPS (Bogue)
South from Sweden and S. Ireland to Mediterranean and Canary Islands. Shallow water amongst rocks.
Trimethylamine 1253; Trimethylamine oxide 1253

BRANCHIOSTEGUS JAPONICUS
S. Japan, Korea.
Astaxanthin 1293; Carotenoids 1293; Inositol 1149; Pyridoxine 1383; Riboflavin 501; Tunaxanthin 1293; Vitamin A 513, 1374; Vitamin D 1374

BREVIRAJA ISOTRACHYS
Japan.
Vitamin A 513

BREVOORTIA PATRONUS (Gulf menhaden)
Gulf of Mexico, coast of Texas.
Chloride 1215; Cholesterol 1215; Haemoglobin 1215; Potassium 1215; Sodium 1215

BREVOORTIA TYRANNUS (Menhaden, Mossbunker, Pogy)   *23, 24, 47, 116, 150*
N. America: Nova Scotia to Florida. Large shoals near shore.
Anserine 783; Carnosine 783; Cerebroside 805, 806; Cholesterol 805, 806;
Haematocrit 737; Histidine 783; Iron 443; Lecithin 805, 806; 1-Methyl
histidine 783; Phospholipid 805, 806; Sphingomyelin 805, 806

BROSME BROSME (Cusk, Torsk, Tusk)   *20, 25*
Both sides of Atlantic, Murman coast, 18 to 550 m. Bottom-living, solitary.
Amino acids 154; Biotin 155, 751; Calcium 1061, 1234; Cyanocobalamin 147,
150, 1234, 1251; Folic acid 751; Iodine 1234; Iron 1234; Magnesium 1061;
Niacin 147, 150, 192, 1234, 1251; Pantothenic acid 147, 150, 751, 1234;
Potassium 1061; Pyridoxine 155; Riboflavin 147, 150, 192, 787, 1234, 1251;
Sodium 1061; Thiamine 192, 742, 787, 1234; Trimethylamine oxide 307;
Ubiquinone 292; Vitamin C 785

CAESIO CHRYSOZONA (Golden-banded fusilier)
Red Sea, Indian Ocean, Philippines, Japan, Formosa, Solomon Islands.
Iron 585 Niacin 585; Riboflavin 585; Thiamine 585

CAESIO CUNING
India, Thailand, Sumatra, Philippines, Okinawa, N. Australia, Solomon
Islands.
Iron 585; Niacin 585; Riboflavin 585; Thiamine 585

CALAMUS CALAMUS (Saucereye porgy)
West Indies, North to Florida Keys.
DNA 862

CALLICHROUS BIMACULATUS† (Butter catfish)
India.
Calcium 918; Cholesterol 1161; Iron 918

CALLIONYMUS LYRA (Dragonet)
Mid-Norway and Iceland southwards to Mediterranean.
Cyanocobalamin 412

CAMBARUS CLARKII
Methionine 846

CANTHERINES UNICORNU
Japan.
Folic acid 503; Pantothenic acid 502; Riboflavin 501

CAPRINUS AORATUS†   *22*
Japan.
Riboflavin 489, 1285; Riboflavin adenine dinucleotide 1285; Riboflavin mono-
nucleotide 1285; Thiamine 839

CARANGOIDES AJAX
Hawaii.
Amino acids 198

CARASSIUS AURATUS† (Goldfish, Johnny carp) *viii, 17, 20, 30, 38, 48, 52, 85, 121, 171, 175, 177, 201, 205, 209, 213, 214, 216, 217, 218, 221, 245, 280*
China, Japan. Introduced widely elsewhere. Tolerates low oxygen concentrations and high temperatures.
Adrenaline 603; γ-Amino butyric acid 949; Calcium 64, 953; Cyanocobalamin 1380; Fatty acids 607, 685; Haematocrit 1097; Haemoglobin 1097; 7-Hydroxy biopterin 842; Isoxanthopterin 842; Magnesium 953, 1024; Noradrenaline 603; RNA 312, 593; Trimethylamine oxide 307; Vitamin A 311, 510, 1374; Vitamin C 579, 840; Vitamin D 1374

CARASSIUS AURATUS BRAZILIENSIS†
Brazil.
Adrenaline 989; Noradrenaline 989

CARASSIUS AURATUS GIBELIO† (Gibel, Gibellian)
Japan.
Adenosine triphosphate 910; Creatine phosphate 910

CARASSIUS CARASSIUS† (Crucian carp) *200, 230, 270*
Japan and Far East, introduced elsewhere. Still waters, slowly-flowing rivers and marshes. Tolerates low oxygen concentrations.
Calcium 918; DNA 1111; Glucose 664; Histidine 532; Hydroxyproline 1238 1239, 1243; Iron 918; Potassium 664; RNA 1111; Sodium 664; Thiamine 382; Vitamin A 508, 510, 513

CARCHARHINUS ALFIMARGNATUS‡ (?ALFIMARGINATUS)
Fibrinogen 1098; Haematocrit 1097; Haemoglobin 1097

CARCHARHINUS BRACHYURUS‡
Vitamin A 513

CARCHARHINUS GANGETICUS‡ (Ground shark)
India, Japan.
Amino acids 141; Hydroxyproline 1239; Sialic acid 325

CARCHARHINUS GLAUCUS‡ = CARCHARIAS GLAUCUS‡ (Blue shark)
Britain.
Carotenoids 347

CARCHARHINUS JAPONICUS‡
Japan.
Cyanocobalamin 1380; Hydroxyproline 1243

CARCHARHINUS LEUCAS‡ (Bull shark, Cub shark, Ground shark)
W. Atlantic from N. Carolina to S. Brazil, inshore. Slow-swimming, viviparous.
Corticosterone 1006; Cortisol 1006

CARCHARHINUS LIMBATUS‡ (probably CARCHARIAS LIMBATUS‡)
(Small black-tipped shark, spot-fin ground shark.) Possibly world-wide in tropical and sub-tropical waters. In W. Atlantic found from N. Carolina to Brazil near the shore. Active, fast-swimming, viviparous.
Chloride 1215; Cholesterol 1215; Haemoglobin 1215; Potassium 1215; Sodium 1215

CARCHARHINUS LONGIMANUS‡ (Whitetip shark)
Japan, tropical and subtropical Atlantic.
DNA 862; Vitamin A 513

CARCHARHINUS MACKIEI‡
Australia.
Copper 88

CARCHARHINUS MACULIPINNIS‡
N. America.
Amino acids 738; Corticosterone 1006; Cortisol 1006

CARCHARHINUS MELANOPTERUS¶
Thailand, Malaya (Perak).
Ammonia 1183; Chloride 1183, 1184; Creatin 1183; Urea 1183, 1184

CARCHARHINUS MILBERTEI‡ (Brown shark).
Both sides of Atlantic, Mediterranean, inshore. Viviparous.
Corticosterone 1006; Cortisol 1006

CARCHARHINUS OBSCURUS‡ (Dusky shark)
Western Atlantic from George's Bank to Brazil. Eastern Atlantic in warm
waters. Inshore and offshore.
Corticosterone 1006; Cortisol 1006; DNA 862

CARCHARIAS AETHALORUS‡
N. America.
Niacin 413; Riboflavin 413; Thiamine 413

CARCHARIAS ARENARIUS‡ (Grey nurse)
Australia: S. Queensland to S. Australia and Tasmania. Viviparous.
Copper 88

CARCHARIAS BRACHYURUS‡
Japan.
Vitamin A 496

CARCHARIAS ELLIOTI‡ (Elliot's grey shark)
India.
Ubiquinone 920; Vitamin E 920

CARCHARIAS LITTORALIS‡
Ammonia 1182; Calcium 1182; Cerebroside 805, 806; Chloride 1182; Cholesterol 805, 806; Creatin 1182; Lecithin 805, 806; Magnesium 1182; Phospholipid 805, 806; Potassium 1182; Sodium 1182; Sphingomyelin 805, 806;
Sulphate 1182; Urea 1182

CARCHARIAS MENISAURAH‡
India.
Amino acids 838; Cholesterol 630; Lecithin 630; Niacin 631; Phospholipid
630; Riboflavin 631; Sphingomyelin 630; Thiamine 631

CARPIOIDES MERIDIONALIS
S. Mexico and Guatemala.
Niacin 413; Riboflavin 413; Thiamine 413

CASPIALOSA KESSLERI PONTICA
Europe.
Calcium 966; Thiamine 966

CATHERINES MODESTUS
Vitamin A 509

CATLA BUCHMANANI† (see C. CATLA)

CATLA CATLA† (Indian carp)   *95, 127*
India: Bengal, Punjab. Burma, Thailand. Introduced into fresh waters of
Ceylon.
Calcium 918, 1327; Cholesterol 1161; Copper 1327; Cyanocobalamin 71, 72;
Folic acid 73; Iron 918, 1327; Niacin 1096, 1231; Potassium 1327; Thiamine
1232; Vitamin C 1095

CATOSTOMUS CATOSTOMUS† (Longnosed sucker, Northern sucker, Red sucker,
Sturgeon sucker)   *40*
N. America: Great Lakes, Alaska.
Corticosterone 1006; Cortisol 1006; Lactic acid 110

CATOSTOMUS COMMERSONII† (Bay mare, Black mullet, Brook sucker, Common
sucker, White sucker)
N. America: Great Lakes to Colorado, Missouri and Georgia.
Amino acids 583; Corticosterone 1006; Cortisol 1006; FREE Fatty acids 365;
Niacin 583, 681; Riboflavin 583; Thiamine 583, 682; Trimethylamine 365;
Trimethylamine oxide 365

CATOSTOMUS SP.†
Potassium 192, 1263, 1274; Sodium 192, 1263, 1274

CATULUS TORAZAME‡
Japan.
Riboflavin 501; Vitamin A 513

CAULOLATILUS PRINCEPS (Ocean whitefish)   *167*
Cape San Lucas to Galapagos.

CENTROLOPHUS JAPONICUS
Japan
Cholesterol 1153; Fatty acids 1153

CENTROPHORUS ATROMARGINATUS‡ (Fin shark)
Japan. Viviparous.
Niacin 494

CENTROPHORUS SQUAMOSUS‡
Carotenoids 347

CENTROPOMUS ARMATUS
N. America.
Niacin 413; Riboflavin 413; Thiamine 413

CENTROPOMUS ROBALITO
N. America.
Niacin 413; Riboflavin 413; Thiamine 413

CENTROPRISTES STRIATUS (Blackfish, Black sea bass, Black perch, Black Will, Tallywag)
Atlantic coast of United States, Cape Ann to N. Florida. Common inshore on rocky bottoms near wrecks and wharves, down to 130 m. Older females often change sex to become fertile males.
Potassium 1263; Sodium 1263

CENTROSCYLLIUM FABRICII‡ (Black dogfish)
Both sides of N. Atlantic, Japan. Found at depths over 280 m.
Carotenoids 347

CENTROSCYMNUS COELOLEPIS‡ (Portuguese shark)
Both sides of N. Atlantic, Azores, Mediterranean, Japan. Found at depths over 330 m.
Carotenoids 347

CENTROSCYMNUS OWSTONI‡
Japan. Deep sea.
Hydroxyproline 1239, 1243; Scale constituents (Ash, Calcium, Carbonate, Phosphate, Protein) 1241; Vitamin A 496, 513

CEPHALOPHOLIS ATROMARGINATUS
Niacin 494

CEPHALOPHOLIS FULVUS (Butter fish, Nigger fish, Yellow fish)
West Indies, Florida.
DNA 862

CEPHALOSCYLLIUM UMBRATILE‡
Japan.
Urea 1226

CERATOCOTTUS NAMIYEI (Ceratocottus, Elf sculpin)
Japan, Korea.
Vitamin E 850

CESTRACION ZYGAENA‡
Japan.
Cyanocobalamin 1381

CETORHINUS MAXIMUS‡ = SELACHUS MAXIMUS‡ (Basking shark)
N. and S. Atlantic and Pacific, Murman coast, Mediterranean, California to
Alaska. Not in Tropics. May exceed 11 m in length. Rather sluggish.
Amino acids 309; Carotenoids 347; Chloride 321; Potassium 321; Sodium 321

CHAENOCEPHALUS ACERATUS (Icefish, White crocodile fish)   *129, 150, 177, 178*
Antarctic.

CHAENOMUGIL PROBOSCIDEUS
N. America.
Niacin 413; Riboflavin 413; Thiamine 413

CHAETODIPTERUS FABER (Angelfish, Moonfish, Spadefish, Three-banded sheeps-
head, Three-tailed porgy, Tripletail)
Cape Cod to Rio de Janeiro, W. Indies. Found on rocky bottoms and in
wrecks.
Calcium 592; Cyanocobalamin 592; Cystine 592; Iron 592; Lysine 592;
Methionine 592; Niacin 592; Riboflavin 592; Thiamine 592; Tryptophan 592

CHANNA ARGUS† (Snake-head fish)   *200*
Japan.
Calcium 950, 951, 952; Cyanocobalamin 1381; Fatty acids 472; Magnesium
950; Potassium 950; Sodium 950; 'Sugar' 950

CHANOS CHANOS* (Milk fish, Salmon herring, White mullet)
Red Sea, India, Indonesia. Coastal waters and lagoons.
Amino acids 306; Iron 585; Niacin 585; Riboflavin 585; Thiamine 585

CHELA CLUPEOIDES†
India: Assam. Burma. Rivers.
Calcium 918; Iron 918

CHELA PHULO†
India.
Calcium 1327; Copper 1327; Iron 1327; Potassium 1327

CHELIDONICHTHYS CAPENSIS
S. Africa.
Vitamin D 1056

CHELIDONICHTHYS KUMU (Gurnard)
Japan, Australia.
Actin 1309; Amino acids 323; Astaxanthin 1293, 1294; Carotenoids 1293,
1294; Cholesterol 872, 1153; Cyanocobalamin 1381; Fatty acids 1153; Folic
acid 503; Pantothenic acid 502; Phospholipid 872; Pyridoxine 1383, 1384;
Riboflavin 891; Tunaxanthin 1293; Vitamin A 510, 513

CHELIDOPERCA HIRUNDINACEA (Princes small porgy)
Japan.
Riboflavin 501

CHILOSCYLLIUM GRISEUM‡
India to Malaya.
Trimethylamine oxide 1319

CHIMAERA BARBOURI‡
Japan.
Folic acid 503; Pantothenic acid 502; Vitamin A 513

CHIMAERA MONSTROSA‡ (Rabbit fish, Rat-tail, Rat-fish)
Europe: N. Norway to Mediterranean, on deep-water trawling grounds.
Calcium 1061; Carotenoids 347; Magnesium 1061; Potassium 1061; Sodium
1061; Vitamin A$_1$ 1020; Vitamin A$_2$ 1020

CHIMAERA PHANTASMA‡ (Ghost shark, Silver shark)
Japan. Oviparous.
Methionine 846; Niacin 494

CHIMAERA SP.‡
Glycogen 672

CHIONODRACO KATHLEENAE   *216*
Antarctic.

CHIROCENTRUS DORAB (Dorab, Wolf herring)
India. Coastal waters.
Iron 585; Niacin 585, 631, 670; Riboflavin 585, 631; Thiamine 585, 631;
Trimethylamine oxide 1319

CHLOROPHTHALMUS ALBATROSSIS
Japan.
Cyanocobalamin 1380; Vitamin A 513

CHPISO MAGARUA (presumably a mistake but could not trace)
India.
Vitamin C 1095

CHROINEMEUS TOLOOPARAH (probably Chrionema) (Leather jacket)
Fatty acids 667

CHRYSOPHRYS DATNIA = SPARUS LATUS (Japanese silver bream)
Madagascar, Red Sea, India, Ceylon, Japan, China, Australia. Coastal waters.
Cholesterol 630, 915; Lecithin 630; Niacin 631; Phospholipid 630; Riboflavin
631; Sphingomyelin 630; Thiamine 631

CHRYSOPHRYS MAJOR (Genuine porgy, Sea bream)   *51, 201*
Japan, Hawaii. Shores.
FREE Amino acids 698; Astaxanthin 1293; Carnosine 698; Carotenoids 1293;
Cholesterol 1153; Fatty acids 1153; Taurine 698; Trimethylamine 1237;
Trimethylamine oxide 1237; Tunaxanthin 1293; Vitamin A 513, 1374;
Vitamin D 1374

CHRYSOSTOMA GARUA†
India, Assam, Burma. Rivers.
Niacin 1096

CIRRHINA CIRRHOSA†
India: Godavary, Krishna and Cauvery rivers.
Calcium 918; Iron 918

CIRRHINA MRIGALA† (Carp)
India: Sind, Punjab. Burma. Rivers.
Adenosine triphosphate 979; Calcium 918, 1327; Cholesterol 1161; Copper
1327; Creatine phosphate 979; Glycogen 979; Iron 918, 1327; Lactic acid
979; Niacin 1096; Potassium 1327; Trimethylamine 979; Vitamin C 1095

CIRRHINA REBA†
India. Rivers.
Calcium 918; Cystine 1090; Iron 918; Tryptophan 1090; Tyrosine 1090

CIRRHINA SP.†
Calcium 918; Iron 918

CITHARICHTHYS SP.
S. America.
Calcium 592; Cyanocobalamin 592; Cystine 592; Iron 592; Lysine 592;
Methionine 592; Niacin 592; Riboflavin 592; Thiamine 592; Tryptophan 592

CITULA DORSALIS (Pampano)
Australia and the Pacific coast of tropical America.
Niacin 413; Riboflavin 413; Thiamine 413

CLARIAS BATRACHUS† = C. MAGUR† (Freshwater catfish, Teysmann's spotted
catfish)
India, Ceylon, Burma and Malaya. Fresh and brackish waters. Amphibious—
comes on land at night or during rain.
Cholesterol 1161; Cyanocobalamin 71, 72; Cystine 1090; Fatty acids 975;
Folic acid 73; Iron 585; Niacin 158, 585, 1096; Riboflavin 585; Thiamine 585;
Tryptophan 1090; Tyrosine 1090; Vitamin C 1095

CLARIAS LAZERA†   50, 92, 98, 120, 123, 202, 223, 252
Egypt.
Glucose 455, 1385, 1387; Glycogen 455, 1385, 1387

CLARIAS MAGUR† (see C. BATRACHUS†)

CLIDODERMA ASPERRIMUM (Roughscale sole)
Japan, S. British Columbia.
Folic acid 503; Pantothenic acid 502; Vitamin A 509, 513

CLUPANODON PSEUDOHISPANICUS
S. America.
Calcium 592; Cyanocobalamin 592; Cystine 592; Iron 592; Lysine 592;
Methionine 592; Niacin 592; Riboflavin 592; Thiamine 592; Tryptophan 592

CLUPANODON PUNCTATUS
Japan.
Arsenic 448; Riboflavin 1285; Riboflavin adenine dinucleotide 1285; Riboflavin mononucleotide 1285; Selenium 448; Thallium 448

CLUPANODON THRISSA
Japan.
Vitamin A 513

CLUPEA ALOSA
Adriatic Sea.
Trimethylamine 1253; Trimethylamine oxide 1253

CLUPEA CASPIOLOSA
Russia.
FREE Amino acids 1329; Creatin + Creatinine 1329

CLUPEA HARENGUS (Atlantic herring) *viii, 21–8, 36, 37, 69, 94–9, 102–5, 116, 117, 119, 126, 149, 152, 153, 155–7, 161, 164, 167, 169, 170, 198, 199, 222, 225, 226, 233, 242, 276, 277*
Both sides of the Atlantic, Spitzbergen to Gibraltar. Pelagic, from surface to 200 m. Different races spawn in spring and autumn.
Acetic acid 543; N-Acetyl histidine 456; Amino acids 34, 125, 240, 924, 1035; FREE Amino acids 400, 542; Ammonia 201, 540; n-Butyric aid 543; Calcium 966, 1061, 1234; Chloride 121; Cholesterol 1369; Collagen 545; Creatin 201, 544; Creatinine 544; Cyanocobalamin 150, 157, 683, 1234; Formic acid 543; Glucose 617, 618; Histidine 546; Hydroxyproline 545; Iodine 1234; Iron 1234; Magnesium 1061; Niacin 150, 157, 683, 690, 708, 785, 1234; Pantothenic acid 150, 157, 1234; Potassium 121, 871, 1061; Propionic acid 543; Riboflavin 150, 157, 517, 683, 785, 787, 1129, 1234; Ribose 617, 618; Sodium 121, 1061; Thiamine 785, 787, 966, 1234; Trimethylamine oxide 307, 541; Ubiquinone 292; Urea 201; Vitamin A_1 157, 311, 1019, 1020, 1021; Vitamin A_2 1020; Vitamin C 355, 785; Vitamin D 785

CLUPEA HARENGUS MEMBRANUS (Baltic herring) *62, 63, 92, 120*
Baltic Sea.

CLUPEA ILISHA* (*see* HILSA ILISHA*)

CLUPEA NORDMANI
Europe.
Calcium 966; Thiamine 966

CLUPEA PALLASII (Pacific herring) *21, 102, 122, 123, 169, 233*
S. California to Bering Sea. Japan.
Amino acids 281, 928, 1110; Calcium 1109; Cerebroside 654, 1396; Chloride 1109; Cholesterol 654, 1153, 1396; Choline 1109; Collagen 796; Creatin 554, 1109; Creatinine 1109; Cyanocobalamin 1381; Fatty acids 1153; Hypoxanthine 1109; Inosinic acid 1109; Inositol 1149; Iron 1109; Lecithin 654, 1396; Magnesium 1109; Methionine 846; Methyl guanidine 1109; Phosphatidyl ethanolamine 1396; Phosphatidyl serine 1396; Phospholipid 1396; Potassium 792, 793, 1109; Riboflavin 1113; Sodium 792, 793, 1109; Sphingomyelin 654, 1396; Sulphate 1109; Taurine 1109; Thiamine 1112; Trimethylamine oxide 307; Vitamin A 513, 1374; Vitamin C 471; Vitamin D 1374

CLUPEA PILCHARDUS (Pilchard)
Europe
Amino acids 1193; Gelatin 1193; Hydroxyproline 1193; Ichthylepidin 1193;
Lead 855

CLUPEA SPRATTUS = SPRATTUS SPRATTUS (Sprat)   *66, 99, 100, 198, 266*
All W. Europe except Iceland. Shallow waters near coasts.
Amino acids 990; FREE Amino acids 1329; Copper 1406; Riboflavin 787;
Urea 1329; Vitamin C 785

CNIDOGLANIS MACROCEPHALUS
Australia: Arafura Sea.
Copper 88

COBITIS TAENIA† (Spined loach)
Europe, Asia, N. Africa. Still or running water with muddy or sandy bottom.
Mainly nocturnal. Swallows bubbles of air under conditions of oxygen lack.
Anserine 1392; Carnosine 1392; Cholesterol 1369; FREE Histidine 1392

COELORHYNCHUS COELORHYNCHUS (Soldier fish)
Europe.
Vitamin A_1 1020; Vitamin A_2 1020

COELORHYNCHUS MULTISPINULOSUS
Japan.
Riboflavin 501

COILIA DUSSUMIERI
India to Malaya, Java, Singapore. Seas and estuaries.
Cholesterol 630; Creatin 631; Lecithin 630; Niacin 631; Phospholipid 630;
Riboflavin 631; Sphingomyelin 630; Thiamine 631; Trimethylamine 631;
Trimethylamine oxide 631; Urea 631

COLOLABIS SAIRA (Saury, Skipper)   *20–4*
Japan, S. California to Alaska. Cold water.
Cholesterol 1153; Cyanocobalamin 1380; Cytochrome C 844; Fatty acids
1153; Folic acid 503; Haemoglobin 844, 845; Manganese 1229; Methionine
846; Myoglobin 844, 845; Pantothenic acid 502; Pyridoxine 1383, 1384;
Riboflavin 501, 1285; Riboflavin adenine dinucleotide 1285; Riboflavin
mononucleotide 1285; Thiamine 839; Trimethylamine 1237; Trimethylamine
oxide 1237; Tryptophan 697; Vitamin A 510, 513, 1374; Vitamin D 1374

COLOTOMUS JAPONICUS
Japan.
Vitamin A 513

CONGER CONGER (Conger eel)   *121*
Atlantic, Mediterranean. Rocky shores and deep water. Active at night.
N-Acetyl histidine 456; FREE Amino acids 1329; Oestradiol 211; Oestriol
211; Oestrone 211; Progesterone 788; Riboflavin 1129; Vitamin A 311;
Vitamin C 399

COTTUS KAZIKA
Japan.
Vitamin A 513

COTTUS POLLUX†
Japan. Rivers.
Cyanocobalamin 1381; Vitamin A 513; Vitamin E 850

COTTUS SCORPIUS (*see* MYOXOCEPHALUS SCORPIUS)

COTTUS SP.
Glucose 1248; Ribose 1248

CRENILABRUS MELOPS (Baillon's wrasse, Corkwing, Gilt-head)
Europe south of Shetland to Mediterranean and Azores, on rocky shores below
mid-tide.
N-Acetyl histidine 456

CRENILABRUS PAVO = C. TINCA (Peacock wrasse)
Europe.
FREE Amino acids 1329; Glycogen 978; 'Sugar' 978

CRENILABRUS QUINQUEMACULATUS
Russia.
Calcium 712; Magnesium 712; Potassium 712; Sodium 712

CRENILABRUS TINCA (*see* C. PAVO)

CRISTIVOMER NAMAYCUSH† (Great Lakes trout, Lake trout, Mackinaw trout)
211, 227
N. America: Great Lakes, headwaters of Columbia and Fraser Rivers, North
to Arctic Circle.
Amino acids 583, 1035; Glycogen 672; Niacin 583; Riboflavin 583; Thiamine
583

CYBIUM COMMERSONII (Spanish mackerel)
Red Sea, Seas of India, Malaya, Philippines.
Iron 585; Niacin 585; Riboflavin 585; Thiamine 585

CYBIUM KUHLI
Seas of India.
Niacin 158

CYCLOPTERUS LUMPUS (Henfish, Lumpfish, Lump-sucker, Sea-hen) *219*
Arctic, both sides of N. Atlantic: Davis Strait to New Jersey; Murman coast,
France, Portugal. Bottom-living, from low-water mark down to 300 m.
N-Acetyl histidine 456; Calcium 1061; Magnesium 1061; Potassium 871,
1061; Sodium 1061; Trimethylamine oxide 307

CYNIAS MANAZO‡
Japan.
Cyanocobalamin 466; Urea 938; Vitamin C 965

Pantothenic acid 341; Phospholipid 946; Potassium 81, 108, 192, 341, 535, 871, 1263, 1274; Riboflavin 52, 341, 489, 583, 1129, 1285; Riboflavin adenine nucleotide 1285; Riboflavin mononucleotide 1285; RNA 1111; Sodium 81, 108, 192, 341, 535, 1263, 1274; 'Sugar' 671, 802; Sulphate 341; Thiamine 583, 682, 839, 966; Ubiquinone 292; Urea 341; Uric acid 341; Vitamin A$_1$ 341, 513, 1020, 1374; Vitamin A$_2$ 1020; Vitamin C 341, 355, 579, 781, 840, 1141; Vitamin D 1374; Vitamin E 581

CYPRINUS CARPIO COMMUNIS†
India.
Calcium 1327; Copper 1327; Iron 1327; Potassium 1327

CYPRINUS CARPIO NUDUS†
India.
Calcium 1327; Copper 1327; Iron 1327; Potassium 1327

CYPRINUS CARPIO SPECULARIS†
India.
Calcium 1327; Copper 1327; Iron 1327; Potassium 1327

CYPSELURUS AGOO   *214*
Japan.
Cyanocobalamin 1381; Folic acid 637; Histidine 532; Methionine 846

CYPSELURUS OLIGOLEPIS
Tanzania, Singapore, Sumatra, Java, Philippines, China.
Iron 585; Niacin 585; Riboflavin 585; Thiamine 585

CYPSELURUS OPISTHOPUS
Java, Celebes.
Manganese 1229

CYPSELURUS SP.
India.
Trimethylamine oxide 1319; Vitamin A 511, 512

DACTYLOPTENA ORIENTALIS
Japan.
Vitamin A 513

DALATIAS ATROMARGINATUS‡
Japan.
Vitamin A 496

DALATIAS LICHA‡ (Armour shark, Dalatias)
Atlantic (deep water), Mediterranean, Japan. Viviparous.
Ubiquinone 292; Vitamin A 513

DANIO AEQUIPINNATUS† = D. MALABARICUS† (Giant danio)
India, Ceylon. Small streams and ponds.
Calcium 918, 1327; Copper 1327; Iron 918, 1327; Potassium 1327

DANIO MALABARICUS† (*see* D. AEQUIPINNATUS†)

DASYATIS AKAJEI‡ (Japanese sting ray, Red skate, Red sting ray)
S. Japan. Viviparous.
Adenosine diphosphate 1224; Adenosine monophosphate 1224; Adenosine triphosphate 1224; Amino acids 323; Ammonia 1224; Creatin phosphate 1224; Cyanocobalamin 1381; Fructose-6-phosphate 1224; Fucose 326; Galactosamine 324; Galactose 326; Glucosamine 324; Glucose 326; Glucose-1-phosphate 1224; Glucose-6-phosphate 1224; Glycogen 1224; Hexose diphosphate 1224; Hexuronic acid 324; Lactic acid 1224; Phosphoglyceric acid 1224; Phosphopyruvic acid 1224; Ribose 326; Ribose phosphate 1224; Sialic acid 325; Triose phosphate 1224; Urea 1226; Vitamin A 513; Vitamin C 965

DASYATIS AMERICANA‡ (Southern stingray)
W. Atlantic: New Jersey to Brazil. Coastal waters.
Corticosterone 1006; Cortisol 1006

DASYATIS CENTROURA‡ (Northern stingray, Roughtail stingray)
Coastal waters from Cape Cod to Cape Hatteras (W. Atlantic). Grows to large size.
Chloride 1184; Urea 1184

DASYATIS SP.‡
Cerebroside 805, 806; Cholesterol 805, 806; Lecithin 805, 806; Phospholipid 805, 806; Sphingomyelin 805, 806

DASYATIS UARNAK*¶ (Banded whip-tail stingray)
Malaya: Perak River.
Ammonia 1183; Chloride 1183, 1184; Creatin 1183; Trimethylamine oxide 1319; Urea 1183, 1184

DASYATIS ZUGEI‡
India.
Amino acids 838; Cholesterol 630; Creatin 631; Lecithin 630; Niacin 631, 1096; Phospholipid 630; Riboflavin 631; Sphingomyelin 630; Thiamine 631; Trimethylamine 631; Trimethylamine oxide 631; Urea 631

DEANIA EGLANTINA‡ (Broad harbour shark)
Japan.
Cyanocobalamin 1381

DECAPTERUS LAJANG
Japan.
Cholesterol 1153; Fatty acids 1153; Vitamin A 513

DECAPTERUS MACROSOMA (Sear)
Natal, Philippines, Formosa, S. Japan, Australia.
Iron 585; Niacin 585; Riboflavin 585; Thiamine 585

DECAPTERUS MUROADSI   22
Japan.
Cholesterol 915, 1153; Cyanocobalamin 466, 1381; Fatty acids 1153; Manganese 1229; Riboflavin 501, 891; Thiamine 382, 839; Vitamin A 510

DECAPTERUS PUNCTATUS (Cigar fish, Dotted scad, Quiaquia, Round robin, Sca d
    W. Atlantic: Cape Cod to Brazil.
    DNA 862

DECAPTERUS RHONCHUS
    Portugal.
    Carotenoids 420; Niacin 420; Riboflavin 420; Thiamine 420; Vitamin C 420

DENTEX FILOSUS
    Portugal. Deep water.
    Carotenoids 420; Niacin 420; Riboflavin 420; Thiamine 420; Vitamin C 420

DENTEX VULGARIS
    Europe.
    Potassium 871

DIAPHUS COERULEUS (Headlight fish)
    Red Sea, India, Sumatra, Philippines, Japan.
    Vitamin A 513

DIAPTERUS EVERMANNI = MOHARRA EVERMANNI
    S. America, Atlantic waters of Panama.
    Calcium 592; Cyanocobalamin 592; Cystine 592; Iron 592; Lysine 592;
    Methionine 592; Niacin 592; Riboflavin 592; Thiamine 592; Tryptophan 592

DIPLECTRUM RADIALE
    Cuba to Brazil.
    Calcium 592; Cyanocobalamin 592; Cystine 592; Iron 592; Lysine 592;
    Methionine 592; Niacin 592; Riboflavin 592; Thiamine 592; Tryptophan 592

DIPLODUS ARGENTEUS
    West Indies to Argentine.
    DNA 862

DIPLODUS SARGUS = D. ANNULARIS = D. VULGARIS (Sargo)
    Portugal, Bermuda.
    Carotenoids 420; Cyanocobalamin 412; Niacin 420; Riboflavin 420; Thiamine
    420; Vitamin C 420

DITREMA TEMMINCKI (Sea chub)
    Japan. Shore. Viviparous.
    Cyanocobalamin 1381; Folic acid 503; Pantothenic acid 502; Trimethylamine
    1237; Trimethylamine oxide 1237; Vitamin A 510, 513

DÖDERLEINIA BERYCOIDES
    Japan, Korea.
    Astaxanthin 1293; Carotenoids 1293; Tunaxanthin 1293

DOROSOMA CEPEDIANUM* (Gizzard shad, Hickory shad)
    E. coast of N. America: Cape Cod to Texas. Enters streams and is sometimes
    landlocked.
    Chloride 553, 1215; Cholesterol 553, 1215; Haemoglobin 553, 1215; Potassium
    553, 1215; Sodium 553, 1215

DOROSOMA PETENSE
Gulf of Mexico.
Chloride 1215; Cholesterol 1215; Haemoglobin 1215; Potassium 1215; Sodium
1215

DOROSOMA THRISSA
Japan.
Cholesterol 1153; Fatty acids 1153

DREPANE PUNCTATA (Sicklefish, Spotted batfish)
Red Sea, E. Africa, Persian Gulf, India, Malaya, China, Australia. Sea and
brackish water of estuaries.
Iron 585; Niacin 585; Riboflavin 585; Thiamine 585

DREPANOPSETTA PLATESSOIDES = HIPPOGLOSSOIDES PLATESSOIDES   219
Arctic.

DUYMAERIA FLAGELLIFERA
Japan, Korea, Formosa. Sub-tropical.
Cyanocobalamin 1381; Vitamin A 513

ELAGATIS BIPINNULATUS
Tanzania, Red Sea, India, Philippines, Japan, Australia, Hawaii.
Iron 585; Niacin 585; Riboflavin 585; Thiamine 585

ELEGINUS NAVAGA
Russia.
FREE Amino acids 1139; Anserine 1139; Creatin + Creatinine 1139

ELEUTHERONEMA TETRADACTYLUM* = POLYNEMUS TETRADACTYLUS* (Cooktown salmon, Giant threadfin)
India, Malaya, Philippines, China to N. and W. Australia. Sea and brackish
waters, ascending rivers to spawn.
Amino acids 838; Cholesterol 630; Creatin 631; Hydroxyproline 58; Lecithin
630; Niacin 631; Phospholipid 630; Proline 58; Riboflavin 631; Sphingomyelin 630; Thiamine 631; Trimethylamine 631; Trimethylamine oxide 631;
Urea 631

ELOPS HAWAIENSIS
Singapore, Java, Philippines, Formosa, Hawaii.
Iron 585; Niacin 585; Riboflavin 585; Thiamine 585

ELOPS SAURUS (Big-eyed herring, Bonefish, Giant herring, John mariggle, Tenpounder)
W. Atlantic: Massachusetts, W. Indies to Brazil. India, Ceylon.
Chloride 1215; Cholesterol 1215; Haemoglobin 1215; Potassium 1215; Sodium
1215

EMBIOTOCA JACKSONI (Black surfperch)   171
N. America: Vancouver Island to Todos Santos Bay.
C.B.F.

EMISSOLA ANTARCTICA‡
  Australia.
  Copper 88

ENEDRIAS NEBULOSUS (Blenny)
  Japan.
  Cyanocobalamin 1381; Vitamin A 513

ENGRAULIS ENCRASICHOLUS (Anchovy)
  Black Sea, Sweden, Britain to Mediterranean. Pelagic.
  FREE Amino acids 1139; Creatin + Creatinine 1139; Cyanocobalamin 412;
  Trimethylamine 1253; Trimethylamine oxide 1253

ENGRAULIS ENCRASICHOLUS PONTICUS
  Russia.
  Aluminium 987, 989; Barium 987; Beryllium 987; Cadmium 987; Chromium
  987, 989; Cobalt 987; Copper 989; Gadolineum 987; Iron 987, 989; Lead 987,
  989; Lithium 987, 989; Manganese 989; Molybdenum 987; Nickel 987, 989;
  Silver 987, 989; Strontium 987, 989; Tin 987, 989; Titanium 987, 989; Vanadium 987, 989; Zinc 987

ENGRAULIS JAPONICUS (Anchovy, Half-mouthed sardine)   *20, 22, 24, 287*
  Japan.
  Amino acids 41; FREE Amino acids 42; Ammonia 42; Carnosine 42;
  Creatinine 42; Cyanocobalamin 1381; Ornithine 42; Taurine 42; Trimethyl-
  amine 1237; Trimethylamine oxide 42; 1237; Vitamin A 513, 1374; Vitamin
  D 1374

ENGRAULIS MORDAX (Anchovy, Northern anchovy)
  N. America: S. California to N. Vancouver Island.
  Haemoglobin 77

ENTOSPHENUS JAPONICUS*§ (River eight-eyes lamprey)   *38, 129, 252, 291*
  Japan. Anadromous. Exceptionally rich in vitamin A.
  Cyanocobalamin 497, 498; Folic acid 498, 503; Pantothenic acid 498, 502;
  Pyridoxine 497, 498; Riboflavin 497, 498, 501; Thiamine 497, 498; Vitamin A
  497, 498, 512, 513, 1374; Vitamin D 1374

ENTOSPHENUS LAMOTTEI*§   *83*
  Amino acids 205

ENTOSPHENUS TRIDENTATUS*§ (Pacific lamprey)
  Japan. S. California to Alaska.
  Vitamin A 1371, 1374; Vitamin D 1374

EOPSETTA GRIGORJEWI (Shotted halibut)   *214*
  Japan, Korea.
  Actin 1309; Arsenic 448; Cyanocobalamin 1381; Selenium 448; Thallium 448

EOPSETTA JORDANI (Brill, Petrale sole)
  N. America: S. California to Alaska.
  Potassium 192, 793, 1263, 1268; Riboflavin 1113; Sodium 192, 793, 1263,
  1268, 1273; Thiamine 1112

EPINEPHELUS AENEUS
Europe.
Carotenoids 420; Niacin 420; Potassium 871; Riboflavin 420; Thiamine 420;
Vitamin C 420

EPINEPHELUS AKAARA
Japan.
Astaxanthin 1293; Carotenoids 1293; Tunaxanthin 1293

EPINEPHELUS CORALLICOLA* (Grouper)
Madras, Singapore, Java, Philippines, New Guinea, N. Australia. In sea,
entering fresh water.
Iron 585; Niacin 585; Riboflavin 585; Thiamine 585

EPINEPHELUS FARIO (Garrupa, Rock-cod, Trout reef-cod)
Japan, China Sea, Java. Coastal waters and pearl banks.
Vitamin A 513

EPINEPHELUS FASCIATUS (Banded reef-cod, Red hata)
Madagascar, Red Sea, India, Philippines, Japan, China, W. Australia. Shores.
Astaxanthin 1293; Carotenoids 1293; Tunaxanthin 1293; Vitamin A 1374;
Vitamin D 1374

EPINEPHELUS GIGAS (Dusky perch)
Portugal, Britain.
Carotenoids 420; Niacin 420; Riboflavin 420; Thiamine 420; Vitamin C 420

EPINEPHELUS GOREËNSIS
Portugal.
Carotenoids 420; Niacin 420; Riboflavin 420; Thiamine 420; Vitamin C 420

EPINEPHELUS GUTTATUS (Cabrilla, Red hind)
E. America: Florida to Brazil. Madagascar, Red Sea, India, Philippines,
N. Australia.
DNA 862

EPINEPHELUS MORIO = E. MOARA (Red grouper)
Atlantic coast of N. and S. America from Virginia to Brazil.
Niacin 413; Potassium 202; Riboflavin 413; Sodium 202; Thiamine 413

EPINEPHELUS SEPTEMFASCIATUS (True bass)
Japan.
Folic acid 503; Pantothenic acid 502; Riboflavin 501; Vitamin A 510, 513

EPINEPHELUS SP.
S. America.
Calcium 592; Cyanocobalamin 592; Cystine 592; Iron 592; Lysine 592;
Methionine 592; Niacin 592; Riboflavin 592; Thiamine 592; Tryptophan 592

EPINEPHELUS STRIATUS (Hamlet, Nassau grouper, Rockfish)
E. America: Florida to Brazil.
DNA 862

EPTATRETUS STOUTII§ (Hagfish)   *89, 142*
Carotenoids 360

ERILEPIS ZONIFER (Skilfish)
Japan, California, Alaska.
Arsenic 448; Niacin 494; Selenium 448; Thallium 448

ERISCION NEBULOSUS (*see* CYNOSCION NEBULOSUS)

ERREX ZACHIRUS (Long-finned sole, Rex sole)
N. Pacific, waters of moderate depth.
Riboflavin 1113; Thiamine 1112

ERYTHRICHTHYS SCHLEGELI
Japan.
Astaxanthin 1293; Carotenoids 1293; Tunaxanthin 1293

ERYTHROCLES SCHLEGELI
Japan, Korea.
Niacin 471

ESOX LUCIUS† (Pike)   *74, 175*
N. America and Europe (except Spain) in streams and lakes near the shore.
N-Acetyl histidine 456; Adenosine triphosphate 972; Amino acids 25, 26, 1015; Betaine 746; Cholesterol 25; Cyanocobalamin 25; DNA 25, 1323; Fatty acids 25; Fucose 1336; Galactose 25; Glucose 25, 664; Glycogen 25, 245; Haematocrit 802; Heparin 25; Hexosamine 1336; Iron 802; Mannose 25; Phospholipids 25; Potassium 462, 664, 871; Riboflavin 25; RNA 25; Sodium 664; 'Sugar' 671, 802; Thiamine 25; Trimethylamine oxide 307, 1065; Ubiquinone 292, 982; Vitamin A_1 25, 982, 1019, 1020; Vitamin A_2 1019, 1020; Vitamin C 861; Vitamin E 982

ESOX NIGER† (Eastern pickerel, Green pike, Jack)   *146*
N. America: Massachusetts to Florida. Lowland streams and swamps.
Trimethylamine 28; Trimethylamine oxide 28

ETELIS EVURUS
Japan.
Cholesterol 1153; Fatty acids 1153; Vitamin A 513

ETMOPTERUS LUCIFER‡
Japan.
Vitamin A 513

ETMOPTERUS SPINAX‡ = SPINAX NIGER‡ (Latern shark, Velvet belly)
Europe, including Iceland and Mediterranean, from 220 to 700 m. Viviparous.
Carotenoids 347; Ubiquinone 292

ETROPLUS MACULATUS† (Spotted etroplus)   *221*
India. Coastal fresh waters.

ETROPLUS SURATENSIS† (Banded etroplus)
India. Fresh and brackish waters.
Calcium 918; Iron 918

ETRUMEUS MICROPUS (Market sardine)
Japan.
Cholesterol 1153; Choline 1236; Cyanocobalamin 1381; Fatty acids 1153; Pyridoxine 1383; Riboflavin 501, 891; Trimethylamine 1236; Trimethylamine oxide 1236; Vitamin A 513

EUCINOSTOMUS GULA (Shad, Silver Jenny)
DNA 862

EUCITHARUS LINGUATULA (Spotted flounder)
Adriatic Sea.
Trimethylamine 1253; Trimethylamine oxide 1253

EUGALEUS GALEUS‡ (Tope)
Britain.
Carotenoids 347

EUMAKAIRA NIGRA
Japan.
Haematocrit 1097; Haemoglobin 1097; Riboflavin 1151

EUPOMOTIS GIBBOSUS† (Bream, Common sunfish, Harlequin roach, Kiver, Northern pomotis, Perch, Pond perch, Pumpkinseed, Quiver, Redbelly, Roach, Robin, Robin perch, Ruff, Sand perch, Sun bass, Tobaccobox, Yellow-belly, Yellow perch) *171*
N. America: Great Lakes to Florida. Introduced to Europe. Still waters with heavy vegetation.

EUTHYNNUS LINEATUS
Pacific coast of Mexico.
Haemoglobin 678

EUTHYNNUS PELAMYS (*see* KATSUWONUS PELAMIS)

EUTHYOPTEROMA VIRGATUM
Japan.
Cyanocobalamin 1380; Thiamine 382, 839

EVYNNIS CARDINALIS
Japan.
Haematocrit 1097; Haemoglobin 1097

EVYNNIS JAPONICA
Japan.
Pyridoxine 1384

FISTULARIA PETIMBA (Flute-mouth)
Indian Ocean, Japan, N. New Guinea. E. Africa to W. tropical America.
Shores.
Astaxanthin 1293; Carotenoids 1293; Tunaxanthin 1293; Vitamin A 513

FISTULARIA SP.
Japan.
Cyanocobalamin 1381

FUGU NIPHOBLES (Grass puffer)   *75, 77*
Japan.
Amino acids 1223

FUGU PARDALIS (Puffer)
Japan.
Vitamin A 513

FUGU RUBRIPES (Tiger puffer)
Japan.
Vitamin A 513

FUGU SP. *34*
Japan.
Adenosine triphosphate 108

FUGU VERMICULARIS PORPHYREUS (Mafugu, Shosaifugu)   *35*
Japan.
Trimethylamine 1237; Trimethylamine oxide 1237

FUNDULUS DIAPHANUS* (Banded killifish)
Eastern N. America: Quebec to Cape Hatteras. Not marine, but a freshwater
fish that is salt tolerant.
Trimethylamine oxide 307

FUNDULUS HETEROCLITUS* (Killifish, Mummichog, Salt water minnow)   *121,
171, 172, 188, 192, 213, 219, 274*
Coast of N. America (Labrador to Mexico) in estuaries and brackish tide
pools. Tolerant of very low oxygen levels, also of big variations in temperature
and salinity. Buries in mud during winter.
Glucose 1312; Trimethylamine oxide 307

FUNDULUS KANSAE† (Plains killifish)   *61, 62, 191, 192, 193, 197*
N. America.
Calcium 1198, 1199; Potassium 1198, 1199; Sodium 1198, 1199

FUNDULUS PARVIPINNIS* (California killifish)   *200*
Coast of California.

FURCINA OSIMAE
Japan.
Vitamin E 850

GADUS AEGLEFINUS = MELANOGRAMMUS AEGLEFINUS (Haddock) *7, 26, 44, 116, 126, 131, 132, 133, 146, 151, 231*
N. Norway to Biscay, W. Greenland to Virginia. Bottom-living, 40–300 m. Not found inshore.
Adenosine diphosphate 653; Adenosine monophosphate 653; Adenosine triphosphate 653; Amino acids 34, 154, 240, 713, 723, 1035, 1042; Ammonia 201; Biotin 751; Caesium 184, 185, 186; Calcium 1061, 1234; Cholesterol 958, 1369; Creatin 201; Cyanocobalamin 147, 149, 150, 526, 527, 1234, 1251; Diphosphopyridine nucleotide 653; Fatty acids 957; FREE Fatty acids 365; Folic acid 751; Glycogen 813, 817, 1142; Hypoxanthine 653; Inosine 653; Inosine monophosphate 653; Iodine 460, 1234; Iron 1234; Lactic acid 813, 817, 1142; Lecithin 958; Lithium 184, 185; Magnesium 1061; Mercury 1337; Niacin 147, 150, 192, 527, 1234, 1251; Nicotinamide 526; Pantothenic acid 147, 150, 526, 527, 751, 1234; Phospholipid 958; Potassium 184, 185, 186, 192, 197, 736, 871, 1061, 1263; Riboflavin 147, 150, 192, 517, 526, 527, 785, 787, 1234, 1251; Rubidium 184, 185, 186; Sodium 184, 185, 186, 192, 736, 1061, 1263; Thiamine 192, 405, 526, 527, 742, 787, 1234; Trimethylamine 365, 1085; Trimethylamine oxide 243, 307, 365, 1085; Urea 201; Vitamin A 311, 1021; Vitamin C 785

GADUS CALLARIAS (Baltic cod) *118, 173*
Baltic Sea and approaches.

GADUS MACROCEPHALUS (Pacific cod) *69, 88, 130, 210, 214*
Japan, Korea, Bering Sea, Alaska, California.
Cholesterol 1153; Cyanocobalamin 1381; Dimethylamine 21; Fatty acids 1089, 1153; Folic acid 503; Formaldehyde 20, 21; Hydroxyproline 1238, 1239, 1243; Insulin 1278; Methionine 846; Pantothenic acid 502; Potassium 792, 793, 1263, 1267; Riboflavin 1113; Sodium 792, 793, 1263, 1267; Thiamine 1112; Trimethylamine 21; Trimethylamine oxide 21; Tryptophan 697; Vitamin A 513, 1374; Vitamin D 1374

GADUS MERLANGUS = MERLANGIUS MERLANGUS (Whiting) *26, 94, 131, 146, 160, 165*
Europe, including Iceland. Commonest between 30 and 100 m. Often close inshore.
Cholesterol 1369; Fucose 1336; Hexosamine 1336; Mercury 1337; Potassium 871; Trimethylamine oxide 1065; Vitamin A 311, 1021

GADUS MERLANGUS EUXINUS
A form of Gadus merlangus found in the Black Sea.
FREE Amino acids 1139; Anserine 1139; Creatin + Creatinine 1139

GADUS MORHUA = GADUS MORRHUA, frequently named GADUS CALLARIAS in the literature. (Atlantic cod, immature form known as Codling.) *viii, 1–13, 15, 16, 20, 21, 23–6, 31, 36, 41, 42, 44–6, 48, 49, 51, 60, 61, 65, 66, 67, 68, 84–96, 98, 103, 105, 106–10, 115–17, 119, 120, 122–4, 126, 131–3, 136, 141, 146, 153, 154, 156–67, 169–71, 173–6, 188, 198–201, 209–11, 213, 214, 219, 221–5, 227–31, 234–9, 242–6, 249, 251–3, 261, 262, 278, 285–7*
Both sides of the Atlantic. Usually bottom-living in shallow offshore waters down to 450 m or more.

N-Acetyl histidine 456; Adenosine diphosphate 622, 623, 624, 894, 1249; Adenosine monophosphate 622, 623, 624, 894, 1249; Adenosine triphosphate 363, 364, 366, 622, 623, 624, 894, 1249; Adrenaline 327; FREE Alanine 1148; Amino acids 2, 34, 48, 83, 124, 154, 239, 240, 309, 318, 528, 924, 1013, 1015, 1035, 1390; FREE Amino acids 269, 615, 1139; Ammonia 201, 364, 366, 645; Anserine 1139, 1148, 1392; Betaine 645; Biotin 148, 155, 751; Calcium 1061, 1234; Carnosine 1392; Chloride 321, 853; Cholesterol 11, 122, 385, 1369; Collagen 1390; Copper 1406; Cortisol 561; Creatin 201, 364, 1139, 1148; Creatin phosphate 363; Creatinine 1148; Cyanocobalamin 147, 148, 149, 150, 526, 527, 1234, 1251; DNA 755; Dihydroxyacetone phosphate 191; Diphosphopyridine nucleotide (nicotinamide adenine dinucleotide) 622, 623, 624, 625, 894, 1249; Elastin 1390; Fatty acids (individual, combined) 6, 7, 11, 173, 595, 957; Fatty acids (total, combined) 237; FREE Fatty acids (total) 122, 959; Folic acid 751; Fructose-6-phosphate 188, 1249; Fructose diphosphate 188, 1249; Fucose 1336; Glucose 188, 616, 618, 640; Glucose-1-phosphate 188, 1249; Glucose-6-phosphate 188, 1249; FREE Glutamic acid 1148; L-α-Glycerophosphate 191; FREE Glycine 1148; Glycogen 85, 364, 640, 797, 798, 813; Guanosine triphosphate 623; Haematocrit 640; Hexosamine 1336; Histidine 1392; Hydrocortisone 1007; Hydroxyproline 294; Inosine monophosphate 622, 623, 624, 894, 1249; Iodine 1234; Iron 1234; Lactic acid 85, 110, 191, 364, 734, 798; Lead 1406; Lecithin 11, 385; FREE Leucine 1148; Lithium 926; Magnesium 1061; Mercury 1337; Methyl guanidine 645; 1-Methyl histidine 615, 1148; Mucopolysaccharides 1390; Niacin 69, 147, 148, 150, 192, 527, 690, 707, 708, 785, 1234, 1251; Nicotinamide 429, 526; Noradrenaline 327, 330; Oestradiol 419; Oestrone 419; Pantothenic acid 145, 147, 148, 150, 526, 527, 751, 1234; Phosphatidyl choline (*see* Lecithin); Phosphatidyl ethanolamine 11, 122; Phosphatidyl serine 11; 3-Phosphoglyceric acid 191; Phospholipid 385; Potassium 192, 197, 321, 462, 736, 871, 926, 1061; Pyridoxine 152, 155; Pyruvic acid 191, 621; Riboflavin 147, 148, 150, 192, 429, 517, 526, 527, 707, 785, 786, 787, 1129, 1234, 1251; Ribose 188, 616, 618; Ribose phosphate 188, 1249; Sodium 192, 321, 736, 926, 1061; Taurine 614, 615; Thiamine 192, 405, 429, 526, 527, 707, 742, 785, 786, 787, 1234; α-Tocopherol (*see* Vitamin E); Triglyceride 11, 122; Trimethylamine 645, 1085; Trimethylamine oxide 243, 307, 645, 1085, 1148; Triphosphopyridine nucleotide 623, 1249; Ubiquinone 157, 982; Urea 201; Uridine triphosphate 623; FREE Valine 1148; Vitamin A 50, 311, 982, 1019, 1021, 1022, 1023; Vitamin C 355, 556, 785; Vitamin D 707, 785; Vitamin E 8, 707, 982

GADUS NEVAGA (Wachna cod)
N. Russia.
Copper 1406; Lead 1406; Tin 1406

GADUS OGAC (Fjord cod, Greenland cod) *219*
Arctic: W. Greenland to Point Barrow, Alaska.
Iron 1126

GADUS POLLACHIUS (Pollack) *271*
N. Atlantic, Mediterranean. Mainly inshore, near rocks.
Calcium 1234; Cyanocobalamin 147, 149, 150, 1234; Iodine 1234; Iron 1234; Niacin 147, 150, 1234; Pantothenic acid 147, 150, 1234; Riboflavin 147, 150, 787, 1234; Thiamine 787, 1234; Trimethylamine 1085; Trimethylamine oxide 1085; Vitamin C 785

GADUS POUTASSOU (Couch's whiting, Poutassou)
W. Europe, including Iceland, Adriatic Sea, western N. Atlantic. Oceanic in large shoals.
Trimethylamine 1253; Trimethylamine oxide 1253

GADUS SP.
Anserine 783; Carnosine 783; Glycogen 813; Histidine 783; Lactic acid 813; 1-Methyl histidine 783; Niacin 810

GADUS VIRENS = POLLACHIUS VIRENS (Blister-back, Boston blue fish, Coalfish, Coalie, Pollock, Saithe) *20–25, 27, 28, 36, 131, 133, 231, 278*
Both sides of N. Atlantic and Greenland, from surface down to 200 m or more. The most active gadoid, occurring in large shoals.
Amino acids 154, 1189; FREE Amino acids 917; Aluminium 1189; Barium 1189; Biotin 155; Calcium 1061, 1234; Cholesterol 1369; Copper 1189; Cyanocobalamin 147, 149, 150, 1234; Glycogen 813; Iodine 1234; Iron 1189, 1234; Lithium 1189; Magnesium 1189; Mercury 1337; Niacin 147, 150, 1234; Pantothenic acid 147, 150, 1234; Potassium 175, 192, 1061, 1189, 1263; Pyridoxine 155; Riboflavin 147, 150, 192, 517, 787, 1234; Silicon 1189; Sodium 175, 192, 1061, 1189, 1263; Strontium 1189; Thiamine 192, 742, 786, 787, 1234; Trimethylamine 1085; Trimethylamine oxide 243, 307, 1085; Ubiquinone 292; Vitamin A 50

GALEICHTHYS FELIS (Sea cat)
N. America: Cape Cod to Texas in bays and harbours. Fertilised eggs carried in the mouth of the male until hatched.
Chloride 1215; Cholesterol 1215; Haemoglobin 1215; Potassium 1215; Sodium 1215

GALEOCERDO ARCTICUS‡ (Leopard shark, Spotted shark, Tiger shark, Tigrone)
Tropical seas, occasionally Iceland.
Fibrinogen 1098; Haematocrit 1097; Haemoglobin 1097

GALEOCERDO CUVIERI‡
World-wide in tropical or sub-tropical waters. In W. Atlantic ranges from Cape Cod to Uruguay. Inshore and offshore, often enters river mouths. A scavenger. Viviparous.
Corticosterone 1006; Cortisol 1006

GALEORHINUS AUSTRALIS‡ (School shark, Snapper shark)
Australia, 2 to 100 fathoms.
Copper 88

GALEORHINUS ZYOPTERUS‡ (Oil shark, Soupfin shark) *91, 95, 105*
N. America: S. California to N. British Columbia.

GALEUS GLAUCUS‡
Japan.
Folic acid 503; Pantothenic acid 502

GAMBUSIA HOLBROOKI* (Top minnow)   *117, 212*
Atlantic coast of N. America, New Jersey to Florida. Feeds at surface, especially on insect larvae. Viviparous.

GARDONUS RUTILUS†
DNA 1323

GARRUPA NIGRITA (Black grouper, Black jewfish)
S. Atlantic, Gulf coast of America, Cuba, Brazil, perhaps Sicily.
Thiamine 405

GASTEROSTEUS ACULEATUS* (Pinfish, Spantickle, Three-spined stickleback, Tiddler)   *110, 195*
Northern hemisphere. Shore fish, equally at home in fresh or salt water. Nestbuilder, eggs guarded by the male. Hardy and pugnacious.
Trimethylamine oxide 307, 727

GENYPTERUS CAPENSIS (Kingklip)
S. Africa.
Amino acids 1341

GEPHYROBERYX JAPONICUS
Japan.
Astaxanthin 1293; Carotenoids 1293

GERMO ALALUNGA (*see* THUNNUS ALALUNGA)

GERMO GERMO (*see* THUNNUS ALALUNGA)

GERMO MACROPTERUS (*see* THUNNUS ALBACARES)

GERRES FILAMENTOSUS* (Longrayed silver-biddy, Spotted mojarras)
India, Malaya, Philippines, New Guinea. Seas and mouths of rivers, pearl banks.
Iron 585; Niacin 585; Riboflavin 585; Thiamine 585

GERRES SP.*
India.
Trimethylamine oxide 1319

GILLICHTHYS MIRABILIS (Long-jawed goby, Mudsucker)   *183*
Pacific coast of N. America.

GIRELLA ELEVATA
Australia.
Cholesterol 872; Phospholipid 872

GIRELLA NIGRICANS (California bluefish, Greenfish, White spot)   *50*
Coast of S. California.

GIRELLA PUNCTATA
Japan.
Cyanocobalamin 1381; Folic acid 637; Riboflavin 501, 891; Vitamin A 510, 513; Vitamin C 579

GIRELLA TRICUSPIDATA* (Blackfish, Darkie, Luderick)
Australia, especially New S. Wales. Rivers and estuaries, sheltered coastal waters in weedy places.
Cholesterol 872; Phospholipid 872

GLOSSANODON SEMIFASCIATUS
Japan.
Vitamin A 513

GLOSSOGOBIUS GIURIS* = GOBIUS GIURIS* (Bar-eyed goby, Flat-head goby)
E. Africa, India, China, Japan, Australia and all parts of the Indo-Australian archipelago. Seas and rivers.
Cyanocobalamin 71, 72; Cystine 1090; Folic acid 73; Hydroxyproline 58; Iron 585; Niacin 585, 1096; Proline 58; Riboflavin 585; Thiamine 585; Tryptophan 1090; Tyrosine 1090; Vitamin C 1095

GLYPHIS GLAUCUS‡ (Great blue shark)
Japan, Europe, America. Viviparous.
Hydroxyproline 1239; Niacin 494

GLYPTOCEPHALUS CYNOGLOSSUS (Grey sole, Pole flounder, Witch flounder)
Both sides of N. Atlantic, bottom-living in fairly deep water (50–1700 m).
Betaine 529; Potassium 175; Sodium 175; Vitamin A 1021

GLYPTOCEPHALUS ZACHIRUS (Rex sole)
S. California to Bering Sea. 10–350 fathoms.
Anserine 783; Carnosine 783; Histidine 783; 1-Methyl histidine 783; Potassium 1268; Sodium 1268

GNATHAGNUS ELONGATUS (Blue mishima puffer fish)
Japan.
Fucose 326; Galactosamine 324; Galactose 326; Glucosamine 324; Glucose 326; Hexuronic acid 324; Ribose 326

GOBIO GOBIO† (Gudgeon)
Europe except S. Italy and Norway. A bottom-living fish of swift waters. Inshore in lakes.
Anserine 1392; Carnosine 1392; FREE Histidine 1392

GOBIUS GIURIS* (see GLOSSOGOBIUS GIURIS*)

GOBIUS LOTA†
Europe.
Vitamin C 399

GOBIUS MELANOSTOMUS
Russia.
Calcium 712; Chromium 989; Copper 989; Iron 989; Magnesium 712; Manganese 989; Potassium 712, 736; Sodium 712, 736; Strontium 989; Titanium 989; Vanadium 989

GOBIUS SP.
Caesium 185; Lithium 184, 185; Potassium 184, 185; Rubidium 184, 185; Sodium 184, 185

GONIISTIUS ZONATUS
Japan, China Sea. Rocky bottom.
Riboflavin 501, 891; Vitamin A 511, 512, 513

GYMNACANTHUS PISTILLIGER
Japan.
Vitamin E 850

GYMNACANTHUS TRICUSPIS (Arctic staghorn sculpin)
Arctic and N. Atlantic Oceans.
Iron 1126

GYMNOCRANIUS GRISEUS (Meichi porgy)
Japan to East Indies. Warm waters.
Riboflavin 501

GYMNOTHORAX KIDAKO
Japan.
Cyanocobalamin 1381; Histidine 532; Vitamin A 513

HAEMULON FLAVOLINEATUM (French grunt, Open-mouthed grunt, Yellow grunt)
Florida, W. Indies to Brazil.
DNA 862

HAEMULON PLUMIERI (Boar grunt, Common grunt, Ronco ronco, Squirrel fish)
W. Indies to Rio de Janeiro.
Niacin 413; Riboflavin 413; Thiamine 413

HAEMULON SCIURUS (Boar grunt, Humpback grunt, Yellow grunt)
Florida to Brazil.
Calcium 592; Cyanocobalamin 592; Cystine 592; DNA 862; Iron 592; Lysine 592; Methionine 592; Niacin 592; Riboflavin 592; Thiamine 592; Tryptophan 592

HAEMULON SP.
Puerta Rica.
Potassium 202; Sodium 202

HALIEUTEA STELLATA (Red batfish, Red rattlefish)
Japan, Korea, China, in medium-deep waters.
Vitamin A 513

HARENGULA SARDINA (Sardina de Ley)
W. Indies.
DNA 862

HARPODON NEHEREUS (Bombay duck)
Tanzania, India, China, Java, Borneo. Coastal and in estuaries.
Amino acids 141, 827; Niacin 631; Riboflavin 631; Thiamine 631

HELICOLENUS HILGENDORFI (Hilgendorf saucord)
Mediterranean, Japan. Deep waters.
Astaxanthin 1293; Carotenoids 1293, 1294; Tunaxanthin 1293

HELOSTOMA TEMMINCKI† (Kissing gourami)
Thailand, Malaya, Sumatra, Borneo, Indonesia. Ponds.
Amino acids 306

HELOTES SEXLINEATUS
Australia.
Copper 88

HEMIBARBUS BARBUS† (Skin-carp)
Japan. Rivers and lakes.
Vitamin A 513; Vitamin C 840

HEMILEPIDOTUS GILBERTI
Japan.
Trimethylamine 1237; Trimethylamine oxide 1237

HEMIRHAMPHUS GEORGII (Long-billed half-beak)
India, Java, Philippines, New Guinea. Tropical and subtropical seas, near
shores.
Iron 585; Niacin 585; Riboflavin 585; Thiamine 585

HEMIRHAMPHUS SAJORI* (Half-beak fish, Japanese needlefish)
Japan. Coastal. Occasionally enters rivers.
Vitamin A 513

HEMITRIPTERUS AMERICANUS (Gurnet, Puff-belly, Sea raven, Whip sculpin)
Atlantic coast of N. America: Newfoundland to Chesapeake Bay, to depth of
182 m.
Trimethylamine oxide 307

HEPTATRETUS OKINOSEANUS§
Japan.
Vitamin A 497, 498

HETERODONTUS FRANCISCI‡
Zeaxanthin 360

HETERODONTUS JAPONICUS‡ (Cat shark, Port Jackson shark)
Japan. Warm waters.
Urea 1226, 1227

HETERODONTUS PHILLIPI‡
  Australia.
  Cholesterol 872; Phospholipid 872

HETEROPNEUSTES FOSSILIS† = SACCOBRANCHUS FOSSILIS† (Stinging catfish)
  India and Burma. Ponds in low country.
  Cholesterol 1161; Cyanocobalamin 71, 72; Cystine 1090; Fatty acids 975;
  Folic acid 73; Niacin 1096; Tryptophan 1090; Tyrosine 1090; Vitamin C 1095

HETEROSCYMNUS LONGUS‡
  Japan
  Riboflavin 501; Vitamin A 496, 513

HEXAGRAMMOS OCTOGRAMMUS (Alaska greenfish)
  Aleutian Islands, westward to Petropaulski and Robben Island.
  Riboflavin 1113; Thiamine 1112

HEXAGRAMMOS OTAKII
  Japan, Korea.
  Trimethylamine 1237; Trimethylamine oxide 1237

HEXAGRAMMOS STELLERI (White spotted greenling)
  Japan, N. California to Bering Sea. Rocky shores, sandy beaches.
  Dimethylamine 21; Formaldehyde 21; Trimethylamine 21; Trimethylamine
  oxide 21

HEXANCHUS GRISEUS‡ = H. CORINUM‡ (Mud shark, Sixgill shark)
  S. California to Alaska, Europe. Temperate areas of all oceans, mainly in
  deep water.
  Carotenoids 347; Vitamin A 496

HILSA HILSA ? = H. ILISHA (could not trace)
  India.
  Cyanocobalamin 72; Folic acid 73

HILSA ILISHA* (Hilsa, River shad, Sable fish)   262
  Persian Gulf ascending the Tigris, Seas of India, Burma, Malaya, ascending
  rivers to breed.
  Amino acids 827; Calcium 1047; Copper 1047; Cyanocobalamin 71; Fatty
  acids 667; Iron 1047; Niacin 158, 670, 1096; Potassium 1047; Vitamin C 1095

HILSA TOLI (Chinese herring)
  India, Malaya, China. Coastal waters.
  Cholesterol 630; Hydroxyproline 58; Lecithin 630; Niacin 631; Phospholipid
  630; Proline 58; Riboflavin 631; Sphingomyelin 630; Thiamine 631

HIPPOGLOSSOIDES DUBIUS (Flathead flounder, Red halibut)
  Japan, Kamchatka, Korea.
  Creatin 1100; Creatinine 1100; Fatty acids 572; Hydroxyproline 1238, 1239,
  1243; Vitamin A 513

HIPPOGLOSSOIDES ELASSODON (Flathead sole, Paper sole)
N. America: Washington to Bering Sea.
Folic acid 503; Pantothenic acid 502; Potassium 1268; Riboflavin 1113; Sodium 1268, 1273; Thiamine 1112; Vitamin A 509; Vitamin E 850

HIPPOGLOSSOIDES PLATESSOIDES (American plaice, Blackback, Canadian plaice, Flounder, Long rough dab, Sand dab, Sole) *126, 230, 238, 250, 262*
Both sides of N. Atlantic, Spitzbergen to English Channel, between 4 and 700 m on mud or fine sand. Tolerates wide ranges of temperature and salinity.
Potassium 175; Sodium 175; Trimethylamine oxide 307; Vitamin A 1021

HIPPOGLOSSUS HIPPOGLOSSUS (Atlantic halibut) *6, 21–25, 27, 28, 36, 93, 131, 145, 172, 200, 286*
Cold waters of the Atlantic, south to Cape Cod (W) and France (E) on sand, gravel or clay bottom at temperatures of 3° to 5°C. May reach 250 Kg in weight. Strongly migratory.
Amino acids 34, 154, 1035; Biotin 217, 751; Calcium 1061, 1234, 1317; Cholesterol 1369; Copper 1406; Cyanocobalamin 146, 150, 1234, 1251; Fatty acids 957; FREE Fatty acids 960; Folic acid 217, 751; Glycogen 780; Inositol 217; Iodine 1234; Iron 1234, 1317; Lead 1406; Magnesium 1061, 1317; Mercury 1337; Niacin 146, 150, 217, 1234, 1251; Pantothenic acid 146, 150, 217, 751, 1234; Phospholipid 960; Potassium 462, 1061, 1271, 1317; Pyridoxine 217; Riboflavin 146, 150, 217, 517, 787, 1113, 1234, 1251; Sodium 1061, 1271; Thiamine 146, 217, 787, 1112, 1234; Tin 1406; Trimethylamine oxide 243, 307; Ubiquinone 292; Vitamin A 311

HIPPOGLOSSUS STENOLEPIS (Pacific halibut) *88, 116, 156*
Pacific coast of N. America. Shallow waters to 600 fathoms.
Anserine 783; Carnosine 783; Histidine 783; 1-Methyl histidine 783; Niacin 192; Potassium 192, 792, 793, 1263; Riboflavin 192; Sodium 192, 792, 793, 1263, 1273; Thiamine 192; Trimethylamine oxide 307

HISTIOPHORUS ORIENTALIS = ISTIOPHORUS ORIENTALIS (Swordfish) *214*
Actin 1309; Folic acid 637

HOLOCENTRUS ASCENSIONIS (Squirrel fish)
Atlantic coast of N. America.
DNA 862

HOPLOPAGRUS GÜNTHERI (Pargo)
Pacific coast of tropical America.
Niacin 413; Riboflavin 413; Thiamine 413

HURO SALMOIDES (Black bass) *212*

HUSO HUSO* (Sturgeon)
Europe.
FREE Amino acids 1139; Anserine 1392; Carnosine 1392; Creatin + Creatinine 1139; FREE Histidine 1392

HYDROLAGUS AFFINIS‡ (Deepwater chimaera)
  Both sides of N. Atlantic, in fairly deep water.
  Trimethylamine 365; Trimethylamine oxide 365

HYDROLAGUS COLLIEI‡ (Ratfish)
  N. America: S. California to S.E. Alaska.
  Creatin 554

HYNNIS MOMSA
  Philippines.
  Iron 585; Niacin 585; Riboflavin 585; Thiamine 585

HYPOLOPHUS SEPHEN¶
  Thailand.
  Ammonia 1183; Chloride 1183, 1184; Creatin 1183; Urea 1183, 1184

HYPOMESUS OLIDUS† (Pond smelt)
  Japan. Can live in brackish water near river mouths.
  Cholesterol 1153; Fatty acids 1153; Vitamin A 513

HYPOPHTHALMICHTHYS MOLITRIX
  Japan.
  DNA 1111; RNA 1111

HYRIOPSIS VELTHUIZENI†
  Indonesia.
  Amino acids 306

ICELUS SPATULA (Spatulate sculpin)   *218*
  Arctic. Bering Sea, Kamchatka coast, Labrador.

ICHTHYOMYZON UNICUSPIS†§ (Silver lamprey)   *82, 237*
  N. America.
  Amino acids 205

ICTALURUS MELAS†   *40, 41, 212*
  N. America.
  Glucose 280; Glycogen 280; Lactic acid 280

ICTALURUS NEBULOSUS† (*see* AMEIURUS NEBULOSUS†)

ICTALURUS PUNCTATUS† (Channel catfish, Fiddler, White cat)   *111, 255, 278*
  N. America: rivers of the Great Lake region, Mississippi Valley, streams leading
  to Gulf of Mexico.
  Carbon dioxide 453; Corticosterone 130; Cortisone 130; Cortisol 130; Epi-
  oestriol 315; Erythrocytes 473, 504; Haematocrit 475, 504; Haemoglobin
  475, 504; Oestradiol 316; Oestriol 316; Oestrone 316

ICTIOBUS SP.†
  California.
  Anserine 783; Carnosine 783; Histidine 783; 1-Methyl histidine 783; Potas-
  sium 192, 1263, 1274; Sodium 192, 1263, 1274

IDUS IDUS† = LEUCISCUS IDUS† (Ide, Orfe)   *97, 213*
Europe, in running waters, lakes and lagoons, also in brackish parts of the
Baltic. In clear water which is not too shallow.
Calcium 966; Potassium 462; Thiamine 966

IDUS MELANOTUS†
Germany.
'Sugar' 671

INEGOCIA MEERDERVOOSTI
Japan.
Cholesterol 1153; Fatty acids 1153

ISOPSETTA ISOLEPIS (Butter sole, Scalyfin flounder)
N. America: S. California to S.E. Alaska. Soft, silty bottom.
Anserine 783; Carnosine 783; Histidine 783; 1-Methyl histidine 783

ISUROPSIS GLAUCUS‡
Japan.
Elastin 1242; Hydroxyproline 1243

ISURUS GLAUCUS‡ (Blue pointer, Blue shark, Mako shark)   *142*
Japan to Tropics. Viviparous.
Folic acid 503; Hydroxyproline 1239; Pantothenic acid 502

JOHNIUS REGIUS (Maigre, Sciaena)
Portugal.
Cyanocobalamin 412

JOHNIUS UMBRA
Portugal.
Cyanocobalamin 412

KAREIUS BICOLORATUS (Stone flounder)   *160*
Japan, Korea, China.
Amino acids 696; Cholesterol 915; Cyanocobalamin 1380; Lecithin 1235;
Riboflavin 584; Vitamin A 509, 513

KATSUWONUS PELAMIS = EUTHYNNUS PELAMIS (Bonita, Ocean bonito, Skipjack,
Watermelon)   *18, 19, 31, 34, 130, 163*
Japan to South Sea Islands. S. California to Vancouver. Mediterranean and
S. Atlantic. Warm water, offshore.
Amino acids 198; Anserine 532, 783; Carnosine 783; Cholesterol 915; Cyanoco-
balamin 891; Haemoglobin 678; Histidine 532, 783; 1-Methyl histidine 783;
Myoglobin 180; Niacin 494; Potassium 649; Pyridoxine 891, 1383, 1384;
Riboflavin 501, 584, 891; Sodium 649, 1273; Tryptophan 1036; Vitamin A
508, 513, 1374; Vitamin D 1374

KATSUWONUS VAGANS (Skipjack)   *19, 20, 21, 25, 204*
Japan.
Aluminium 531; Amino acids 639, 847, 1214; Biotin 636; Calcium 531;
Chloride 531; Cholesterol 1228; Cyanocobalamin 466, 635, 867, 1380, 1382;

LABRAX LUPUS
  Europe.
  Potassium 871

LABRUS BERGYLTA (Ballan wrasse, Bergylt) *119, 120*
  Europe apart from Iceland. Mid-Norway south to Canary Islands. Rocky
  shores down to 9 m. A nest-builder.
  N-Acetyl histidine 456

LABRUS SP.
  Cholesterol 872; Phospholipid 872

LABRUS TURDUS (Green wrasse)
  Europe.
  Vitamin C 399

LACHNOLAIMUS MAXIMUS (Capitaine, Hogfish)
  Puerta Rica, W. Indies.
  Potassium 202; Sodium 202

LAGOCEPHALUS LUNARIS
  Japan.
  Fucose 326; Galactosamine 324; Galactose 326; Glucosamine 324; Glucose
  326; Hexuronic acid 324; Ribose 326; Vitamin A 513

LAGODON RHOMBOIDES (Bream, Pinfish, Sailor's choice)
  Atlantic and Gulf coast of United States. Cape Cod to Cuba.
  Chloride 1215; Cholesterol 1215; Potassium 1215; Sodium 1215

LAMNA CORNUBICA‡ (Porbeagle) *21, 22, 23, 25, 27, 28*
  Japan. Europe.
  Calcium 1234; Carotenoids 347; Cholesterol 1153; Cyanocobalamin 1234;
  Fatty acids 1153; Iodine 1234; Iron 1234; Niacin 1234; Pantothenic acid
  1234; Riboflavin 1234; Thiamine 1234

LAMNA NASUS‡ (Mackerel shark, Porbeagle) *21, 23, 25*
  Murman coast to Mediterranean and N.W. Africa. Newfoundland to S. Caro-
  lina. Japan and Australia. Surface down to 150 m or deeper. Strong-swimming.
  Trimethylamine oxide 307

LAMPETRA FLUVIATILIS*§ (*see* PETROMYZON FLUVIATILIS*§)

LAMPETRA JAPONICA†§ (Arctic lamprey)
  Japan.
  Cyanocobalamin 1381

LAMPETRA LAMOTTEI*§ (American brook lamprey) *82, 237*

LAMPETRA MARINUS*§
  Arginine 1039; Histidine 1039

LAMPETRA PLANERI*§ (Brook lamprey, Planer's lamprey)
Japan, Europe (not Iceland), N. Asia and western N. America. Upper reaches of rivers at spawning time. Non-parasitic.
Vitamin A 497, 498

LATEOLABRAX JAPONICUS   *7, 24, 25*
Japan, Korea, China Sea. Shores.
Actin 1309; Adenosine diphosphate 901; Adenosine monophosphate 901; Adenosine triphosphate 901; Arsenic 448; Cholesterol 1153; Fatty acids 1153; Fructose diphosphate 901; Fructose-6-phosphate 901; Glucose 901; Glucose-1-phosphate 901; Glucose-6-phosphate 901; Glycogen 901; 'Hexose' 901; Inositol 1149; Lactic acid 901; Lecithin 1235; Manganese 1229; Methionine 846; 'Pentose' 901; Riboflavin 584; Selenium 448; Thallium 448; Vitamin A 510, 513

LATES CALCARICES
Philippines
Iron 585; Niacin 585; Riboflavin 585; Thiamine 585

LATES CALCARIFER* (Barramundi, Cock-up, Giant perch)
Persion Gulf, Seas of India, China and Australia. Coastal waters, estuaries and lagoons, ascending rivers for food.
Cholesterol 630; Creatin 631; Cyanocobalamin 71, 72; Folic acid 73; Lecithin 630; Niacin 158, 631; Phospholipid 630; Riboflavin 52, 631; Sphingomyelin 630; Thiamine 631; Trimethylamine 631; Trimethylamine oxide 631; Urea 631; Vitamin C 1095

LATICAUDA LATICAUDATA
Japan
Ophidin 1295

LATICAUDA SEMIFASCIATA
Japan.
Ophidin 1295

LATIMERIA CHALUMNAE (Coelacanth)   *137, 139, 140, 141, 142*
Madagascar. Survivor of primitive Crossopterygians; not discovered until 1938.
Aluminium 251; Arginine 1039; Barium 251; Bicarbonate 1011; Bromine 251; Calcium 251, 1011; Carotenoids 360; Chloride 251, 1011; Chromium 251; Cobalt 251; Copper 88, 251; Fatty acids 927; Fluoride 251; Germanium 251; Histidine 1039; Iodine 251; Iron 251; Lead 251; Magnesium 251, 1011; Manganese 251; Nickel 251; Potassium 251, 1011; Rubidium 251; Selenium 251; Silicon 251; Sodium 251, 1011; Strontium 251; Sulphate 251; Titanium 251; Tryptophan 1039; Tyrosine 1039; Urea 177, 1011; Wax esters 927; Zinc 251

LEBISTES RETICULATUS† (Belly-fish, Guppy, Millions, Rainbow-fish)   *117, 127, 200, 213*
Barbados, Trinidad and Venezuela, in pools and streams.

LEIOGNATHUS ARGENTEUS
  Japan.
  Thiamine 382

LEIOGNATHUS BINDUS (Orange-finned pony fish)
  India: Coromandel coast. China, Philippines, Java, Borneo.
  Amino acids 1324

LEIOGNATHUS DAURA (Golden-striped pony fish)
  S. Arabia, India, Thailand, Philippines, Queensland (Australia).
  Iron 585; Niacin 585; Riboflavin 585; Thiamine 585

LEIOGNATHUS EQUULUS* (Common slipmouth, Greater pony fish)
  Red Sea, Tanzania, Philippines, Australia. In sea, brackish water and rivers.
  Iron 585; Niacin 585; Riboflavin 585; Thiamine 585

LEIOGNATHUS NUCHALIS
  Japan
  Arsenic 448; Selenium 448; Thallium 448

LEIOGNATHUS SP.
  Niacin 670

LEIOSTOMUS XANTHURUS (Cape May goody, Goody, Lafayette, Oldwife, Porgy,
  Postcroaker, Spot, Yellowtail)
  S. Atlantic and Gulf coasts of United States. Cape Cod to Texas.
  Chloride 1215; Cholesterol 1215; Haemoglobin 1215; Potassium 1215; Sodium
  1215

LEPIDION INOSIMAE
  Japan.
  Vitamin A 513

LEPIDOCYBIUM FLAVOBRUNNEUM (Escolar)
  Atlantic.
  Vitamin A 513

LEPIDOPSETTA BILINEATA (Rock sole)
  Japan, S. California to Bering Sea. Coastal.
  Potassium 1268; Riboflavin 1113; Sodium 1268; Thiamine 1112; Vitamin E
  850

LEPIDOPSETTA MOCHIGAREI
  Japan.
  Hydroxyproline 1239; Vitamin A 513

LEPIDORHOMBUS WHIFFIAGONIS (Megrim, Sail-fluke)
  Europe, including Iceland, south to W. Mediterranean. 10–400 m on soft
  bottoms.
  Ubiquinone 292

LEPIDOTRIGLA GÜNTHERI
  Japan.
  Astaxanthin 1293; Carotenoids 1293; Tunaxanthin 1293

LEPIDOTRIGLA MICROPTERA
  Japan.
  Trimethylamine 1237; Trimethylamine oxide 1237

LEPISOSTEUS OSSEUS† (Billfish, Billy gar, Common gar-pike, Long-nosed gar,
  Ohio gar)
  N. America: Maryland to Florida in streams. Also Great Lakes and Mississippi
  Valley.
  Chloride 1215; Cholesterol 1215; Haemoglobin 1215; Potassium 1215; Sodium
  1215

LEPISOSTEUS PRODUCTUS†
  Mexico.
  Chloride 1215; Cholesterol 1215; Haemoglobin 1215; Potassium 1215; Sodium
  1215

LEPISOSTEUS SPATULA† (Mississippi alligator gar)
  Lower Mississippi Valley (N. America).
  Chloride 1215; Cholesterol 1215; Haemoglobin 1215; Potassium 1215; Sodium
  1215

LEPOMIS GIBBOSUS† (Pumpkinseed)   *146*
  Chloride 553; Cholesterol 553; Haemoglobin 553; Potassium 553; Sodium
  553; Trimethylamine 28; Trimethylamine oxide 28

LEPOMIS MACROCHIRUS† (Bluegill, Bream, Chain-sided perch, Gilded sunfish,
  Gold perch, Perch, Sunfish)   *41, 146, 175, 212*
  N. America: Ohio valley, South-westward to Missouri and Kentucky.
  Glucose 280, 479; Glycogen 280, 479; Lactic acid 280, 479; Trimethylamine
  28; Trimethylamine oxide 28

LEPOPHIDIUM BREVIBARBE
  W. Indies to Brazil.
  Calcium 592; Cyanocobalamin 592; Cystine 592; Iron 592; Lysine 592;
  Methionine 592; Niacin 592; Riboflavin 592; Thiamine 592; Tryptophan 592

LEPTOCOTTUS ARMATUS (Staghorn sculpin)
  S. California to Gulf of Alaska. Coastal shallow waters.
  Creatin 554

LEPTOSCARUS JAPONICUS (Japanese parrotfish)
  Japan.
  Folic acid 503; Pantothenic acid 502; Riboflavin 501

LETHRINUS CINEREUS—a doubtful species, according to Weber and de Beaufort:
  probably Lethrinus frenatus. (Bridled pig-face bream)
  India, coastal waters.
  Trimethylamine oxide 1319

LETHRINUS OPERCULARIS (Starry pig-face bream)
Aden, India, Philippines, Formosa to Samoa. Coastal waters, entering harbours. Pearl banks and trawling grounds.
Iron 585; Niacin 585; Riboflavin 585; Thiamine 585

LEUCICHTHYS ARTEDI† (Cisco, Greyback, Lake herring, Shallow-water cisco)
N. America: Lakes Erie, St. Clair and Huron.
Amino acids 583, 1035; Niacin 583, 681; Potassium 192, 1263, 1274; Riboflavin 583; Sodium 192, 1263, 1274; Thiamine 405, 583, 682; Trimethylamine oxide 243, 307

LEUCISCUS ERYTHROPHTHALMUS† *224*

LEUCISCUS HAKONENSIS† *22*
Japan.
Adenosine triphosphate 108; Calcium 108; Magnesium 108; Potassium 108; Pyridoxine 1384; Riboflavin 501; Sodium 108; Thiamine 839

LEUCISCUS IDUS† (*see* IDUS IDUS†)

LEUCISCUS LEUCISCUS† (Dace) *200*
Europe, except for Iceland, Scotland and Norway. Rivers and streams, near the surface. Gregarious.
Anserine 1392; Carnosine 1392; FREE Histidine 1392

LEUCISCUS RUTILUS†
Glycogen 245; Potassium 462; Vitamin C 781

LEURESTHES TENUIS (Grunion) *156*
California. Sandy coasts.

LIMANDER ANGUSTIROSTRIS
Japan.
Folic acid 503; Pantothenic acid 502; Urea 938; Vitamin A 509; Vitamin E 850

LIMANDER FERRUGINEA (Rusty dab, Yellow tail flounder)
E. side of N. America (Labrador to Virginia), confined to the continental shelf.
Potassium 175, 192, 1263; Sodium 175, 192, 1263; Trimethylamine oxide 307

LIMANDER HERZENSTEINI (Small-mouthed sole) *232*
Japan.
Hydroxyproline 1239, 1243; Vitamin A 513

LIMANDER LIMANDER (Dab) *146*
Europe: White Sea to France. 20–150 m on sandy banks.
Vitamin A 1021

LIMANDER YOKOHAMAE
Japan.
Inositol 1149; Vitamin A 509, 513

LIPARIS KOEFOEDI (Gelatinous seasnail)   *218*
Circumpolar.
Iron 1126

LIZA DUSSUMIERI* (see MUGIL DUSSUMIERI*)

LOPHIOMUS SETIGERUS (Angler)
Japan, Korea, China. Rocky or weedy bottom.
Cholesterol 1153; Fatty acids 1153; Vitamin A 1374; Vitamin D 1374

LOPHIUS AMERICANUS (All-mouth, Angler, Goosefish, Monkfish)
E. coast of America from Gulf of St. Lawrence to Brazil.
Glucose 823

LOPHIUS LITULON
Japan.
Vitamin A 513

LOPHIUS PISCATORIUS (All-mouth, Angler, Bellowsfish, Fishing frog, Goosefish, Monk)   *150, 278*
Both sides of N. Atlantic, Mediterranean. Intertidal to 550 m or more, on a variety of bottoms.
N-Acetyl histidine 456; Amino acids (of insulin) 548; Haematocrit 737; Iron 443; 'Sugar' 428; Thiamine 405; Trimethylamine oxide 307; Ubiquinone 292

LOPHIUS SETIGERUS
Japan.
Cyanocobalamin 1381

LOPHOPSETTA MACULATA (Sundial, Windowpane)
Atlantic coast of United States: Gulf of St. Lawrence to S. Carolina. Bottom-living in shallow water.
Iron 443; 'Sugar' 428

LOTA LOTA† (Burbot, Eel-pout)   *232, 234, 235, 255*
N. and central Europe and Asia in lakes and streams. Prefers bottom of clear waters, under rocks or in holes. The only gadoid living entirely in fresh water.
N-Acetyl histidine 456; Amino acids 25; Cholesterol 25; Cyanocobalamin 25; DNA 25; Fatty acids 25; Galactose 25; Glucose 25; Glycogen 25; Heparin 25; Mannose 25; Mercury 1337; Phospholipids 25; Potassium 462; Riboflavin 25; RNA 25; Thiamine 25; Vitamin A 25

LOTA LOTA MACULOSA† (Alekey trout, Burbot, Eel-pout, Lake lawyer, Ling, Mud blower)
N. America: New England northwards to Arctic. Rivers and lakes.
Amino acids 26, 583; Niacin 583, 681; Riboflavin 583; Thiamine 405, 583, 682

LOTA MOLVA†
Potassium 871

LOTELLA MAXIMOWICZI
Japan.
Vitamin A 513

LUCIOPERCA LUCIOPERCA† = L. SANDRA† (Pike-perch, Sander)
Central Europe, Baltic. Warm shallow water with hard bottom.
N-Acetyl histidine 456; Anserine 1392; Calcium 966; Carnosine 1392; FREE
Histidine 1392; Potassium 462; Riboflavin 1129; Thiamine 966; Vitamin C 781

LUTIANUS ANALIS (Mutton fish, Pargo)
E. America: Woods Hole to Brazil.
Thiamine 405

LUTIANUS AYA
United States to Brazil.
Potassium 948; Sodium 948

LUTIANUS BLACKFORDII (Pensacola snapper, Red snapper)
N. America: Florida.
Amino acids 1035; Niacin 413; Potassium 192, 1258, 1263; Riboflavin 413;
Sodium 192, 1258, 1263; Thiamine 405, 413

LUTIANUS CAMPECHANUS (Mexican snapper, Red snapper)
E. America: Long Island to Texas, Puerta Rica.
Potassium 202; Sodium 202

LUTIANUS GRISEUS (Cabelellerote, Grey snapper, Lawyer, Mangrove snapper)
E. America: New York to Brazil.
DNA 862; Thiamine 405

LUTIANUS HASTINGSI (Bermuda silk snapper)
Bermuda.
DNA 862

LUTIANUS MALABARICUS (Malabar snapper)
India, Malaya, Philippines. Pearl banks and trawling grounds.
Iron 585; Niacin 585; Riboflavin 585; Thiamine 585

LUTIANUS RIVULATUS (Flute porgy, Snapper)
India, Red Sea, Japan, China.
Fatty acids 667

LUTIANUS SP.
S. America.
Calcium 592; Cyanocobalamin 592; Cystine 592; Iron 592; Lysine 592;
Methionine 592; Niacin 592; Riboflavin 592; Thiamine 592; Tryptophan 592

LUTIANUS SYNAGRIS (Biajaiba, Lane snapper, Red tail snapper)
E. America: Florida to Brazil, Puerta Rica.
Potassium 202; Sodium 202

LYCODES TURNERI (Polar eel-pout) *218*
Arctic Ocean, Labrador coast.

MABULA JAPONICA‡
  Japan.
  Cyanocobalamin 1381

MACQUARIA AUSTRALASICA† (Macquarie perch, Mountain perch, Murray perch)
  Australia. Fast-flowing rivers.
  Cholesterol 872; Phospholipid 872

MACRODON ANCYLODON
  S. America.
  Calcium 592; Cyanocobalamin 592; Cystine 592; Iron 592; Lysine 592;
  Methionine 592; Niacin 592; Riboflavin 592; Thiamine 592; Tryptophan 592

MACRONES AOR† (see M. CAVASIUS†)

MACRONES CAVASIUS† = M. AOR† = M. NIGRICEPS† (Dwarf catfish)
  India, Assam, Burma, Java, Borneo, Sumatra. Rivers and lakes.
  Amino acids 629; Calcium 918; Iron 918

MACRONES PUNCTATUS†
  India: Bowany River.
  Calcium 918; Iron 918

MACRONES SEENGHALA†
  India. Rivers.

MACRONES SP.*
  India. Brackish waters.
  Haematocrit 1038; Haemoglobin 1038

MACRONES VITTATUS† = MYSTUS VITTATUS† (Striped dwarf catfish)
  India and Burma. Ponds and streams up to 3000 ft.
  Cholesterol 1161; Cyanocobalamin 71, 72; Cystine 1090; Folic acid 73;
  Tryptophan 1090; Tyrosine 1090

MACRORHAMPHOSUS SAGIFUE (Egret-piper)
  Japan. Deep sea.
  Vitamin A 513

MACROURUS BERGLAX (Smooth-spined rat-tail)
  United States to Greenland and Norway.
  Iron 266; Trimethylamine oxide 307

MACROZOARCES AMERICANUS (Eel-pout, Muttonfish, Ocean pout)
  Western N. Atlantic, Newfoundland to Delaware. 15–180 m on bottom.
  Trimethylamine oxide 243, 307

MAKAIRA MARLINA (Giant black marlin)
  California South to Cape San Lucas.
  Niacin 494

MAKAIRA MAZARA (Black marlin, Black spearfish, Real swordfish)   *20, 21*
Japan, Hawaii, California.
Cytochrome C 844; Haemoglobin 844; Myoglobin 844; Pyridoxine 891;
Riboflavin 501, 891, 1152; Vitamin A 513, 1374; Vitamin D 1374

MAKAIRA MITSUKURII (Pacific marlin, Spear fish, Striped marlin)   *20, 21*
Japan, Formosa, Hawaii, California. Surface, Oceanic.
Cytochrome C 844; Haemoglobin 844, 845; Myoglobin 844, 845; Riboflavin
1152; Tryptophan 697; Vitamin A 513

MAKAIRA NIGRICANS (Blue marlin)
Haemoglobin 77

MARLINA MARLINA
Riboflavin 1151

MASTACEMBALUS ARMATUS† (Spiny eel)
India, Ceylon, Burma, China. Fresh and brackish waters of the plains and
hills up to 4000 ft.
Calcium 918; Cholesterol 1161; Iron 918

MASTURUS LANCEOLATUS (Nipple-tailed ocean sunfish, Sharp tail ocean sunfish)   *33*
Cosmopolitan in temperate and tropical waters.

MEGALASPIS CORDYLA (Torpedo trevally)
Red Sea, Tanzania, S. Arabia, India, Malaya, Hong-Kong, Formosa, Philip-
pines, Queensland, Hawaii. Coastal waters.
Iron 585; Niacin 585; Riboflavin 585; Thiamine 585

MEGALOPS CYPRINOIDES* (Ox-eye herring, Tarpon)
E. Africa, India, China, Philippines, Australia. Seas and estuaries, entering
fresh water. Ponds.
Iron 585; Niacin 585; Riboflavin 585; Thiamine 585

MEGALOPS SP.
India.
Haematocrit 1038; Haemoglobin 1038

MELANOGRAMMUS AEGLEFINUS (*see* GADUS AEGLEFINUS)

MENACANTHUS CIRRHIFER
Japan.
Vitamin A 510

MENE MACULATA
Aden, Tanzania, Japan, East Indies, China, Philippines, Queensland, Hawaii.
Deep coastal waters.
Iron 585; Niacin 585; Riboflavin 585; Thiamine 585

MENIDIA MENIDIA NOTATA (Atlantic silverside, Sand smelt)
Western Atlantic. Shore waters and estuaries. Tolerates brackish water.
Trimethylamine oxide 307

MENTICIRRHUS LITTORALIS (Gulf kingfish, King whiting)
Atlantic coast of N. America.
Potassium 948; Sodium 948

MERLANGUS CARBONARIUS
Europe.
Potassium 871

MERLANGIUS MERLANGUS (*see* GADUS MERLANGUS)

MERLANGUS VULGARIS (*see* GADUS MERLANGUS)

MERLUCCIUS BILINEARIS (American hake, New England hake, Old England
hake, Silverfish, Silver hake, Stockfish, Whiting)
Eastern N. America: Newfoundland to N. Carolina and in deeper water to the
Bahamas. Found down to 122 m.
Iron 266, 443; Potassium 175, 192, 1263; Sodium 175, 192, 1263; 'Sugar' 428;
Trimethylamine oxide 307

MERLUCCIUS CAPENSIS (Stockfish)
S. Africa.
Amino acids 1341; Cardiolipid 692; Lyso-phosphatidyl choline 692; Phosphatidyl choline = Lecithin 692; Phosphatidyl ethanolamine 692; Phosphatidyl inositol 692; Phosphatidyl serine 692; Phospholipid 692; Sphingomyelin 692; Vitamin D 1054

MERLUCCIUS MERLUCCIUS (Hake)   *91, 116, 126, 171, 174, 260*
Coasts of Europe and N. Africa straying to Greenland.
N-Acetyl histidine 456; Cobalt 120; Copper 120; Cyanocobalamin 412; Iron
120; Potassium 871; Trimethylamine 1253; Trimethylamine oxide 1253;
Ubiquinone 292; Vitamin A 311

MERLUCCIUS PRODUCTUS (Pacific hake)
S. California to Gulf of Alaska. Coastal.
Fatty acids 1347

MICROGADUS PROXIMUS (Pacific tomcod)
N. California to Gulf of Alaska. Coastal.
Adenosine diphosphate + Adenosine triphosphate 1247; Adenosine mono-
phosphate 1247

MICROGADUS TOMCOD* (Atlantic tomcod, Frostfish, Snig)
N. American coasts: Newfoundland to Virginia, inshore or in brackish water.
Eggs laid in river estuaries. Occasionally found in fresh water.
Riboflavin 517

MICROPOGON UNDULATUS (Corvina, Croaker, Hardhead, Roncodina)   *149*
Atlantic coast of N. America: Cape Cod to Texas. Shallow, sandy shores in
summer, deeper waters in winter.
Amino acids 1035; Chloride 1215; Cholesterol 1215; Haematocrit 320; Haemoglobin 320, 1215; Potassium 948, 1215; Sodium 948, 1215; Thiamine 405

MICROPTERUS DOLOMIEU† (Bass, Bass hogfish, Black perch, Little bass, Small-mouthed black bass and many other names) *146*
N. America: Lake Champlain to Manitoba and south to Carolina and Arkansas. Introduced to Europe. Prefers deep water.
Calcium 1144; Chloride 1144; Cholesterol 1144; Creatinine 1144; Glucose 1144; Iron 1144; Potassium 1144; Sodium 1144; Trimethylamine 28; Trimethyl-amine oxide 28; Uric acid 1144

MICROPTERUS SALMOIDES† (Largemouth bass and many other names) *40, 41, 176, 212*
Rivers of the United States. Introduced to Europe.
Carnitine 949; Chloride 553; Cholesterol 553; Glucose 280; Glycogen 280; Haemoglobin 553; Lactic acid 110, 280; Potassium 553; Sodium 553

MICROSTOMUS HIREGURO
Japan.
Vitamin E 850

MICROSTOMUS KITAHARAE
Japan.
Vitamin A 509

MICROSTOMUS KITT (*see* PLEURONECTES MICROCEPHALUS)

MICROSTOMUS PACIFICUS (Dover sole, Slime sole, Slippery sole) *245*
S. California to Bering Sea. Muddy bottoms less than 55 m.
Potassium 1268; Riboflavin 1113; Sodium 1268; Thiamine 1112

MICROSTOMUS STELLERI
Japan.
Choline 869; Folic acid 503; Pantothenic acid 502; Vitamin E 850

MIICHTHYS IMBRICATUS
Japan.
Cholesterol 1153; Fatty acids 1153

MISGURNUS ANGUILLICAUDATUS† (Loach) *154*
Japan, China.
Amino acids 323; Fucose 326; Galactosamine 324; Galactose 326; Glucosamine 324; Glucose 326; Hexuronic acid 324; Ribose 326; Vitamin A 513

MISGURNUS FOSSILIS† (Mudfish, Pond loach, Weatherfish) *71, 74*
Japan. Central and E. Europe and Baltic. Not Britain, France or Scandinavia. Still waters with muddy bottom. Swallows bubbles of air under conditions of oxygen lack.
Adenosine triphosphate 108; Calcium 108; DNA + RNA 12; Magnesium 108; Potassium 108; Sodium 108; 'Sugar' 671

MOLA MOLA (Headfish, Ocean sunfish)
Wide distribution in tropical and temperate seas. Preferred depth unknown,
but sometimes found drifting at the surface.
Trimethylamine oxide 307

MOLLIENESIA SP.† (Black mollie)   *14*

MOLVA BYRKELANGE (Blue ling, Lesser ling)
Both sides of Atlantic in deep water.
Ubiquinone 292

MOLVA MOLVA (Ling)   *20, 25*
Iceland, Murman coast to France. Occasionally W. Atlantic. Commonest at
depths between 300–400 m.
Amino acids 154; Biotin 155; Calcium 1061, 1234; Cholesterol 1369; Cyanocobalamin 147, 149, 150, 1234; Iodine 1234; Iron 1234; Magnesium 1061; Niacin
147, 150, 1234; Pantothenic acid 147, 150, 1234; Potassium 1061; Pyridoxine
155; Riboflavin 147, 150, 787, 1234; Sodium 1061; Thiamine 742, 787, 1234;
Trimethylamine 1085; Trimethylamine oxide 243, 1085; Ubiquinone 292

MONACANTHUS CIRRHIFER
Japan.
Arsenic 448; Pyridoxine 1383; Riboflavin 1285; Riboflavin adenine dinucleo-
tide 1285; Riboflavin mononucleotide 1285; Selenium 448; Thallium 448

MONOPTERUS ALBUS† = M. ALBA†
Burma, Malaya, Indonesia, China, Formosa, Japan. Fresh or brackish waters.
Scale-less, can live for long periods out of water.
Amino acids 306

MONOTAXIS GRANDOCULIS (Round-toothed large-eyed bream)
Red Sea, Ceylon, Pacific Islands eastwards to Hawaii, N. Australia. Coastal
reefs and trawling grounds.
Iron 585; Niacin 585; Riboflavin 585; Thiamine 585

MORONE AMERICANA* (Sea perch, Silver perch, White perch)   *146*
Atlantic coast of N. America: Nova Scotia to S. Carolina. Brackish water,
ascending streams. Frequently landlocked.
Trimethylamine 28; Trimethylamine oxide 28, 307

MORONE LABRAX (Bass)
Europe.
Oestriol 221; Oestrone 221; Progesterone 221

MOXOSTOMA AUREOLUM† (Large-scaled sucker, Mullet, Northern redhorse, White
sucker)
N. America: Great Lakes, rivers.
Trimethylamine oxide 307

MUGIL AURATUS (Golden-grey mullet)
Britain and S. Norway south to Mediterranean. Black Sea.
Calcium 652; Iron 652; Magnesium 652; Potassium 652

MUGIL CEPHALUS* = M. JAPONICUS* = M. OEUR* (Haader, Springer, Striped mullet, True mullet)
Widely distributed in tropical and temperate waters. Not anadromous, but found in fresh and salt water.
Amino acids 838; FREE Amino acids 698; Arsenic 448; Calcium 966; Carnosine 698; Chloride 1215; Cholesterol 630, 872, 915, 1215; Copper 88; Cyanocobalamin 1380; Fatty acids 789; Folic acid 503; Haemoglobin 1215; Hydroxyproline 58; Lecithin 630, 1235; Niacin 631; Pantothenic acid 502; Phospholipid 630, 872; Potassium 192, 1215, 1263; Proline 58; Pyridoxine 1383, 1384; Riboflavin 489, 501, 584, 631, 891, 1285; Riboflavin adenine nucleotide 1285; Riboflavin mononucleotide 1285; Selenium 448; Sodium 192, 1215, 1263; Sphingomyelin 630; Taurine 698; Thallium 448; Thiamine 631, 839, 966; Triglycerides 789; Trimethylamine 1253; Trimethylamine oxide 1253; Vitamin A 510, 513; Vitamin C 56; Wax esters 789

MUGIL CHELO (Thick-lipped grey mullet)
Iceland and mid-Norway south to Mediterranean. Black Sea. Inshore and estuarine.
Potassium 871

MUGIL CUREMA (Blue-black mullet, Lisa, White mullet)
Warm and temperate seas. Shallow waters in schools near the surface.
Chloride 1215; Cholesterol 1215; DNA 862; Haemoglobin 1215; Potassium 1215; Sodium 1215

MUGIL DUSSUMIERII* = LIZA DUSSUMIERI* (Dussumier's mullet)
India, Ceylon, Singapore, Java, Sumatra, Philippines, New Guinea, Australia.
Calcium 55; Vitamin C 56, 57

MUGIL JAPONICUS* (see M. CEPHALUS*)

MUGIL MELINOPTERUS (Black-finned mullet)
Philippines, Vanicolo, Tonga, Samoa, Fiji.
Iron 585; Niacin 585; Riboflavin 585; Thiamine 585

MUGIL OEUR* (see M. CEPHALUS*)

MUGIL PARSIA* (Gold-spot mullet)
Red Sea, E. Africa, India, China, Fiji, Samoa. Fresh and brackish waters (Weber and Beaufort); seas and estuaries (Day).
Cyanocobalamin 71, 72; Folic acid 73; Niacin 1096; Vitamin C 1095

MUGIL SP.*
Amino acids 1035; Niacin 670; Thiamine 405; Trimethylamine oxide 1319; Ubiquinone 292

MUGIL SPEIGLERI (Grey mullet)
Seas of India, Malaya, Java, Borneo.
Amino acids 827; Fatty acids 667

MUGIL TADE*
Red Sea, India, Philippines, China, Australia. Seas and rivers.
Cystine 1090; Tryptophan 1090; Tyrosine 1090

MUGIL VAIGIENSIS* (Diamond-scale mullet, Long-finned mullet)
Red Sea, E. Africa, India, Malaya, China, Philippines, Australia. Seas, estuaries
and fresh water.
Iron 585; Niacin 585; Riboflavin 585; Thiamine 585

MULLOIDES FLAVOLINEATUS (Golden-banded goat fish)
Red Sea, India, Malaya, Philippines, Japan, China, Australia. Harbours.
Trimethylamine oxide 1319

MULLUS BARBATUS (Red mullet, Striped mullet)   *120*
Russia.
FREE Amino acids 1139; Trimethylamine 1253; Trimethylamine oxide 1253;
Ubiquinone 292

MULLUS BARBATUS PONTICUS
Calcium 712; Magnesium 712; Potassium 712; Sodium 712

MULLUS SURMULLETUS (Red mullet)
Puerta Rica. S. Norway and Denmark to Britain, France, Mediterranean and
Canaries. Mostly on rough ground.
Potassium 202; Sodium 202

MURAENA HELENA (Moray eel)   *121, 144*
S. England, France, Mediterranean. Inshore amongst rocks.
Calcium 1075, 1076; Chloride 1075, 1076; Magnesium 1075, 1076; Oestradiol
211; Oestriol 211; Oestrone 211; Potassium 1075, 1076; Sodium 1075, 1076;
Sulphate 1076

MURAENA PARDALIS
Japan.
Cyanocobalamin 1381; Vitamin A 513

MURAENA SP.
Philippines.
Iron 585; Niacin 585; Riboflavin 585; Thiamine 585

MURAENESOX CINEREUS (Silver conger eel)
Wide distribution. Brackish and salt waters of lagoons and shallow coastal
inlets.
Amino acids 696; Cyanocobalamin 1381; Methionine 846; Vitamin A 513

MURAENESOX TELABONOIDES*
India and Malaya. Seas and estuaries.
Cholesterol 630; Creatin 631; Lecithin 630; Niacin 631; Phospholipid 630;
Riboflavin 631; Sphingomyelin 630; Thiamine 631; Trimethylamine 631;
Trimethylamine oxide 631; Urea 631

MUSTELUS CANIS‡ = SCYLIORHINUS CANICULA‡ (Lesser spotted dogfish, Smooth dogfish) *20, 112*
Atlantic. Bays, estuaries and ocean beaches down to 18 m.
Ammonia 1182; Calcium 293, 592, 1182; Carnitine 361; Carotenoids 982; Chloride 293, 1182; Creatin 1182; Cyanocobalamin 412, 592; Cystine 592; DNA 1404; Glucose 128, 293; Glycogen 135; Iron 443, 592; Lysine 592; Magnesium 293, 1182; Methionine 592; Niacin 592; Oestradiol 1171; Oestrone 1171; Potassium 293, 1182; Riboflavin 592; RNA 1404; Sodium 293, 1182; Sulphate 293, 1182; Thiamine 592; Trimethylamine oxide 293; Tryptophan 592; Ubiquinone 292; Urea 293, 1182; Vitamin C 293

MUSTELUS GRISEUS‡ (Dog-shark)
Japan. Viviparous.
Urea 1226

MUSTELUS KANEKONIS‡
Japan.
Urea 1226

MUSTELUS LAEVIS‡ (*see* MUSTELUS MUSTELUS‡)

MUSTELUS MANAZO‡ (Gummy shark, Star-spotted shark) *146*
Japan, in shallow bays. Viviparous.
Actin 1309; Amino acids 696; Creatin 1100; Creatinine 1100; Cyanocobalamin 867; Niacin 867; Riboflavin 867; Thiamine 867; Trimethylamine oxide 1227; Urea 1226, 1227; Vitamin A 1374; Vitamin D 1374; Vitamin E 581

MUSTELUS MUSTELUS‡ = M. LAEVIS‡ (Smooth hound, Sweet William)
Britain, France, Mediterranean, occasionally America.
Carotenoids 347; Urea 674

MYCTEROPERCA TIGRIS (Rockfish)
W. Indies, north to Bermuda.
DNA 862

MYLIO AUSTRALIS* (Bream)
Australia. Creeks, estuaries, rivers and coastal waters.
Cholesterol 872; Phospholipid 872

MYLIO BUTCHERI
Australia.
Copper 88

MYLIO MACROCEPHALUS
Vitamin A 513

MYLIOBATIS AQUILA‡ (Eagle ray)
Britain to Mediterranean. Active, pelagic, viviparous.
Carotenoids 347

MYLIOBATIS MACULATA‡
Seas of India to Malaya.
Trimethylamine oxide 1319

MYOXOCEPHALUS GROENLANDICUS (Shorthorn sculpin)
Atlantic coast of N. America.
Trimethylamine oxide 307

MYOXOCEPHALUS NIVOSUS
Japan.
Folic acid 503; Pantothenic acid 502

MYOXOCEPHALUS OCTODECIMSPINOSUS (Longhorn sculpin)
Western N. Atlantic: Newfoundland to Virginia. Coastal, down to 200 m.
Glycogen 813; Trimethylamine oxide 307

MYOXOCEPHALUS SCORPIUS = COTTUS SCORPIUS (Bullhead, Daddy sculpin,
Father lasher, Greenland sculpin, Shorthorn sculpin, short-spined cottus) *219*
Both sides of N. Atlantic and the Arctic. Littoral on sandy or muddy grounds,
also estuaries.
N-Acetyl histidine 456; FREE Amino acids 1139; Caesium 184, 185; Chloride
321; Iron 1126; Lithium 184, 185, 926; Potassium 184, 185, 321, 736, 926;
Rubidium 185; Sodium 184, 185, 321, 736, 926

MYSTUS AOR† (probably MACRONES CAVASIUS†)
India.
Cholesterol 1161

MYSTUS SEENGHALA†
India.
Calcium 1327; Cholesterol 1161; Copper 1327; Iron 1327; Potassium 1327

MYSTUS VITTATUS† (*see* MACRONES VITTATUS†)

MYXINE GLUTINOSA§ (Atlantic hagfish, Borer, Hagfish, Northern hagfish) *24, 31,
46, 98, 137, 140, 186, 251*
Wide distribution in Arctic seas and both coasts of N. Atlantic. Over 15
fathoms on muddy bottom. Parasitic.
Adenosine triphosphate 1077; Adrenaline 327; FREE Amino acids (sum of)
220; Betaine 1077; Calcium 92, 220, 874, 1075, 1076, 1077; Chloride 92, 220,
874, 1075, 1076, 1077; Corticosterone 1008; Cortisol 1008; Creatine 1077;
Fucose 1336; Glucose 332, 1077; Glycerol 1077; Haematocrit 332, 604;
Hexosamines 1336; Lactic acid 1077; Magnesium 92, 220, 874, 1075, 1076,
1077; Noradrenaline 327; Potassium 92, 220, 874, 1075, 1076, 1077; Sodium
92, 220, 874, 1075, 1076, 1077; Sulphate 874, 1076, 1077; Trimethylamine
oxide 92, 220, 243, 1077; Ubiquinone 292; Urea 1077

NARCACION NOBILIANUS‡ *148*
N. America.
Iron 443

NARKE JAPONICA‡ (Electric ray, Torpedo)
Japan. Coastal. Viviparous.
Coenzyme A 719; Vitamin A 513

NAVODON MODESTUS (Black scraper, File fish)
Japan, Korea. Coastal.
Adenosine triphosphate 108; Vitamin A 513

NEMACHEILUS BARBATULUS† (Loach, Stone loach)
All Europe except extreme S. and N. Pure waters of brooks and shore regions
of clear lakes.
'Sugar' 671

NEMADACTYLUS DOUGLASII (Morwong)
Australia.
Cholesterol 872; Phospholipid 872

NEMIPTERUS JAPONICUS = SYNAGRIS JAPONICUS (Japanese threadfin bream)
Tanzania, Red Sea, Aden, India, Japan, China, Philippines. Coastal.
Iron 585; Niacin 585; Riboflavin 585; Thiamine 585; Trimethylamine oxide
1319

NEMIPTERUS TAENIOPTERUS (Ribbon-finned nemipterid)
Tanzania, India, Thailand, China, Philippines, Australia.
Iron 585; Niacin 585; Riboflavin 585; Thiamine 585

NEMIPTERUS VIRGATUS
Japan, Formosa. Muddy bottom.
Folic acid 637

NEOCERATODUS FORSTERI† (Burnett salmon, Lungfish)
Australia: Mary and Burnett Rivers (S. Queensland). Introduced elsewhere.
Amino acids 309; 8-arginine oxytocin 354; Serine ethanolamine phosphate
1088; Threonine ethanolamine phosphate 1088

NEOGOBIUS MELANOSTOMUS (Goby)   *117*
Calcium 652; Iron 652; Magnesium 652; Potassium 652

NEOPLATYCEPHALUS RICHARDSONI (Tiger flathead)
S. Australia.
Cholesterol 872; Phospholipid 872

NEOTHUNNUS ALBACORA (*see* THUNNUS ALBACARES)

NEOTHUNNUS MACROPTERUS (*see* THUNNUS ALBACARES)

NEOTHUNNUS SP.
Niacin 494

NEOTROPIUS KAVALCHOR†
India.
Calcium 1327; Copper 1327; Iron 1327; Potassium 1327

NEPTUNUS TRITUBERCULATUS
Arsenic 448; Selenium 448; Thallium 448

NIBEA ARGENTATA
    Japan.
    Cyanocobalamin 867; Niacin 867; Riboflavin 867; Thiamine 867

NIBEA SCHLEGELI
    Japan.
    Arsenic 448; Cyanocobalamin 1381; Riboflavin 584; Selenium 448; Thallium
    448

NIPHON SPINOSUS
    Japan, Philippines, in deep water.
    Folic acid 503; Pantothenic acid 502; Riboflavin 501; Vitamin A 513

NOTACANTHUS NASUS (Largescale tapirfish, Spiny eel)
    Atlantic, in deep water.
    Iron 266 (given as 'Notocanthus phasganorus' but prob. the same species);
    Trimethylamine 365; Trimethylamine oxide 307, 365

NOTACANTHUS PHASGANORUS (see N. NASUS)

NOTEMIGONUS CRYSOLEUCAS† (Bitterhead, Bream, Chub, Dace, Gudgeon,
    Roach, Shiner, Sunfish, Windfish, Young shad)
    N. America: Nova Scotia, Maryland, Dakota.
    Trimethylamine 28; Trimethylamine oxide 28

NOTEMIGONUS CRYSOLEUCAS BOSCII† (Golden shiner)   *184*
    N. America.

NOTOPTERUS CHITALA†
    India: fresh waters of Sind, Bengal, Assam. Burma, Thailand, Malaya, Java,
    Sumatra, Borneo.
    Cholesterol 1161; Niacin 1231; Thiamine 1232

NOTOPTERUS KAPIRAT† (see N. NOTOPTERUS†)

NOTOPTERUS NOTOPTERUS† = N. KAPIRAT†
    India, Burma, Thailand, Sumatra, Java.
    Calcium 918, 1327; Copper 1327; Glucose 1219; Glycogen 1219; Iron 918,
    1327; Niacin 158; Potassium 1327; Vitamin C 1095

NOTOTHENIA GIBBERIFRONS
    Antarctic.
    Haemoglobin 328

NOTOTHENIA LARSONI   *220*
    Antarctic.
    Haemoglobin 1306

NOTOTHENIA NEGLECTA
    Antarctic.
    Haematocrit 328; Haemoglobin 328

ONCORHYNCHUS MASOU* (Masu, Trout)   *134, 141*
Japan.
Inositol 1129

ONCORHYNCHUS NERKA* (Blueback, Red salmon, Sockeye salmon)   *40, 47, 55, 67, 68, 98, 99, 105, 106, 107, 108, 110, 112, 114, 115, 118, 119, 121, 134, 156, 163, 208, 225, 230, 245, 278*
S. Oregon (USA) to Bering Sea.
Acetone 608; Adenosine diphosphate 1249; Adenosine monophosphate 1249; Adenosine triphosphate 1249; Adrenosterone 565; Aldosterone 1006, 1009; Amino acids 696, 1035, 1135, 1136; Anserine 1359; Astaxanthin 643; Cholesterol 559; Choline 1401; Corticosterone 1006, 1009; Cortisol 329, 563, 564, 1006, 1009, 1124; Cortisone 563, 564, 1006, 1009, 1124; Creatin 216, 1359; Creatinine 1359; Cyanocobalamin 893, 1381; DNA 127, 258; 20 β-Dihydrocortisone 567; 20 β-Dihydro 17 α-hydroxyprogesterone 1124; 17 α- 20 β-Dihydroxy-pregn-4 ene-3 one 560; Fatty acids 1401; Folic acid 893; Fructose diphosphate 1249; Fructose-6-phosphate 1249; Glucose 611; Glucose-1-phosphate 1249; Glucose-6-phosphate 1249; Glycerol 1401; Glycogen 215; Haematocrit 1186; Haemoglobin 111; FREE Histidine 1359, 1360; β-Hydroxy-butyrate 608; 17-α-Hydroxyprogesterone 560, 1124; Inosine monophosphate 1249; Inositol 216; 11-Ketotestosterone 566, 1124; Lactic acid 111; Pantothenic acid 893; Potassium 736, 792, 793, 814, 1284; Pyridoxine 891, 893, 1384; Riboflavin 501, 893, 1113; RNA 127, 258; Ribose-5-phosphate 1249; Sodium 736, 792, 793, 814, 1284; Testosterone 422, 423, 1124; Thiamine 405, 1112; Trimethylamine 1237, 1359; Trimethylamine oxide 1237, 1359; Triphosphopyridine nucleotide 1249; Vitamin A 508, 513; Vitamin D 60

ONCORHYNCHUS NERKA KENNERLYI[†] (Kickaninny, Kokanee, Little redfish, Silver trout)   *115, 117, 126, 127*
N. America.

ONCORHYNCHUS RHODURUS[†]
Land locked.
Vitamin A 499

ONCORHYNCHUS SP.*
Biotin 217; Folic acid 217; Inositol 217; Niacin 217, 810; Pantothenic acid 217; Pyridoxin 217; Riboflavin 217, 1285; Riboflavin adenine dinucleotide 1285; Riboflavin mononucleotide 1285; Thiamine 217

ONCORHYNCHUS TSCHAWYTSCHA* (Chinook salmon, King salmon, Spring salmon)   *49, 54, 88, 98, 99, 106, 111, 112, 113, 119, 134, 141, 145, 163, 188, 207, 208, 209, 226, 240, 242, 243, 252*
S. California to Bering Sea.
Amino acids 281, 924, 1035, 1135, 1136; Anserine 783; Astaxanthin 643; Carnosine 783; Cholesterol 1080; DNA 127; Glucose 1080; Glycogen 1277; Haemoglobin 1080; Histidine 783; 17-Hydroxycorticoids 452, 1080; Iodine (protein-bound) 1080; 1-Methyl histidine 783; Niacin 192; Potassium 792, 793, 814, 1080; Riboflavin 192, 1113; RNA 127; Sodium 792, 793, 814, 1080; Thiamine 192, 1112; Trimethylamine oxide 307; Urea 1080; Vitamin A 1374; Vitamin D 60, 1374

OPHICEPHALUS ARGUS†
    Japan.
    Histidine 532
    (Note: all the following OPHICEPHALUS† SP. can also be spelt OPHIOCEPHALUS†)

OPHICEPHALUS MARULIUS† (Giant snake-head)
    India, Ceylon, Sumatra, Borneo, China. Rivers and inland fresh waters up to
    1500 feet.
    Calcium 918; Iron 918

OPHICEPHALUS PUNCTATUS† (Green snake-head, Murrel)   *91, 122*
    India and Burma. Stagnant fresh or brackish waters in low country.
    Calcium 1162; Cholesterol 1161; Cystine 1090; Niacin 1096; Tryptophan
    1090; Tyrosine 1090; Vitamin C 1095, 1162

OPHICEPHALUS STRIATUS† (Mudfish, Murrel, Striped snake-head)
    Plains of India, Ceylon, Burma, China, Philippines. Introduced to Hawaii.
    Fresh waters and swamps. Can live for considerable periods out of water.
    Cholesterol 1161; Cyanocobalamin 71, 72; Folic acid 73; Glucose 1138;
    Hydroxyproline 58; Iron 585; Niacin 585, 1096; Proline 58; Riboflavin 585;
    Thiamine 585; Vitamin C 1095

OPHICEPHALUS TADIANUS†
    Japan.
    Vitamin C 840

OPHICHTHYS BORO*
    India and Malaya. Seas and estuaries, ascending large rivers. A scale-less fish.
    Vitamin C 56

OPHIODON BARBATUM (Snake blenny)
    Adriatic and North Seas.
    Trimethylamine 1253; Trimethylamine oxide 1253

OPHIODON ELONGATUS (Cultus cod, Lingcod)   *17, 20, 30, 31, 88, 278*
    S. California to Bering Sea.
    Adenosine diphosphate 1249, 1280; Adenosine monophosphate 1249, 1280;
    Adenosine triphosphate 1249, 1280; Anserine 783; Carnosine 783; Creatin
    554; DNA 127, 1281; Diphosphopyridine nucleotide 1249; Fructose diphos-
    phate 1249; Fructose-6-phosphate 1249; Glucose-1-phosphate 1249; Glucose-
    6-phosphate 1249; Histidine 783; Hypoxanthine 1280; Inosine 1280; Inosine
    monophosphate 1249, 1280; Magnesium 196; 1-Methyl histidine 783; Potas-
    sium 192, 792, 793, 1263, 1267; Riboflavin 1113; Ribose 1280; RNA 127,
    1280, 1281; Ribose-5-phosphate 1249; Sodium 192, 792, 793, 1263, 1267;
    Thiamine 1112; Trimethylamine oxide 307; Triphosphopyridine nucleotide
    1249

OPHIOSCION VENEZUELAE
    S. America.
    Calcium 592; Cyanocobalamine 592; Cystine 592; Iron 592; Lysine 592;
    Methionine 592; Niacin 592; Riboflavin 592; Thiamine 592; Tryptophan 592

OPHISURUS MACRORHYNCHUS (Off-shore snake, Sandsnake)
Japan.
Vitamin A 513

OPHTHALMOLEPIS LINEOLATUS (Maori)
S. Australia.
Cholesterol 872; Phospholipid 872

OPISTHOPTERUS TARTOOR
India, Malaya, Java, Sumatra.
Hydroxyproline 58; Proline 58

OPLEGNATHUS FASCIATUS (Japanese parrot fish)
Japan.
Adenosine diphosphate 1224; Adenosine monophosphate 1224; Adenosine
triphosphate 1224; Ammonia 1224; Creatin phosphate 1224; Fructose-6-
phosphate 1224; Glucose-1-phosphate 1224; Glucose-6-phosphate 1224;
Glycogen 1224; Hexose diphosphate 1224; Lactic acid 1224; Phosphoglyceric
acid 1224; Phosphopyruvic acid 1224; Ribose phosphate 1224; Triose phosphate 1224

OPSANUS TAU (Oysterfish, Sapo, Scorpion, Slimer, Toadfish)   *99, 147, 148, 149,
150, 169, 221, 250*
N. America: Massachusetts coast to W. Indies. In shallow water on sandy or
muddy bottom.
Chloride 553; Cholesterol 553; Glycogen 1250; Haematocrit 320; Haemoglobin 320, 553; Iron 443; Potassium 553; Sodium 553; 'Sugar' 428, 731, 897,
898, 1132

ORTHAGORISCUS MOLA
Europe.
Potassium 871

ORYZIAS LATIPES† (High-eyes)   *117*
Japan, China.

OSMERUS EPERLANUS* (may be same as O. MORDAX*) (European smelt, Sparling)
E. Atlantic from France to Spitzbergen, inshore. Also found in streams. Some
populations landlocked in Europe and America.
N-Acetyl histidine 456; FREE Amino acids 1139; Creatin + Creatinine
1139

OSMERUS MORDAX* (American smelt)
Atlantic coast of N. America: Labrador to Virginia. Rivers and lakes.
Amino acids 583; Biotin 751; Cyanocobalamin 1251; Folic acid 751; Niacin
583, 1251; Pantothenic acid 751; Riboflavin 517, 583, 1251; Thiamine 583;
Trimethylamine oxide 243, 307

OSPHRONEMUS GORAMI† (Gouramy)
Originally from E. Indian islands, Malaya, Sumatra, Java, China. Introduced
to Australia, India, Ceylon. Rivers and brackish water. Prefers shallow,
weedy ponds.
Amino acids 306; Calcium 918; Iron 918

OSTEOCHILUS HASSELTI†
Indonesia, Malacca, Thailand, Sumatra, Java, Borneo. Rivers.
Amino acids 306

OTOLITHUS RUBER (Rosy jewfish)
India to Malaya. Coastal.
Fatty acids 667

OXYURICHTHYS MICROLEPIS (Small-scaled goby)
India, Thailand, Philippines, China, Japan. Seas and estuaries; harbours.
Iron 585; Niacin 585; Riboflavin 585; Thiamine 585

PAGELLUS BELLOTTI
Portugal.
Carotenoids 420; Niacin 420; Riboflavin 420; Thiamine 420; Vitamin C 420

PAGELLUS ERYTHRINUS (Pandora, Red sea bream)
S. Britain to Angola, in shallow water.
Potassium 871; Trimethylamine 1253; Trimethylamine oxide 1253

PAGELLUS MORMYRUS (Marmor bream)
Portugal.
Carotenoids 420; Niacin 420; Riboflavin 420; Thiamine 420; Trimethylamine
1253; Trimethylamine oxide 1253; Vitamin C 420

PAGROSOMUS AURATUS
Australia.
Cholesterol 872; Phospholipid 872

PAGROSOMUS MAJOR   22
Japan.
Amino acids 696; Arsenic 448; Choline 1236; Cyanocobalamin 466, 1380;
Methionine 846; Riboflavin 584, 1285; Riboflavin adenine dinucleotide 1285;
Riboflavin mononucleotide 1285; Selenium 448; Thallium 448; Thiamine
839; Trimethylamine 1236; Trimethylamine oxide 1236

PAGROSOMUS UNICOLOR
Japan.
Folic acid 503; Pantothenic acid 502

PAGRUS EHRENBERGII
Portugal.
Carotenoids 420; Niacin 420; Riboflavin 420; Thiamine 420; Vitamin C 420

PAGRUS PAGRUS (Couch's sea bream)
Britain, Portugal.
Carotenoids 420; Cyanocobalamin 412; Niacin 420; Riboflavin 420; Thiamine
420; Vitamin C 420

PALINURICHTHYS PERCIFORMIS (American barrel fish, Barrel fish, Black rudder fish)
Wide distribution in the Atlantic. Often found under floating wreckage or seaweed.
Iron 443; 'Sugar' 428; Trimethylamine oxide 307

PALOMETA MEDIA
N. America.
Niacin 413; Riboflavin 413; Thiamine 413

PAMPUS ARGENTEUS (see STROMATEUS CINEREUS)

PANGASIUS PANGASIUS†
India, Burma, Java. Large rivers and estuaries.
Calcium 918; Iron 918; Vitamin C 1095

PARACAESIO CAERULEUS
Japan.
Folic acid 503; Pantothenic acid 502; Riboflavin 501; Vitamin A 513

PARACHAENICHTHYS CHARCOTI
Antarctic.
Haemoglobin 328

PARACHAENICHTHYS GEORGIANUS   *220*
Antarctic.
Haemoglobin 328

PARALABRAX CLATHRATUS (Kelp bass)
Pacific coast of N. America.
Aluminium 1201; Barium 1201; Cadmium 1201; Calcium 1201; Chromium 1201; Cobalt 1201; Copper 1201; Haemoglobin 77; Iron 1201; Lead 1201; Lithium 1201; Magnesium 1201; Manganese 1201; Molybdenum 1201; Niacin 413; Nickel 1201; Riboflavin 413; Strontium 1201; Thiamine 413; Vanadium 1201; Zinc 1201

PARALICHTHYS LETHOSTIGMUS (Southern flounder)
Gulf of Mexico to New York coast.
Potassium 948; Sodium 948

PARALICHTHYS OLIVACEUS (Japanese flounder)   *38, 39*
Japan.
Amino acids 1214; Cholesterol 915; Cyanocobalamin 1381; Glucose 314; Hydroxyproline 1239, 1243; Inositol 1149; Pyridoxine 1383, 1384; Riboflavin 501, 584, 891; Ribose 314; Tryptophan 697; Vitamin A 509, 511, 513, 1374; Vitamin D 1374; Vitamin E 581

PARALICHTHYS SP.   *149*
Haematocrit 320; Haemoglobin 320

PERCA FLAVESCENS†, probably = PERCA FLUORESCENS† (American perch, Lake perch, Raccoon perch, Ringed perch, River perch, Yellow Ned, Yellow perch) *210, 211*
Fresh waters of Eastern United States.
Amino acids 583; Anserine 783; Carnosine 783; Cerebroside 805, 806; Cholesterol 805, 806; Histidine 783; Lecithin 805, 806; 1-Methyl histidine 783; Niacin 583; Phospholipid 803, 806; Potassium 192, 1263, 1274; Riboflavin 583; Sodium 192, 1263, 1274; Sphingomyelin 805, 806; Thiamine 583; Trimethylamine 28; Trimethylamine oxide 28, 307

PERCA FLUORESCENS† (*see* PERCA FLAVESCENS†)

PERCA FLUVIATILIS† = PERCA PERCA† (Perch)   *116, 130, 172, 200, 204, 210*
Europe (apart from Iceland and Norway), Russia, N. America, N. Asia. Rivers and lakes, warm and cold.
N-Acetyl histidine 456; Anserine 1392; Carnosine 1392; FREE Histidine 1392; Potassium 462, 871; 'Sugar' 671; Trimethylamine oxide 1065; Ubiquinone 292; Vitamin A_1 1019; Vitamin A_2 1019; Vitamin C 781

PERCA PERCA† (*see* PERCA FLUVIATILIS†)

PERCA SP.†
FREE Amino acids 917

PERIOPHTHALMODON AUSTRALIS (Mud skipper)
Lactic acid 70; Potassium 70; Sodium 70

PERIOPHTHALMUS SP.
India. Brackish waters.
Haematocrit 1038; Haemoglobin 1038

PETROMYZON FLUVIATILIS*§ = LAMPETRA FLUVIATILIS*§ (Lampern, Lamprey, River lamprey)   *99, 114, 119, 218, 251*
Coastal waters of Europe, Siberia and S. Greenland. Enters rivers to spawn. Parasitic.
Amino acids (in haemoglobin) 16; Betaine 1211; Calcium 1075; Chloride 1075, 1342; DNA 862; Glucose 96; Glutamine 1407; Glycogen 96, 1025; Magnesium 1075; Potassium 1075; Sodium 1075; Ubiquinone 982; Vitamin A_1 982, 1020; Vitamin A_2 1020; Vitamin E 982

PETROMYZON MARINUS*§ (Lamper eel, Sea lamprey)   *82, 83, 121, 166, 231, 237*
E. and W. Atlantic. Mediterranean. Landlocked in Great Lakes (N. America).
Amino acids 205, 1094; Corticosterone 219, 1006; Cortisol 219, 1006; Haematocrit 1261; Oestradiol 142; Potassium 871; Ubiquinone 982; Vitamin A_1 982, 1020; Vitamin A_2 1020; Vitamin E 982

PHANERODON FURCATUS (White seaperch)
S. California to Vancouver Island (N. America, Pacific coast).
Creatin 554; Sodium 1273

PHINOPLAGUSIA JAPONICA
Japan.
Arsenic 448; Selenium 448; Thallium 448

PHOXINUS PHOXINUS† = PHOXINUS LAEVIS† (Minnow)
All Europe except S. Spain, S. Italy, Norway and Iceland. Clear waters.
N-Acetyl histidine 456; 'Sugar' 671

PLANIPLORA SP.
Australia.
Copper 88

PLATESSA LIMANDA *46*

PLATICHTHYS FLESUS* = PLEURONECTES FLESUS* (Flounder) *187, 190, 192,
193, 195, 197*
Europe (apart from Iceland), Arctic Ocean to Black Sea, migrating to fresh
water for part of its early life. Common in inshore waters within the 55 m
line.
N-Acetyl histidine 456; Calcium 724, 1234; Chloride 724, 727, 877, 878;
Cyanocobalamin 150, 1234; Iodine 1234; Iron 1234; Niacin 150, 1234; Pantothenic acid 150, 1234; Potassium 724, 727; Riboflavin 150, 1234; Sodium
724, 727, 877, 878; Thiamine 1234; Trimethylamine oxide 727

PLATICHTHYS FLESUS LUSCUS
Russia.
Chromium 989; Copper 989; Iron 989; Manganese 989; Nickel 989; Strontium
989; Titanium 989; Vanadium 989

PLATICHTHYS STELLATUS* (Emerywheel, Grindstone, Starry flounder) *42*
California to Bering Sea. Shallow water on sandy bottom. Occasionally deep
water. Young travel upstream for some distance.
Adenosine diphosphate + Adenosine triphosphate 1247; Adenosine monophosphate 1247; Creatin 554; DNA 127; Lactic acid 1279; Potassium 192,
1263, 1268; Riboflavin 1113; RNA 127; Sodium 192, 1263, 1268

PLATOPHRYS PANTHERINUS (Leopard flounder)
Red Sea, E. Africa, India, Malaya, Philippines, Japan, N. Australia, Hawaii,
Tahiti. Coastal waters.
Trimethylamine oxide 1319

PLATYCEPHALUS INDICUS (Indian flathead, River gurnard, Sand gurnard)
E. Africa, Red Sea, India, Philippines, Japan, China, W. Australia. Sandy
bottom near shore. Sea and brackish water.
Arsenic 448; Iron 585; Manganese 1229; Niacin 585; Selenium 448; Thallium
448; Thiamine 585; Vitamin A 513

PLATYRHINOIDIS TRISERIATUS‡
N. America: Californian coast.
Zeaxanthin 360

PLECOGLOSSUS ALTIVELIS* (Sweet smelt)
Japan, China, Formosa.
Cholesterol 1153, 1154; Cyanocobalamin 1381, 1382; Fatty acids 1153, 1154; Folic acid 503; Pantothenic acid 502; Pyridoxine 1383, 1384; Riboflavin 584; Thiamine 382; Vitamin A 510, 511, 512, 513, 1374

PLEUROGRAMMUS AZONUS (Atka mackerel)
Japan.
Hydroxyproline 1239, 1243; Methionine 846; Trimethylamine 1237; Trimethylamine oxide 1237; Vitamin A 513, 1374; Vitamin D 1374

PLEUROGRAMMUS MONOPTERYGNIS
Japan.
Folic acid 503; Pantothenic acid 502

PLEURONECTES CYNOGLOSSUS (Witch)   *133*
Europe.

PLEURONECTES FLESUS* (*see* PLATICHTHYS FLESUS*)

PLEURONECTES FLESUS LUSCUS (perhaps same as PLATICHTHYS FLESUS LUSCUS, *see above*)
Russia.
FREE Amino acids 1329; Creatin + Creatinine 1329

PLEURONECTES LIMANDA (Mud dab)
Europe.
Potassium 871

PLEURONECTES MICROCEPHALUS = MICROSTOMUS KITT (Lemon sole, Smear dab)
131, 133, 188, 238
Europe: N. Spain to White Sea and Iceland. Found on any type of bottom between 40 and 200 m.
Amino acids 240; FREE Amino acids 620; Adenosine diphosphate 653; Adenosine monophosphate 653; Adenosine triphosphate 653; Cyanocobalamin 150; Diphosphopyridine nucleotide = Nicotinamide adenine dinucleotide 653; Fatty acids 957; FREE Fatty acids 960; Hypoxanthine 653; Inosine 653; Inosine monophosphate 653; Niacin 150; Pantothenic acid 150; Phospholipid 960; Riboflavin 150; Trimethylamine oxide 1065

PLEURONECTES PLATESSA (Plaice)   *55, 93, 124, 126, 133, 146, 187*
Europe, including Iceland, south to Cadiz and W. Mediterranean, from shore line to 120 m on sandy grounds, occasionally on mud or gravel.
N-Acetyl histidine 456; Adenosine diphosphate 653; Adenosine monophosphate 653; Adenosine triphosphate 653; Amino acids 154; Calcium 1061; Copper 1406; Cyanocobalamin 149, 150; Diphosphopyridine nucleotide = Nicotinamide adenine dinucleotide 653; Fucose 1336; Haematocrit 1040; Haemoglobin 1040; Hexosamine 1336; Hypoxanthine 653; Inosine 653; Inosine monophosphate 653; Iodine 460; Lead 1406; Magnesium 1061; Mercury 1337; Niacin 150; Pantothenic acid 150; Potassium 871, 1061; Riboflavin 150; Sodium 1061; Thiamine 785; Tin 1406; Vitamin A_1 1019, 1020; Vitamin A_2 1020

PLEURONECTES SP.
Amino acids 725; Manganese 1229; Riboflavin 787; Thiamine 787

PLEURONICHTHYS CORNUTUS
Japan.
Niacin 494; Vitamin A 1374; Vitamin D 1374

PLEURONICHTHYS PROMETHEUS
Cyanocobalamin 1382

PLOTOSUS ANGUILLARIS (Sea catfish, Striped catfish eel)
Japan. Shallow seas.
Arsenic 448; Selenium 448; Thallium 448

PNEUMATOPHORUS COLIAS (Chub mackerel, Spanish mackerel)   *150*
N. America: Nova Scotia to Virginia. Europe.
Iron 443; 'Sugar' 428

PNEUMATOPHORUS DIEGO (*see* P. JAPONICUS). May be same as SCOMBER JAPONICUS

PNEUMATOPHORUS JAPONICUS = P. DIEGO (Pacific mackerel)   *23, 24*
S. California to S.E. Alaska.
Amino acids 924; Anserine 783; Arsenic 380; Carnosine 783; Gold 380; Histidine 532, 783; Manganese 1229; 1-Methyl histidine 783; Rhenium 380; Tungsten 380; Vitamin A 510, 511, 512, 513, 1374; Vitamin D 1374

PNEUMATOPHORUS JAPONICUS TAPEINOCEPHALUS
Vitamin A 513

POGONIAS CROMIS (Banded drum, Big drum, Black drum, Drumfish, Grey drum)
E. America: Long Island to mouth of Rio Grande, rarely Bay of Fundy, Gulf of Mexico. Bottom feeder.
Cholesterol 553, 1215; Haemoglobin 1215; Potassium 948, 1215; Sodium 948, 1215

POLISTOTREMA STOUTII§ (Pacific hagfish)   *46, 137*
S. California to S.E. Alaska. Parasitic.
Chloride 807; Corticosterone 219, 1006; Cortisol 219, 1006; Sodium 807

POLLACHIUS SP.
Glycogen 813; Lactic acid 813

POLLACHIUS VIRENS (*see* GADUS VIRENS)

POLYMIXIA JAPONICA (Japanese salmon de alto)
Japan.
Vitamin A 513

POLYNEMUS INDICUS* (Indian tasselfish, Threadfin)
Madagascar, India to Australia. Seas and estuaries.
Cholesterol 630; Creatin 631; Fatty acids 667; Lecithin 630; Niacin 631; Phospholipid 630; Riboflavin 631; Sphingomyelin 630; Thiamine 631; Trimethylamine 631; Trimethylamine oxide 631; Urea 631

POLYNEMUS MICROSTOMA
Formosa, Philippines, Borneo, New Guinea.
Iron 585; Niacin 585; Riboflavin 585; Thiamine 585

POLYNEMUS PARADISEUS*
India, Burma, Malaya. Enters rivers to spawn.
Cyanocobalamin 71, 72; Folic acid 73

POLYNEMUS SP.
Philippines.
Iron 585; Niacin 585; Riboflavin 585; Thiamine 585

POLYNEMUS TETRADACTYLUS* (see ELEUTHERONEMA TETRADACTYLUM*)

POLYPRION AMERICANUS = SERRANUS GUAZA (Atlantic wreckfish, Cernier, Stone
bass)
Wide distribution: Atlantic, Mediterranean, Cape of Good Hope, Indian
Ocean. Found near floating debris and down to 545 m or more.
Cyanocobalamin 412; Vitamin D 1052

POLYPRION OXYGENEIOS   252
Vitamin A 1156

POMADASYS JUBELINA
Portugal.
Carotenoids 420; Niacin 420; Riboflavin 420; Thiamine 420; Vitamin C 420

POMATOMUS PEDICA
Australia.
Cholesterol 872; Phospholipid 872

POMATOMUS SALTATRIX (Bluefish, Fatback, Greenfish, Skip mackerel, Snap
mackerel)   149
Widespread in warm seas, for example off Bermuda, W. Africa, Malaya,
Australia. Inshore and offshore in large schools.
FREE Amino acids 1329; Calcium 966; Creatin + Creatinine 1329; Haemato-
crit 320; Haemoglobin 320; Niacin 192; Riboflavin 192; Thiamine 192, 966

POMOLOBUS PSEUDOHARENGUS* (Alewife, Bang, Big-eyed herring, Branch
herring, Sawbelly, Wall-eyed herring)   104, 145, 180, 233
Atlantic coast of N. America: Nova Scotia to N. Carolina. Lake Ontario and
permanently landlocked in the 'Finger Lakes' of New York.
Trimethylamine oxide 307

POMOXIS ANNULARIS† (Bachelor, Crappie, Shad, Silver perch, Speckled perch,
Timber crappie, Tinmouth, Tin perch, White crappie, White perch)   41, 212
E. United States.
Glucose 280; Glycogen 280; Lactic acid 280

POMOXIS NIGROMACULATUS† (Black crappie)   146
Trimethylamine 28; Trimethylamine oxide 28

PORONOTUS TRIACANTHUS (Butterfish, Dollarfish, Harvestfish, Shiner) *150*
  Atlantic coast of N. America: Nova Scotia to Florida, usually inshore.
  Iron 443; Potassium 175; Sodium 175; 'Sugar' 428; Trimethylamine oxide 307

PRIACANTHUS BOOPS
  Warm waters south of Japan
  Astaxanthin 1293; Carotenoids 1293; Tunaxanthin 1293; Vitamin A 513

PRIACANTHUS HAMRUR
  Japan.
  Riboflavin 501, 891

PRIACANTHUS JAPONICUS
  Japan.
  Pyridoxine 1383

PRIONACE GLAUCA‡ (Blue dog, Blue shark) *38*
  World-wide in sub-tropical and temperate waters of all oceans. Pelagic, usually
  offshore. Viviparous.
  Amino acids 715; Collagen 1242; Elastin 1242; Hydroxyproline 1238, 1243;
  Methionine 846; Riboflavin 501; Urea 1226; Vitamin A 496

PRIONOTUS CAROLINUS (Common gurnard, Common searobin, Northern searobin)
  E. coast of United States: Bay of Fundy to S. Carolina. Inshore waters in
  summer, deeper offshore in winter.
  Iron 443; 'Sugar' 428

PRIONOTUS SP.
  Thiamine 405

PRIONURUS MICROLEPIDOTUS
  Japan. Shore.
  Vitamin C 579

PRIONURUS MICROLEPIS
  Japan.
  Vitamin A 513

PRISTIPOMA COMMERSONII
  E. Africa, Red Sea, India, China, Formosa, Philippines, Australia.
  Cholesterol 630; Lecithin 630; Niacin 631; Phospholipid 630; Riboflavin 631;
  Sphingomyelin 630; Thiamine 631

PRISTIPOMA OLIVACEUM (Olive grunter)
  Madagascar, S. Arabia, India, Malay Straits. Trawling grounds.
  Fatty acids 667

PRISTIPOMOIDES AMOENUS
  Japan.
  Vitamin A 513

PRISTIPOMOIDES SIEBOLDII
  Japan.
  Fibrinogen 1098; Haematocrit 1097; Haemoglobin 1097

PRISTIS MICRODON*¶ (Sawfish, Small-toothed sawfish)
  Thailand, Malaya (Perak).
  Ammonia 1183; Calcium 1183; Chloride 1183, 1184; Creatin 1183; Magnesium 1183; Potassium 1183; Sulphate 1183; Urea, 1183, 1184

PRISTIURUS MELANOSTOMUS‡ (Black-mouthed dogfish)
  Europe, United States.
  Carotenoids 347; Vitamin A_1 1020; Vitamin A_2 1020

PROCHILODUS LATICEPS
  S. America.
  Calcium 592; Cyanocobalamin 592; Cystine 592; Iron 592; Lysine 592; Methionine 592; Niacin 592; Riboflavin 592; Thiamine 592; Tryptophan 592

PROGNICHTHYS AGOO (Flying fish)
  Japan, Formosa.
  Cholesterol 1153; Fatty acids 1153; Vitamin A 513, 1374; Vitamin D 1374

PROMETHICHTHYS PROMETHEUS (Black tuna)
  Japan, Hawaii, Australia.
  Cholesterol 1153; Cyanocobalamin 1381; Fatty acids 1153; Pyridoxine 1384; Riboflavin 501, 891; Vitamin A 509, 510, 511, 512, 513

PROSOPIUM WILLIAMSONI† (Rocky mountain whitefish)   *122*
  N. America: Rivers of Sierra Nevada, W. slope of Rocky mountains.
  Haematocrit 812; Haemoglobin 812

PROTOPTERUS AETHIOPICUS† (Lungfish)
  Africa. Amphibious.
  8-Arginine oxytocin 354

PROTOPTERUS ANNECTENS† (Lungfish)   *222*
  Africa. Amphibious.
  Hydrocortisone 1007

PSENOPSIS ANOMALA (Wart perch)
  Japan, Korea.
  Vitamin A 513

PSETTICHTHYS MELANOSTICTUS (Sand flounder, Sand sole)
  N. California to Bering Sea. Sandy bottom.
  Potassium 1268; Sodium 1268, 1273

PSETTODES BELCHERI
  Portugal and elsewhere.
  Cyanocobalamin 412; Potassium 871

PSETTODES ERUMEI (Indian halibut, Indian turbot)
W. coast of Africa, India, Malaya, China, Japan, Philippines. Coastal down to 90 m.
Cholesterol 630; Lecithin 630; Niacin 631; Phospholipid 630; Riboflavin 631; Sphingomyelin 630; Thiamine 631

PSEUDOBAGRUS AURANTIACUS†
Japan. Rivers.
Vitamin C 840

PSEUDOENTROPIUS GARUS†
India.
Cholesterol 1161

PSEUDOLABRUS JAPONICUS
Japan.
Cyanocobalamin 1381; Pyridoxine 1383; Vitamin A 510, 513

PSEUDOPLEURONECTES AMERICANUS (Blackback, George's Bank flounder, Winter flounder)
Atlantic coast of N. America: Labrador to Georgia. Bottom-dwelling from shallow waters to 90 m.
Glycogen 813; Riboflavin 517; Trimethylamine oxide 307

PSEUDOPLEURONECTES SP.
Glycogen 813; Lactic acid 813

PSEUDORASBORA PARVA† (Stone moroko)
Japan, Korea, China.
Vitamin A 513

PSEUDORHOMBUS OLIGODON
Bay of Bengal, Philippines, Formosa, Japan.
Iron 585; Niacin 585; Riboflavin 585; Thiamine 585

PSEUDOSCARUS GUACAMAIA (Green parrotfish)
E. America: Florida to Rio de Janeiro.
DNA 862

PSEUDOSCIAENA ANEA*
India, Philippines, S. China. Sea and mouths of rivers.
Iron 585; Niacin 585; Riboflavin 585; Thiamine 585

PSEUDOSCIAENA CROCEA
Japan.
Cholesterol 1153; Fatty acids 1153

PSILOCRANIUM NIGRICANS
Australia.
Copper 88

PTEROGOBIUS ELAPOIDES (Stretched silk)
  Japan, Korea.
  Vitamin A 513

PTYCHOCHEILUS OREGONENSIS† (Squawfish, Whitefish)   *40*
  N. America: Oregon, Washington, British Columbia. Rivers.
  Lactic acid 110

PUNTIUS JAVANICUS†
  Thailand, Sumatra, Java, Indonesia.
  Amino acids 306

RAJA ASTERIAS‡ (Starry ray)
  Europe.
  Urea 674

RAJA BATIS‡ (Blue skate, Flapper skate, Grey skate)   *91, 95, 96, 146*
  Europe: N. Iceland to Madeira, Mediterranean.
  Carotenoids 347; Thiamine 742; Trimethylamine oxide 1065

RAJA BINOCULATA‡ (Big skate)   *139*
  S. California to Gulf of Alaska.
  Creatin 554

RAJA BRACHYURA‡ (Blonde ray)
  Britain to Mediterranean and Madeira. Shallow waters.
  Carotenoids 347; Chloride 895; Potassium 895; Sodium 895; Ubiquinone 292;
  Urea 895

RAJA CIRCULARIS‡ (Sandy ray)
  W. Europe (except Iceland). Mediterranean. Deep waters on sandy bottom.
  Carotenoids 347

RAJA CLAVATA‡ (Roker, Thornback ray)
  Europe: Iceland to Madeira.
  FREE Amino acids 1139; Betaine 1148; Caesium 184, 185, 186; Carotenoids
  347; Chloride 321, 895; Corticosterone 1007; Creatin 1148; Creatin +
  Creatinine 1139; Lithium 184, 185; Potassium 184, 185, 186, 321, 736, 871,
  895; Rubidium 184, 185, 186; Sodium 184, 185, 186, 321, 736, 895; Tri-
  methylamine 1253; Trimethylamine oxide 1148, 1253; Urea 895, 1148;
  Vitamin A_1 1020; Vitamin A_2 1020

RAJA DIAPHENES‡ (Clear ray)
  E. coast of United States.
  Ammonia 1182; Calcium 1182; Chloride 1182, 1184; Creatin 1182; Magnesium
  1182; Potassium 1182; Sodium 1182; Sulphate 1182; Urea 1182, 1184

RAJA EGLANTERIA‡ (Bob-tailed skate, Brier ray, Clear-nosed skate, Possum ray,
  Sea possum, Skate, Summer skate)
  E. coast of N. America: Cape Cod to Florida. Shallow waters along beaches
  and down to 120 m.
  Corticosterone 1006; Cortisol 1006

RAJA SCABRATA‡ (Atlantic prickly skate)
Trimethylamine oxide 307

RAJA SP.‡
Chloride 1184; Fucose 1336; Hexosamine 1336; Thiamine 405; Urea 1184

RAJA STABULIFORIS‡ (Barn-door skate, Peck-nosed skate, Winter skate)
N. America: Massachusetts to Florida.
Ammonia 201, 1182; Calcium 1182; Chloride 1182, 1184; Creatin 201, 1182;
Magnesium 1182; Potassium 1182; Sodium 1182; Sulphate 1182; Urea 201,
1182, 1184

RAJA UNDULATA‡ (Undulate ray) *124*
S. England and Ireland to Mediterranean and N. Africa. Sandy bottoms
offshore.

RASBORA DANICONIUS† (Common rasbora)
India, Ceylon, Burma, Malaya, Tanzania. Rivers and ponds.
Calcium 918, 1327; Copper 1327; Iron 918, 1327; Potassium 1327

RASTRELLIGER BRACHYSOMA (Short-bodied mackerel)
Philippines, Java.
Iron 585; Niacin 585; Riboflavin 585; Thiamine 585

RASTRELLIGER CHRYZOZONUS (*see* R. KANAGURTA)

RASTRELLIGER KANAGURTA = R. CHRYZOZONUS (Rake-gilled mackerel) *17, 21*
E. Africa, India to Queensland, China and Japan. Open sea.
Amino acids 1324; Calcium 919; Cholesterol 630; Copper 919; Creatin 631;
Iron 585, 919; Lecithin 630; Niacin 585, 631, 919; Phospholipid 630; Potassium 919; Riboflavin 585, 631, 919; Sodium 919; Sphingomyelin 630; Thiamine
585, 631, 919; Trimethylamine 631, 919; Trimethylamine oxide 631; Urea
631; Vitamin E 919

REINHARDTIUS HIPPOGLOSSOIDES (Blue halibut, Greenland halibut, Greenland
turbot, Little halibut, Newfoundland turbot, Turbot)
Arctic and N. Atlantic in deep water, usually 250–1600 m, northwards of
Iceland and Faroes.
FREE Amino acids 917; Calcium 1234; Cyanocobalamin 1234; Iodine 1234;
Iron 1234; Niacin 1234; Pantothenic acid 1234; Riboflavin 1234; Thiamine
1234

REINHARDTIUS MATSUURAE
Japan.
Folic acid 503; Pantothenic acid 502

REPORHAMPHUS MELANOCHIR
Australia.
Copper 88

RHABDOSARGUS SARBA = SPARUS SARBA (Silver bream, Tarwhine)
  Madagascar, Tanzania, Red Sea, Mauritius, India, Japan, China, Australia.
  Coastal.
  Vitamin A 513; Vitamin C 579

RHIGOPHILA DEARBORNI *212*

RHINEODON TYPUS‡
  Japan.
  Riboflavin 501

RHINOPLAGUSIA JAPONICA (Black cow tongue)
  Japan, Korea, Formosa.
  Vitamin A 509, 513

RHOMBUS MAXIMUS = SCOPHTHALMUS MAXIMUS (Turbot)
  Europe including Iceland. Mediterranean. Inshore, 0–80 m.
  Calcium 1061; Magnesium 1061; Niacin 690; Potassium 871, 1061; Riboflavin
  1129; Sodium 1061; Trimethylamine 1253; Trimethylamine oxide 1253;
  Vitamin A 311, 1021

RHOMBUS MEOTICUS
  Europe.
  Calcium 966; Thiamine 966

RHYNCHOBATUS DJIDDENSIS‡ (White-spotted shovelnose ray)
  Red Sea, E. Africa, India, Malaya. Coastal.
  Amino acids 23; Arginine 22; Cystine 22; Trimethylamine oxide 1319;
  Tryptophan 22; Tyrosine 22

RHYNCHOCYMBA NYSTROMI
  Japan.
  Vitamin A 513

RITA RITA†
  India: Indus, Jumna, Ganges and Irrawaddy rivers.
  Cholesterol 1161

ROCCUS AMERICANUS* (Sea perch, White perch)
  Atlantic coast of N. America, usually in brackish water. Freshwater ponds and
  lakes near the sea. Tolerates high temperatures.
  Chloride 553; Cholesterol 553; Haemoglobin 553; Potassium 553; Sodium 553

ROCCUS SAXATILIS* (Rock, Rockfish, Striped bass, Striper) *149*
  Atlantic coast of N. America: Gulf of St. Lawrence to Gulf of Mexico. Coastal
  or in brackish or fresh water.
  Cholesterol 553; Haematocrit 320; Haemoglobin 320

ROOSEVELTIELLA NATTERERI (Natterer's piranha, Red piranha) *50, 51, 250*

RUTILUS RUTILUS† (Roach)   *97*
Europe eastwards to Russia. Baltic Sea. Still and slowly-flowing water situated
at heights up to 900 m. Lagoons and weedy marshes.
Ubiquinone 292

SACCOBRANCHUS FOSSILIS† (*see* HETEROPNEUSTES FOSSILIS†)

SACCOBRANCHUS SP.†
India.
Haematocrit 1038; Haemoglobin 1038

SALANGICHTHYS MICRODON* (Whitefish)
Japan, Korea.
Cholesterol 1153; Fatty acids 1153; Vitamin A 1374; Vitamin D 1374

SALMO CLARKII* (Coastal cutthroat trout, Sea trout)   *175*
N. California to S.E. Alaska. Marine coastal, streams and lakes. Some remain
permanently in fresh water.
Fructose 434; Glucose 479; Glycogen 479, 520; Lactic acid 479; Riboflavin
1113; Thiamine 1112

SALMO FARIO* (*see* S. TRUTTA*)

SALMO GAIRDNERII* = S. IRIDEUS* (Rainbow trout, Steelhead)   *viii, 7, 20, 23, 24,*
31, 40, 41, 43, 46, 47, 48, 54, 56, 60, 69, 70–76, 78, 79, 104, 111, 114, 115, 116,
118, 123, 134, 160, 186, 187, 202, 203, 207–212, 217, 223, 229, 232, 233, 242,
251, 254, 255, 256, 262, 266, 267, 271, 277, 281
Acetone 608; N-Acetyl histidine 456; Adenosine diphosphate 425, 1099, 1249;
Adenosine monophosphate 425, 912, 1099, 1249; Adenosine triphosphate 425,
1099, 1249, 1283; Adrenaline 912; Amino acids 195, 247, 1221, 1222; Anserine
783; Astaxanthin 461, 511, 892; Biotin 892; Calcium 538, 892, 918, 947, 966,
1104; Carbon dioxide 116; Carnosine 783; β-Carotene 461; Carotenoids 461;
Chloride 321, 322, 534, 538; Cholesterol 872, 1081, 1153; Choline 609; Copper
947; Creatin 248, 1104, 1283; Creatinine 1104; Cyanocobalamin 892, 1381;
Cytidine triphosphate 425; DNA 1323; Diphosphopyridine nucleotide 425,
1249; Fatty acids 31, 1153; FREE Fatty acids 105, 609; Folic acid 892;
Fructose diphosphate 1249; Fructose-6-phosphate 1249; Glucose 117, 912,
1081; Glucose-1-phosphate 1249; Glucose-6-phosphate 1249; Glutamine
1407; Glycerylphosphoryl choline 609; Glycogen 114, 115, 117, 427, 859, 912;
Guanosine triphosphate 425; Haematocrit 1104, 1186; Haemoglobin 114, 115,
116, 117; Histidine 783; β-Hydroxybutyrate 608; 17-Hydroxycorticosteroid
452, 1081; Hypoxanthine 1099; Inosine monophosphate 425, 1099, 1249; Iron
892, 918, 947; Lactic acid 114, 115, 116, 117, 859, 1279, 1283; Lecithin 1235;
Lutein 461; Magnesium 947, 1283; 1-Methyl histidine 783; Noradrenaline
330, 912; Oxygen 116; Pantothenic acid 892; Phospholipid 609, 872; Potassium 310, 321, 322, 538, 947, 1081, 1283; Pyridoxine 892; Pyruvate 115, 116;
Riboflavin 501, 511, 891, 892, 1113; Ribose-5-phosphate 1249; Serine ethanolamine phosphate 1088; Silicon 947; Sodium 310, 321, 322, 538, 947, 1081,
1283; 'Sugar' 671, 1104; Thiamine 966, 1112; Threonine ethanolamine phosphate 1088; Triphosphopyridine nucleotide 1249; Urea 1104; Uridine diphosphate 425; Uridine triphosphate 425; Vitamin A 499, 511, 513; Vitamin C
579; Vitamin D 1374

SALMO GAIRDNERII KAMLOOPS† (Kamloops trout) *40*
N. America.
Glucose 117; Glycogen 117; Haemoglobin 117; Lactic acid 110, 117

SALMO MILKTSCHITSCH*
Japan.
Folic acid 503; Pantothenic acid 502; Riboflavin 501

SALMO SALAR* (Atlantic salmon, Black salmon) *21–5, 27, 28, 53, 65, 68, 70, 71, 80, 81, 82, 94, 98, 99, 102, 106, 111, 112, 115, 118, 119, 121, 124, 141, 146, 164, 166, 188, 189–95, 209, 223, 238, 242, 243, 250, 254, 266, 287*
Both sides of N. Atlantic: N.E. Labrador to New York, Arctic Circle to Portugal.
N-Acetyl histidine 456; Amino acids 249, 1388, 1391; FREE Amino acids 249, 250, 1139; Ammonia 201; Anserine 250; Biotin 751; Calcium 356, 971, 1234; Carbon dioxide 971; Chloride 356, 971; Cortisol 369, 562, 1124; Cortisone 562, 1124; Creatin 201, 250, 1139; Creatinine 250, 1139; Cyanocobalamin 150, 1234; 20-β-dihydro 17-α-hydroxyprogesterone 1124; Folic acid 751; Glucosamine 1388; Glycogen 357; Iodine 1234; Iron 1234; 11-ketotestosterone 562, 1124; Niacin 150, 690, 1234; Oestradiol 210; Oestriol 210; Oestrone 210; Pantothenic acid 150, 751, 1234; Potassium 462, 971; Riboflavin 150, 517, 785, 1234; Sodium 971; Taurine 250; Thiamine 742, 785, 1044, 1234; Trimethylamine 971; Trimethylamine oxide 243, 307; Ubiquinone 292; Urea 201; Vitamin A_1 311, 1019, 1020; Vitamin A_2 1019, 1020; Vitamin C 355, 1044

SALMO TRUTTA* = S. FARIO* (Brown trout, Sea trout) *49, 50, 62, 64, 67, 69, 71, 72, 73, 96, 110, 116, 121, 122, 123, 153, 156, 172, 189, 201, 202, 208, 210, 213, 217, 231*
N. coast of Europe. Introduced widely elsewhere: now present in all continents except Antarctica.
N-Acetyl histidine 456; Adenosine monophosphate 679; Adenosine diphosphate 679; Adenosine triphosphate 679; Amino acids 1322; Astacene or astaxanthin 1205, 1257; Calcium 992, 998, 1234; Canthaxanthin 1257; β-Carotene 1205; Chloride 341, 992, 998; Cholesterol 799, 800, 872, 991, 999; Copper 992, 998; Creatin 991, 999; Creatinine 991, 999; Cyanocobalamin 150, 1234; Cytidine monophosphate 679; Cytidine triphosphate 679; Diphosphopyridine nucleotide 679; Fibrinogen 999; Glucose 991, 999; Glucose diphosphate 679; Glucose monophosphate 679; Glucose triphosphate 679; Glycogen 1352; Haemoglobin 1005; Iron 992; 998, 1234; Lactic acid 991, 999, 1352; Lutein 1205; Magnesium 992, 998; Mercury 1337; Niacin 150, 1234; Pantothenic acid 150, 1234; Phospholipid 872; Potassium 341, 462, 871, 992, 998; Pyruvate 1352; Riboflavin 150, 1234; Sodium 341, 992, 998; Sulphate 998; Thiamine 742, 1234; Trimethylamine 1085; Trimethylamine oxide 243, 1065, 1085; Ubiquinone 292; Urea 991, 999; Uridine diphosphate 679; Uridine diphosphogalactose 679; Uridine triphosphate 679; Vitamin A_1 311, 1019, 1020; Vitamin A_2 1019, 1020; Vitamin C 355

SALVELINUS ALPINUS* (Arctic char, Hudson Bay salmon, Sea trout) *192*
Circumpolar. May be landlocked. Prefers considerable depths.
Chloride 415; Potassium 462; Ubiquinone 982; Vitamin A 982; Vitamin E 982

SALVELINUS FONTINALIS* (Coaster, Eastern brook trout, Sea trout, Speckled char, Speckled trout) *48, 49, 52, 54, 61, 62, 63, 73, 84, 92, 117, 119, 121, 123, 174, 176, 183, 186, 189, 199, 201, 202, 203, 205, 206–211, 213, 225, 227, 243, 251, 252*
N. America, introduced elsewhere. Essentially freshwater but may go to sea. Found in cold swift streams.
Ammonia 341; Calcium 136, 341, 995; Carotene 341; Chloride 341, 1001; Cholesterol 341, 991, 999; Creatin 341, 991, 999; Creatinine 991, 999; Cyanocobalamin 1381; Fibrinogen 999; Fructose 434; Glucose 341, 991, 999; Haematocrit 341; Haemoglobin 341; Iron 341; Lactic acid 991, 999; Magnesium 341, 995; Manganese 341; Niacin 341; Pantothenic acid 341; Potassium 341; Riboflavin 341, 517; Sodium 341; 'Sugar' 671, 995; Sulphate 341; Trimethylamine oxide 307; Urea 341, 991, 999; Uric acid 341, 991, 999; Vitamin A 341, 499, 513; Vitamin C 341

SALVELINUS MALMA* (Malma trout)
Waters of Kamchatka and Alaska, descending to the sea.
Riboflavin 1113; Thiamine 1112

SALVELINUS NAMAYCUSH NAMAYCUSH† (Lake trout) *51, 69, 129, 183, 199*
N. America.
Potassium 1269; Sodium 1269

SALVELINUS NAMAYCUSH SISCOWET† (Siscowet trout) *6, 21, 36, 129, 261*
N. America. Extremely fatty.
Potassium 1269; Sodium 1269

SALVELINUS WILLUGHBII† (Char, Windermere char)
England: Lake Windermere. May not be genetically different from *S. alpinus*. Divided into spring and autumn spawners.
Vitamin A_1 1019, 1020; Vitamin A_2 1019, 1020

SARDA CHILENSIS
Chile. May be the same as S. SARDA
Cholesterol 872; Haemoglobin 77, 678; Phospholipid 872; Tryptophan 1036

SARDA SARDA (Atlantic bonito, Pelamid, Short-finned tunny) *148, 169*
Warmer parts of Atlantic, occasionally Britain and S. Norway; Mediterranean. Strongly migratory.
FREE Amino acids 1139; Calcium 652, 966; Creatin + Creatinine 1139; Iron 443, 652; Magnesium 652; Potassium 652; 'Sugar' 428; Thiamine 966

SARDINA PILCHARDUS (Pilchard) *225, 243*
Black Sea, Norway to Britain and Canary Islands. Perhaps same as CLUPEA PILCHARDUS. Pelagic.
Cyanocobalamin 412

SARDINELLA ALBELLA (Short-bodied sardine)
India, Ceylon. Coastal waters.
Hydroxyproline 58; Proline 58; Trimethylamine oxide 1319

SARDINELLA AURITA *155*
Portugal.
Calcium 1370; Carotenoids 420; Iron 1370; Magnesium 1370; Niacin 420; Potassium 1370; Riboflavin 420; Thiamine 420; Vitamin C 420

SARDINELLA EBA
    Portugal.
    Carotenoi ds 420; Niacin 420; Riboflavin 420; Thiamine 420; Vitamin C 420

SARDINELLA FIMBRIATA (Fringe-scale sardine)
    Red Sea, India, Malaya. Coastal waters.
    Amino acids 1324; Iron 585; Niacin 585, 670; Riboflavin 585; Thiamine 585

SARDINELLA LONGICEPS (Indian sardine, Oil sardine)   *65, 91, 116*
    India, Malaya, Philippines, Java. Coastal waters.
    Amino acids 1324; Cholesterol 630; Iron 585; Lecithin 630; Niacin 585;
    Phospholipid 630; Riboflavin 585; Sphingomyelin 630; Thiamine 585

SARDINELLA PERFORATA (Perforated scale sardine)
    S. Arabia, Malaya, Thailand, Sumatra, Java, Borneo, Philippines, China.
    Coastal waters.
    Iron 585; Niacin 585; Roboflavin 585; Thiamine 585

SARDINIA MELANOSTICTA (*see* SARDINOPS MELANOSTICTA)

SARDINOPS CAERULEA (California sardine, Pacific sardine, Pilchard)   *23, 24, 199*
    S. California to S.E. Alaska.
    Amino acids 305, 924, 1035; Anserine 783; Carnosine 783; Cyanocobalamin
    646; Histidine 783; 1-Methyl histidine 783; Niacin 192; Riboflavin 192;
    Thiamine 192

SARDINOPS MELANOSTICTA = SARDINIA MELANOSTICTA (True sardine)   *19, 20–
25, 38, 279*
    Japan, Korea. Pelagic.
    Actin 1309; Amino acids 696; Calcium 377; Cholesterol 915; Choline 869;
    Cobalt 864; Cyanocobalamin 466, 1381; Folic acid 503, 637; Iron 377;
    Lecithin 841; Methionine 846; Pantothenic acid 502; Riboflavin 489, 932,
    1285; Riboflavin adenine dinucleotide 1285; Riboflavin mononucleotide 1285;
    Sulphur 377; Thiamine 839; Tryptophan 697; Urea 938; Vitamin A 509, 513,
    1374; Vitamin D 1374

SARDINOPS OCELLATA (Pilchard)   *225*
    S. Africa.
    Amino acids 183

SAURIDA TUMBIL (Greater lizard-fish)
    Red Sea, India, Malaya, China, Japan.
    Iron 585; Niacin 585, 670; Riboflavin 585; Thiamine 585; Trimethylamine
    oxide 1319

SAURIDA UNDOSQUAMIS (True lizard-fish)
    Japan, Philippines, China, Formosa. Coastal, muddy bottom.
    Actin 1309

SAWARA NIPHONIA
    Japan.
    Cyanocobalamin 1381

SCAPHIODON SP.†
Rivers of W. Asia.
Calcium 918; Iron 918

SCARDINIUS ERYTHROPHTHALMUS† (Rudd)   *183*
Europe to Asia Minor, except the Iberian peninsula and S. Italy. Still and
slowly-flowing waters, sometimes brackish.
'Sugar' 671

SCARUS CROICENSIS
DNA 862

SCARUS GUACAMAIA (Parrot fish)   *95*
Bermuda.
Iodine (protein-bound) 848

SCARUS MECHIPUNCTATUS
Tanzania, Hong Kong, Sumatra, Java to New Guinea.
Iron 585; Niacin 585; Riboflavin 585; Thiamine 585

SCATOPHAGUS ARGUS* (Spotted butterfish)   *21, 22, 24, 25*
Indian Ocean to China and Australia, entering rivers.
Iron 14, 585; Niacin 585; Riboflavin 585; Thiamine 585; Trimethylamine
oxide 1319

SCIAENA ANTARCTICA* (Butterfish, Jewfish, Kingfish, Mulloway, River kingfish,
Silver jew)
Australia. Coastal, reefs, ascending rivers.
Cholesterol 872; Phospholipid 872

SCIAENA AQUILA (Meagre)
Shetland and Kattegat to Mediterranean, W. Africa and Gulf of Guinea.
Shallow waters, sometimes entering estuaries.
Potassium 871

SCIAENA COITOR*
India, Burma, Malaya, Sumatra, Java, Australia. Large rivers, descending to
sea at certain seasons.
Niacin 1096; Vitamin C 1095

SCIAENA DIACANTHUS* (Two-spined jewfish)
India, Malaya, China, Hong Kong, Philippines. Sea and mouths of rivers.
Cholesterol 630; Fatty acids 667; Lecithin 630; Niacin 631; Phospholipid 630;
Riboflavin 631; Sphingomyllin 630; Thiamine 631

SCIAENA DUSSUMIERI (Dussumier's silver jewfish)
India, Philippines, Singapore, Sumatra, S. China. Sea and brackish water.
Iron 585; Niacin 585; Riboflavin 585; Thiamine 585

SCIAENA HOLOLEPIDOTA
Vitamin D 1055

SCIAENA SCHLEGELI
  Japan.
  Vitamin A 510

SCIAENA SP.
  Niacin 670

SCIAENOIDES BRUNNEUS*
  India, Sumatra, China. Sea, entering mouths of rivers.
  Cholesterol 630; Lecithin 630; Niacin 631; Phospholipid 630; Riboflavin 631;
  Sphingomyelin 630; Thiamine 631

SCIAENOPS OCELLATA (Bass, Channel bass, Red bass, Red drum, Redfish, Sea
  bass, Spottail, Spotted bass)
  S. Atlantic and Gulf coasts of United States, Texas to New Jersey on sandy
  shores.
  Chloride 1215; Cholesterol 1215; Haemoglobin 1215; Potassium 948, 1215;
  Sodium 948, 1215

SCOLIODON SORRAKOWAH‡ (Yellow dog shark)
  India.
  Amino acids 23; Arginine 22; Cholesterol 630; Cystine 22; Lecithin 630;
  Phospholipid 630; Sphingomyelin 630; Tryptophan 22; Tyrosine 22

SCOLIODON SP.‡
  India.
  Trimethylamine oxide 1319

SCOLIODON WALBEEHMII‡ (Milk shark, Sharpnosed shark)
  Japan, Indian Ocean.
  Riboflavin 501

SCOMBER COLIAS (Chub mackerel, Spanish mackerel)
  Both sides of Atlantic, Mediterranean and Black Seas. More southern than
  Atlantic mackerel (S. SCOMBRUS). May be same species as S. JAPONICUS. Migra-
  tory, swimming in shoals.
  Calcium 592, 1370; Cyanocobalamin 592; Cystine 592; Iron 592, 1370;
  Lysine 592; Magnesium 1370; Methionine 592; Niacin 592; Potassium 1370;
  Riboflavin 592; Thiamine 592; Tryptophan 592

SCOMBER JAPONICUS (Japanese mackerel, Matreel)   *20, 21, 23, 24, 25*
  Japan, Formosa, Korea. Coastal, fairly shallow water.
  Actin 1309; Adenosine monophosphate 1101; Adenosine triphosphate 108,
  910, 911; Amino acids 847; Calcium 108; Cephalin 658; Cerebroside 658,
  1396; Cholesterol 658, 915; Choline 1236; Creatin 910, 911, 1100, 1101;
  Creatinine 1100, 1101; Cyanocobalamin 466, 867, 1380; Cytochrome C 844;
  Folic acid 503; Haemoglobin 678, 844, 845; Hydroxyproline 1238, 1239, 1243;
  Hypoxanthin 1101; Inosine monophosphate 1101; Inositol 1149; Insulin
  1278; Lecithin 658, 1396; Magnesium 108; Methionine 846; Myoglobin 844,
  845; Niacin 867; Pantothenic acid 502; Phosphatidyl ethanolamine 1396;
  Phosphatidyl serine 1396; Potassium 108; Pyridoxine 891, 1383, 1384;

Riboflavin 489, 501, 584, 867, 891, 1285; Riboflavin adenine dinucleotide 1285; Riboflavin mononucleotide 1285; Sodium 108; Sphingomyelin 658, 1396; Taurine 1101; Thiamine 867; Trimethylamine 1236, 1237; Trimethylamine oxide 1101, 1236, 1237; Tryptophan 697; Vitamin C 965

SCOMBER SCOMBRUS (Atlantic mackerel)   *17, 18, 22–28, 32, 148, 150, 225, 226, 231*
Both sides of N. Atlantic, including Iceland. Restricted to continental shelf. Mediterranean. Avoids colder waters. Pelagic, swimming in large shoals.
N-Acetyl histidine 456; Aluminium 987; Amino acids 34, 154, 924, 1035; Barium 987; Beryllium 987; Biotin 751; Cadmium 987; Calcium 1061, 1234; Cholesterol 1369; Chromium 987, 989; Cobalt 987; Copper 989; Cyanocobalamin 146, 150, 157, 1234, 1251; Folic acid 751; Gadolineum 987; Iodine 1234; Iron 443, 987, 989, 1234; Lead 987, 989; Lithium 987, 989; Magnesium 1061; Manganese 989; Molybdenum 987; Niacin 146, 150, 157, 192, 1234, 1251; Nickel 987, 989; Pantothenic acid 146, 150, 157, 751, 1234; Potassium 192, 871, 1061; Riboflavin 146, 150, 157, 192, 517, 787, 1234, 1251; Silver 987; Sodium 192, 1061; Strontium 987, 989; 'Sugar' 428; Thiamine 146, 192, 405, 742, 785, 787, 1234; Tin 987; Titanium 987, 989; Trimethylamine 1085, 1253; Trimethylamine oxide 307, 1085, 1253; Ubiquinone 292; Vanadium 987, 989, 1194; Vitamin A 157; Vitamin C 785; Vitamin D 47, 60, 785; Vitamin E 8; Zinc 987

SCOMBER TAPEINOCEPHALUS (Spotted mackerel)
Japan, Korea, Formosa.
Folic acid 637; Haematocrit 1097; Haemoglobin 1097

SCOMBERESOX SAURUS (Atlantic saury, Billfish, Needlefish, Saurel, Saury pike, Skipjack, Skipper)
Temperate parts of Atlantic, Pacific and Indian Oceans. Coast and open sea, in shoals near the surface.
Trimethylamine oxide 307

SCOMBEROIDES LYSAN
Red Sea, Tanzania, India, Thailand, Philippines, Formosa, N. Australia.
Iron 585; Niacin 585; Riboflavin 585; Thiamine 585

SCOMBEROMORUS CAVALLA (King mackerel)   *149*
Atlantic coast of America: Cape Cod to Brazil.
Haematocrit 320; Haemoglobin 320

SCOMBEROMORUS COMMERSONII (Barred Spanish mackerel)
Madagascar, Tanzania, Red Sea, India, Philippines, China, Japan, Queensland, Tasmania, Fiji. Sea and brackish water.
Trimethylamine oxide 1319

SCOMBEROMORUS GUTTATUM* (Spotted Spanish mackerel)
India, Malaya, Sumatra, Java, Borneo, China. Sea and coastal waters, entering rivers.

Cholesterol 630; Creatin 631; Lecithin 630; Niacin 631; Phospholipid 630; Riboflavin 631; Sphingomyelin 630; Thiamine 631; Trimethylamine 631; Trimethylamine oxide 631; Urea 631

SCOMBEROMORUS MACULATUS (Bay mackerel, Spanish mackerel, Spotted cybium, Spotted mackerel) *149*
E. America: Maine to Brazil.
Amino acids 1035; Calcium 592; Chloride 1215; Cholesterol 1215; Cyanocobalamin 592; Cystine 592; Haematocrit 320; Haemoglobin 320; Iron 592; Lysine 592; Methionine 592; Niacin 413, 592; Potassium 192, 202, 1215, 1263; Riboflavin 413, 592; Sodium 192, 202, 1215, 1263; Thiamine 405, 413, 592; Tryptophan 592

SCOMBEROMORUS NIPHONIUS (Spanish mackerel) *23*
Japan, Korea, China.
Thiamine 839; Vitamin A 513

SCOMBEROMORUS REGALIS (Black-spotted Spanish mackerel, Kingfish, Sierra, Spotted cero)
E. America: Cape Cod to Brazil, Cuba.
Thiamine 405

SCOMBEROMORUS SP.
Niacin 670; Riboflavin 489

SCOMBROPS BOOPS
Japan.
Folic acid 637; Inositol 1149; Riboflavin 501, 584, 891; Thiamine 891; Vitamin A 513

SCOPHTHALMUS MAEOTICUS MAEOTICUS
Russia.
Chromium 989; Iron 989; Lithium 989; Nickel 989; Strontium 989; Titanium 989; Vanadium 989

SCOPHTHALMUS MAXIMUS (*see* RHOMBUS MAXIMUS)

SCORPAENA PORCUS (Small-scaled scorpion fish)
Europe.
Calcium 712; Glycogen 245, 978; Magnesium 712; Potassium 712; Sodium 712; 'Sugar' 978; Trimethylamine 1253; Trimethylamine oxide 1253

SCORPAENA SCROFA (Large-scaled scorpion fish)
France to Mediterranean and Madeira, from 20–110 m on sandy or stony ground.
Glycogen 978; 'Sugar' 978

SCORPAENICHTHYS MARMORATUS (Cabezon, Giant marbled sculpin)
S. California to N. British Columbia. Coastal on rocky, sandy or muddy bottoms. Sluggish.
Creatin 554

SCYLLIORHINUS CANICULA‡ (*see* MUSTELUS CANIS‡)

SCYLLIORHINUS STELLARIS‡ = SCYLLIUM CATULUS‡ (Bounce, Bull huss, Greater spotted dogfish, Huss, Nursehound)   *146*
Italy, Britain, Biscay. Inshore to 60 m on rough ground.
Androstenedione 221; Glucose 933; Glycogen 933; Inositol 933; Oestradiol-17-β 221; Progesterone 221; Testosterone 221; Trimethylamine oxide 1065; Ubiquinone 292; Urea 1130

SCYLLIORHINUS TORAZAME‡ (Tiger shark)
Japan, Korea. Cold waters.
Niacin 494

SCYLLIUM CANICULA‡ (Rough hound, Small spotted dogfish)   *124, 146, 231*
W. Europe except Iceland. Mediterranean. Mainly bottom-living, 3–110 m.
Glycogen 245; Trimethylamine oxide 1065; Urea 674

SCYLLIUM CATULUS‡ (*see* SCYLLIORHINUS STELLARIS‡)

SCYLLIUM STELLARE‡ perhaps SCYLLIORHINUS STELLARIS (Large spotted dogfish)
Glycogen 978; 'Sugar' 978; Urea 674

SCYMNODON JONSONII‡
Europe.
Carotenoids 347

SCYMNODON SQUAMULOSUS‡
Japan.
Folic acid 503; Pantothenic acid 502; Vitamin A 496

SCYMNORHINUS LICHA‡
Japan.
Carotenoids 347; Urea 1226

SEBASTES DACTYLOPTERUS (Rock fish)
Europe.
Potassium 871

SEBASTES FLAMMEUS (Rock fish)
Japan.
Astaxanthin 1293; Carotenoids 1293; Vitamin A 513

SEBASTES INERMIS (perhaps SEBASTODES INERMIS)
Japan.
Creatin 1100; Creatinine 1100; Vitamin A 513

SEBASTES MARAMENUKE (perhaps SEBASTODES BARAMENUKE)
Japan.
Astaxanthin 1293; Carotenoids 1293

SEBASTES MARINUS (Norway haddock, Ocean perch, Redfish, Rosefish, Soldier) *59, 225, 226*

Both sides of N. Atlantic, in cold waters of gullies and deep water slopes, 100–500 m. Viviparous.

Amino acids 154; Calcium 1061, 1234; Cholesterol 1369; Cyanocobalamin 150, 1234; Iodine 1234; Iron 266, 1234; Magnesium 1061; Niacin 150, 1234; Pantothenic acid 150, 1234; Potassium 192, 197, 1061, 1263; Riboflavin 150, 787, 1129, 1234; Sodium 192, 1061, 1263; Thiamine 787, 1234; Trimethylamine oxide 243, 307

SEBASTES MATSUBARAE (perhaps SEBASTODES MATSUBARAE)
Japan.
Riboflavin 501; Vitamin A 513

SEBASTES SP.
Japan.
Cholesterol 1153; Fatty acids 1153

SEBASTES TOMPSONI
Japan.
Astaxanthin 1293; Carotenoids 1293; Tunaxanthin 1293

SEBASTES VULPES
Japan.
Trimethylamine 1237; Trimethylamine oxide 1237

SEBASTICHTHYS CAPENSIS (Jacopever)
S. Africa.
Vitamin D 1057

SEBASTISCUS ALBOFASCIATUS
Japan.
Folic acid 503; Pantothenic acid 502

SEBASTISCUS MARMORATUS (Rockfish, Scorpion-fish)   *119, 130, 187*
Japan, Korea, China. Shore, rocky bottom. Viviparous.
Astaxanthin 1293; Carotenoids 1293; Cyanocobalamin 1381; Pyridoxine 1383, 1384; Riboflavin 501, 891; Tunaxanthin 1293; Vitamin A 511, 512, 513

SEBASTODES ALASKANUS
N. America.
Potassium 1266; Sodium 1266

SEBASTODES ALUTUS (Long jaw rockfish, Pacific Ocean perch)   *88*
S. California to Bering Sea.
Anserine 783; Carnosine 783; Histidine 783; 1-Methyl histidine 783; Potassium 192, 1263, 1267; Sodium 192, 1263, 1267

SEBASTODES BARAMENUKE (Scorpion fish)
Japan. Cold waters.
Hydroxyproline 1238

C.B.F.

SEBASTODES CAURINUS (Copper rockfish)
   S. California to S.E. Alaska.
   Creatin 554

SEBASTODES ELONGATUS (Greenstriped rockfish)
   S. California to Strait of Georgia. Fairly deep waters.
   Potassium 1266; Sodium 1266, 1273

SEBASTODES FLAMMEUS
   Japan.
   Insulin 1278

SEBASTODES FLAVIDUS (Yellowtail rockfish)
   S. California to Vancouver Island.
   Potassium 1263, 1266; Sodium 1263, 1266, 1273

SEBASTODES GOODEI (Chili-pepper)
   Californian coast.
   Potassium 1266; Sodium 1266, 1273

SEBASTODES INERMIS (Japanese stingfish)
   Japan.
   Actin 1309

SEBASTODES IRACUNDUS
   Japan.
   Cyanocobalamin 1381; Folic acid 503; Pantothenic acid 502

SEBASTODES MALIGER (Orange-spotted rockfish, Quillback rockfish)
   S. California to Gulf of Alaska. All depths down to 270 m.
   Creatin 554

SEBASTODES MATSUBARAE (Matsubara stingfish)
   Japan. Deep waters.
   Folic acid 503; Niacin 494; Pantothenic acid 502; Riboflavin 501; Vitamin A
   1374; Vitamin D 1374

SEBASTODES MELANOPS (Black rockfish)
   N. California to Gulf of Alaska. Shores, among the rocks.
   Potassium 192, 1263; Sodium 192, 1263, 1273; Trimethylamine oxide 307

SEBASTODES PAUCISPINIS (Bocaccio)
   S. California to Queen Charlotte Sound, below 70 m.
   Potassium 1266; Sodium 1266

SEBASTODES PINNIGER (Canary rockfish, Orange rockfish)
   S. California to Dixon Entrance. Coastal.
   Potassium 192, 1263, 1266; Sodium 192, 1263, 1266, 1273

SEBASTODES RUBERRIMUS (Rasphead rockfish, Red cod, Red snapper, Turkey rockfish)
S. California to Gulf of Alaska.
Creatin 554; Potassium 192, 1263; Sodium 192, 1263; Trimethylamine oxide 307

SEBASTODES SP.
Amino acids 281, 928; Anserine 783; Carnosine 783; Histidine 783; 1-Methyl histidine 783; Riboflavin 1113; Sodium 1273; Thiamine 1112

SEBASTOLOBUS MACROCHIR
Japan.
Astaxanthin 1293; Carotenoids 1293; Folic acid 503; Pantothenic acid 502; Trimethylamine 1237; Trimethylamine oxide 1237; Tunaxanthin 1293; Vitamin A 513

SEBASTOPYR RUBERRIMUS (Red rockfish, Tambor)
Pacific coast of N. America.
Riboflavin 1113

SELACHUS MAXIMUS‡ (see CETORHINUS MAXIMUS‡)

SELAR CRUMENOPHTHALMUS (Bigeye scad, Goggle eye Jack)
Warm seas: W. Indies, Pacific coast of Mexico, Portugal.
Carotenoids 420; Niacin 420; Riboflavin 420; Thiamine 420; Vitamin C 420

SELENE VOMER (Atlantic lookdown, Horsehead, Moonfish)
Warm waters of the Atlantic and Pacific coasts of the Americas.
Calcium 592; Cyanocobalamin 592; Cystine 592; Iron 592; Lysine 592; Methionine 592; Niacin 592; Riboflavin 592; Thiamine 592; Tryptophan 592

SEMOTILUS ATROMACULATUS† (Creek chub, Horned dace, Mud chub, Silver chub)
N. America: Maine, New Jersey, Kansas, Wyoming.
Trimethylamine oxide 307

SERIOLA AUREOVITTATA
Japan, Korea. Warmer waters.
Cholesterol 915; Cyanocobalamin 1382; Vitamin C 965

SERIOLA DORSALIS (White salmon, Yellowtail)
Pacific coast of N. America, Santa Barbara Islands.
Haemoglobin 77

SERIOLA DUMERILI (Amberjack, Rudderfish)
Mediterranean to W. Indies, Massachusetts to Brazil.
Trimethylamine oxide 307

SERIOLA PURPURASCENS (Rudder fish)
Japan, Korea.
Folic acid 637; Vitamin C 579

SPARUS MACROCEPHALUS
Japan.
Thiamine 382; Urea 938

SPARUS SARBA (*see* RHABDOSARGUS SARBA)

SPHAEROIDES MACULATUS (Balloonfish, Northern puffer, Swellfish)
Atlantic coast of United States from Florida to Cape Cod. Shallow water on
sandy bottom, in which it often burrows.
Calcium 315; Chloride 315; Iron 443; Magnesium 315; Potassium 315;
Sodium 315; 'Sugar' 428; Thiamine 405; Zinc 315

SPHAEROIDES PARDALIS
Japan.
Cyanocobalamin 1381

SPHAEROIDES SPADICEUS
Japan.
Fibrinogen 1098; Haematocrit 1097; Haemoglobin 1097

SPHAEROIDES SPENGLERI (Southern puffer, Swelltoad, Tambor)
Portugal, W. Indies, Madeiras and Canaries.
Cyanocobalamin 412

SPHAEROIDES VERMICULARIS
Japan.
Cholesterol 1153; Fatty acids 1153

SPHYRAENA ARGENTEA (Pacific barracuda)
S. California to Gulf of Alaska. Coastal.
Anserine 783; Carnosine 783; Histidine 783; 1-Methyl histidine 783

SPHYRAENA BARRACUDA (Great barracuda)
Atlantic coast of S. America, W. Indies.
Calcium 592; Cyanocobalamin 592; Cystine 592; DNA 862; Iron 592; Lysine
592; Methionine 592; Niacin 592; Potassium 202; Riboflavin 592; Sodium
202; Thiamine 592; Tryptophan 592

SPHYRAENA GUACHANCHO
Portugal, W. Indies.
Carotenoids 420; Niacin 420; Riboflavin 420; Thiamine 420; Vitamin C 420

SPHYRAENA JAPONICA (Japanese barracuda, Seapike, Snock)
Japan.
Cyanocobalamin 1381; Riboflavin 501; Vitamin A 510, 511, 512

SPHYRAENA JELLO (Giant sea pike)
Natal, Seychelles, Madagascar, Red Sea, India, Malaya, China, Philippines.
Sea and brackish water.
Iron 585; Niacin 585; Riboflavin 585; Thiamine 585

SPHYRAENA OBTUSATA (Blunt-jawed sea pike, Striped barracuda)
E. Africa, Red Sea, India, Thailand, China, Philippines, Australia, New Zealand, Fiji.
Iron 585; Niacin 585; Riboflavin 585; Thiamine 585

SPHYRAENA PINGUIS (Good salmon, Red barracuda)
Japan.
Pyridoxine 1383, 1384; Riboflavin 891; Thiamine 891

SPHYRAENA SCHLEGELI
Cholesterol 1153; Fatty acids 1153; Vitamin A 513

SPHYRNA MALLEUS‡ (see S. ZYGAENA‡)

SPHYRNA TIBURA‡ (Bonnetnose shark, Shovelhead)
Both sides of Atlantic, and American Pacific coast. Shallow coastal waters. Sluggish. Viviparous.
Chloride 1215; Cholesterol 1215; Haemoglobin 1215; Potassium 1215; Sodium 1215

SPHYRNA ZYGAENA‡ = S. MALLEUS‡ (Cross-staff shark, Hammer head shark, Smooth hammerhead)
Warm parts of Atlantic and Pacific. India. Often seen near surface, both inshore and offshore. Viviparous.
Amino acids 738; Riboflavin 501; Sialic acid 325; Trimethylamine oxide 1319; Urea 674; Vitamin A 496

SPINAX NIGER (see ETMOPTERUS SPINAX)

SPONDYLIOSOMA CANTHARUS = SALPA SALPA (Black bream, Old wife)
Mid-Norway to Canaries. Deep water in winter, inshore in summer near rocks.
Cyanocobalamin 412

SPRATTUS SPRATTUS (see CLUPEA SPRATTUS)

SPRATTUS SPRATTUS PHALERICUS
Russia.
Aluminium 987, 989; Barium 987; Beryllium 987; Cadmium 987; Chromium 987, 989; Cobalt 987; Copper 989; Gadolineum 987; Iron 987, 989; Lead 987, 989; Lithium 987, 989; Manganese 989; Molybdenum 987; Nickel 987, 989; Silver 987, 989; Strontium 987, 989; Tin 987, 989; Titanium 987, 989; Vanadium 987, 989; Zinc 987

SQUALIUS CEPHALUS† (Chub)
Europe and Asia Minor, except Denmark and Sicily. Rivers and lakes.
Anserine 1392; Calcium 538; Carnosine 1392; Chloride 538; FREE Histidine 1392; Potassium 538; Sodium 538

SQUALUS ACANTHIAS‡ given variously as ACANTHIAS ACANTHIAS‡, ACANTHIAS VULGARIS‡, SQUALUS SUCKLEYI‡ (Atlantic spiny dogfish, Grayfish, Pacific spiny dogfish, Piked dogfish, Spined dogfish, Spur dog) *ix, 10, 22, 38, 88, 94–96, 131, 139*

Wide distribution in cold waters, between surface and 185 m. Rather sluggish. Viviparous.

Adrenaline 327; Amino acids 1014, 1222; FREE Amino acids 1329; Androstene dione 1170; Androsterone 1170; Calcium 1061, 1184, 1234; Carbon dioxide 832; Carotenoids 347; Cerebroside 805, 806; Chloride 392, 832, 1083, 1184; Cholesterol 729, 805, 806, 822, 1153, 1369; Creatin 554, 1184; Cyanocobalamin 1234, 1381; 11-Deoxycorticosterone 1170, 1172; Dehydroepiandrosterone 1170; Fatty acids 822, 957, 1153; FREE Fatty acids 729, 822, 960; Folic acid 503; Galactosamine 295; Glucosamine 295; Glycogen 672; Haematocrit 737; Hydrocortisone 1007; Hydroxyproline 392, 1014, 1239, 1243; Insulin 43; Iodine 1234; Iron 1234; Lecithin 805, 806; Magnesium 1061, 1184; Niacin 1234; Oestradiol 1368; Ornithine 1329; Pantothenic acid 502, 1234; Phosphatidyl choline 729; Phosphatidyl ethanolamine 729; Phosphatidyl serine 729; Phospholipid 729, 805, 806, 822, 960; Potassium 262, 601, 736, 832, 871, 1061, 1083, 1184; Pregnenolone 1170; Progesterone 1170; Riboflavin 501, 787, 932, 1113, 1234; Sarcosine 1329; Sodium 601, 736, 832, 1061, 1083; Sphingomyelin 729, 805, 806; Sulphate 1184; Thiamine 405, 787, 932, 1112, 1234; Triglyceride 729, 822; Trimethylamine 1085; Trimethylamine oxide 231, 307, 1085; Tyrosine 392; Ubiquinone 292; Urea 1184; Uronic acid 295; Vitamin A_1 495, 513, 1020; Vitamin A_2 1020; Vitamin C 932; Vitamin D 47; Vitamin E 8

SQUALUS BREVIROSTRIS‡
Japan.
Cyanocobalamin 1381; Trimethylamine oxide 1227; Urea 1226, 1227; Vitamin A 496, 513

SQUALUS MITSUKURII‡
Japan.
Vitamin A 496

SQUALUS SUCKLEYI‡ (see S. ACANTHIAS‡)

SQUATINA ANGELUS‡ (see SQUATINA SQUATINA‡)

SQUATINA JAPONICA‡ (Canopy shark, Japanese angel-fish, Japanese monk-fish)
Japan. Buried in sand.
Urea 1226; Vitamin A 496

SQUATINA SQUATINA‡ = S. ANGELUS‡ (Angel fish, Angel ray, Monkfish)
W. Europe: Shetlands to Canary Islands, Mediterranean.
Carotenoids 347; Urea 674

STENOTOMUS CHRYSOPS (Porgy, Scup)
E. coast of N. America: Cape Cod to N. Carolina. On sandy bottoms in large schools. Inshore in summer, offshore in winter.
Carnitine 361; Iron 443; Potassium 1263; Sodium 1263; 'Sugar' 428

STENOTOMUS VERSICOLOR (Bream, Common scup, Fair maid, Porgy, Scuppang)
Atlantic coast of United States.
Potassium 192; Sodium 192

STEPHANOLEPIS CIRRHIFER (File fish, Porky)
Japan, Korea, E. China Sea.
Vitamin A 513

STEREOLEPIS GIGAS (California jewfish)
Californian coast.
Anserine 783; Carnosine 783; Histidine 783; 1-Methyl histidine 783; Niacin 413; Riboflavin 413; Thiamine 413

STIZOSTEDION VITREUM† (Blue pike, Dory, Glass-eye, Jack salmon, Pike-perch, Spike, Walleye, Wall-eyed pike, White-eye, Yellow pike)   *164*
N. America: Great Lakes to Georgia.
Amino acids 583; Anserine 783; Carnosine 783; Histidine 783; Hypoxanthine 302; 1-Methyl histidine 783; Niacin 583; Potassium 192, 1263, 1274; Riboflavin 583; Sodium 192, 1263, 1274; Thiamine 583

STOLEPHORUS COMMERSONII (Commerson's anchovy, Long-jawed anchovy)
Madagascar to India to Philippines. Coastal.
Iron 585; Niacin 585; Riboflavin 585; Thiamine 585

STOLEPHORUS SP.
Niacin 670

STROMATEUS CINEREUS* = PAMPUS CINEREUS* (Grey pomfret, Harvest fish, Silver pomfret)
India, Malaya, China, Japan, Philippines; introduced to Hawaii.
Amino acids 723, 827, 838; Cholesterol 630; Creatin 631; Lecithin 630; Niacin 631; Phospholipid 630; Riboflavin 631; Sphingomyelin 630; Thiamine 631; Trimethylamine 631; Trimethylamine oxide 631, 1319; Urea 631; Vitamin A 509, 513

STROMATEUS NIGER (*see* PARASTROMATEUS NIGER)

STROMATEUS SINENSIS (White pomfret)
India, Malaya, China.
Fatty acids 667

STROMATEUS SP.
Niacin 158, 670

SYNAGRIS JAPONICUS (*see* NEMIPTERUS JAPONICUS)

SYNAPHOBRANCHUS AFFINIS
Japan.
Vitamin A 513

SYNAPHOBRANCHUS KAUPI = S. PINNATUS (Gray's cutthroat eel, Longnose eel)
Wide distribution in deep water.
Iron 266

SYNAPHOBRANCHUS PINNATUS (*see* S. KAUPI)

15*

TACHYSURUS SP.
  India.
  Adenosine triphosphate phosphorus 979; Creatine phosphate 979; Glycogen
  979; Lactic acid 979; Trimethylamine 979

TACHYSURUS VENOSUS
  Madagascar, India, Malaya, Java, Borneo.
  Vitamin C 56, 57

TAENIOTOCA LATERALIS (Striped surffish)
  W. America: Vancouver to Todos Santos Bay.
  Adenosine diphosphate + Adenosine triphosphate 1247; Adenosine mono-
  phosphate 1247; Creatin 554

TAIUS TUMIFRONS (Yellow porgy)
  Japan, Korea.
  Cholesterol 1153; Fatty acids 1153; Folic acid 637; Vitamin A 511, 512, 513,
  1374; Vitamin D 1374

TANAKIUS KITAHARAE (Flounder)
  Japan.
  Hydroxyproline 1238, 1239, 1243; Vitamin A 513

TARPON ATLANTICUS (Silverfish, Tarpon)
  E. America: Long Island to Brazil.
  Trimethylamine oxide 307

TAUTOGA ONITIS (Blackfish, Tautog)
  Atlantic coast of N. America: Nova Scotia to S. Carolina. Coastal. Can enter
  brackish water.
  Carnitine 361

TAUTOGOLABRUS ADSPERSUS (Bergall, Blue perch, Cunner, Nipper, Perch, Sea
  perch)
  Atlantic coast of N. America within a few miles of shore, on sea bottom, also
  around rocks and wrecks.
  Iron 443; 'Sugar' 428

TEATHIS JAVUS
  Philippines.
  Iron 585; Niacin 585; Riboflavin 585; Thiamine 585

TETRANARCE OCCIDENTALIS‡ = TORPEDO OCCIDENTALIS‡ (Atlantic torpedo,
  Crampfish, Electric fish, Numbfish)
  Atlantic coast of United States: Cape Cod to Cuba.
  Carnitine 361; Trimethylamine oxide 307

TETRAPTURUS ANGUSTIROSTRIS
  Japan, America.
  Haemoglobin 77; Vitamin A 513

TETRAPTURUS AUDAX
N. America
Haemoglobin 77

TETRAPTURUS MITSUKURII
Japan.
Cholesterol 915; Pyridoxine 891; Riboflavin 891; Thiamine 839

THALEICHTHYS PACIFICUS* (Candlefish, Euchalon) *287*
N. California to Bering Sea.
Phospholipid 5; Pristane 5; Squalene 5; Triglyceride 5

THERAGRA CHALCOGRAMMA (Alaska pollack)   *215*
Japan, W. America.
Adenosine diphosphate + Adenosine triphosphate 1247; Adenosine mono-
phosphate 1247; Amino acids 696, 725; Cyanocobalamin 466, 1380; Dimethyl-
amine 21; Fatty acids 1244, 1347, 1397; Folic acid 503; Formaldehyde 20, 21;
Hydroxyproline 1238, 1239, 1243; Pantothenic acid 502; Pyridoxine 1383,
1384; Riboflavin 501, 725, 891; Thiamine 725, 891; Trimethylamine 21;
Trimethylamine oxide 21; Vitamin A 513; Vitamin C 965

THERAPON BIDYANA†
Australia.
Cholesterol 872; Phospholipid 872

THERAPON JARBUA* (Crescent perch)
E. Africa, Red Sea, India, Philippines, Japan, N. Australia. Coastal waterᵉ and
estuaries.
Iron 585; Niacin 585; Riboflavin 585; Thiamine 585

THERAPON OXYRHYNCHUS*
India, Japan, Formosa, Philippines.
Arsenic 448; Selenium 448; Thallium 448; Vitamin A 510, 513; Vitamin C 579

THERAPON THERAPS (Large-scaled banded grunter)
E. Africa, India, Malaya, Philippines, China.
Iron 585; Niacin 585; Riboflavin 585; Thiamine 585

THUNNUS ALALUNGA = GERMO ALALUNGA, GERMO GERMO, THUNNUS GERMO
(Albacore, Long-finned albacore, Long-finned tuna)
All warm seas: Japan, Hawaii, California, Atlantic, Mediterranean. Surface
waters down to 185 m. Migratory.
Anserine 532, 783; Carnosine 783; Cephalin 1158; Cyanocobalamin 646, 1381;
DNA 375; Glucose 1248; Haemoglobin 77; Histidine 532, 783; Insulin 1278;
Lecithin 1158; 1-Methyl histidine 783; Myoglobin 180; Niacin 646; Phospho-
inositide 1158; Phospholipid 1158; Potassium 192, 649, 1263; Riboflavin 646,
1151; Ribose 1248; Sodium 192, 649, 1263, 1273; Sphingomyelin 1158;
Trimethylamine oxide 691; Tryptophan 1036; Urea 938; Vitamin A 513;
Vitamin C 471

THUNNUS ALBACARES = GERMO MACROPTERUS, NEOTHUNNUS ALBACORA, NEOTHUNNUS MACROPTERUS, THUNNUS ALBACORA (Allison's tuna, Autumn albacore, Yellowfin tuna)   *20, 21, 23, 38, 163, 209, 289*
Circumtropical. Pelagic.
Amino acids 198; Anserine 532, 783; Carnosine 783; Cephalin 1158; Cyano-cobalamin 466, 506, 1381; Cytochrome C 844; DNA 375; Fibrinogen 1098; Folic acid 506, 507, 637; Haematocrit 1097; Haemoglobin 77, 179, 678, 844, 1097; Histidine 532, 783; Insulin 1278; Iron 585; Lecithin 1158; Methionine 846; 1-Methyl histidine 783; Myoglobin 179, 180, 844; Niacin 585; Panto-thenic acid 506, 507; Phosphoinositide 1158; Phospholipid 1158; Potassium 649; Pyridoxine 506, 507, 891; Riboflavin 506, 507, 585, 891, 1151, 1152; Sodium 649; Sphingomyelin 1158; Thiamine 585; Trimethylamine oxide 1373; Tryptophan 697; Vitamin A 513, 1374; Vitamin D 1374

THUNNUS ALBACORA (*see* THUNNUS ALBACARES)

THUNNUS GERMO (*see* THUNNUS ALALUNGA)

THUNNUS MACCOII
Southern Oceans: S. Australia, Tasmania, New Zealand, Chile, S. Africa.
Cholesterol 1153; DNA 375; Fatty acids 1153; Riboflavin 1152

THUNNUS OBESUS = PARATHUNNUS MEBACHI, PARATHUNNUS OBESUS, PARA-THUNNUS SIBI (Big-eye tuna)   *19, 20, 21, 25, 31, 38, 87, 209*
Both sides of the Atlantic, Pacific, Azores, Canary Islands, Indian Ocean, Japan. Absent from Mediterranean.
Amino acids 657, 847; Anserine 783; Carnosine 783; Choline 395; Cyano-cobalamin 867, 1380; Cytochrome C 844; DNA 375; Haemoglobin 77, 844; Histidine 783; Insulin 1278; 1-Methyl histidine 783; Myoglobin 844; Niacin 494, 867; Pyridoxine 73; Riboflavin 501, 867, 891, 1151, 1152; Thiamine 867; Vitamin A 513, 1374; Vitamin D 1374

THUNNUS SALIENS (*see* THUNNUS THYNNUS ORIENTALIS)

THUNNUS SP.
Amino acids 924; Vitamin A 508

THUNNUS THYNNUS ORIENTALIS = THUNNUS SALIENS, THYNNUS ORIENTALIS (Pacific bluefin tuna)   *20–23, 29*
Kodiak Island, Gulf of Alaska, Vancouver, S. California, Okhotsk Sea, Japan, Philippines, Hawaii.
Amino acids 695; Cerebroside 655, 1396; Cholesterol 573, 574, 655, 915, 1396; Cephalin 576; Cyanocobalamin 1381; Cytochrome C 844; Haemoglobin 844, 845; Lecithin 575, 655, 1396; Manganese 1229; Myoglobin 844, 845; Phos-phatidyl ethanolamine 655, 1396; Phosphatidyl serine 655, 1396; Phospholipid 655, 1396; Riboflavin 1285; Riboflavin adenine dinucleotide 1285; Riboflavin mononucleotide 1285; Sphingomyelin 655, 1396; Thiamine 839; Tryptophan 1036; Vitamin A 513

THUNNUS THYNNUS (*see* THUNNUS THYNNUS THYNNUS)

TINCA VULGARIS† (*see* T. TINCA†)

TORPEDO MARMORATA‡ (Marbled electric ray)
W. France to Mediterranean in shallow waters.
Acetyl choline 873; Oestradiol 222; Oestriol 222; Urea 674; Zinc 344

TORPEDO NOBILIANA‡ (Atlantic torpedo, Electric ray, Numbfish, Torpedo)
Both sides of Atlantic, Mediterranean, tropical W. Africa. Grows to considerable size. Lives partly buried in sand or mud in fairly deep water.
Carotenoids 347; Ubiquinone 292

TORPEDO OCCIDENTALIS‡ (*see* TETRANARCE OCCIDENTALIS‡)

TORPEDO OCELLATA‡
Urea 674; Zinc 344

TRACHICHTHODES AFFINIS
Australia.
Cholesterol 872; Phospholipid 872

TRACHINOCEPHALUS MYOPS (Offshore lizzard fish).
Pacific and Atlantic Oceans.
Arsenic 448; Selenium 448; Thallium 448

TRACHINOTUS CAROLINUS (Butterfish, Carolina pompano, Cobbler fish, Common pampano)
Gulf of Mexico, Cape Code, W. Indies, Brazil.
Potassium 948; Sodium 948

TRACHINOTUS SP.
Thiamine 405

TRACHINUS DRACO (Greater weever)
S. Norway, Britain to Mediterranean, 10 to 100 m, buried in sand.
FREE Amino acids 1139; Potassium 871; Trimethylamine 1253; Trimethylamine oxide 1253

TRACHIPTERUS SP.
Japan.
Vitamin A 513

TRACHURUS JAPONICUS (Jack mackerel, Japanese horse mackerel, Rungh scad)
214
Japan, Korea. Offshore.
Adenosine triphosphate 108; Amino acids 696, 1214; Arsenic 448; Calcium 108; Cholesterol 915, 1153; Choline 869; Creatin 1100; Creatinine 1100; Cyanocobalamin 466, 868, 1380; Fatty acids 1153; Hydroxyproline 1239, 1243; Magnesium 108; Manganese 1229; Methionine 846; Potassium 108; Riboflavin 489, 584, 1285; Riboflavin adenine dinucleotide 1285; Riboflavin mononucleotide 1285; Selenium 448; Sodium 108; Thallium 448; Thiamine 839; Trimethylamine 1237; Trimethylamine oxide 1237; Vitamin A 513, 1374; Vitamin C 965; Vitamin D 1374; Vitamin E 581

TRACHURUS MEDITERRANEUS PONTICUS (Black Sea scad)
Aluminium 987, 989; Barium 987; Beryllium 987; Cadmium 987; Chromium 987, 989; Cobalt 987; Copper 989; Gadolinium 987; Iron 987, 989; Lead 987, 989; Lithium 987, 989; Manganese 989; Molybdenum 987; Nickel 987, 989; Potassium 736; Silver 987; Sodium 736; Strontium 987, 989; Tin 987, 989; Titanium 987, 989; Vanadium 987, 989; Zinc 987

TRACHURUS TRACHURUS (Horse mackerel, Rough scad, Scad) *20, 91, 92, 226, 227, 242*
Japan, W. Europe apart from Iceland, Florida. Forms large shoals in shallow water.
Caesium 184, 185, 926; Calcium 712, 1370; Cyanocobalamin 412, 867; Folic acid 503; Iron 1370; Lithium 184, 185, 926; Magnesium 712, 1370; Niacin 867; Pantothenic acid 502; Potassium 184, 185, 712, 926, 1370; Pyridoxine 1383, 1384; Riboflavin 867, 891; Rubidium 184, 185, 926; Sodium 184, 185, 712, 926; Thiamine 867; Vitamin A 510

TREMATOMUS BERNACCHII
Antarctic.
Haematocrit 699; Haemoglobin 328, 699

TREMATOMUS BORCHGREVINKI *220*
Antarctic.
Haematocrit 699; Haemoglobin 699, 1306

TREMATOMUS HANSONI
Antarctic.
Haematocrit 699; Haemoglobin 699

TREMATOMUS LOENNBERGII
Antarctic.
Haematocrit 699; Haemoglobin 699

TRIAKIS SCYLLIA‡ (Incense burner)
India, Japan. Weedy shore-bottom.
Adenosine diphosphate 1224; Adenosine monophosphate 1224; Adenosine triphosphate 1224; Ammonia 1224; Creatin phosphate 1224; Fructose-6-phosphate 1224; Glucose-1-phosphate 1224; Glucose-6-phosphate 1224; Glycogen 1224; Hexose diphosphate 1224; Lactic acid 1224; Phosphoglyceric acid 1224; Phosphopyruvic acid 1224; Ribose phosphate 1224; Triose phosphate 1224; Vitamin A 1374; Vitamin D 1374

TRIAKIS SEMIFASCIATUM‡ (Cat shark, Leopard shark)
California.
Anserine 783; Carnosine 783; Histidine 783; 1-Methyl histidine 783

TRIBOLODON HAKONENSIS*
Japan. The only Cyprinoid that can inhabit salt water.
Vitamin A 510, 513, 1374; Vitamin D 1374

TRICHIURUS HAUMELA (Hairtail, Large-headed ribbon-fish)
India: Bay of Bengal, Ceylon. Coastal waters and trawling grounds.
Iron 585; Niacin 585, 670; Riboflavin 585; Thiamine 585

TRICHIURUS JAPONICUS
Japan.
Cyanocobalamin 1381; Riboflavin 584; Vitamin A 510

TRICHIURUS LEPTURUS (Bandfish, Cutlass fish, Hair-tail, Ribbon-fish, Snakefish)
Britain, Portugal, W. Atlantic: N. Carolina to W. Indies, Japan. Shallow water.
Carotenoids 420; Niacin 420; Riboflavin 420; Thiamine 420; Vitamin A 513;
Vitamin C 420

TRICHIURUS SAVALA (Small-headed ribbon-fish)
India, Malaya, China.
Niacin 631; Riboflavin 631; Thiamine 631

TRICHIURUS SP.
India.
Amino acids 141

TRICHOGASTER PECTORALIS† (Bubble-nest builder, Siamese goramy)
Native to Thailand, Malaya, Indonesia. Introduced to Ceylon.
Amino acids 306

TRICHOGASTER TRICHOPTERUS†
Indonesia.
Amino acids 306

TRICHODON STELLERI   *23*
Japan.
Thiamine 839

TRIGLA CORAX (*see* TRIGLA LUCERNA)

TRIGLA CUCULUS = T. PINI (Elleck, Piper, Red gurnard)
Europe.
Vitamin A_1 1019, 1020; Vitamin A_2 1020

TRIGLA GURNARDUS (Grey gurnard)
Europe.
Potassium 871; Vitamin A_1 1020; Vitamin A_2 1020

TRIGLA LUCERNA = T. CORAX (Tub-fish, Yellow gurnard)
W. Europe (apart from Iceland), Mediterranean and Black Seas. Found
between 5–200 m; common close inshore on sand, mud or gravel.
Trimethylamine 1253; Trimethylamine oxide 1253; Vitamin C 399

TRIGLA PINI (*see* T. CUCULUS)

TRISOTROPIS VENENOSUS (Rockfish, Yellow-finned grouper)
Florida, Bahamas.
DNA 862

TRUDIS BASSENSIS WESTRALIAE (Cliff flathead)
Australia.
Copper 88

TRYGON IMBRICATA‡ (Scaly stingray)
India: Coromandel coast.
Trimethylamine oxide 1319

TRYGON MICROPS‡
India.
Trimethylamine oxide 1319

TRYGON PASTINACA‡ (Sting ray)
Russia, N. Atlantic.
FREE Amino acids 1329; Caesium 184, 185; Carotenoids 347; Lithium 184,
185, 926; Potassium 184, 185, 736, 926; Rubidium 184, 185; Sarcosine 1329;
Sodium 184, 185, 736, 926; Urea 674, 1329

TRYGON UARNAK¶ (see DASYATIS UARNAK¶)

TRYGON VIOLACEA‡ (Blue sting-ray)   *144*
Europe.
Urea 674

TRYPAUCHEN WAKAE
Japan.
Riboflavin 489

TYLOSURUS ACUS (Agujon, Houndfish)
W. Indies.
DNA 862

TYLOSURUS GIGANTEUS
Seychelles, India, Philippines, Japan, N. Australia, Sandwich Islands.
Iron 585; Niacin 585; Riboflavin 585; Thiamine 585

UMBRINA SINUTA
India: Sind
Cholesterol 630; Lecithin 630; Phospholipid 630; Sphingomyelin 630

UPENEOIDES BENSASI (Goatfish, Salmonet, Surmullet)
Japan. Shore, on muddy bottom.
Arsenic 448; Selenium 448; Thallium 448

UPENEOIDES SULPHUREUS (Yellow goatfish)
Madagascar, India, Thailand, Philippines, S. China, S. Japan, Fiji, New
Hebrides. Trawling grounds.
Iron 585; Niacin 585; Riboflavin 585; Thiamine 585

URANOSCOPUS JAPONICUS (Japanese stargazer, Mishima puffer fish)
Japan, Korea.
Cyanocobalamin 1381; Vitamin A 513

URANOSCOPUS SCABER
Russia.
Calcium 712; Glycogen 978; Magnesium 712; Potassium 712; Sodium 712;
'Sugar' 978; Trimethylamine 1253; Trimethylamine oxide 1253

UROLOPHUS MUCOSUS‡
Australia.
Copper 88

UROPHYCIS BLENNOIDES (Forked-beard hake)
Ubiquinone 292

UROPHYCIS CHESTERI (Longfin hake)
Eastern N. America on the continental slope.
Iron 266

UROPHYCIS CHUSS (Forkbeard, Ling, Mud hake, Red hake, Squirrel hake, Thimble-
eyed ling, White hake)
N.W. Atlantic: Newfoundland to Virginia. Shallow water to over 900 m.
Tolerates wide temperature range.
Iron 266; Potassium 175; Sodium 175; Trimethylamine oxide 307

UROPHYCIS TENUIS (Codling, Hake, Ling, Old English hake, Squirrel hake, White
hake)
Distribution as for U. chuss.
Iron 266

USACARANX GEORGIANUS (Silver bream, Silver trevally, Skipjack, White trevally)
Australia. Coastal.
Copper 88

VERASPER MOSERI
Japan.
Vitamin A 509, 513; Vitamin C 965

VIMBA VIMBA†
Sweden, Austria, Black and Caspian Sea basins. Lower reaches of rivers and
lakes.
Glutamine 1407

WALLAGO ATTU† (Fresh water shark)
India, Ceylon, Burma. Deep waters of rivers. Predatory.
Calcium 918, 1327; Cholesterol 1161; Copper 1327; Cyanocobalamin 71, 72;
Folic acid 73; Iron 918, 1327; Niacin 1096; Potassium 1327; Vitamin C 1095

XESURUS SCALPRUM
Japan.
Cyanocobalamin 1381; Riboflavin 501, 891; Vitamin A 510

XIPHIAS GLADIUS (Broadbill swordfish, Swordfish)
Wide range over Atlantic, N. Norway to S. Africa. A solitary oceanic traveller, swimming in surface waters.
Anserine 783; Biotin 750, 751; Carnosine 783; Cholesterol 915; Cyanocobalamin 1251; Folic acid 751; Haemoglobin 77; Histidine 783; 1-Methyl histidine 783; Niacin 494, 750, 1251; Pantothenic acid 751; Riboflavin 750, 1251; Thiamine 750; Trimethylamine oxide 243, 307; Vitamin A 750

ZACCO PLATYPUS‡ (Common minnow)
Japan, China, Korea.
Pyridoxine 1383; Vitamin A 510, 511, 512, 513, 1374; Vitamin D 1374

ZEBRIAS ZEBRINUS (Striped sole)
Japan, Formosa.
Vitamin A 509, 513

ZEUS AUSTRALIS (John Dory)
Australia.
Cholesterol 872; Phospholipid 872

ZEUS FABER (John Dory, St. Peter's fish)
Japan, W. Europe apart from Iceland, Portugal, western N. Atlantic. Found from close inshore to 200 m. Solitary.
Cyanocobalamin 412; Potassium 871; Riboflavin 891; Trimethylamine oxide 1065; Vitamin A_1 1020; Vitamin A_2 1020

ZEUS JAPONICUS
Japan.
Adenosine triphosphate 108; Cyanocobalamin 1381; Riboflavin 501; Vitamin A 513

ZOARCES SP.
Glycogen 813; Lactic acid 813

ZOARCES VIVIPARUS (Eel pout, Viviparous blenny) *152, 165*
S. and E. Britain to White Sea. Baltic. Commonest between 5.5 and 27.5 m. Fertilisation of the egg is internal.
FREE Amino acids 1139; Creatin + Creatinine 1139

ZONICHTHYS FALCATUS (Madregal, Rock salmon)
W. Indies, Florida.
DNA 862

ZYGAENA BLOCHII‡ (Arrow-headed hammerhead shark)
India, Malaya and beyond.
Amino acids 1324

FAMILY RELATIONSHIPS OF FISH GENERA

All the genera mentioned in the text (Part I) have been grouped here according to the classification of Starr Jordan (1963) to show which are closely related and, incidentally, which are cyclostomes, elasmobranchs or teleosts. The distinction between fresh-water and marine fish is not made, but that information can be found in Part III, the Chemical Index of Fish Names. Numbers in the left hand margin are Starr Jordan's family numbers.

Class CYCLOSTOMI

Order HYPEROTRETA

4   MYXINIDAE   *Myxine*
5   EPTATRETIDAE   *Eptatretus, Polistotrema*

Order HYPEROARTIA

6   PETROMYZONIDAE   *Entosphenus, Ichthyomyzon, Lampetra, Petromyzon*

Class ELASMOBRANCHII

Order EUSELACHII

52   SCYLLIORHINIDAE   *Scylliorhinus, Scyllium*
60   LAMNIDAE   *Isurus, Lamna*
63   GALEIDAE   *Galeorhinus, Prionace*

Order TECTOSPONDYLI

67   SQUALIDAE   *Squalus*

Order BATOIDEI

77   RAJIDAE   *Raja*
79   TORPEDINIDAE   *Benthobatis, Narcacion*
80   DASYATIDAE   *Trygon*

Class PISCES

Order SIRENOIDEI

107   PROTOPTERIDAE   *Protopterus*

Order GLANIOSTOMI

116   ACIPENSERIDAE   *Acipenser*

Order HALECOMORPHI

127 AMIIDAE *Amia*

Superorder TELEOSTEI

(The bony fishes)

Order ISOSPONDYLI

147 CLUPEIDAE *Alosa, Brevoortia, Clupea, Pomolobus, Sardina, Sardinella, Sardinia*
150 ENGRAULIDAE *Engraulis*
163 SALMONIDAE *Cristivomer, Oncorhynchus, Salmo, Salvelinus*
165 COREGONIDAE *Coregonus, Prosopium*
168 ARGENTINIDAE *Argentina*

Order APODES

202 ANGUILLIDAE *Anguilla*
211 CONGRIDAE *Conger*
223 MURAENIDAE *Muraena*

Order HETEROGNATHI

226 CHARACINIDAE *Astyanax, Rooseveltiella*

Order EVENTOGNATHI

236 CATOSTOMIDAE *Catostomus*
237 CYPRINIDAE *Abramis, Carassius, Catla, Cyprinus, Idus, Labeo, Leuciscus, Notemigonus, Ptychocheilus, Rutilis, Scardinius, Tinca*
239 COBITIDAE *Misgurnus*

Order NEMATOGNATHII

247 AMEIURIDAE *Ameiurus, Ictalurus*
255 CLARIIDAE *Clarias*

Order HAPLOMI

288 ESOCIDAE *Esox*

Order CYPRINODONTES

290 CYPRINODONTIDAE *Cynolebias, Cyprinodon, Fundulus, Lebistes, Oryzias*
294 POECILIDAE *Belonesox, Gambusia, Mollienesia*

Order SYNENTOGNATHI

303 SCOMBERESOCIDAE *Cololabis*
305 EXOCOETIDAE *Cypselurus*

Order ANACANTHINI

310 GADIDAE *Boreogadus, Brosme, Gadus, Lota, Molva, Theragra*
311 MERLUCCIIDAE *Merluccius*

Order HETEROSOMATA

326 BOTHIDAE *Solea*
327 PARALICHTHIDAE *Paralichthys*
328 HIPPOGLOSSIDAE *Drepanopsetta, Eopsetta, Hippoglossoides, Hippoglossus*
329 PLEURONECTIDAE *Kareius, Limanda, Microstomus, Parophrys, Platessa,
Platichthys, Pleuronectes*

Order THORACOSTEI

352 GASTEROSTEIDAE *Gasterosteus*

Order LABYRINTHICI

365 OPHICEPHALIDAE *Channa, Ophicephalus (=Ophiocephalus)*

Order PERCOMORPHI

373 ATHERINIDAE *Leuresthes*
374 MUGILIDAE *Mugil*
377 SCOMBRIDAE *Pneumatophorus, Rastrelliger, Scomber, Scomberomorus*
378 THUNNIDAE *Auxis, Euthynnus, Sarda, Thunnus*
383 ISTIOPHORIDAE *Histiophorus, Makaira*
393 STROMATEIDAE *Poronotus*
401 CARANGIDAE *Caranx, Decapterus, Seriola, Trachurus*
404 POMATOMIDAE *Pomatomus*
410 PERCIDAE *Perca, Stizostedion*
418 CENTRARCHIDAE *Eupomotis, Huro, Lepomis, Micropterus, Pomoxis*
423 MORONIDAE *Roccus*
424 OLIGORIDAE *Lateolabrax*
426 EPINEPHELIDAE *Polyprion*
427 SERRANIDAE *Serranus*
449 SPARIDAE *Chrysophrys, Pagrosomus*
451 GIRELLIDAE *Girella*
460 MULLIDAE *Mullus*
461 SCIAENIDAE *Aplodinotus, Micropogon*
467 BRANCHIOSTEGIDAE *Caulolatilus*
471 TRICHODONTIDAE *Trichodon*
487 SCATOPHAGIDAE *Scatophagus*

Order CATAPHRACTI

493 SCORPAENIDAE *Sebastes, Sebastiscus, Sebastodes*
499 ANOPLOPOMIDAE *Anoplopoma*
502 OPHIODONTIDAE *Ophiodon*
508 ICELIDAE *Icelus*
511 COTTIDAE *Cottus, Myoxocephalus*
524 CYCLOPTERIDAE *Cyclopterus*
526 LIPARIDAE *Liparis*

Order HOLCONOTI

530 EMBIOTOCIDAE *Embiotoca*

Order CHROMIDES

534 CICHLIDAE *Etroplus, Tilapia*

Order PHARYNGOGNATHI

536 LABRIDAE *Labrus*
540 SCARIDAE *Scarus*

Order GOBIOIDEA

545 GOBIIDAE *Gillichthys*

Order JUGULARES

555 NOTOTHENIIDAE *Notothenia*
557 CHANNICHTHYIDAE *Chaenocephalus*
589 BLENNIIDAE *Blennius*
601 ANARHICHADIDAE *Anarrhichas (Anarhichas)*
608 ZOARCIDAE *Lycodes, Zoarces*
615 BATRACHOIDIDAE *Opsanus*

Order PLECTOGNATHI

627 MOLIDAE *Masturus*

Order PEDICULATI

628 LOPHIIDAE *Lophius*

The following genera, mentioned in the text, are not classified by Starr Jordan (1963):

Anoptichthys, Astroconger, Caprinus, Chionodraco, Fugu, Katsuwonus, Latimeria, Neogobius, Neothunnus, Parachaenichthys, Parathunnus, Rhigophila, Sardinops, Sprattus, Trematomus.

The reason for this is that the bulk of the material in Starr Jordan was compiled before 1920, so new genera such as the coelacanth, *Latimeria,* had not been discovered, neither probably had the Antarctic genera *Parachaenichthys* and *Trematomus.* New names for known genera, such as *Neothunnus* and *Parathunnus* probably account for the remainder.

COMMON NAMES OF FISH AND THEIR LATIN EQUIVALENTS

Where a name consists of several separate words, these are individually listed, apart from the word 'fish' as in Toad-fish. It has not been easy to decide which words should be separated and which run together, as in dollar fish, dollarfish or dollar-fish. They have therefore been left in the form given in the appropriate reference book, apart from having all but the essential hyphens removed. Common names in languages other than English can be found in the "Multilingual Dictionary of Fish and Fish Products" (1968) 431 pp. Fishing News (Books), London.

AFRICAN LUNGFISH   *Protopterus aethiopicus, Protopterus annectens*
AGUJON   *Tylosurus acus*
AGULHAS SOLE   *Austroglossus pectoralis*
ALASKA GREENFISH   *Hexagrammos octogrammus*
ALBACORE   *Thunnus thynnus thynnus, Thunnus alalunga*
ALBACORE, AUTUMN   *Thunnus albacares*
ALBACORE, LONG-FINNED   *Thunnus alalunga*
ALEKEY TROUT   *Lota lota maculosa*
ALEWIFE   *Alosa pseudoharengus, Pomolobus pseudoharengus*
ALFONCINO   *Beryx splendens*
ALL-MOUTH   *Lophius americanus, Lophius piscatorius*
ALLIGATOR GAR, MISSISSIPPI   *Lepisosteus spatula*
ALLISON'S TUNA   *Thunnus albacares*
AMBER JACK   *Seriola dumerili*
AMERICAN BARRELFISH   *Palinurichthys perciformis*
AMERICAN BROOK LAMPREY   *Lampetra lamottei*
AMERICAN EEL   *Anguilla bostoniensis, Anguilla rostrata*
AMERICAN HAKE   *Merluccius bilinearis*
AMERICAN PERCH   *Perca flavescens*
AMERICAN PLAICE   *Hippoglossoides platessoides*
AMERICAN SHAD   *Alosa sapidissima*
AMERICAN SMELT   *Osmerus mordax*
ANCHOVY   *Engraulis encrasicholus, Engraulis japonicus, Engraulis mordax*
ANCHOVY, COMMERSON'S   *Stolephorus commersonii*
ANCHOVY, LONG-JAWED   *Stolephorus commersonii*
ANCHOVY, NORTHERN   *Engraulis mordax*
ANGEL FISH   *Angelichthys isabelita, Chaetodipterus faber*
ANGEL RAY   *Squatina squatina*
ANGEL SHARK, JAPANESE   *Squatina japonica*
ANGLER   *Lophiomus setigerus, Lophius piscatorius*
ANNUAL FISH   *Cynolebias adloffi*
ARCTIC CHAR   *Salvelinus alpinus*

ARCTIC COD   *Boreogadus saida*
ARCTIC LAMPREY   *Lampetra japonica*
ARCTIC SANDLANCE   *Ammodytes tobianus*
ARCTIC STAGHORN SCULPIN   *Gymnocanthus tricuspis*
ARGENTINE   *Argentina silus*
ARGENTINE, JAPANESE   *Argentina semifasciata*
ARMOUR SHARK   *Dalatias licha*
ARROW-HEADED HAMMERHEAD SHARK   *Zygaena blochii*
ARROWTOOTH FLOUNDER   *Atheresthes stomias*
ASP   *Aspius aspius*
ATKA MACKEREL   *Pleurogrammus asotus*
ATLANTIC BONITO   *Sarda sarda*
ATLANTIC COD   *Gadus morhua*
ATLANTIC HAGFISH   *Myxine glutinosa*
ATLANTIC HALIBUT   *Hippoglossus hippoglossus*
ATLANTIC HERRING   *Clupea harengus*
ATLANTIC LOOKDOWN   *Selene vomer*
ATLANTIC MACKEREL   *Scomber scombrus*
ATLANTIC PRICKLY SKATE   *Raja radiata, Raja scabrata*
ATLANTIC SAURY   *Scomberesox saurus*
ATLANTIC SILVERSIDE   *Menidia menidia notata*
ATLANTIC SPINY DOGFISH   *Squalus acanthias*
ATLANTIC TOMCOD   *Microgadus tomcod*
ATLANTIC TORPEDO   *Tetranarce occidentalis, Torpedo nobiliana*
ATLANTIC WOLF FISH   *Anarhichas lupus*
ATLANTIC WRECKFISH   *Polyprion americanus*
AUTUMN ALBACORE   *Thunnus albacares*

BACHELOR   *Pomoxis annularis*
BAILLON'S WRASSE   *Crenilabrus melops*
BALLAN WRASSE   *Labrus bergylta*
BALLOONFISH   *Sphaeroides maculatus*
BALTIC COD   *Gadus callarias*
BALTIC HERRING   *Clupea harengus membranus*
BANDED CAVALLA   *Caranx sexfasciatus*
BANDED DRUM   *Pogonias cromis*
BANDED ETROPLUS   *Etroplus suratensis*
BANDED KILILFISH   *Fundulus diaphanus*
BANDED REEF-COD   *Epinephelus fasciatus*
BANDED WHIPTAIL STINGRAY   *Dasyatis uarnak*
BANDFISH   *Trichiurus lepturus*
BANG   *Pomolobus pseudoharengus*
BARB, OLIVE   *Barbus chrysopoma*
BAR-EYED GOBY   *Glossogobius giuris*
BARN-DOOR SKATE   *Raja stabuliforis*
BARRACUDA, GREAT   *Sphyraena barracuda*
BARRACUDA, JAPANESE   *Sphyraena japonica*
BARRACUDA, PACIFIC   *Sphyraena argentea*
BARRACUDA, RED   *Sphyraena pinguis*
BARRACUDA, STRIPED   *Sphyraena obtusata*

BARRAMUNDI   *Lates calcarifer*
BARRED SPANISH MACKEREL   *Scomberomorus commersonii*
BARREL FISH   *Palinurichthys perciformis*
BARREL FISH, AMERICAN   *Palinurichthys perciformis*
BASKING SHARK   *Cetorhinus maximus*
BASS   *Micropterus dolomieu, Morone labrax, Sciaenops ocellata*
BASS, BLACK   *Huro salmoides*
BASS, BLACK SEA   *Centropristes striatus*
BASS, BLACK, SMALL-MOUTHED   *Micropterus dolomieu*
BASS, CHANNEL   *Sciaenops ocellata*
BASS HOGFISH   *Micropterus dolomieu*
BASS, KELP   *Paralabrax clathratus*
BASS, LARGEMOUTH   *Micropterus salmoides*
BASS, LITTLE   *Micropterus dolomieu*
BASS, RED   *Sciaenops ocellata*
BASS, SEA   *Sciaenops ocellata*
BASS, SPOTTED   *Sciaenops ocellata*
BASS, STONE   *Polyprion americanus*
BASS, STRIPED   *Roccus saxatilis*
BASS, SUN   *Eupomotis gibbosus*
BASS, TRUE   *Epinephelus septemfasciatus*
BATFISH, RED   *Halieutea stellata*
BATFISH, SPOTTED   *Drepane punctata*
BAY MACKEREL   *Scomberomorus maculatus*
BAY MARE   *Catostomus commersonii*
BELLOWS FISH   *Lophius piscatorius*
BELLY FISH   *Lebistes reticulatus*
BELLY, PUFF   *Hemitripterus americanus*
BELLY, VELVET   *Etmopterus spinax*
BENGAL TONGUE SOLE   *Cynoglossus bengalensis*
BERGALL   *Tautogolabrus adspersus*
BERGYLT   *Labrus bergylta*
BERMUDA SILK SNAPPER   *Lutianus hastingsi*
BIAJAIBA   *Lutianus synagris*
BIG DRUM   *Pogonias cromis*
BIG-EYE SCAD   *Selar crumenophthalmus*
BIG-EYE TUNA   *Thunnus obesus*
BIG-EYED HERRING   *Elops saurus, Pomolobus pseudoharengus*
BIG SKATE   *Raja binoculata, Raja ocellata*
BILLFISH   *Lepisosteus osseus, Scomberesox saurus*
BILLY GAR   *Lepisosteus osseus*
BITTERHEAD   *Notemigonus crysoleucas*
BLACKBACK   *Hippoglossoides platessoides, Pseudopleuronectes americanus*
BLACK BASS   *Huro salmoides*
BLACK BASS, SMALL-MOUTHED   *Micropterus dolomieu*
BLACK BREAM   *Sparus berda, Spondyliosoma cantharus*
BLACK BULLHEAD   *Ameiurus melas melas*
BLACK COD   *Anoplopoma fimbria*
BLACK COW TONGUE   *Rhinoplagusia japonica*
BLACK CRAPPIE   *Pomoxis nigro-maculatus*

BLACK DOGFISH *Centroscyllium fabricii*
BLACK DRUM *Pogonias cromis*
BLACK-FINNED MULLET *Mugil melinopterus*
BLACKFISH *Centropristes striatus, Girella tricuspidata, Tautoga onitis.*
BLACK GROUPER *Garrupa nigrita*
BLACK JEWFISH *Garrupa nigrita*
BLACK MARLIN *Makaira mazara*
BLACK MARLIN, GIANT *Makaira marlina*
BLACK MOLLIE *Mollienesia* sp.
BLACK-MOUTHED DOGFISH *Pristiurus melanostomus*
BLACK MULLET *Catostomus commersonii*
BLACK PERCH *Centropristes striatus, Micropterus dolomieu*
BLACK POMFRET *Parastromateus niger*
BLACK ROCKFISH *Sebastodes melanops*
BLACK RUDDER FISH *Palinurichthys perciformis*
BLACK SCRAPER *Navodon modestus*
BLACK SEA BASS *Centropristes striatus*
BLACK SEA SCAD *Trachurus mediterraneus ponticus*
BLACK SPEARFISH *Makaira mazara*
BLACK-SPOTTED SPANISH MACKEREL *Scomberomorus regalis*
BLACK SURFPERCH *Embiotoca jacksoni*
BLACK-TIPPED SHARK, SMALL *Carcharhinus limbatus*
BLACK TUNA *Promethichthys prometheus*
BLACK WILL *Centropristes striatus*
BLEAK *Alburnus lucidus*
BLEEKER'S LINED SURGEON-FISH *Acanthurus bleekeri*
BLENNY *Enedrias nebulosus*
BLENNY, PEACOCK *Blennius pavo*
BLENNY, RED-SPECKLED *Blennius sanguinolentus*
BLENNY, SNAKE *Ophiodon barbatum*
BLENNY, VIVIPAROUS *Zoarces viviparus*
BLIND CAVE-FISH *Anoptichthys jordani*
BLISTER-BACK *Gadus virens*
BLONDE RAY *Raja brachyura*
BLOWER, MUD *Lota lota maculosa*
BLUEBACK *Oncorhynchus nerka*
BLUE DOG *Prionace glauca*
BLUEFIN *Thunnus thynnus thynnus*
BLUEFIN TUNA *Thunnus thynnus thynnus*
BLUEFIN TUNA, PACIFIC *Thunnus thynnus orientalis*
BLUEFISH *Pomatomus saltatrix*
BLUEFISH, BOSTON *Gadus virens*
BLUEFISH, CALIFORNIA *Girella nigricans*
BLUEGILL *Lepomis macrochirus*
BLUE GROPER *Achoerodus gouldii*
BLUE HALIBUT *Reinhardtius hippoglossoides*
BLUE LING *Molva byrkelange*
BLUE MARLIN *Makaira nigricans*
BLUE MISHIMA PUFFER FISH *Gnathagnus elongatus*
BLUE PERCH *Tautogolabrus adspersus*

BLUE PIKE   *Stizostedion vitreum*
BLUE POINTER   *Isurus glaucus*
BLUE SHARK   *Carcharhinus glaucus, Isurus glaucus, Prionace glauca*
BLUE SHARK, GREAT   *Glyphis glaucus*
BLUE SKATE   *Raja batis*
BLUE SMELT, CALIFORNIA   *Atherinops californiensis*
BLUE STING-RAY   *Trygon violacea*
BLUE-BLACK MULLET   *Mugil curema*
BLUNT-JAWED SEA PIKE   *Sphyraena obtusata*
BOAR GRUNT   *Haemulon plumieri, Haemulon sciurus*
BOB-TAILED SKATE   *Raja eglantaria*
BOCACCIO   *Sebastodes paucispinis*
BOGUE   *Box boops*
BOMBAY DUCK   *Harpodon nehereus*
BONITA   *Katsuwonus pelamis*
BONITO, ATLANTIC   *Sarda sarda*
BONITO, OCEAN   *Katsuwonus pelamis*
BONITO, PLAIN   *Auxis rochei, Auxis thazard*
BONNETNOSE SHARK   *Sphyrna tiburo*
BOSTON BLUE-FISH   *Gadus virens*
BOTTOM PERCH   *Apogon semilineatus*
BOUNCE   *Scylliorhinus stellaris*
BOWFIN   *Amia calva*
BRANCH HERRING   *Pomolobus pseudoharengus*
BREAM   *Abramis brama, Eupomotis gibbosus, Lagodon rhomboides, Lepomis macrochirus, Mylio australis, Notemigonus crysoleucas, Stenotomus versicolor*
BREAM, BLACK   *Sparus berda, Spondyliosoma cantharus*
BREAM, BRIDLED PIG-FACE   *Lethrinus cinereus*
BREAM, BRONZE   *Abramis brama*
BREAM, COUCH'S SEA   *Pagrus pagrus*
BREAM, JAPANESE SILVER   *Chrysophrys datnia*
BREAM, JAPANESE THREADFIN   *Nemipterus japonicus*
BREAM, MARMOR   *Pagellus mormyrus*
BREAM, RED SEA   *Pagellus erythrinus*
BREAM, ROUND-TOOTHED LARGE-EYED   *Monotaxis grandoculis*
BREAM, SEA   *Chrysophrys major*
BREAM, SILVER   *Rhabdosargus sarba, Usacaranx georgianus*
BREAM, STARRY PIG-FACE   *Lethrinus opercularis*
BRIDLED PIG-FACE BREAM   *Lethrinus cinereus*
BRIER RAY   *Raja eglantaria*
BRILL   *Eopsetta jordani*
BROADBILL SWORDFISH   *Xiphias gladius*
BROAD HARBOUR SHARK   *Deania eglantina*
BROAD HEADED CATFISH   *Anarhichas latifrons*
BRONZE BREAM   *Abramis brama*
BROOK LAMPREY   *Lampetra planeri*
BROOK LAMPREY, AMERICAN   *Lampetra lamottei*
BROOK SUCKER   *Catostomus commersonii*
BROOK TROUT, EASTERN   *Salvelinus fontinalis*
BROWN BULLHEAD   *Ictalurus nebulosus*

BROWN MEAGRE   *Corvina nigra*
BROWN SHARK   *Carcharhinus milbertei*
BROWN TROUT   *Salmo trutta*
BUBBLE NEST BUILDER   *Trichogaster pectoralis*
BUBBLER   *Aplodinotus grunniens*
BUILDER, BUBBLE NEST   *Trichogaster pectoralis*
BULLHEAD   *Cottus gobio, Myoxocephalus scorpius*
BULLHEAD, BLACK   *Ameiurus melas melas*
BULLHEAD, BROWN   *Ictalurus nebulosus*
BULLHEAD, COMMON   *Ameiurus nebulosus*
BULL HUSS   *Scylliorhinus stellaris*
BULL SHARK   *Carcharhinus leucas*
BURBOT   *Lota lota, Lota lota maculosa*
BURNETT SALMON   *Neoceratodus forsteri*
BUTTER CATFISH   *Callichrous bimaculatus*
BUTTERFISH   *Cephalopholis fulvus, Poronotus triacanthus, Sciaena antarctica, Trachinotus carolinus*
BUTTER SOLE   *Isopsetta isolepis*

CABELELLEROTE   *Lutianus griseus*
CABEZON   *Scorpaenichthys marmoratus*
CABRILLA   *Epinephelus guttatus*
CALIFORNIA BLUEFISH   *Girella nigricans*
CALIFORNIA BLUE SMELT   *Atherinopsis californiensis*
CALIFORNIA KILLIFISH   *Fundulus parvipinnis*
CALIFORNIA JEWFISH   *Stereolepis gigas*
CALIFORNIA SARDINE   *Sardinops caerula*
CANADIAN PLAICE   *Hippoglossoides platessoides*
CANARY ROCKFISH   *Sebastodes pinniger*
CANDLEFISH   *Thaleichthys pacificus*
CANOPY SHARK   *Squatina japonica*
CAPE MAY GOODY   *Leiostomus xanthurus*
CAPITAINE   *Lachnolaimus maximus*
CAROLINA POMPANO   *Trachinotus carolinus*
CARP   *Cirrhina mrigala, Cyprinus carpio*
CARP BREAM   *Abramis brama*
CARP, CRUCIAN   *Carassius carassius*
CARP, INDIAN   *Catla catla*
CARP, JOHNNY   *Carassius auratus*
CARP, SKIN   *Hemibarbus barbus*
CATFISH   *Anarhichas lupus, Arius serratus, Parasilurus asotus, Silurus glanis*
CATFISH, BROAD HEADED   *Anarhichas latifrons*
CATFISH, BUTTER   *Callichrous bimaculatus*
CATFISH, CHANNEL   *Ictalurus punctatus*
CATFISH, DUSKY   *Arius sona*
CATFISH, DWARF   *Macrones cavasius*
CATFISH, DWARF, STRIPED   *Macrones vittatus*
CATFISH EEL, STRIPED   *Plotosus anguillaris*
CATFISH, FRESHWATER   *Clarias batrachus*

CATFISH, LESSER *Anarhichas minor*
CATFISH, MANILA SEA *Arius manillensis*
CATFISH, SAW-EDGED *Arius serratus*
CATFISH, SEA *Bagre morina, Plotosus anguillaris*
CATFISH, SMALL *Ameiurus melas melas, Ameiurus nebulosus*
CATFISH, SPOTTED *Anarhichas minor*
CATFISH, STINGING *Heteropneustes fossilis*
CATFISH, TEYSMANN'S SPOTTED *Clarias batrachus*
CAT, SEA *Galeichthys felis*
CAT SHARK *Heterodontus japonicus, Triakis semifasciatum*
CAT, WHITE *Ictalurus punctatus*
CAVALLA, BANDED *Caranx sexfasciatus*
CAVE FISH, BLIND *Anoptichthys jordani*
CERO, SPOTTED *Scomberomorus regalis*
CHAIN-SIDED PERCH *Lepomis macrochirus*
CHANNEL BASS *Sciaenops ocellata*
CHANNEL CATFISH *Ictalurus punctatus*
CHAR *Salvelinus willughbii*
CHAR, ARCTIC *Salvelinus alpinus*
CHAR, SPECKLED *Salvelinus fontinalis*
CHAR, WINDERMERE *Salvelinus willughbii*
CHARACIN, MEXICAN CAVE *Anoptichthys jordani*
CHICKWICK *Cynoscion regalis*
CHILI-PEPPER *Sebastodes goodei*
CHIMAERA, DEEPWATER *Hydrolagus affinis*
CHINESE HERRING *Hilsa toli*
CHINOOK SALMON *Oncorhynchus tschawytscha*
CHOICE, SAILORS' *Lagodon rhomboides*
CHUB *Notemigonus crysoleucas, Squalius cephalus*
CHUB, CREEK *Semotilus atromaculatus*
CHUB MACKEREL *Pneumatophorus colias, Scomber colias*
CHUB, MUD *Semotilus atromaculatus*
CHUB, SEA *Ditrema temmincki*
CHUB, SILVER *Semotilus atromaculatus*
CHUM SALMON *Oncorhynchus keta*
CIGARFISH *Decapterus punctatus*
CISCO *Leucichthys artedi*
CISCO, SHALLOW WATER *Leucichthys artedi*
CLEAR-NOSED SKATE *Raja eglantaria*
CLEAR RAY *Raja diaphenes*
CLIFF FLATHEAD *Trudis bassensis westraliae*
CLIMBING PERCH *Anabas scandens*
COALFISH *Anoplopoma fimbria, Gadus virens*
COALIE *Gadus virens*
COASTAL CUTTHROAT TROUT *Salmo clarkii*
COASTER *Salvelinus fontinalis*
COBBLERFISH *Trachinotus carolinus*
COCK-UP *Lates calcarifer*
COD, ARCTIC *Boreogadus saida*
COD, ATLANTIC *Gadus morhua*

COD, BALTIC   *Gadus callarias*
COD, BANDED REEF-   *Epinephelus fasciatus*
COD, CULTUS   *Ophiodon elongatus*
COD, FJORD   *Gadus ogac*
COD, GREENLAND   *Gadus ogac*
COD, PACIFIC   *Gadus macrocephalus*
COD, POLAR   *Boreogadus saida*
COD, RED   *Sebastodes ruberrimus*
COD, ROCK   *Epinephelus fario*
COD, TROUT REEF-   *Epinephelus fario*
COD, WACHNA   *Gadus nevaga*
CODLING   *Urophycis tenuis* (also used of the immature form of *Gadus morhua*)
COELACANTH   *Latimeria chalumnae*
COHO SALMON   *Oncorhynchus kisutch*
COMBER, PAINTED   *Serranus scriba*
COMMERSON'S ANCHOVY   *Stolephorus commersonii*
COMMON BULLHEAD   *Ameiurus nebulosus*
COMMON CARP   *Cyprinus carpio*
COMMON EEL   *Anguilla anguilla*
COMMON GAR PIKE   *Lepisosteus osseus*
COMMON GRUNT   *Haemulon plumieri*
COMMON GURNARD   *Prionotus carolinus*
COMMON JAPANESE CONGER   *Astroconger myriaster*
COMMON MINNOW   *Zacco platypus*
COMMON PAMPANO   *Trachinotus carolinus*
COMMON RASBORA   *Rasbora daniconius*
COMMON SCUP   *Stenotomus versicolor*
COMMON SEAROBIN   *Prionotus carolinus*
COMMON SHAD   *Alosa sapidissima*
COMMON SKATE   *Raja inornata*
COMMON SLIPMOUTH   *Leiognathus equulus*
COMMON SUCKER   *Catostomus commersonii*
COMMON SUNFISH   *Eupomotis gibbosus*
COMMON SURGEON   *Acanthurus hepatus*
CONGER, COMMON JAPANESE   *Astroconger myriaster*
CONGER EEL   *Conger conger*
CONGER EEL, SILVER   *Muraenesox cinereus*
CONGER, SILVERY   *Anago anago*
COOKTOWN SALMON   *Eleutheronema tetradactylum*
COPPER ROCKFISH   *Sebastodes caurinus*
CORKWING   *Crenilabrus melops*
CORVINA   *Micropogon undulatus*
COUCH'S SEA BREAM   *Pagrus pagrus*
COUCH'S WHITING   *Gadus poutassou*
CRAMPFISH   *Tetranarce occidentalis*
CRAPPIE   *Pomoxis annularis*
CRAPPIE, BLACK   *Pomoxis nigro-maculatus*
CRAPPIE, TIMBER   *Pomoxis annularis*
CRAPPIE, WHITE   *Pomoxis annularis*
CREEK CHUB   *Semotilus atromaculatus*

CRESCENT PERCH *Therapon jarbua*
CREVALLE JACK *Caranx sexfasciatus*
CROAKER *Aplodinotus grunniens, Micropogon undulatus*
CROCODILE FISH, WHITE *Chaenocephalus aceratus*
CROSS-STAFF SHARK *Sphyrna zygaena*
CRUCIAN CARP *Carassius carassius*
CUB SHARK *Carcharhinus leucas*
CUCKOO RAY *Raja naevus*
CULTUS COD *Ophiodon elongatus*
CUNNER *Tautogolabrus adspersus*
CUSK *Brosme brosme*
CUTLASS FISH *Trichiurus lepturus*
CUTTHROAT EEL, GRAY'S *Synaphobranchus kaupi*
CUTTHROAT TROUT, COASTAL *Salmo clarkii*
CYBIUM, SPOTTED *Scomberomorus maculatus*

DAB *Limander limander*
DAB, LONG ROUGH *Hippoglossoides platessoides*
DAB, MUD *Pleuronectes limanda*
DAB, RUSTY *Limander ferruginea*
DAB, SAND *Hippoglossoides platessoides*
DAB, SMEAR *Pleuronectes microcephalus*
DACE *Leuciscus leuciscus, Notemigonus crysoleucas*
DACE, HORNED *Semotilus atromaculatus*
DADDY SCULPIN *Myoxocephalus scorpius*
DALATIAS *Dalatias licha*
DANIO, GIANT *Danio aequipinnatus*
DARKIE *Girella tricuspidata*
DEEPWATER CHIMAERA *Hydrolagus affinis*
DIAMOND-SCALE MULLET *Mugil vaigiensis*
DOCTOR FISH *Acanthurus hepatus*
DOG, BLUE *Prionace glauca*
DOGFISH, ATLANTIC SPINY *Squalus acanthias*
DOGFISH, BLACK *Centroscyllium fabricii*
DOGFISH, BLACK-MOUTHED *Pristiurus melanostomus*
DOGFISH, GREATER SPOTTED *Scylliorhinus stellaris*
DOGFISH, LARGE SPOTTED *Scyllium stellare*
DOGFISH, LESSER SPOTTED *Mustelus canis*
DOGFISH, PACIFIC SPINY *Squalus acanthias*
DOGFISH, PIKED *Squalus acanthias*
DOGFISH, SMALL SPOTTED *Scyllium canicula*
DOGFISH, SPINED *Squalus acanthias*
DOGFISH, SMOOTH *Mustelus canis*
DOG SALMON *Oncorhynchus keta*
DOG SHARK *Mustelus griseus*
DOG SHARK, YELLOW *Scoliodon sorrakowah*
DOG, SPUR *Squalus acanthias*
DOLLARFISH *Poronotus triacanthus*
DOLPHIN *Coryphaena hippurus*
DORAB *Chirocentrus dorab*

DORADO   *Coryphaena hippurus*
DORY   *Stizostedion vitreum*
DORY, JOHN   *Zeus australis, Zeus faber*
DOTTED SCAD   *Decapterus punctatus*
DOVER SOLE   *Microstomus pacificus*
DRAGONET   *Callionymus lyra*
DRUM, BANDED   *Pogonias cromis*
DRUM, BIG   *Pogonias cromis*
DRUM, BLACK   *Pogonias cromis*
DRUMFISH   *Pogonias cromis*
DRUM, FRESHWATER   *Aplodinotus grunniens*
DRUM, GREY   *Pogonias cromis*
DRUM, RED   *Sciaenops ocellata*
DUCK, BOMBAY   *Harpodon nehereus*
DUSKY CATFISH   *Arius sona*
DUSKY PERCH   *Epinephelus gigas*
DUSKY SHARK   *Carcharhinus obscurus*
DUSSUMIER'S MULLET   *Mugil dussumierii*
DUSSUMIER'S SILVER JEWFISH   *Sciaena dussumierii*
DWARF CATFISH   *Macrones cavasius*
DWARF CATFISH, STRIPED   *Macrones vittatus*

EAGLE RAY   *Myliobatis aquila*
EASTERN BROOK TROUT   *Salvelinus fontinalis*
EASTERN PICKEREL   *Esox niger*
EEL, AMERICAN   *Anguilla bostoniensis, Anguilla rostrata*
EEL, COMMON   *Anguilla anguilla*
EEL, CONGER   *Conger conger*
EEL, GRAY'S CUTTHROAT   *Synaphobranchus kaupi*
EEL, JAPANESE   *Anguilla japonica*
EEL, LAMPER   *Petromyzon marinus*
EEL, LONGNOSE   *Synaphobranchus kaupi*
EEL, MORAY   *Muraena helena*
EEL, SILVER   *Anguilla rostrata*
EEL, SILVER CONGER   *Muraenesox cinereus*
EEL, SLIME   *Simenchelys parasiticus*
EEL, SNUBNOSE   *Simenchelys parasiticus*
EEL, SPINY   *Mastacembelus armatus, Notacanthus nasus*
EEL, STRIPED CATFISH   *Plotosus anguillaris*
EEL-POUT   *Lota lota, Lota lota maculosa, Macrozoarces americanus, Zoarces viviparus*
EGRET PIPER   *Macrorhamphosus sagifue*
EIGHT-EYES LAMPREY, RIVER   *Entosphenus japonicus*
ELECTRIC FISH   *Tetranarce occidentalis*
ELECTRIC RAY   *Narke japonica, Torpedo nobiliana*
ELECTRIC RAY, MARBLED   *Torpedo marmorata*
ELF SCULPIN   *Ceratocottus namiyei*
ELLECK   *Trigla cuculus*
ELLIOT'S GREY SHARK   *Carcharias ellioti*
EMERYWHEEL   *Platichthys stellatus*

C.B.F.

ENGLISH SOLE   *Parophrys vetulus*
ESCOLAR   *Lepidocybium flavobrunneum*
ETROPLUS, BANDED   *Etroplus suratensis*
ETROPLUS, SPOTTED   *Etroplus maculatus*
EUCHALON   *Thaleichthys pacificus*
EUROPEAN SMELT   *Osmerus eperlanus*
EYED SKATE   *Raja ocellata*

FAIR MAID   *Stenotomus versicolor*
FATBACK   *Pomatomus saltatrix*
FATHER LASHER   *Myoxocephalus scorpius*
FIDDLER   *Ictalurus punctatus*
FILE FISH   *Balistes capriscus, Navodon modestus, Stephanolepsis cirrhifer*
FIN SHARK   *Centrophorus atromarginatus*
FISHING FROG   *Lophius piscatorius*
FJORD COD   *Gadus ogac*
FLAPPER SKATE   *Raja batis*
FLAT BACK   *Raja kenoji*
FLATHEAD, CLIFF   *Trudis bassensis westraliae*
FLATHEAD FLOUNDER   *Hippoglossoides dubius*
FLATHEAD GOBY   *Glossogobius giuris*
FLATHEAD, INDIAN   *Platycephalus indicus*
FLATHEAD SOLE   *Hippoglossoides elassodon*
FLATHEAD, TIGER   *Neoplatycephalus richardsoni*
FLOUNDER   *Hippoglossoides platessoides, Platichthys flesus, Tanakius kitaharae*
FLOUNDER, ARROWTOOTH   *Atheresthes stomias*
FLOUNDER, FLATHEAD   *Hippoglossoides dubius*
FLOUNDER, GEORGE'S BANK   *Pseudopleuronectes americanus*
FLOUNDER, JAPANESE   *Paralichthys olivaceus*
FLOUNDER, LEOPARD   *Platophrys pantherinus*
FLOUNDER, LONG-JAW   *Atheresthes stomias*
FLOUNDER, POLE   *Glyptocephalus cynoglossus*
FLOUNDER, SAND   *Psettichthys melanostictus*
FLOUNDER, SCALYFIN   *Isopsetta isolepis*
FLOUNDER, SOUTHERN   *Paralichthys lethostigmus*
FLOUNDER, SPOTTED   *Eucitharus linguatula*
FLOUNDER, STARRY   *Platichthys stellatus*
FLOUNDER, STONE   *Kareius bicoloratus*
FLOUNDER, WINTER   *Pseudopleuronectes americanus*
FLOUNDER, WITCH   *Glyptocephalus cynoglossus*
FLOUNDER, YELLOWTAIL   *Limander ferruginea*
FLUKE, SAIL-   *Lepidorhombus whiffiagonis*
FLUTE-MOUTH   *Fistularia petimba*
FLUTE PORGY   *Lutianus rivulatus*
FLYING FISH   *Prognichthys agoo*
FORKBEARD   *Urophycis chuss*
FORKED-BEARD HAKE   *Urophycis blennoides*
FOX SHARK   *Alopias pelagicus*
FRENCH GRUNT   *Haemulon flavolineatum*
FRESHWATER CATFISH   *Clarias batrachus*

FRESHWATER DRUM   *Aplodinotus grunniens*
FRESHWATER SHARK   *Wallago attu*
FRIGATE MACKEREL   *Auxis rochei, Auxis tapeinosoma, Auxis thazard*
FRINGE-SCALE SARDINE   *Sardinella fimbriata*
FROG, FISHING   *Lophius piscatorius*
FROSTFISH   *Microgadus tomcod*
FULLER'S RAY   *Raja fullonica*
FUSILIER, GOLDEN-BANDED   *Caesio chrysozona*

GAFFTOPSAIL   *Bagre morina*
GAR, BILLY   *Lepisosteus osseus*
GARFISH   *Belone belone*
GAR, LONG-NOSED   *Lepisosteus osseus*
GAR, MISSISSIPPI ALLIGATOR   *Lepisosteus spatula*
GAR, OHIO   *Lepisosteus osseus*
GARPIKE   *Belone belone*
GAR PIKE, COMMON   *Lepisosteus osseus*
GARRUPA   *Epinephelus fario*
GELATINOUS SEASNAIL   *Liparis koefoedi*
GENUINE GOBY   *Acanthogobius flavimanus*
GENUINE PORGY   *Chrysophrys major*
GEORGE'S BANK FLOUNDER   *Pseudopleuronectes americanus*
GHOST SHARK   *Chimaera phantasma*
GIANT BLACK MARLIN   *Makaira marlina*
GIANT DANIO   *Danio aequipinnatus*
GIANT HERRING   *Elops saurus*
GIANT MARBLED SCULPIN   *Scorpaenichthys marmoratus*
GIANT PERCH   *Lates calcarifer*
GIANT SEA PIKE   *Sphyraena jello*
GIANT SNAKE-HEAD   *Ophicephalus marulius*
GIANT THREADFIN   *Eleutheronema tetradactylum*
GIBEL   *Carassius auratus gibelio*
GIBELLIAN   *Carassius auratus gibelio*
GILDED SUNFISH   *Lepomis macrochirus*
GILT HEAD   *Crenilabrus melops*
GIZZARD SHAD   *Anodontostoma chacunda, Dorosoma cepedianum*
GLASS-EYE   *Stizostedion vitreum*
GLUT HERRING   *Alosa pseudoharengus*
GOATFISH   *Upeneoides bensasi*
GOATFISH, GOLDEN-BANDED   *Mulloides flavolineatus*
GOATFISH, YELLOW   *Upeneoides sulphureus*
GOBY   *Neogobius melanostomus*
GOBY, BAR-EYED   *Glossogobius giuris*
GOBY, FLATHEAD   *Glossogobius giuris*
GOBY, GENUINE   *Acanthogobius flavimanus*
GOBY, GREEN-SPOTTED   *Acentrogobius viridipunctatus*
GOBY, LONG-JAWED   *Gillichthys mirabilis*
GOBY, POINTED-TAILED   *Apocryptes lanceolatus*
GOBY, SMALL-SCALED   *Oxyurichthys microlepis*
GOGGLE-EYE JACK   *Selar crumenophthalmus*

GOLDFISH *Carassius auratus*
GOLD PERCH *Lepomis macrochirus*
GOLD-SPOT MULLET *Mugil parsia*
GOLDEN-BAND FUSILIER *Caesio chrysozona*
GOLDEN-BANDED GOAT FISH *Mulloides flavolineatus*
GOLDEN-GREY MULLET *Mugil auratus*
GOLDEN SCAD *Caranx kalla*
GOLDEN SHINER *Notemigonus crysoleucas boscii*
GOLDEN-STRIPED PONY FISH *Leiognathus daura*
GOOD SALMON *Sphyraena pinguis*
GOODY *Leiostomus xanthurus*
GOODY, CAPE MAY *Leiostomus xanthurus*
GOOSEFISH *Lophius americanus, Lophius piscatorius*
GORAMY, SIAMESE *Trichogaster pectoralis*
GOURAMI, KISSING *Helostoma temmincki*
GRASS PUFFER *Fugu niphobles*
GRAYFISH *Squalus acanthias*
GRAYLING *Thymallus thymallus*
GRAY'S CUTTHROAT EEL *Synaphobranchus kaupi*
GREAT BARRACUDA *Sphyraena barracuda*
GREAT BLUE SHARK *Glyphis glaucus*
GREAT LAKES TROUT *Cristivomer namaycush*
GREATER LIZARD FISH *Saurida tumbil*
GREATER PONY FISH *Leiognathus equulus*
GREATER SPOTTED DOGFISH *Scylliorhinus stellaris*
GREATER WEEVER *Trachinus draco*
GREENFISH *Girella nigricans, Pomatomus saltatrix*
GREENFISH, ALASKA *Hexagrammos octogrammus*
GREENLAND COD *Gadus ogac*
GREENLAND HALIBUT *Reinhardtius hippoglossoides*
GREENLAND SCULPIN *Myoxocephalus scorpius*
GREENLAND SHARK *Somniosus microcephalus*
GREENLING, WHITE SPOTTED *Hexagrammos stelleri*
GREEN PARROTFISH *Pseudoscarus guacamaia*
GREEN PIKE *Esox niger*
GREEN SNAKE-HEAD *Ophicephalus punctatus*
GREEN-SPOTTED GOBY *Acentrogobius viridipunctatus*
GREENSTRIPED ROCKFISH *Sebastodes elongatus*
GREEN WRASSE *Labrus turdus*
GRENADIER, ROCK *Coryphaenoides rupestris*
GREYBACK *Leucichthys artedi*
GREY DRUM *Pogonias cromis*
GREY GURNARD *Trigla gurnardus*
GREY MULLET *Mugil speigleri*
GREY MULLET, THICK LIPPED *Mugil chelo*
GREY NURSE *Carcharias arenarius*
GREY POMFRET *Stromateus cinereus*
GREY SHARK, ELLIOT'S *Carcharias ellioti*
GREY SKATE *Raja batis*
GREY SNAPPER *Lutianus griseus*

GREY SOLE *Glyptocephalus cynoglossus*
GREY TRIGGER FISH *Balistes capriscus*
GRINDSTONE *Platichthys stellatus*
GROPER, BLUE *Achoerodus gouldii*
GROUND SHARK *Carcharhinus gangeticus, Carcharhinus leucas, Somniosus micro-
  cephalus*
GROUPER *Epinephelus corallicola*
GROUPER, BLACK *Garrupa nigrita*
GROUPER, NASSAU *Epinephelus striatus*
GROUPER, RED *Epinephelus morio*
GROUPER, YELLOW-FINNED *Trisotropis venenosus*
GRUNION *Leuresthes tenuis*
GRUNT, BOAR *Haemulon plumieri, Haemulon sciurus*
GRUNT, COMMON *Haemulon plumieri*
GRUNT, FRENCH *Haemulon flavolineatum*
GRUNT, HUMPBACK *Haemulon sciurus*
GRUNT, OPEN-MOUTHED *Haemulon flavolineatum*
GRUNT, YELLOW *Haemulon flavolineatum, Haemulon sciurus*
GRUNTER, LARGE-SCALED BANDED *Therapon theraps*
GRUNTER, OLIVE *Pristipoma olivaceum*
GUDGEON *Gobio gobio, Notemigonus crysoleucas*
GULF KINGFISH *Menticirrhus littoralis*
GULF MENHADEN *Brevoortia patronus*
GUMMY SHARK *Mustelus manazo*
GUPPY *Lebistes reticulatus*
GURNARD *Chelidonichthys kumu*
GURNARD, COMMON *Prionotus carolinus*
GURNARD, GREY *Trigla gurnardus*
GURNARD, RED *Trigla cuculus*
GURNARD, RIVER *Platycephalus indicus*
GURNARD, SAND *Platycephalus indicus*
GURNARD, YELLOW *Trigla lucerna*
GURNET *Hemitripterus americanus*
GURRY SHARK *Somniosus microcephalus*
GWYNIAD *Coregonus clupeoides*

HAADER *Mugil cephalus*
HADDOCK *Gadus (Melanogrammus) aeglefinus*
HADDOCK, NORWAY *Sebastes marinus*
HAGFISH *Eptatretus stoutii, Myxine glutinosa*
HAGFISH, ATLANTIC *Myxine glutinosa*
HAGFISH, NORTHERN *Myxine glutinosa*
HAGFISH, PACIFIC *Polistotrema stoutii*
HAIR-TAIL *Trichiurus haumela, Trichiurus lepturus*
HAKE *Merluccius merluccius, Urophycis tenuis*
HAKE, AMERICAN *Merluccius bilinearis*
HAKE, FORKED-BEARD *Urophycis blennoides*
HAKE, LONGFIN *Urophycis chesteri*
HAKE, MUD *Urophycis chuss*
HAKE, NEW ENGLAND *Merluccius bilinearis*
HAKE, OLD ENGLAND *Merluccius bilinearis*

HAKE, OLD ENGLISH   *Urophycis tenuis*
HAKE, PACIFIC   *Merluccius productus*
HAKE, RED   *Urophycis chuss*
HAKE, SILVER   *Merluccius bilinearis*
HAKE, SQUIRREL   *Urophycis chuss, Urophycis tenuis*
HAKE, WHITE   *Urophycis chuss, Urophycis tenuis*
HALF BEAK FISH   *Hemirhamphus sajori*
HALF-BEAK, LONG-BILLED   *Hemirhamphus georgii*
HALF-MOUTHED SARDINE   *Engraulis japonicus*
HALIBUT, ATLANTIC   *Hippoglossus hippoglossus*
HALIBUT, BLUE   *Reinhardtius hippoglossoides*
HALIBUT, GREENLAND   *Reinhardtius hippoglossoides*
HALIBUT, INDIAN   *Psettodes erumei*
HALIBUT, LITTLE   *Reinhardtius hippoglossoides*
HALIBUT, PACIFIC   *Hippoglossus stenolepis*
HALIBUT, RED   *Hippoglossoides dubius*
HALIBUT, SHOTTED   *Eopsetta grigorjewi*
HAM   *Epinephelus striatus*
HAMLET   *Epinephelus striatus*
HAMMERHEAD SHARK   *Sphyrna zygaena*
HAMMERHEAD SHARK, ARROW-HEADED   *Zygaena blochii*
HAMMERHEAD, SMOOTH   *Sphyrna zygaena*
HARBOUR SHARK, BROAD   *Deania eglantina*
HARDHEAD   *Micropogon undulatus*
HARLEQUIN ROACH   *Eupomotis gibbosus*
HARVEST FISH   *Poronotus triacanthus, Stromateus cinereus*
HATA, RED   *Epinephelus fasciatus*
HEADFISH   *Mola mola*
HEAD, GILT   *Crenilabrus melops*
HEADLIGHT FISH   *Diaphus coeruleus*
HENFISH   *Cyclopterus lumpus*
HERRING, ATLANTIC   *Clupea harengus*
HERRING, BALTIC   *Clupea harengus membranus*
HERRING, BIG-EYED   *Elops saurus, Pomolobus pseudoharengus*
HERRING, BRANCH   *Pomolobus pseudoharengus*
HERRING, CHINESE   *Hilsa toli*
HERRING, GIANT   *Elops saurus*
HERRING, GLUT   *Alosa pseudoharengus*
HERRING, LAKE   *Leucichthys artedi*
HERRING, OX-EYE   *Megalops cyprinoides*
HERRING, PACIFIC   *Clupea pallasii*
HERRING, SALMON   *Chanos chanos*
HERRING, SEA   *Arripis georgianus*
HERRING SMELT   *Argentina silus*
HERRING, WALL-EYED   *Pomolobus pseudoharengus*
HERRING, WOLF   *Chirocentrus dorab*
HICKORY SHAD   *Dorosoma cepedianum*
HIGH-EYES   *Oryzias latipes*
HILGENDORF SAUCORD   *Helicolenus hilgendorfi*
HILSA   *Hilsa ilisha*

HIND, RED   *Epinephelus guttatus*
HOGFISH   *Lachnolaimus maximus*
HOGFISH, BASS   *Micropterus dolomieu*
HOMELYN RAY   *Raja montagui*
HORNED DACE   *Semotilus atromaculatus*
HORNED POUT   *Ameiurus nebulosus*
HORSEHEAD   *Selene vomer*
HORSE MACKEREL   *Thunnus thynnus thynnus, Trachurus trachurus*
HORSE MACKEREL, JAPANESE   *Trachurus japonicus*
HOUNDFISH   *Tylosurus acus*
HOUND, SMOOTH   *Mustelus mustelus*
HOUTING   *Coregonus lavaretus*
HUDSON BAY SALMON   *Salvelinus alpinus*
HUMPBACK GRUNT   *Haemulon sciurus*
HUSS   *Scylliorhinus stellaris*

ICEFISH   *Chaenocephalus aceratus*
IDE   *Idus idus*
INCENSE BURNER   *Triakis scyllia*
INDIAN CARP   *Catla catla*
INDIAN FLATHEAD   *Platycephalus indicus*
INDIAN HALIBUT   *Psettodes erumei*
INDIAN LITTLE FISH   *Apogon semilineatus*
INDIAN SARDINE   *Sardinella longiceps*
INDIAN TASSEL FISH   *Polynemus indicus*
INDIAN TURBOT   *Psettodes erumei*

JACK   *Esox niger*
JACK, CREVALLE   *Caranx sexfasciatus*
JACK, GOGGLE-EYE   *Selar crumenophthalmus*
JACK, HORSE-EYE   *Caranx sexfasciatus*
JACK MACKEREL   *Trachurus japonicus*
JACK SALMON   *Stizostedion vitreum*
JACK, STRIPED   *Caranx delicatissimus*
JACKET, LEATHER   *Chroinemeus tolooparah, Tilapia mossambica*
JACOPEVER   *Sebastichthys capensis*
JAPANESE ANGEL SHARK   *Squatina japonica*
JAPANESE ARGENTINE   *Argentina semifasciata*
JAPANESE BARRACUDA   *Sphyraena japonica*
JAPANESE CONGER, COMMON   *Astroconger myriaster*
JAPANESE EEL   *Anguilla japonica*
JAPANESE FLOUNDER   *Paralichthys olivaceus*
JAPANESE HORSE MACKEREL   *Trachurus japonicus*
JAPANESE MACKEREL   *Scomber japonicus*
JAPANESE MONKFISH   *Squatina japonica*
JAPANESE NEEDLEFISH   *Hemirhamphus sajori*
JAPANESE PARROTFISH   *Leptoscarus japonicus, Oplegnathus fasciatus*
JAPANESE SALMON DE ALTO   *Polymixia japonica*
JAPANESE SILVER BREAM   *Chrysophrys datnia*
JAPANESE STARGAZER   *Uranoscopus japonicus*

JAPANESE STINGFISH   *Sebastodes inermis*
JAPANESE STING RAY   *Dasyatis akajei*
JAPANESE THREADFIN BREAM   *Nemipterus japonicus*
JENNY, SILVER   *Eucinostomus gula*
JEWFISH   *Sciaena antarctica*
JEWFISH, CALIFORNIA   *Stereolepis gigas*
JEWFISH, BLACK   *Garrupa nigrita*
JEWFISH, DUSSUMIER'S SILVER   *Sciaena dussumieri*
JEWFISH, ROSY   *Otolithus ruber*
JEWFISH, TWO-SPINED   *Sciaena diacanthus*
JEW, SILVER   *Sciaena antarctica*
JOHN DORY   *Zeus australis, Zeus faber*
JOHN MARIGGLE   *Elops saurus*
JOHNNY CARP   *Carassius auratus*
JUREL   *Caranx sexfasciatus*

KAMLOOPS TROUT   *Salmo gairdnerii kamloops*
KELP BASS   *Paralabrax clathratus*
KICKANINNY   *Oncorhynchus nerka kennerlyi*
KILLIFISH   *Fundulus heteroclitus*
KILLIFISH, BANDED   *Fundulus diaphanus*
KILLIFISH, CALIFORNIA   *Fundulus parvipinnis*
KINGFISH   *Caranx equula, Sciaena antarctica, Scomberomorus regalis*
KINGFISH, GULF   *Menticirrhus littoralis*
KINGFISH, RIVER   *Sciaena antarctica*
KING GEORGE WHITING   *Sillaginodes punctatus*
KINGKLIP   *Genypterus capensis*
KING MACKEREL   *Scomberomorus cavalla*
KING SALMON   *Oncorhynchus tschawytscha*
KING WHITING   *Menticirrhus littoralis*
KISSING GOURAMI   *Helostoma temmincki*
KIVER   *Eupomotis gibbosus*
KOKANEE   *Oncorhynchus nerka kennerlyi*

LABEO, ORANGE-FIN   *Labeo calbasu*
LAFAYETTE   *Leiostomus xanthurus*
LAKE HERRING   *Leucichthys artedi*
LAKE LAWYER   *Lota lota maculosa*
LAKE PERCH   *Perca flavescens*
LAKE TROUT   *Salvelinus namaycush namaycush*
LAKE WHITEFISH   *Coregonus clupeaformis*
LAMPER EEL   *Petromyzon marinus*
LAMPREY   *Petromyzon fluviatilis*
LAMPREY, AMERICAN BROOK   *Lampetra lamottei*
LAMPREY, ARCTIC   *Lampetra japonica*
LAMPREY, BROOK   *Lampetra planeri*
LAMPREY, PACIFIC   *Entosphenus tridentatus*
LAMPREY, PLANER'S   *Lampetra planeri*
LAMPREY, RIVER EIGHT-EYES   *Entosphenus japonicus*
LAMPREY, SEA   *Petromyzon marinus*

LAMPREY, SILVER   *Ichthyomyzon unicuspis*
LANCET FISH   *Acanthurus hepatus*
LANE SNAPPER   *Lutianus synagris*
LARGE-EYED BREAM, ROUND-TOOTHED   *Monotaxis grandoculis*
LARGE-HEADED RIBBONFISH   *Trichiurus haumela*
LARGEMOUTH BASS   *Micropterus salmoides*
LARGE-SCALED BANDED GRUNTER   *Therapon theraps*
LARGE-SCALED SCORPION FISH   *Scorpaena scrofa*
LARGE-SCALED SUCKER   *Moxostoma aureolum*
LARGE-SCALE TAPIRFISH   *Notacanthus nasus*
LARGE SPOTTED DOGFISH   *Scyllium stellare*
LASHER, FATHER   *Myoxocephalus scorpius*
LATERN SHARK   *Etmopterus spinax*
LAWYER   *Amia calva, Lutianus griseus*
LAWYER, LAKE   *Lota lota maculosa*
LEATHERCOAT   *Oligoplites saurus*
LEATHER JACKET   *Chroinemeus tolooparah, Oligoplites saurus, Tilipa mossambica*
LEMON SOLE   *Parophrys vetulus, Pleuronectes microcephalus*
LEOPARD FISH   *Anarhichas minor*
LEOPARD FLOUNDER   *Platophrys pantherinus*
LEOPARD SHARK   *Galeocerdo arcticus, Triakis semifasciatum*
LESSER CATFISH   *Anarhichas minor*
LESSER LING   *Molva byrkelange*
LESSER SAND-EEL   *Ammodytes tobianus*
LESSER SPOTTED DOGFISH   *Mustelus canis*
LING   *Lota lota maculosa, Molva molva, Urophycis chuss, Urophycis tenuis*
LING, BLUE   *Molva byrkelange*
LINGCOD   *Ophiodon elongatus*
LING, LESSER   *Molva byrkelange*
LING, THIMBLE-EYED   *Urophycis chuss*
LISA   *Mugil curema*
LITTLE BASS   *Micropterus dolomieu*
LITTLE FISH, INDIAN   *Apogon semilineatus*
LITTLE HALIBUT   *Reinhardtius hippoglossoides*
LITTLE REDFISH   *Oncorhynchus nerka kennerlyi*
LITTLE SKATE   *Raja erinacea*
LITTLE TUNNY   *Thynnus thunnina*
LIZARD FISH, GREATER   *Saurida tumbil*
LIZARD FISH, TRUE   *Saurida undosquamis*
LIZZARD FISH, OFFSHORE   *Trachinocephalus myops*
LOACH   *Misgurnus anguillicaudatus, Nemacheilus barbatulus*
LOACH, POND   *Misgurnus fossilis*
LOACH, SPINED   *Cobitis taenia*
LOACH, STONE   *Nemacheilus barbatulus*
LONG-BILLED HALF-BEAK   *Hemirhamphus georgii*
LONGFIN HAKE   *Urophycis chesteri*
LONG-FINNED ALBACORE   *Thunnus alalunga*
LONG-FINNED MULLET   *Mugil vaigiensis*
LONG-FINNED SOLE   *Errex zachirus*
LONG-FINNED TUNA   *Thunnus alalunga*

16*

LONGHORN SCULPIN *Myoxocephalus octodecimspinosus*
LONG JAW FLOUNDER *Atheresthes stomias*
LONG JAW ROCKFISH *Sebastodes alutus*
LONG JAWED ANCHOVY *Stolephorus commersonii*
LONG JAWED GOBY *Gillichthys mirabilis*
LONGNOSE EEL *Synaphobranchus kaupi*
LONG NOSED GAR *Lepisosteus osseus*
LONG NOSED SKATE *Raja oxyrhynchus*
LONG NOSED SUCKER *Catostomus catostomus*
LONG RAYED SILVER BIDDY *Gerres filamentosus*
LONG ROUGH DAB *Hippoglossoides platessoides*
LOOKDOWN, ATLANTIC *Selene vomer*
LUDERICK *Girella tricuspidata*
LUMPFISH *Cyclopterus lumpus*
LUMP SUCKER *Cyclopterus lumpus*
LUNGFISH *Neoceratodus forsteri*
LUNGFISH, AFRICAN *Protopterus aethiopicus, Protopterus annectens*

MACKEREL, ATKA *Pleurogrammus asotus*
MACKEREL, ATLANTIC *Scomber scombrus*
MACKEREL, BARRED SPANISH *Scomberomorus commersonii*
MACKEREL, BAY *Scomberomorus maculatus*
MACKEREL, BLACK-SPOTTED SPANISH *Scomberomorus regalis*
MACKEREL, CHUB *Pneumatophorus colias, Scomber colias*
MACKEREL, FRIGATE *Auxis rochei, Auxis tapeinosoma, Auxis thazard*
MACKEREL, HORSE *Thunnus thynnus thynnus, Trachurus trachurus*
MACKEREL, JACK *Trachurus japonicus*
MACKEREL, JAPANESE *Scomber japonicus*
MACKEREL, KING *Scomberomorus cavalla*
MACKEREL, PACIFIC *Pneumatophorus japonicus*
MACKEREL, RAKE-GILLED *Rastrelliger kanagurta*
MACKEREL, SHORT-BODIED *Rastrelliger brachysoma*
MACKEREL SHARK *Lamna nasus*
MACKEREL, SKIP *Pomatomus saltatrix*
MACKEREL, SNAP *Pomatomus saltatrix*
MACKEREL, SPANISH *Cybium commersonii, Pneumatophorus colias, Scomber colias, Scomberomorus maculatus, Scomberomorus niphonius*
MACKEREL, SPOTTED *Scomber tapeinocephalus, Scomberomorus maculatus*
MACKEREL, SPOTTED SPANISH *Scomberomorus guttatum*
MACKEREL, STRIPED *Pelamys chilensis*
MACQUARIE PERCH *Macquaria australasica*
MADREGAL *Zonichthys falcatus*
MAID, FAIR *Stenotomus versicolor*
MAIGRE *Johnius regius*
MAKO SHARK *Isurus glaucus*
MALABAR SNAPPER *Lutianus malabaricus*
MALMA TROUT *Salvelinus malma*
MANGROVE SNAPPER *Lutianus griseus*
MANILA SEA CATFISH *Arius manillensis*

MAORI   *Ophthalmolepis lineolatus*
MARBLED ELECTRIC RAY   *Torpedo marmorata*
MARBLED SCULPIN, GIANT   *Scorpaenichthys marmoratus*
MARE, BAY   *Catostomus commersonii*
MARIGGLE, JOHN   *Elops saurus*
MARKET SARDINE   *Etrumeus micropus*
MARLIN, BLACK   *Makaira mazara*
MARLIN, BLUE   *Makaira nigricans*
MARLIN, GIANT BLACK   *Makaira marlina*
MARLIN, PACIFIC   *Makaira mitsukurii*
MARLIN, STRIPED   *Makaira mitsukurii*
MARMOR BREAM   *Pagellus mormyrus*
MASU   *Oncorhynchus masou*
MATREEL   *Scomber japonicus*
MATSUBARA STINGFISH   *Sebastodes matsubarae*
MEAGRE   *Sciaena aquila*
MEAGRE, BROWN   *Corvina nigra*
MEGRIM   *Lepidorhombus whiffiagonis*
MEICHI PORGY   *Gymnocranius griseus*
MENHADEN   *Brevoortia tyrannus*
MENHADEN, GULF   *Brevoortia patronus*
MEXICAN CAVE CHARACIN   *Anoptichthys jordani*
MEXICAN SNAPPER   *Lutianus campechanus*
MILK FISH   *Chanos chanos*
MILK SHARK   *Scoliodon walbeehmii*
MILLER'S THUMB   *Cottus gobio*
MILLIONS   *Lebistes reticulatus*
MINNOW   *Phoxinus phoxinus*
MINNOW, COMMON   *Zacco platypus*
MINNOW, SALTWATER   *Fundulus heteroclitus*
MINNOW, TOP   *Gambusia holbrooki*
MISHIMA PUFFER FISH   *Uranoscopus japonicus*
MISHIMA PUFFER FISH, BLUE   *Gnathagnus elongatus*
MISSISSIPPI ALLIGATOR GAR   *Lepisosteus spatula*
MOJARRAS, SPOTTED   *Gerres filamentosus*
MOJARRON   *Anisotremus interruptus*
MOLLIE, BLACK   *Mollienesia* sp.
MONKFISH   *Lophius americanus, Lophius piscatorius, Squatina squatina*
MONKFISH, JAPANESE   *Squatina japonica*
MOONFISH   *Chaetodipterus faber, Selene vomer*
MORAY EEL   *Muraena helena*
MOROKO, STONE   *Pseudorasbora parva*
MORWONG   *Nemadactylus douglasii*
MOSSBUNKER   *Brevoortia tyrannus*
MOUNTAIN PERCH   *Macquaria australasica*
MOUTH, FLUTE-   *Fistularia petimba*
MUD BLOWER   *Lota lota maculosa*
MUD CHUB   *Semotilus atromaculatus*
MUD DAB   *Pleuronectes limander*
MUDFISH   *Amia calva, Misgurnus fossilis, Ophicephalus striatus, Parasilurus asotus*

MUD HAKE   *Urophycis chuss*
MUD SHARK   *Hexanchus griseus*
MUD SKIPPER   *Periophthalmodon australis*
MUDSUCKER   *Gillichthys mirabilis*
MULLET   *Moxostoma aureolum, Mugil cephalus*
MULLET, BLACK   *Catostomus commersonii*
MULLET, BLACK-FINNED   *Mugil melinopterus*
MULLET, BLUE-BLACK   *Mugil curema*
MULLET, DIAMOND-SCALE   *Mugil vaigiensis*
MULLET, DUSSUMIER'S   *Mugil dussumierii*
MULLET, GOLDEN-GREY   *Mugil auratus*
MULLET, GOLD-SPOT   *Mugil parsia*
MULLET, GREY   *Mugil speigleri*
MULLET, THICK-LIPPED GREY   *Mugil chelo*
MULLET, LONG-FINNED   *Mugil vaigiensis*
MULLET, RED   *Mullus barbatus, Mullus surmulletus*
MULLET, STRIPED   *Mugil cephalus, Mullus barbatus*
MULLET, TRUE   *Mugil cephalus*
MULLET, WHITE   *Chanos chanos, Mugil curema*
MULLOWAY   *Sciaena antarctica*
MUMMICHOG   *Fundulus heteroclitus*
MURRAY PERCH   *Macquaria australasica*
MURREL   *Ophicephalus punctatus, Ophicephalus striatus*
MUTTONFISH   *Lutianus analis, Macrozoarces americanus*

NASSAU GROUPER   *Epinephelus striatus*
NEEDLEFISH   *Scomberesox saurus*
NEEDLEFISH, JAPANESE   *Hemirhamphus sajori*
NED, YELLOW   *Perca flavescens*
NEMIPTERID, RIBBON-FINNED   *Nemipterus taeniopterus*
NEW ENGLAND HAKE   *Merluccius bilinearis*
NEWFOUNDLAND TURBOT   *Reinhardtius hippoglossoides*
NIGGERFISH   *Cephalopholis fulvus*
NIPPER   *Tautogolabrus adspersus*
NIPPLE-TAILED OCEAN SUNFISH   *Masturus lanceolatus*
NORTHERN ANCHOVY   *Engraulis mordax*
NORTHERN HAGFISH   *Myxine glutinosa*
NORTHERN POMOTIS   *Eupomotis gibbosus*
NORTHERN PUFFER   *Sphaeroides maculatus*
NORTHERN REDHORSE   *Moxostoma aureolum*
NORTHERN SEAROBIN   *Prionotus carolinus*
NORTHERN STINGRAY   *Dasyatis centroura*
NORTHERN SUCKER   *Catostomus catostomus*
NORWAY HADDOCK   *Sebastes marinus*
NUMBFISH   *Tetranarce occidentalis, Torpedo nobiliana*
NURSE, GREY   *Carcharias arenarius*
NURSEHOUND   *Scylliorhinus stellaris*

OCEAN BONITO   *Katsuwonus pelamis*
OCEAN PERCH   *Sebastes marinus*

OCEAN PERCH, PACIFIC   *Sebastodes alutus*
OCEAN POUT   *Macrozoarces americanus*
OCEAN SUNFISH   *Mola mola*
OCEAN SUNFISH, NIPPLE-TAILED   *Masturus lanceolatus*
OCEAN SUNFISH, SHARP TAIL   *Masturus lanceolatus*
OCEAN WHITEFISH   *Caulolatilus princeps*
OFFSHORE LIZZARD FISH   *Trachinocephalus myops*
OFFSHORE SNAKE   *Ophisurus macrorhynchus*
OHIO GAR   *Lepisosteus osseus*
OIL SARDINE   *Sardinella longiceps*
OIL SHARK   *Galeorhinus zyopterus*
OLD ENGLAND HAKE   *Merluccius bilinearis*
OLD ENGLISH HAKE   *Urophycis tenuis*
OLD WIFE   *Leiostomus xanthurus, Spondyliosoma cantharus*
OLIVE BARB   *Barbus chrysopoma*
OLIVE GRUNTER   *Pristipoma olivaceum*
OPEN-MOUTHED GRUNT   *Haemulon flavolineatum*
ORANGE-FIN LABEO   *Labeo calbasu*
ORANGE-FINNED PONY FISH   *Leiognathus bindus*
ORANGE ROCKFISH   *Sebastodes pinniger*
ORANGE-SPOTTED ROCKFISH   *Sebastodes maliger*
OX-EYE HERRING   *Megalops cyprinoides*
OYSTERFISH   *Opsanus tau*

PACIFIC BARRACUDA   *Sphyraena argentea*
PACIFIC BLUEFIN TUNA   *Thunnus thynnus orientalis*
PACIFIC COD   *Gadus macrocephalus*
PACIFIC HAGFISH   *Polistotrema stoutii*
PACIFIC HAKE   *Merluccius productus*
PACIFIC HALIBUT   *Hippoglossus stenolepis*
PACIFIC HERRING   *Clupea pallasii*
PACIFIC LAMPREY   *Entosphenus tridentatus*
PACIFIC MACKEREL   *Pneumatophorus japonicus*
PACIFIC MARLIN   *Makaira mitsukurii*
PACIFIC OCEAN PERCH   *Sebastodes alutus*
PACIFIC SARDINE   *Sardinops caerula*
PACIFIC SPINY DOGFISH   *Squalus acanthias*
PACIFIC TOMCOD   *Microgadus proximus*
PAINTED COMBER   *Serranus scriba*
PALLID SCULPIN   *Cottunculus thompsoni*
PAMPANO   *Citula dorsalis*
PAMPANO, COMMON   *Trachinotus carolinus*
PANDORA   *Pagellus erythrinus*
PAPER SOLE   *Hippoglossoides elassodon*
PARGO   *Hoplopagrus güntheri, Lutianus analis*
PARROT FISH   *Scarus guacamaia*
PARROT FISH, GREEN   *Pseudoscarus guacamaia*
PARROT FISH, JAPANESE   *Leptoscarus japonicus, Oplegnathus fasciatus*
PEACOCK BLENNY   *Blennius pavo*
PEACOCK WRASSE   *Crenilabrus pavo*

PECK-NOSED SKATE *Raja stabuliforis*
PELAMID *Sarda sarda*
PENSACOLA SNAPPER *Lutianus blackfordii*
PERCH *Eupomotis gibbosus, Lepomis macrochirus, Perca fluviatilis, Tautogolabrus adspersus*
PERCH, AMERICAN *Perca flavescens*
PERCH, BLACK *Micropterus dolomieu*
PERCH, BLUE *Tautogolabrus adspersus*
PERCH, BOTTOM *Apogon semilineatus*
PERCH, CLIMBING *Anabas scandens*
PERCH, CRESCENT *Therapon jarbua*
PERCH, DUSKY *Epinephelus gigas*
PERCH, GIANT *Lates calcarifer*
PERCH, GOLD *Lepomis macrochirus*
PERCH, LAKE *Perca flavescens*
PERCH, MACQUARIE *Macquaria australasica*
PERCH, MOUNTAIN *Macquaria australasica*
PERCH, MURRAY *Macquaria australasica*
PERCH, OCEAN *Sebastes marinus*
PERCH, PACIFIC OCEAN *Sebastodes alutus*
PERCH, PIKE- *Lucioperca lucioperca*
PERCH, POND *Eupomotis gibbosus*
PERCH, RINGED *Perca flavescens*
PERCH, RIVER *Perca flavescens*
PERCH, SAND *Eupomotis gibbosus*
PERCH, SEA *Morone americana, Roccus americanus, Tautogolabrus adspersus*
PERCH, SILVER *Morone americana, Pomoxis annularis*
PERCH, SPECKLED *Pomoxis annularis*
PERCH, TIN *Pomoxis annularis*
PERCH, WART *Psenopsis anomala*
PERCH, WHITE *Aplodinotus grunniens, Morone americana, Pomoxis annularis, Roccus americanus*
PERCH, YELLOW *Eupomotis gibbosus, Perca flavescens*
PERFORATED SCALE SARDINE *Sardinella perforata*
PETRALE SOLE *Eopsetta jordani*
PICKEREL, EASTERN *Esox niger*
PIG-FACE BREAM, BRIDLED *Lethrinus cinereus*
PIG-FACE BREAM, STARRY *Lethrinus opercularis*
PIKE *Esox lucius*
PIKE, BLUE *Stizostedion vitreum*
PIKE, BLUNT-JAWED SEA *Sphyraena obtusata*
PIKE, GIANT SEA *Sphyraena jello*
PIKE, GREEN *Esox niger*
PIKE, SAURY *Scomberesox saurus*
PIKE, SEA *Sphyraena japonica*
PIKE, WALL-EYED *Stizostedion vitreum*
PIKE, YELLOW *Stizostedion vitreum*
PIKE-PERCH *Lucioperca lucioperca, Stizostedion vitreum*
PIKED DOGFISH *Squalus acanthias*

PILCHARD *Clupea pilchardus, Sardina pilchardus, Sardinops caerula, Sardinops ocellata*

PINFISH *Gasterosteus aculeatus, Lagodon rhomboides*

PINK SALMON *Oncorhynchus gorbuscha*

PIPER *Trigla cuculus*

PIPER, EGRET *Macrorhamphosus sagifue*

PIRANHA, NATTERER'S *Rooseveltiella nattereri*

PIRANHA, RED *Rooseveltiella nattereri*

PLAICE *Pleuronectes platessa*

PLAICE, AMERICAN *Hippoglossoides platessoides*

PLAICE, CANADIAN *Hippoglossoides platessoides*

PLAIN BONITO *Auxis rochei, Auxis thazard*

PLAINS KILLIFISH *Fundulus kansae*

PLANER'S LAMPREY *Lampetra planeri*

POGY *Brevoortia tyrannus*

POINTED-TAILED GOBY *Apocryptes lanceolatus*

POINTER, BLUE *Isurus glaucus*

POLAR COD *Boreogadus saida*

POLAR EEL-POUT *Lycodes turneri*

POLE FLOUNDER *Glyptocephalus cynoglossus*

POLLACK *Gadus pollachius, Gadus virens*

POMFRET, BLACK *Parastromateus niger*

POMFRET, GREY *Stromateus cinereus*

POMFRET, SILVER *Stromateus cinereus*

POMFRET, WHITE *Stromateus sinensis*

POMOTIS, NORTHERN *Eupomotis gibbosus*

POMPANO, CAROLINA *Trachinotus carolinus*

POND LOACH *Misgurnus fossilis*

POND SMELT *Hypomesus olidus*

PONY FISH, GOLDEN STRIPED *Leiognathus daura*

PONY FISH, GREATER *Leiognathus equulus*

PONY FISH, ORANGE-FINNED *Leiognathus bindus*

PORBEAGLE *Lamna cornubica, Lamna nasus*

PORGY *Leiostomus xanthurus, Stenotomus chrysops, Stenotomus versicolor*

PORGY, FLUTE *Lutianus rivulatus*

PORGY, GENUINE *Chrysophrys major*

PORGY, MEICHI *Gymnocranius griseus*

PORGY, PRINCE'S SMALL *Chelidoperca hirundinacea*

PORGY, SAUCEREYE *Calamus calamus*

PORGY, SHEEPSHEAD *Archosargus probatocephalus*

PORGY, THREE-TAILED *Chaetodipterus faber*

PORGY, YELLOW *Taius tumifrons*

PORKY *Stephanolepsis cirrhifer*

PORT JACKSON SHARK *Heterodontus japonicus*

PORTUGUESE SHARK *Centroscymnus coelolepis*

POSSUM RAY *Raja eglantaria*

POSSUM, SEA *Raja eglantaria*

POSTCROAKER *Leiostomus xanthurus*

POUT, HORNED *Ameiurus nebulosus*

POUT, OCEAN *Macrozoarces americanus*

POUTASSOU   *Gadus poutassou*
POWAN   *Coregonus clupeoides*
PRICKLY SKATE, ATLANTIC   *Raja radiata, Raja scabrata*
PRINCE'S SMALL PORGY   *Chelidoperca hirundinacea*
PUFF-BELLY   *Hemitripterus americanus*
PUFFER   *Fugu pardalis*
PUFFER FISH, BLUE MISHIMA   *Gnathagnus elongatus*
PUFFER FISH, MISHIMA   *Uranoscopus japonicus*
PUFFER, GRASS   *Fugu niphobles*
PUFFER, NORTHERN   *Sphaeroides maculatus*
PUFFER, SOUTHERN   *Sphaeroides spengleri*
PUFFER, TIGER   *Fugu rubripes*
PUMPKINSEED   *Eupomotis gibbosus, Lepomis gibbosus*

QUIAQUIA   *Decapterus punctatus*
QUILLBACK ROCKFISH   *Sebastodes maliger*
QUIVER   *Eupomotis gibbosus*

RABBIT FISH   *Chimaera monstrosa*
RACCOON PERCH   *Perca flavescens*
RAINBOW FISH   *Lebistes reticulatus*
RAINBOW TROUT   *Salmo gairdnerii*
RAKE-GILLED MACKEREL   *Rastrelliger kanagurta*
RASBORA, COMMON   *Rasbora daniconius*
RASPHEAD ROCKFISH   *Sebastodes ruberrimus*
RATFISH   *Chimaera monstrosa, Hydrolagus colliei*
RAT-TAIL   *Chimaera monstrosa*
RAT-TAIL, SMOOTH SPINED   *Macrourus berglax*
RATTLEFISH, RED   *Halieutea stellata*
RAVEN, SEA   *Hemitripterus americanus*
RAY, ANGEL   *Squatina squatina*
RAY, BANDED WHIPTAIL STING-   *Dasyatis uarnak*
RAY, BLONDE   *Raja brachyura*
RAY, BRIER   *Raja eglantaria*
RAY, CLEAR   *Raja diaphenes*
RAY, CUCKOO   *Raja naevus*
RAY, EAGLE   *Myliobatis aquila*
RAY, ELECTRIC   *Narke japonica, Torpedo nobiliana*
RAY, FULLER'S   *Raja fullonica*
RAY, HOMELYN   *Raja montagui*
RAY, JAPANESE STING   *Dasyatis akajei*
RAY, MARBLED ELECTRIC   *Torpedo marmorata*
RAY, POSSUM   *Raja eglantaria*
RAY, RED STING   *Dasyatis akajei*
RAY, ROUGHTAIL STING   *Dasyatis centroura*
RAY, SANDY   *Raja circularis*
RAY, SEA WALL   *Raja kenoji*
RAY, SHAGREEN   *Raja fullonica*
RAY, SPOTTED   *Raja montagui*
RAY, STARRY   *Raja asterias*

RAY, STING   *Trygon pastinaca*
RAY, THORNBACK   *Raja clavata*
RAY, UNDULATE   *Raja undulata*
RAY, WHITE-SPOTTED SHOVELNOSE   *Rhynchobatus djiddensis*
REAL SWORDFISH   *Makaira mazara*
RED BARRACUDA   *Sphyraena pinguis*
RED BASS   *Sciaenops ocellata*
RED BATFISH   *Halieutea stellata*
REDBELLY   *Eupomotis gibbosus*
RED COD   *Sebastodes ruberrimus*
RED DRUM   *Sciaenops ocellata*
REDFISH   *Sciaenops ocellata, Sebastes marinus*
REDFISH, LITTLE   *Oncorhynchus nerka kennerlyi*
RED GROUPER   *Epinephelus morio*
RED GURNARD   *Trigla cuculus*
RED HAKE   *Urophycis chuss*
RED HALIBUT   *Hippoglossoides dubius*
RED HATA   *Epinephelus fasciatus*
RED HIND   *Epinephelus guttatus*
REDHORSE, NORTHERN   *Moxostoma aureolum*
RED MULLET   *Mullus barbatus, Mullus surmulletus*
RED PIRANHA   *Rooseveltiella nattereri*
RED RATTLEFISH   *Halieutea stellata*
RED ROCKFISH   *Sebastopyr ruberrimus*
RED SALMON   *Oncorhynchus nerka*
RED SEA BREAM   *Pagellus erythrinus*
RED SKATE   *Dasyatis akajei*
RED SNAPPER   *Lutianus blackfordii, Lutianus campechanus, Sebastodes ruber-rimus*
RED-SPECKLED BLENNY   *Blennius sanguinolentus*
RED STING RAY   *Dasyatis akajei*
RED SUCKER   *Catostomus catostomus*
RED TAIL SNAPPER   *Lutianus synagris*
REEF-COD, BANDED   *Epinephelus fasciatus*
REEF-COD, TROUT   *Epinephelus fario*
REX SOLE   *Errex zachirus, Glyptocephalus zachirus*
RIBBON-FINNED NEMIPTERID   *Nemipterus taeniopterus*
RIBBONFISH   *Trichiurus lepturus*
RIBBONFISH, LARGE-HEADED   *Trichiurus haumela*
RIBBONFISH, SMALL-HEADED   *Trichiurus savala*
RINGED PERCH   *Perca flavescens*
RIVER EIGHT-EYES LAMPREY   *Entosphenus japonicus*
RIVER GURNARD   *Platycephalus indicus*
RIVER KINGFISH   *Sciaena antarctica*
RIVER PERCH   *Perca flavescens*
RIVER SHAD   *Hilsa ilisha*
ROACH   *Eupomotis gibbosus, Notemigonus crysoleucas, Rutilus rutilus*
ROACH, HARLEQUIN   *Eupomotis gibbosus*
ROBIN   *Eupomotis gibbosus*
ROBIN, ROUND   *Decapterus punctatus*

Rock   *Roccus saxatilis*
Rock cod   *Epinephelus fario*
Rockfish   *Epinephelus striatus, Mycteroperca tigris, Roccus saxatilis, Sebastes dactylopterus, Sebastes flammeus, Sebastiscus marmoratus, Trisotropis venenosus*
rockfish, Black   *Sebastodes melanops*
rockfish, Canary   *Sebastodes pinniger*
rockfish, Copper   *Sebastodes caurinus*
rockfish, Green striped   *Sebastodes elongatus*
rockfish, Longjaw   *Sebastodes alutus*
rockfish, Orange-spotted   *Sebastodes maliger*
rockfish, Quillback   *Sebastodes maliger*
rockfish, Rasphead   *Sebastodes ruberrimus*
rockfish, Red   *Sebastopyr ruberrimus*
rockfish, Turkey   *Sebastodes ruberrimus*
rockfish, Yellowtail   *Sebastodes flavidus*
Rock grenadier   *Coryphaenoides rupestris*
Rock salmon   *Zonichthys falcatus*
Rock sole   *Lepidopsetta bilineata*
Rocky mountain whitefish   *Prosopium williamsoni*
Roker   *Raja clavata*
Roncodina   *Micropogon undulatus*
Ronco ronco   *Haemulon plumieri*
Rose fish   *Sebastes marinus*
Rosy jewfish   *Otolithus ruber*
rough dab, Long   *Hippoglossoides platessoides*
Rough hound   *Scyllium canicula*
Rough scad   *Trachurus trachurus*
rough, Tommy   *Arripis georgianus*
Roughscale sole   *Clidoderma asperrimum*
Roughtail stingray   *Dasyatis centroura*
Round robin   *Decapterus punctatus*
Round-toothed large-eyed bream   *Monotaxis grandoculis*
Rudd   *Scardinius erythrophthalmus*
Rudderfish   *Seriola dumerili, Seriola purpurascens*
rudderfish, Black   *Palinurichthys perciformis*
Ruff   *Arripis georgianus, Eupomotis gibbosus*
Rungh scad   *Trachurus japonicus*
Runner   *Oligoplites saurus*
Rusty dab   *Limander ferruginea*

Sablefish   *Anoplopoma fimbria, Hilsa ilisha*
Sailor's choice   *Lagodon rhomboides*
Saint Peter's fish   *Zeus faber*
Saithe   *Gadus virens*
salmon, Burnett   *Neoceratodus forsteri*
salmon, Chinook   *Oncorhynchus tschawytscha*
salmon, Chum   *Oncorhynchus keta*
salmon, Coho   *Oncorhynchus kisutch*
salmon, Cooktown   *Eleutheronema tetradactylum*
salmon de alto, Japanese   *Polymixia japonica*

SALMON, DOG   *Oncorhynchus keta*
SALMON, GOOD   *Sphyraena pinguis*
SALMON HERRING   *Chanos chanos*
SALMON, HUDSON BAY   *Salvelinus alpinus*
SALMON, JACK   *Stizostedion vitreum*
SALMON, PINK   *Oncorhynchus gorbuscha*
SALMON, RED   *Oncorhynchus nerka*
SALMON, ROCK   *Zonichthys falcatus*
SALMON, SILVER   *Oncorhynchus kisutch*
SALMON, SOCKEYE   *Oncorhynchus nerka*
SALMON, SPRING   *Oncorhynchus tschawytscha*
SALMON TROUT   *Arripis trutta*
SALMON, WHITE   *Seriola dorsalis*
SALMONET   *Upeneoides bensasi*
SALT WATER MINNOW   *Fundulus heteroclitus*
SAND DAB   *Hippoglossoides platessoides*
SAND-EEL, LESSER   *Ammodytes tobianus*
SANDER   *Lucioperca lucioperca*
SAND FLOUNDER   *Psettichthys melanostictus*
SAND GURNARD   *Platycephalus indicus*
SANDLANCE, ARCTIC   *Ammodytes tobianus*
SAND PERCH   *Eupomotis gibbosus*
SAND SMELT   *Menidia menidia notata*
SAND SNAKE   *Ophisurus macrorhynchus*
SAND SOLE   *Psettichthys melanostictus*
SANDY RAY   *Raja circularis*
SAPO   *Opsanus tau*
SARDINA DE LEY   *Harengula sardina*
SARDINE, CALIFORNIA   *Sardinops caerula*
SARDINE, FRINGE-SCALE   *Sardinella fimbriata*
SARDINE, HALF-MOUTHED   *Engraulis japonicus*
SARDINE, INDIAN   *Sardinella longiceps*
SARDINE, MARKET   *Etrumeus micropus*
SARDINE, OIL   *Sardinella longiceps*
SARDINE, PACIFIC   *Sardinops caerula*
SARDINE, PERFORATED SCALE   *Sardinella perforata*
SARDINE, SHORT-BODIED   *Sardinella albella*
SARDINE, TRUE   *Sardinops melanosticta*
SARGO   *Diplodus sargus*
SAUCEREYE PORGY   *Calamus calamus*
SAUCORD, HILGENDORF   *Helicolenus hilgendorfi*
SAUREL   *Scomberesox saurus*
SAURY   *Cololabis saira*
SAURY, ATLANTIC   *Scomberesox saurus*
SAURY PIKE   *Scomberesox saurus*
SAW-BELLY   *Pomolobus pseudoharengus*
SAW-EDGED CATFISH   *Arius serratus*
SAWFISH   *Pristis microdon*
SAWFISH, SMALL-TOOTHED   *Pristis microdon*
SCAD   *Trachurus trachurus*

SCAD, BIG-EYE   *Selar crumenophthalmus*
SCAD, BLACK SEA   *Trachurus mediterraneus ponticus*
SCAD, GOLDEN   *Caranx kalla*
SCAD, ROUGH   *Trachurus trachurus*
SCAD, RUNGH   *Trachurus japonicus*
SCAD, SLENDER-SCALED   *Caranx leptolepis*
SCALYFIN FLOUNDER   *Isopsetta isolepis*
SCALY STINGRAY   *Trygon imbricata*
SCHOOL SHARK   *Galeorhinus australis*
SCIAENA   *Johnius regius*
SCORPION   *Opsanus tau*
SCORPION-FISH   *Sebastiscus marmoratus, Sebastodes baramenuke*
SCORPION-FISH, LARGE-SCALED   *Scorpaena scrofa*
SCORPION-FISH, SMALL-SCALED   *Scorpaena porcus*
SCRAPER, BLACK   *Navodon modestus*
SCULPIN, ARCTIC STAGHORN   *Gymnocanthus tricuspis*
SCULPIN, DADDY   *Myoxocephalus scorpius*
SCULPIN, ELF   *Ceratocottus namiyei*
SCULPIN, GIANT MARBLED   *Scorpaenichthys marmoratus*
SCULPIN, GREENLAND   *Myoxocephalus scorpius*
SCULPIN, LONGHORN   *Myoxocephalus octodecimspinosus*
SCULPIN, PALLID   *Cottunculus thompsoni*
SCULPIN, SHORTHORN   *Myoxocephalus groenlandicus, Myoxocephalus scorpius*
SCULPIN, SPATULATE   *Icelus spatula*
SCULPIN, STAGHORN   *Leptocottus armatus*
SCULPIN, WHIP   *Hemitripterus americanus*
SCUP   *Stenotomus chrysops*
SCUP, COMMON   *Stenotomus versicolor*
SCUPPANG   *Stenotomus versicolor*
SEA BASS   *Sciaenops ocellata*
SEA BASS, BLACK   *Centropristes striatus*
SEA BREAM   *Chrysophrys major*
SEA BREAM, COUCH'S   *Pagrus pagrus*
SEA BREAM, RED   *Pagellus erythrinus*
SEA CAT   *Galeichthys felis*
SEA CATFISH   *Bagre morina, Plotosus anguillaris*
SEA CHUB   *Ditrema temmincki*
SEA HEN   *Cyclopterus lumpus*
SEA HERRING   *Arripis georgianus*
SEA LAMPREY   *Petromyzon marinus*
SEA PERCH   *Morone americana, Roccus americanus, Tautogolabrus adspersus*
SEA PERCH, WHITE   *Phanerodon furcatus*
SEA PIKE   *Sphyraena japonica*
SEA PIKE, BLUNT-JAWED   *Sphyraena obtusata*
SEA PIKE, GIANT   *Sphyraena jello*
SEA POSSUM   *Raja eglantaria*
SEA RAVEN   *Hemitripterus americanus*
SEA ROBIN, COMMON   *Prionotus carolinus*
SEA ROBIN, NORTHERN   *Prionotus carolinus*
SEA SNAIL, GELATINOUS   *Liparis koefoedi*

SEA TROUT   *Cynoscion regalis, Salmo trutta, Salvelinus alpinus, Salvelinus fontinalis*
SEA TROUT, SPOTTED   *Eriscion nebulosus*
SEA WALL RAY   *Raja kenoji*
SEAR   *Decapterus macrosoma*
SHAD   *Eucinostomus gula, Pomoxis annularis*
SHAD, AMERICAN   *Alosa sapidissima*
SHAD, COMMON   *Alosa sapidissima*
SHAD, GIZZARD   *Anodontostoma chacunda, Dorosoma cepedianum*
SHAD, HICKORY   *Dorosoma cepedianum*
SHAD, RIVER   *Hilsa ilisha*
SHAD, YOUNG   *Notemigonus crysoleucas*
SHAGREEN RAY   *Raja fullonica*
SHALLOW-WATER CISCO   *Leucichthys artedi*
SHARK, ARMOUR   *Dalatias licha*
SHARK, ARROW-HEADED HAMMERHEAD   *Zygaena blochii*
SHARK, BASKING   *Cetorhinus maximus*
SHARK, BLUE   *Carcharhinus glaucus, Isurus glaucus, Prionace glauca*
SHARK, BONNETNOSE   *Sphyrna tiburo*
SHARK, BROAD HARBOUR   *Deania eglantina*
SHARK, BROWN   *Carcharhinus milbertei*
SHARK, BULL   *Carcharhinus leucas*
SHARK, CANOPY   *Squatina japonica*
SHARK, CAT   *Heterodontus japonicus, Triakis semifasciatum*
SHARK, CROSS-STAFF   *Sphyrna zygaena*
SHARK, CUB   *Carcharhinus leucas*
SHARK, DOG   *Mustelus griseus*
SHARK, DUSKY   *Carcharhinus obscurus*
SHARK, ELLIOT'S GREY   *Carcharias ellioti*
SHARK, FIN   *Centrophorus atromarginatus*
SHARK, FOX   *Alopias pelagicus*
SHARK, FRESH WATER   *Wallago attu*
SHARK, GHOST   *Chimaera phantasma*
SHARK, GREAT BLUE   *Glyphis glaucus*
SHARK, GREENLAND   *Somniosus microcephalus*
SHARK, GROUND   *Carcharhinus gangeticus, Carcharhinus leucas, Somniosus microcephalus*
SHARK, GUMMY   *Mustelus manazo*
SHARK, GURRY   *Somniosus microcephalus*
SHARK, HAMMERHEAD   *Sphyrna zygaena*
SHARK, LATERN   *Etmopterus spinax*
SHARK, LEOPARD   *Galeocerdo arcticus, Triakis semifasciatum*
SHARK, MACKEREL   *Lamna nasus*
SHARK, MAKO   *Isurus glaucus*
SHARK, MILK   *Scoliodon walbeehmii*
SHARK, MUD   *Hexanchus griseus*
SHARK, OIL   *Galeorhinus zyopterus*
SHARK, PORT JACKSON   *Heterodontus japonicus*
SHARK, PORTUGUESE   *Centroscymnus coelolepis*
SHARK, SCHOOL   *Galeorhinus australis*
SHARK, SHARPNOSED   *Scoliodon walbeehmii*

SHARK, SILVER *Chimaera phantasma*
SHARK, SIXGILL *Hexanchus griseus*
SHARK, SLEEPER *Somniosus microcephalus*
SHARK, SMALL BLACK-TIPPED *Carcharhinus limbatus*
SHARK, SMOOTH-TOOTH *Aprionodon isodon*
SHARK, SNAPPER *Galeorhinus australis*
SHARK, SOUPFIN *Galeorhinus zyopterus*
SHARK, SPOT-FIN GROUND *Carcharhinus limbatus*
SHARK, SPOTTED *Galeorcerdo arcticus*
SHARK, STAR-SPOTTED *Mustelus manazo*
SHARK, THRESHER *Alopias profundus*
SHARK, TIGER *Galeocerdo arcticus, Scylliorhinus torazame*
SHARK, WHIP-TAIL *Alopias pelagicus.*
SHARK, WHITETIP *Carcharhinus longimanus*
SHARK, YELLOW DOG *Scoliodon sorrakowah*
SHARPNOSED SHARK *Scoliodon walbeehmii*
SHARP TAIL OCEAN SUNFISH *Masturus lanceolatus*
SHECUTTS *Cynoscion regalis*
SHEEPSHEAD *Aplodinotus grunniens, Archosargus probatocephalus*
SHEEPSHEAD, THREE-BANDED *Chaetodipterus faber*
SHEEPSHEAD PORGY *Archosargus probatocephalus*
SHINER *Notemigonus crysoleucas, Poronotus triacanthus*
SHINER, GOLDEN *Notemigonus crysoleucas boscii*
SHORT-BODIED MACKEREL *Rastrelliger brachysomus*
SHORT-BODIED SARDINE *Sardinella albella*
SHORT-FINNED TUNNY *Sarda sarda*
SHORTHORN SCULPIN *Myoxocephalus groenlandicus, Myoxocephalus scorpius*
SHORT-SPINED COTTUS *Myoxocephalus scorpius*
SHOTTED HALIBUT *Eopsetta grigorjewi*
SHOVELHEAD *Sphyrna tibura*
SIAMESE GORAMY *Trichogaster pectoralis*
SICKLEFISH *Drepane punctata*
SIERRA *Scomberomorus regalis*
SILK SNAPPER, BERMUDA *Lutianus hastingsi*
SILK, STRETCHED *Pterogobius elapoides*
SILVER-BIDDY, LONGRAYED *Gerres filamentosus*
SILVER BREAM *Rhabdosargus sarba, Usacaranx georgianus*
SILVER BREAM, JAPANESE *Chrysophrys datnia*
SILVER CHUB *Semotilus atromaculatus*
SILVER CONGER EEL *Muraenesox cinereus*
SILVER EEL *Anguilla rostrata*
SILVERFISH *Merluccius bilinearis, Tarpon atlanticus*
SILVER HAKE *Merluccius bilinearis*
SILVER JENNY *Eucinostomus gula*
SILVER JEW *Sciaena antarctica*
SILVER JEWFISH, DUSSUMIER'S *Sciaena dussumieri*
SILVER LAMPREY *Ichthyomyzon unicuspis*
SILVER PERCH *Morone americana, Pomoxis annularis*
SILVER POMFRET *Stromateus cinereus*
SILVER SALMON *Oncorhynchus kisutch*

SILVER SHARK *Chimaera phantasma*
SILVERSIDE, ATLANTIC *Menidia menidia notata*
SILVER TREVALLY *Usacaranx georgianus*
SILVER TROUT *Oncorhynchus nerka kennerlyi*
SILVERY CONGER *Anago anago*
SISCOWET TROUT *Salvelinus namaycush siscowet*
SIX-BANDED TREVALLY *Caranx sexfasciatus*
SIX-GILL SHARK *Hexanchus griseus*
SKATE *Raja batis, Raja eglantaria*
SKATE, ATLANTIC PRICKLY *Raja radiata, Raja scabrata*
SKATE, BARN-DOOR *Raja stabuliforis*
SKATE, BIG *Raja binoculata, Raja ocellata*
SKATE, BLUE *Raja batis*
SKATE, BOB-TAILED *Raja eglantaria*
SKATE, CLEAR-NOSED *Raja eglantaria*
SKATE, COMMON *Raja inornata*
SKATE, EYED *Raja ocellata*
SKATE, FLAPPER *Raja batis*
SKATE, GREY *Raja batis*
SKATE, LITTLE *Raja erinacea*
SKATE, LONG-NOSED *Raja oxyrhynchus*
SKATE, PECK-NOSED *Raja stabuliforis*
SKATE, RED *Dasyatis akajei*
SKATE, SPINY RASP *Raja kenoji*
SKATE, STARRY *Raja radiata*
SKATE, SUMMER *Raja eglantaria*
SKATE, THORNY *Raja radiata*
SKATE, WINTER *Raja ocellata, Raja stabuliforis*
SKIL *Anoplopoma fimbria*
SKILFISH *Erilepis zonifer*
SKIN CARP *Hemibarbus barbus*
SKIPJACK *Katsuwonus pelamis, Katsuwonus vagans, Scomberesox saurus, Usacaranx georgianus*
SKIP MACKEREL *Pomatomus saltatrix*
SKIPPER *Cololabis saira, Scomberesox saurus*
SLEEPER SHARK *Somniosus microcephalus*
SLENDER-SCALED SCAD *Caranx leptolepis*
SLIME EEL *Simenchelys parasiticus*
SLIME SOLE *Microstomus pacificus*
SLIMER *Opsanus tau*
SLIPMOUTH, COMMON *Leiognathus equulus*
SLIPPERY SOLE *Microstomus pacificus*
SMALL BLACK-TIPPED SHARK *Carcharhinus limbatus*
SMALL CATFISH *Ameiurus melas melas, Ameiurus nebulosus*
SMALL-HEADED RIBBON-FISH *Trichiurus savala*
SMALL-MOUTHED BLACK BASS *Micropterus dolomieu*
SMALL-MOUTHED SOLE *Limander herzensteini*
SMALL PORGY, PRINCE'S *Chelidoperca hirundinacea*
SMALL-SCALED GOBY *Oxyurichthys microlepis*
SMALL-SCALED SCORPION FISH *Scorpaena porcus*

SMALL SPOTTED DOGFISH   *Scyllium canicula*
SMALL-TOOTHED SAWFISH   *Pristis microdon*
SMEAR DAB   *Pleuronectes microcephalus*
SMELT   *Sillago sihama*
SMELT, AMERICAN   *Osmerus mordax*
SMELT, CALIFORNIA BLUE   *Atherinopsis californiensis*
SMELT, EUROPEAN   *Osmerus eperlanus*
SMELT, HERRING   *Argentina silus*
SMELT, POND   *Hypomesus olidus*
SMELT, SAND   *Menidia menidia notata*
SMELT, SWEET   *Plecoglossus altivelis*
SMOOTH DOGFISH   *Mustelus canis*
SMOOTH HAMMERHEAD   *Sphyrna zygaena*
SMOOTH HOUND   *Mustelus mustelus*
SMOOTH-SPINED RAT-TAIL   *Macrourus berglax*
SMOOTH-TOOTH SHARK   *Aprionodon isodon*
SNAKE BLENNY   *Ophiodon barbatum*
SNAKEFISH   *Trichiurus lepturus*
SNAKE-HEAD FISH   *Channa argus*
SNAKE-HEAD, GIANT   *Ophicephalus marulius*
SNAKE-HEAD, GREEN   *Ophicephalus punctatus*
SNAKE-HEAD, STRIPED   *Ophicephalus striatus*
SNAKE, OFFSHORE   *Ophisurus macrorhynchus*
SNAKE, SAND   *Ophisurus macrorhynchus*
SNAP MACKEREL   *Pomatomus saltatrix*
SNAPPER   *Lutianus rivulatus*
SNAPPER, BERMUDA SILK   *Lutianus hastingsi*
SNAPPER, GREY   *Lutianus griseus*
SNAPPER, LANE   *Lutianus synagris*
SNAPPER, MALABAR   *Lutianus malabaricus*
SNAPPER, MANGROVE   *Lutianus griseus*
SNAPPER, MEXICAN   *Lutianus campechanus*
SNAPPER, PENSACOLA   *Lutianus blackfordii*
SNAPPER, RED   *Lutianus blackfordii, Lutianus campechanus, Sebastodes ruber-rimus*
SNAPPER, RED TAIL   *Lutianus synagris*
SNAPPER SHARK   *Galeorhinus australis*
SNAPPER, YELLOWTAIL   *Ocyurus chrysurus*
SNIG   *Microgadus tomcod*
SNOCK   *Sphyraena japonica*
SNOEK   *Thyrsites atun*
SNUBNOSE EEL   *Simenchelys parasiticus*
SOCKEYE SALMON   *Oncorhynchus nerka*
SOLDIER   *Sebastes marinus*
SOLDIER FISH   *Coelorhynchus coelorhynchus*
SOLE   *Hippoglossoides platessoides*
SOLE, AGULHAS   *Austroglossus pectoralis*
SOLE, BENGAL TONGUE   *Cynoglossus bengalensis*
SOLE, BUTTER   *Isopsetta isolepis*
SOLE, DOVER   *Microstomus pacificus*

SOLE, ENGLISH   *Parophrys vetulus*
SOLE, FLATHEAD   *Hippoglossoides elassodon*
SOLE, GREY   *Glyptocephalus cynoglossus*
SOLE, LEMON   *Parophrys vetulus, Pleuronectes microcephalus*
SOLE, LONG-FINNED   *Errex zachirus*
SOLE, PAPER   *Hippoglossoides elassodon*
SOLE, PETRALE   *Eopsetta jordani*
SOLE, REX   *Errex zachirus, Glyptocephalus zachirus*
SOLE, ROCK   *Lepidopsetta bilineata*
SOLE, ROUGHSCALE   *Clidoderma asperrimum*
SOLE, SAND   *Psettichthys melanostictus*
SOLE, SLIME   *Microstomus pacificus*
SOLE, SLIPPERY   *Microstomus pacificus*
SOLE, SMALL-MOUTHED   *Limander herzensteini*
SOLE, STRIPED   *Zebrias zebrinus*
SOUPFIN SHARK   *Galeorhinus zyopterus*
SOUTHERN FLOUNDER   *Paralichthys lethostigmus*
SOUTHERN PUFFER   *Sphaeroides spengleri*
SOUTHERN STINGRAY   *Dasyatis americana*
SPADEFISH   *Chaetodipterus faber*
SPANISH MACKEREL   *Cybium commersonii, Pneumatophorus colias, Scomber colias,
    Scomberomorus maculatus, Scomberomorus niphonius*
SPANISH MACKEREL, BARRED   *Scomberomorus commersonii*
SPANISH MACKEREL, BLACK-SPOTTED   *Scomberomorus regalis*
SPANISH MACKEREL, SPOTTED   *Scomberomorus guttatum*
SPANTICKLE   *Gasterosteus aculeatus*
SPARLING   *Osmerus eperlanus*
SPATULATE SCULPIN   *Icelus spatula*
SPEARFISH   *Makaira mitsukurii*
SPEARFISH, BLACK   *Makaira mazara*
SPECKLED CHAR   *Salvelinus fontinalis*
SPECKLED PERCH   *Pomoxis annularis*
SPECKLED TROUT   *Salvelinus fontinalis*
SPIKE   *Stizostedion vitreum*
SPINED DOGFISH   *Squalus acanthias*
SPINED LOACH   *Cobitis taenia*
SPINY DOGFISH, ATLANTIC   *Squalus acanthias*
SPINY DOGFISH, PACIFIC   *Squalus acanthias*
SPINY EEL   *Mastacembelus armatus, Notacanthus nasus*
SPINY RASP SKATE   *Raja kenoji*
SPOT   *Leiostomus xanthurus*
SPOT-FIN GROUND SHARK   *Carcharhinus limbatus*
SPOTTAIL   *Sciaenops ocellata*
SPOT, WHITE   *Girella nigricans*
SPOTTED BASS   *Sciaenops ocellata*
SPOTTED BATFISH   *Drepane punctata*
SPOTTED BUTTERFISH   *Scatophagus argus*
SPOTTED CATFISH   *Anarhichas minor*
SPOTTED CATFISH, TEYSMANN'S   *Clarias batrachus*
SPOTTED CERO   *Scomberomorus regalis*

SPOTTED CYBIUM *Scomberomorus maculatus*
SPOTTED DOGFISH, GREATER *Scylliorhinus stellaris*
SPOTTED DOGFISH, LARGE *Scyllium stellare*
SPOTTED DOGFISH, LESSER *Mustelus canis*
SPOTTED DOGFISH, SMALL *Scyllium canicula*
SPOTTED ETROPLUS *Etroplus maculatus*
SPOTTED GREENLING, WHITE *Hexagrammos stelleri*
SPOTTED FLOUNDER *Eucitharus linguatula*
SPOTTED MACKEREL *Scomber tapeinocephalus, Scomberomorus maculatus*
SPOTTED MOJARRAS *Gerres filamentosus*
SPOTTED RAY *Raja montagui*
SPOTTED SEA TROUT *Eriscion nebulosus*
SPOTTED SHARK *Galeocerdo arcticus*
SPOTTED SPANISH MACKEREL *Scomberomorus guttatum*
SPOTTED SQUETEAGUE *Eriscion nebulosus*
SPOTTED WEAKFISH *Eriscion nebulosus*
SPOTTED WHITING *Sillaginodes punctatus*
SPOTTED WOLF FISH *Anarhichas minor*
SPRAT *Clupea sprattus*
SPRING SALMON *Oncorhynchus tschawytscha*
SPRINGER *Mugil cephalus*
SPUR DOG *Squalus acanthias*
SQUAWFISH *Ptychocheilus oregonensis*
SQUETEAGUE *Cynoscion regalis*
SQUETEAGUE, SPOTTED *Eriscion nebulosus*
SQUIRREL FISH *Haemulon plumieri, Holocentrus ascensionis*
SQUIRREL HAKE *Urophycis chuss, Urophycis tenuis*
STAGHORN SCULPIN *Leptocottus armatus*
STAGHORN SCULPIN, ARCTIC *Gymnocanthus tricuspis*
STAR-SPOTTED SHARK *Mustelus manazo*
STARRY PIG-FACE BREAM *Lethrinus opercularis*
STARRY FLOUNDER *Platichthys stellatus*
STARRY RAY *Raja asterias*
STARRY SKATE *Raja radiata*
STEELHEAD *Salmo gairdnerii*
STERLET *Acipenser ruthenus*
STICKLEBACK, THREE-SPINED *Gasterosteus aculeatus*
STINGFISH, JAPANESE *Sebastodes inermis*
STINGFISH, MATSUBARA *Sebastodes matsubarae*
STINGING CATFISH *Heteropneustes fossilis*
STING RAY *Trygon pastinaca*
STING RAY, BLUE *Trygon violacea*
STING RAY, BANDED WHIPTAIL *Dasyatis uarnak*
STING RAY, JAPANESE *Dasyatis akajei*
STING RAY, NORTHERN *Dasyatis centroura*
STING RAY, RED *Dasyatis akajei*
STING RAY, ROUGHTAIL *Dasyatis centroura*
STING RAY, SCALY *Trygon imbricata*
STING RAY, SOUTHERN *Dasyatis americana*
STOCKFISH *Merluccius bilinearis, Merluccius capensis*

STONE BASS *Polyprion americanus*
STONE FLOUNDER *Kareius bicoloratus*
STONE, LOACH *Nemacheilus barbatulus*
STONE MOROKO *Pseudorasbora parva*
STRETCHED SILK *Pterogobius elapoides*
STRIPED BARRACUDA *Sphyraena obtusata*
STRIPED BASS *Roccus saxatilis*
STRIPED CATFISH EEL *Plotosus anguillaris*
STRIPED DWARF CATFISH *Macrones vittatus*
STRIPED JACK *Caranx delicatissimus*
STRIPED MACKEREL *Pelamys chilensis*
STRIPED MARLIN *Makaira mitsukurii*
STRIPED MULLET *Mugil cephalus, Mullus barbatus*
STRIPED SNAKE-HEAD *Ophicephalus striatus*
STRIPED SOLE *Zebrias zebrinus*
STRIPED SURF FISH *Taeniotoca lateralis*
STRIPED WOLF FISH *Anarhichas lupus*
STRIPER *Roccus saxatilis*
STURGEON *Acipenser sturio, Huso huso*
STURGEON SUCKER *Catostomus catostomus*
SUCKER, BROOK *Catostomus commersonii*
SUCKER, COMMON *Catostomus commersonii*
SUCKER, LARGE-SCALED *Moxostoma aureolum*
SUCKER, LONG-NOSED *Catostomus catostomus*
SUCKER, NORTHERN *Catostomus catostomus*
SUCKER, RED *Catostomus catostomus*
SUCKER, STURGEON *Catostomus catostomus*
SUCKER, WHITE *Catostomus commersonii, Moxostoma aureolum*
SUMMER SKATE *Raja eglantaria*
SUN BASS *Eupomotis gibbosus*
SUNDIAL *Lophopsetta maculata*
SUNFISH *Lepomis macrochirus, Notemigonus crysoleucas*
SUNFISH, COMMON *Eupomotis gibbosus*
SUNFISH, GILDED *Lepomis macrochirus*
SUNFISH, NIPPLE-TAILED OCEAN *Masturus lanceolatus*
SUNFISH, OCEAN *Mola mola*
SUNFISH, SHARP-TAIL OCEAN *Masturus lanceolatus*
SURF FISH, STRIPED *Taeniotoca lateralis*
SURF PERCH, BLACK *Embiotoca jacksoni*
SURGEON, COMMON *Acanthurus hepatus*
SURGEON-FISH, BLEEKER'S LINED *Acanthurus bleekeri*
SURMULLET *Upeneoides bensasi*
SWEET SMELT *Plecoglossus altivelis*
SWEET WILLIAM *Mustelus mustelus*
SWELLFISH *Sphaeroides maculatus*
SWELLTOAD *Sphaeroides spengleri*
SWORDFISH *Histiophorus orientalis, Xiphias gladius*
SWORDFISH, BROADBILL *Xiphias gladius*
SWORDFISH, REAL *Makaira mazara*

TALLYWAG *Centropristes striatus*
TAMBOR *Sebastopyr ruberrimus, Sphaeroides spengleri*
TAPIRFISH, LARGESCALE *Notacanthus nasus*
TARPON *Megalops cyprinoides, Tarpon atlanticus*
TARWHINE *Rhabdosargus sarba*
TASSEL FISH, INDIAN *Polynemus indicus*
TAUTOG *Tautoga onitis*
TENCH *Tinca tinca*
TENPOUNDER *Elops saurus*
TEYSMANN'S SPOTTED CATFISH *Clarias batrachus*
THICK-LIPPED GREY MULLET *Mugil chelo*
THIMBLE-EYED LING *Urophycis chuss*
THORNBACK RAY *Raja clavata*
THORNY SKATE *Raja radiata*
THREADFIN *Polynemus indicus*
THREADFIN BREAM, JAPANESE *Nemipterus japonicus*
THREADFIN, GIANT *Eleutheronema tetradactylum*
THREE-BANDED SHEEPSHEAD *Chaetodipterus faber*
THREE-SPINED STICKLEBACK *Gasterosteus aculeatus*
THREE-TAILED PORGY *Chaetodipterus faber*
THRESHER *Alopias pelagicus*
THRESHER SHARK *Alopias profundus*
THUMB, MILLER'S *Cottus gobio*
THUNDERPUMPER *Aplodinotus grunniens*
TIDDLER *Gasterosteus aculeatus*
TIGER FLATHEAD *Neoplatycephalus richardsoni*
TIGER PUFFER *Fugu rubripes*
TIGER SHARK *Galeocerdo arcticus, Scylliorhinus torazame*
TIGRONE *Galeocerdo arcticus*
TILAPIA *Tilapia mossambica*
TIMBER CRAPPIE *Pomoxis annularis*
TINMOUTH *Pomoxis annularis*
TIN PERCH *Pomoxis annularis*
TOADFISH *Opsanus tau*
TOBACCO BOX *Eupomotis gibbosus, Raja erinacea*
TOMCOD, ATLANTIC *Microgadus tomcod*
TOMCOD, PACIFIC *Microgadus proximus*
TOMMY ROUGH *Arripis georgianus*
TONGUE, BLACK COW *Rhinoplagusia japonica*
TONGUE SOLE, BENGAL *Cynoglossus bengalensis*
TOP MINNOW *Gambusia holbrooki*
TOPE *Eugaleus galeus*
TORPEDO *Narke japonica, Torpedo nobiliana*
TORPEDO, ATLANTIC *Tetranarce occidentalis, Torpedo nobiliana*
TORPEDO TREVALLY *Megalaspis cordyla*
TORSK *Brosme brosme*
TREVALLY, SILVER *Usacaranx georgianus*
TREVALLY, SIX-BANDED *Caranx sexfasciatus*
TREVALLY, TORPEDO *Megalaspis cordyla*
TREVALLY, WHITE *Usacaranx georgianus*

TRIGGER FISH, GREY   *Balistes capriscus*
TRIPLE TAIL   *Chaetodipterus faber*
TROUT, ALEKEY   *Lota lota maculosa*
TROUT, BROWN   *Salmo trutta*
TROUT, COASTAL CUTTHROAT   *Salmo clarkii*
TROUT, EASTERN BROOK   *Salvelinus fontinalis*
TROUT, GREAT LAKES   *Cristivomer namaycush*
TROUT, GREY   *Cynoscion regalis*
TROUT, KAMLOOPS   *Salmo gairdnerii kamloops*
TROUT, LAKE   *Cristivomer namaycush, Salvelinus namaycush*
TROUT, MACKINAW   *Cristivomer namaycush*
TROUT, MALMA   *Salvelinus malma*
TROUT, RAINBOW   *Salmo gairdnerii*
TROUT REEF-COD   *Epinephelus fario*
TROUT, SALMON   *Arripis trutta*
TROUT, SEA   *Cynoscion regalis, Salvelinus alpinus, Salvelinus fontinalis, Salmo trutta*
TROUT, SILVER   *Oncorhynchus nerka kennerlyi*
TROUT, SISCOWET   *Salvelinus namaycush siscowet*
TROUT, SPECKLED   *Salvelinus fontinalis*
TROUT, SPOTTED SEA-   *Eriscion nebulosus*
TRUE BASS   *Epinephelus septemfasciatus*
TRUE LIZARD FISH   *Saurida undosquamis*
TRUE MULLET   *Mugil cephalus*
TRUE SARDINE   *Sardinops melanosticta*
TRUMPET FISH   *Aulostomus maculatus*
TRUMPETER WHITING   *Sillago maculata*
TUB FISH   *Trigla lucerna*
TUNA   *Thunnus thynnus thynnus*
TUNA, ALLISON'S   *Thunnus albacares*
TUNA, BIG-EYE   *Thunnus obesus*
TUNA, BLACK   *Promethichthys prometheus*
TUNA, BLUEFIN   *Thunnus thynnus thynnus*
TUNA, LONG-FINNED   *Thunnus alalunga*
TUNA, PACIFIC BLUEFIN   *Thunnus thynnus orientalis*
TUNA, YELLOWFIN   *Thunnus albacares*
TUNNY   *Thunnus thynnus thynnus*
TUNNY, LITTLE   *Thynnus thunnina*
TUNNY, SHORT-FINNED   *Sarda sarda*
TURBOT   *Atheresthes stomias, Reinhardtius hippoglossoides, Rhombus maximus*
TURBOT, INDIAN   *Psettodes erumei*
TURBOT, NEWFOUNDLAND   *Reinhardtius hippoglossoides*
TURKEY ROCKFISH   *Sebastodes ruberrimus*
TUSK   *Brosme brosme*
TWO-SPINED JEWFISH   *Sciaena diacanthus*

UNDULATE RAY   *Raja undulata*

VELVET BELLY   *Etmopterus spinax*
VIVIPAROUS BLENNY   *Zoarces viviparus*

WACHNA COD *Gadus nevaga*
WALLEYE *Stizostedion vitreum*
WALL-EYED HERRING *Pomolobus pseudoharengus*
WALL-EYED PIKE *Stizostedion vitreum*
WART PERCH *Psenopsis anomala*
WATERMELON *Katsuwonus pelamis*
WEAKFISH *Cynoscion regalis*
WEAKFISH, SPOTTED *Eriscion nebulosus*
WEATHERFISH *Misgurnus fossilis*
WEEVER, GREATER *Trachinus draco*
WELS *Silurus glanis*
WHIP SCULPIN *Hemitripterus americanus*
WHIP-TAIL SHARK *Alopias pelagicus*
WHIP-TAIL STINGRAY, BANDED *Dasyatis uarnak*
WHITE CAT *Ictalurus punctatus*
WHITE CRAPPIE *Pomoxis annularis*
WHITE CROCODILE FISH *Chaenocephalus aceratus*
WHITE EYE *Stizostedion vitreum*
WHITEFISH *Coregonus clupeaformis, Ptychocheilus oregonensis, Salangichthys microdon*
WHITEFISH, LAKE *Coregonus clupeaformis*
WHITEFISH, OCEAN *Caulolatilus princeps*
WHITEFISH, ROCKY MOUNTAIN *Prosopium williamsoni*
WHITE HAKE *Urophycis chuss, Urophycis tenuis*
WHITE MULLET *Chanos chanos, Mugil curema*
WHITE PERCH *Aplodinotus grunniens, Morone americana, Pomoxis annularis, Roccus americanus*
WHITE POMFRET *Stromateus sinensis*
WHITE SALMON *Seriola dorsalis*
WHITE SEAPERCH *Phanerodon furcatus*
WHITE SPOT *Girella nigricans*
WHITE SPOTTED GREENLING *Hexagrammos stelleri*
WHITE SPOTTED SHOVELNOSE RAY *Rhynchobatus djiddensis*
WHITE SUCKER *Catostomus commersonii, Moxostoma aureolum*
WHITE TIP SHARK *Carcharhinus longimanus*
WHITE TREVALLY *Usacaranx georgianus*
WHITING *Gadus (Merlangius) merlangus, Merluccius bilinearis*
WHITING, COUCH'S *Gadus poutassou*
WHITING, KING *Menticirrhus littoralis*
WHITING, KING GEORGE *Sillaginodes punctatus*
WHITING, SPOTTED *Sillaginodes punctatus*
WHITING, TRUMPETER *Sillago maculata*
WIFE, OLD *Spondyliosoma cantharus*
WILL, BLACK *Centropristes striatus*
WILLIAM, SWEET *Mustelus mustelus*
WINDERMERE CHAR *Salvelinus willughbii*
WINDFISH *Notemigonus crysoleucas*
WINDOWPANE *Lophopsetta maculata*
WINTER FLOUNDER *Pseudopleuronectes americanus*
WINTER SKATE *Raja ocellata, Raja stabuliforis*

WIRRAH   *Acanthistius serratus*
WITCH FLOUNDER   *Glyptocephalus cynoglossus*
WOLF FISH, ATLANTIC   *Anarhichas lupus*
WOLF FISH, SPOTTED   *Anarhichas minor*
WOLF FISH, STRIPED   *Anarhichas lupus*
WOLF HERRING   *Chirocentrus dorab*
WRASSE, BAILLON'S   *Crenilabrus melops*
WRASSE, BALLAN   *Labrus bergylta*
WRASSE, GREEN   *Labrus turdus*
WRASSE, PEACOCK   *Crenilabrus pavo*
WRECKFISH, ATLANTIC   *Polyprion americanus*

YELLOWBELLY   *Eupomotis gibbosus*
YELLOW DOG SHARK   *Scoliodon sorrakowah*
YELLOWFIN TUNA   *Thunnus albacares*
YELLOW-FINNED GROUPER   *Trisotropis venenosus*
YELLOWFISH   *Cephalopholis fulvus*
YELLOW GOATFISH   *Upeneoides sulphureus*
YELLOW GRUNT   *Haemulon flavolineatum, Haemulon sciurus*
YELLOW GURNARD   *Trigla lucerna*
YELLOW NED   *Perca flavescens*
YELLOW PERCH   *Eupomotis gibbosus, Perca flavescens*
YELLOW PIKE   *Stizostedion vitreum*
YELLOW PORGY   *Taius tumifrons*
YELLOWTAIL   *Leiostomus xanthurus, Seriola dorsalis, Seriola quinqueradiata*
YELLOWTAIL FLOUNDER   *Limander ferruginea*
YELLOWTAIL ROCKFISH   *Sebastodes flavidus*
YELLOWTAIL SNAPPER   *Ocyurus chrysurus*
YOUNG SHAD   *Notemigonus crysoleucas*

BIBLIOGRAPHY AND AUTHOR INDEX

References marked with an asterisk (*) have yielded chemical data for Parts II and III, where they are identified by the numbers in the left hand margin. Figures in italics refer to pages in the text where references are quoted.

1. Abdallah, M. M. and Salah, M. K. (1961). Relation between vitamin A content in livers and the feeding habitat of fishes in the Red Sea. *J. Pharm. Sci. U. Arab. Rep.* **2,** 135–7. *200*

*2. Abderhalden, E., Baertich, E. and Ziesecke, W. (1936). On the content of amino acids in cod muscle. *Hoppe-Seyler's Z.physiol. Chem.* **240,** 152–62.

3. Ackman, R. G. (1967a). The influence of lipids on fish quality. *J. Fd Technol.* **2,** 169–81. *292*

4. Ackman, R. G. (1967b). Characteristics of the fatty acid composition and biochemistry of some freshwater fish oils and lipids in comparison with marine oils and lipids. *Comp. Biochem. Physiol.* **22,** 907–22.

*5. Ackman, R. G., Addison, R. F. and Eaton, C. A. (1968). Unusual occurrence of squalene in a fish, the Euchalon, *Thaleichthys pacificus. Nature, Lond.* **220,** 1033–4. *287*

*6. Ackman, R. G. and Burgher, R. D. (1964a). Cod flesh: component fatty acids as determined by gas-liquid chromatography. *J. Fish. Res. Bd Can.* **21,** 367–71.

*7. Ackman, R. G. and Burgher, R. D. (1964b). Cod roe: component fatty acids as determined by gas-liquid chromatography. *J. Fish. Res. Bd Can.* **21,** 469–76.

*8. Ackman, R. G. and Cormier, M. G. (1967). α-tocopherol in some Atlantic fish and shellfish with particular reference to live-holding without food. *J. Fish. Res. Bd Can.* **24,** 357–73. *21, 22, 25, 200, 252, 292*

9. Ackman, R. G., Eaton, C. A., Bligh, E. G. and Lantz, A. W. (1967). Freshwater fish oils: yields and composition of oils from reduction of sheepshead, tullibee, maria and alewife. *J. Fish. Res. Bd Can.* **24,** 1219–27. *147*

*10. Ackman, R. G., Eaton, C. A. and Ke, P. J. (1967). Canadian marine oils of low iodine value: fatty acid composition of oils from Newfoundland turbot (Greenland halibut), certain Atlantic herring, and a sablefish. *J. Fish. Res. Bd Can.* **24,** 2563–72.

*11. Addison, R. F., Ackman, R. G. and Hingley, J. (1968). Distribution of fatty acids in cod flesh lipids. *J. Fish. Res. Bd Can.* **25,** 2083–90.

*12. Aitkhozhin, M. A., Belitsina, N. V. and Spirin, A. S. (1964). Nucleic acids during early development of fish embryos (*Misgurnus fossilis*). *Biokhimiya* **29,** 169–75. *74*

13. Alderdice, D. F. and Forrester, C. R. (1968). Some effects of salinity and temperature on early development and survival of the English sole (*Parophrys vetulus*). *J. Fish. Res. Bd Can.* **25,** 495–521. *69*

*14. Alexander, K. M. (1955). A comparison of the gross chemical composition of the red and white muscles in the two fishes, *Scatophagus argus* and *Labeo rohita. J. Anim. Morph. Physiol.* **1** (2), 58–61. *21, 23, 24, 25*

15. Ali, S. M., Haq, S. A. and Mahdihassan, S. (1958). Studies on shark liver oil. Part 1—physico-chemical constants and vitamin 'A' content of liver oil from sharks of the Karachi coast. *Pakist. J. scient. ind. Res.* **1,** 70–2. *92*

*16. Allison, A. C., Cecil, R., Charlwood, P. A., Gratzer, W. B., Jacobs, S. and Snow, N. S. (1960). Haemoglobin of the lamprey, *Lampetra fluviatilis. Biochim. biophys. Acta* **42,** 43–8. *137*

17. Alm, G. (1959). Connection between maturity, size and age in fishes. *Rep. Inst. Freshwat. Res. Drottningholm* **40,** 5–145. *117, 127, 211*

18. Amano, K. and Bito, M. (1951). Consequence of free amino acids generated from decomposing fish muscle. *Bull. Jap. Soc. scient. Fish.* **16,** (12), 10–16. *20*

*19. Amano, K., Bito, M. and Kawabata, T. (1953). Handling effect upon biochemical change in the fish muscle immediately after catch—1. Difference of glycolysis in the frigate mackerel killed by various methods. *Bull. Jap. Soc. scient. Fish.* **19,** 487–98. *7, 31*

*20. Amano, K., Yamada, K. and Bito, M. (1963a). Detection and identification of formaldehyde in gadoid fish. *Bull. Jap. Soc. scient. Fish.* **29,** 695–701.

*21. Amano, K., Yamada, K. and Bito, M. (1963b). Contents of formaldehyde and volatile amines in different tissues of gadoid fish. *Bull. Jap. Soc. scient. Fish.* **29,** 860–4.

*22. Ambe, K. S. and Sohonie, K. (1957a). A comparative study of the protein of shark and skate casein. I. Isolation, analysis and comparison of amino-acid make-up. *Indian J. Fish.* **4,** 113–23.

*23. Ambe, K. S. and Sohonie, K. (1957b). A comparative study of the proteins of shark and skate casein. III. Essential amino-acid content and the nutritive value. *Indian J. Fish.* **4,** 130–33.

*24. Ananichev, A. V. (1959). Digestive enzymes of fish and seasonal changes in their activity. *Biokhimiya* **24,** 952–8. *170, 254*

*25. Ananichev, A. V. (1961). Comparative biochemical data for some freshwater invertebrates and fish. *Biochemistry, N.Y.* **26,** 16–26.

*26. Ananichev, A. V. (1963). Amino acid content of proteins of some freshwater invertebrates and fish. *Data on biology and hydrology of the Volga region reservoirs. USSR Acad. Sci. Biol., Institute of Internal waters* 38–41.

27. Ancellin, J. (1953). Observations on the cod of Terra Nova and Labrador. *Rapp. P.- v. Réun. Cons. perm. int. Explor. Mer* **136,** 72–6. *117*

*28. Anderson, D. W. and Fellers, C. R. (1952). The occurrence of trimethylamine and trimethylamine oxide in freshwater fishes. *Fd Res.* **17,** 472–4. *202*

29. Anderson, M. L. and Steinberg, M. A. (1964). Effect of lipid content on protein-sodium linolenate interaction in fish muscle homogenates. *J. Food Sci.* **29,** 327–30. *131*

30. Ando, K. (1962a). Change in the lipid during development of rainbow trout eggs. *Bull. Jap. Soc. scient. Fish.* **28,** 73–6. *71*

*31. Ando, K. (1962b). Change in fatty acids composition of acetone soluble lipids during development of rainbow trout eggs. *Bull. Jap. Soc. scient. Fish.* **28,** 340–3. *78*

32. Ando, K. (1965). Ultracentrifugal analysis of yolk proteins in rainbow trout and their changes during development. *Can. J. Biochem.* **43,** 373–9. *73*

33. Annegers, J. (1954). Total body water in rats and mice. *Proc. Soc. exp. Biol. Med.* **87,** 454–9. *230*

*34. Anon. (1959). Amino acid content of fillets of various fishes. *Rep. Fish. Res. Bd Can.* 132.

35. Anon. (1960). Definitive rules for the nomenclature of the vitamins. *J. Am. chem. Soc.* **82,** 5581–3. *259, 292*

36. Anon. (1965). Tentative rules: trivial names of miscellaneous compounds of importance in biochemistry. *Biochim. biophys. Acta* **107,** 1–4. *67*

37. Anon. (1966a). Analytical methods committee. Report prepared by the fish products sub-committee. Nitrogen factor for cod flesh. *Analyst, Lond.* **91,** 540–2. *36, 96, 169, 173, 239*

38. Anon. (1966b). Farmed fish are easy prey. *New Scient.* **30,** 74–5. *55*

39. Anon. (1966c). Relationship between fat and water in mackerel (*Scomber scombrus*). *Torry Res. Handl. Preserv. Fish* 56. *225*

40. Arai, K. and Saito, T. (1963). Studies on the organic phosphates in muscle of aquatic animals. XIII. Muscle levels of uric acid and nicotinamide-adenine dinucleotide in fresh and frozen stored fish. *Bull. Fac. Fish. Hokkaido Univ.* **13,** 193–9. *23, 24*

*41. Arakaki, J. and Suyama, M. (1966a). Amino acid composition of the protein of anchovy. *Bull. Jap. Soc. scient. Fish.* **32,** 70–3.

*42. Arakaki, J. and Suyama, M. (1966b). Free and conjugated amino acids in the extractives of anchovy. *Bull. Jap. Soc. scient. Fish.* **32,** 74–9. *20, 24*

*43. Arakawa, K. (1949). Study of fish-insulin. 1. The value of aburazame (*Squalus suckleyi* Girard) pancreas for insulin source. *Bull. Jap. Soc. scient. Fish.* **15,** 402–6.

44. Arevalo, A. (1948). Study of the variation in the chemical composition of the *Trachurus trachurus* L. *Boln Inst. esp. Oceanogr.* no. 8, 13 pp. *91, 227, 242*

45. Arnheim, N., Cocks, G. T. and Wilson, A. C. (1967). Molecular size of hagfish muscle lactate dehydrogenase. *Science, N.Y.* **157**, 568–9. *142*

46. Asboe-Hansen, G. (1963). Connective tissue. *A. Rev. Physiol.* **25**, 41–60. *101*

*47. Aschehoug, V., Kringstad, H. and Lunde, G. (1939). The vitamin D potency of different fish and fish products. *J. Soc. chem. Ind., Lond.*, **58**, 220–3.

*48. Astrup, H. N., Marko, A. M. and Young, E. G. (1958). Some physical and chemical properties of acid-soluble ichthyocol. *In* "Recent Advances in Gelatin and Glue Research" (G. Stainsby, ed.), pp. 76–81. Pergamon Press, London.

*49. Aten, A. H. W., Dalenberg, J. W. and Bakkum, W. C. M. (1961). Concentration of uranium in sea fish. *Hlth Phys.* **5**, 225–6.

*50. Aure, L. (1951). Vitamin A in pyloric caecae of cod and coalfish. *FiskDir. Skr. Serie Teknologiske undersøkelser* **2** (1), 12 pp.

51. Baalsrud, K. (1956). Astaxanthin in the muscle of cod. *Nature, Lond.* **178**, 1182–3. *266*

*52. Baars, J. K. (1938). Content of riboflavin (vitamin B_2) in foodstuffs. *Geneesk. Tijdschr. Ned-Indië* **78**, 3145–51.

53. Bachelard, H. S., Campbell, W. J. and McIlwain, H. (1962). The sodium and other ions of mammalian cerebral tissues, maintained and electrically stimulated in vitro. *Biochem. J.* **84**, 225–32. *43*

54. Baggerman, B. (1962). Some endocrine aspects of fish migration. *Gen. Comp. Endocrinol—Suppl.* **1**, 188–205. *110*

*55. Bai, P. A. and Kalyani, M. (1960a). On the composition of the scales and skin of *Boleophthalmus boddaerti* Pall and *Mugil dussumieri* (Val). *J. Anim. Morph. Physiol.* **7**, 71–7.

*56. Bai, P. A. and Kalyani, M. (1960b). Studies on ascorbic acid in fish tissues. 1. *J. Anim. Morph. Physiol.* **7**, 162–6. *291*

*57. Bai, P. A. and Kalyani, M. (1960c). Studies on the ascorbic acid content of fish tissues. 2. *J. zool. Soc. India.* **12**, 216–9. *291*

*58. Bai, P. A. and Kalyani, M. (1961). The relative content of imino acids in the skin and scales of some teleosts. *J. Anim. Morph. Physiol.* **8**, 126–9.

59. Bailey, B., Koran, P. and Bradley, H. C. (1942). The autolysis of muscle of highly active and less active fish. *Biol. Bull. mar. biol. Lab., Woods Hole* **83**, 129–36. *151, 231*

*60. Bailey, B. E., Carter, N. M. and Swain, L. A. (1952). Marine oils, with particular reference to those of Canada. *Bull. Fish. Res. Bd Can.* **89**, 413 pp., Ottawa. *291*

61. Bailey, J. E. (1964). Russian theories on the inferior quality of hatchery-reared chum salmon fry. *Progve Fish Cult.* **26**, 130 only. *56*

62. Bailey, K. (1937). Composition of the myosins and myogen of skeletal muscle. *Biochem. J.* **31**, 1406–13. *238*

63. Bailey, K. (1954). Structure proteins. II. Muscle. *In* "The Proteins" (H. Neurath and K. Bailey, eds.) Chapter 24, Vol. 2B, pp. 951–1055. Academic Press, New York. *16*

*64. Bailey, R. E. (1957). The effect of oestradiol on serum calcium, phosphorus and protein of goldfish. *J. exp. Zool.* **136**, 455–69. *61, 62, 120, 267*

65. Bainbridge, R. (1963). Caudal fin and body movement in the propulsion of some fish. *J. exp. Biol.* **40**, 23–56. *11*

66. Baldwin, E. (1948). "An Introduction to Comparative Biochemistry" 3rd. edn., Cambridge University Press. *129, 138, 261*

67. Baldwin, E. (1951). 1. Some comparative aspects of the biochemistry of fish. *Biochem. Soc. Symp.* **6**, 3–7. *187*

68. Bams, R. A. (1967). Differences in performance of naturally and artificially propagated sockeye salmon migrant fry, as measured with swimming and predation tests. *J. Fish. Res. Bd Can.* **24**, 1117–53. *55*

*69. Bandier, E. (1939). Quantitative estimation of nicotinic acid in biological material. *Biochem. J.* **33**, 1130–4.

*70. Bandurski, R. S., Bradstreet, E. and Scholander, P. F. (1968). Metabolic changes in the mud-skipper during asphyxia or exercise. *Comp. Biochem. Physiol.* **24**, 271–4.

*71. Banerjee, D. K. and Chatterjea, J. B. (1963a). Vitamin B_{12} content of some articles of Indian diets and effect of cooking on it. *Br. J. Nutr.* **17**, 385–9.

*72. Banerjee, D. K. and Chatterjea, J. B. (1963b). Vitamin B_{12} content of Indian fishes and the effect of boiling on its availability. *Bull. Calcutta Sch. trop. Med. Hyg.* **11**, 11–12.

*73. Banerjee, D. K. and Chatterjea, J. B. (1963c). Effect of cooking on the availability of folic acid in Indian fishes. *Bull. Calcutta Sch. trop. Med. Hyg.* **11**, 49–50.

*74. Bara, G. (1965). Glucose-6-phosphate dehydrogenase activity in the ovaries of *Scomber scomber* L. *Experientia* **21**, 638–40.

75. Barets, A. (1961). Contribution to the study of 'slow' and 'fast' motor systems in the lateral muscle of teleosts. *Archs Anat. microsc. Morph. exp.* **50**, Suppl., 91–187. *29*

76. Barnes, H., Barnes, M. and Finlayson, D. M. (1963). The metabolism during starvation of *Balanus balanoides*. *J. mar. biol. Ass. U.K.* **43**, 213–23. *250*

*77. Barrett, I. and Williams, A. A. (1965). Haemoglobin content of the blood of fifteen species of marine fishes. *Calif. Fish Game* **51**, 612–8.

78. Barrington, E. J. W. (1957). The alimentary canal and digestion. *In* "The Physiology of Fishes" (M. E. Brown, ed.), Vol. 1, pp. 109–161. Academic Press, New York. *203, 205*

79. Barry, J. M. and o'Rourke, F. J. (1959). Species specificity of fish mucus. *Nature, Lond.* **184**, 2039 only. *135*

*80. Baruh, J. and Gillard, J. (1959). Amino acid composition of local food-fishes in Katanga. *Bull. Soc. chim. Fr.* **41**, 1017–25.

*81. Baslow, M. H. (1967). N-acetyl-L-histidine metabolism in the fish eye: evidence for ocular fluid-lens L-histidine recycling. *Expl Eye Res.* **6**, 336–42.

82. Baslow, M. H. and Nigrelli, R. F. (1964). The effect of thermal acclimation on brain cholinesterase activity of the killifish, *Fundulus heteroclitus*. *Zoologica* **49**, 41–51. *171, 213*

*83. Beach, E. F., Munks, B. and Robinson, A. (1943). The amino acid composition of animal tissue protein. *J. biol. Chem.* **148**, 431–9. *58, 265*

84. Beamish, F. W. H. (1966). Muscular fatigue and mortality in haddock, *Melanogrammus aeglefinus*, caught by otter trawl. *J. Fish. Res. Bd Can.* **23**, 1507–21. *44*

*85. Beamish, F. W. H. (1968). Glycogen and lactic acid concentrations in Atlantic cod (*Gadus morhua*) in relation to exercise. *J. Fish. Res. Bd Can.* **25**, 837–51.

86. Beatty, D. D. (1966). A study of the succession of visual pigments in Pacific salmon (*Oncorhynchus*). *Can. J. Zool.* **44**, 429–55. *184, 185*

87. Beatty, S. A. (1939). Studies of fish spoilage. III. The trimethylamine oxide content of the muscles of Nova Scotia fish. *J. Fish. Res. Bd Can.* **4**, 229–32. *145, 202*

*88. Beck, A. B. (1956). The copper content of the liver and blood of some vertebrates. *Aust. J. Zool.* **4**, 1–18.

89. Belding, D. L. (1934). The cause of the high mortality in the Atlantic salmon after spawning. *Trans. Am. Fish. Soc.* **64**, 219–24. *112, 119*

90. Bellamy, D. (1966). On the lipochromes in the skin of marine teleost fish with special reference to the painted comber (*Serranus scriba* L.). *Comp. Biochem. Physiol.* **17**, 1137–40. *50, 268*

91. Bellamy, D. (1968). Metabolism of the red piranha (*Rooseveltiella nattereri*) in relation to feeding behaviour. *Comp. Biochem. Physiol.* **25**, 343–7. *50, 250*

*92. Bellamy, D. and Chester Jones, I. (1961). Studies on *Myxine glutinosa*. I. The chemical composition of the tissues. *Comp. Biochem. Physiol.* **3**, 175–83. *137*

93. Bendall, J. R. and Voyle, C. A. (1967). A study of the histological changes in the growing muscles of beef animals. *J. Fd Technol.* **2**, 259–83. *85*

94. Benditt, E., Morrison, P. and Irving, L. (1941). The blood of the Atlantic salmon during migration. *Biol. Bull. mar. biol. Lab., Woods Hole* **80**, 429–40. *176, 188*

95. Benoit, G. J. and Norris, E. R. (1945). Studies on trimethylamine oxide. II. The origin of trimethylamine oxide in young salmon. *J. biol. Chem.* **158**, 439–42. *145, 202, 288*

*96. Bentley, P. J. and Follett, B. K. (1965). Fat and carbohydrate reserves in the river lamprey during spawning migration. *Life Sci.*, **4**, 2003–7. *99, 114, 119, 251*

97. Ben-Tuvia, A. (1963a). Influence of temperature on the vertebral number of *Sardinella aurita* from the eastern Mediterranean. *Israel J. Zool.* **12**, 59–66. *155*

98. Ben-Tuvia, A. (1963b). Variation in vertebral number of young *Sardinella aurita* in relation to temperature during spawning season. *Rapp. P.-v. Réun. Commn int. Explor. scient. Mer Méditerr.* **17**, 313–8. *155*

99. Berdyshev, G. D., Korotaev, G. K., Boyarskikh, G. V. and Vanyushin, B. F. (1967). Investigation of DNA nucleotide composition in somatic tissues of spawning humpback salmon. *Tsitologiya i genetika* **1**, 56–60. *109*

*100. Berlin, E. and Kutscher, Fr. (1924). *Zh. obshch. Biol.* **81**, 87. Quoted by Shewan (1951).

101. Beverton, R. J. H. and Holt, S. J. (1959). A review of the lifespans and mortality rates of fish in nature, and their relation to growth and other physiological characteristics. *Ciba Fdn Colloq. Ageing* **5**, 142–80. *126*

102. Bhushana Rao, K. S. P. (1965). Biochemical studies on red and white muscles of *Caranx sexfasciatus* Quoy and Gaimard. *Proc. Indian Acad. Sci. Sci.* **62**, 87–91. *107, 108*

103. Bilinski, E. (1963). Utilisation of lipids by fish. 1. Fatty acid oxidation by tissue slices from dark and white muscle of rainbow trout (*Salmo gairdnerii*). *Can. J. Biochem. Physiol.* **41**, 107–12. *31*

104. Bilinski, E. (1964). Biosynthesis of trimethylammonium compounds in aquatic animals. IV. Precursors of trimethylamine oxide and betaine in marine teleosts. *J. Fish. Res. Bd Can.* **21**, 765–71. *288*

*105. Bilinski, E. and Gardner, L. J. (1968). Effect of starvation on free fatty acid level in blood plasma and muscular tissues of rainbow trout (*Salmo gairdneri*). *J. Fish. Res. Bd Can.* **25**, 1555–60. *242*

*106. Bilinski, E. and Jonas, R. E. E. (1966). Lecithinase activity in the muscle of rainbow trout (*Salmo gairdnerii*). *J. Fish. Res. Bd Can.* **23**, 207–20.

107. Bishop, C. M. and Odense, P. H. (1967). The ultrastructure of the white striated myotomal muscle of the cod, *Gadus morhua*. *J. Fish. Res. Bd Can.* **24**, 2549–53. *11, 16*

*108. Bito, M. and Amano, K. (1962). Significance of adenosine triphosphate decomposition in fish muscle at approximately —2°C. *Bull. Tokai reg. Fish. Res. Lab.* **32**, 149–53.

109. Black, E. C. (1940). The transport of oxygen by the blood of freshwater fish. *Biol. Bull. mar. biol. Lab.*, *Woods Hole* **79**, 215–29. *149*

*110. Black, E. C. (1955). Blood levels of haemoglobin and lactic acid in some freshwater fishes following exercise. *J. Fish. Res. Bd Can.* **12**, 917–29. *39, 40*

*111. Black, E. C. (1957). Alterations in the blood level of lactic acid in certain salmonoid fishes following muscular activity. III. Sockeye salmon, *Onco-rhynchus nerka*. *J. Fish. Res. Bd Can.* **14**, 807–14. *40, 47*

112. Black, E. C. (1958). Hyperactivity as a lethal factor in fish. *J. Fish. Res. Bd Can.* **15**, 573–86. *47*

113. Black, E. C., Bosomworth, N. J. and Docherty, G. E. (1966). Combined effect of starvation and severe exercise on glycogen metabolism of rainbow trout, *Salmo gairdneri*. *J. Fish. Res. Bd Can.* **23**, 1461–3. *41, 42, 43*

*114. Black, E. C. and Connor, A. R. (1964). Effects of MS 222 on glycogen and lactate levels in rainbow trout (*Salmo gairdneri*). *J. Fish. Res. Bd Can.* **21**, 1539–42.

*115. Black, E. C., Connor, A. R., Lam, K.-C. and Chiu, W.-G. (1962). Changes in glycogen, pyruvate and lactate in rainbow trout (*Salmo gairdneri*) during and following muscular activity. *J. Fish. Res. Bd Can.* **19**, 409–36. *7*

*116. Black, E. C., Manning, G. T. and Hayashi, K. (1966). Changes in levels of haemoglobin, oxygen, carbon dioxide, pyruvate and lactate in venous blood of rainbow trout (*Salmo gairdnerii*) during and following severe muscular activity. *J. Fish. Res. Bd Can.* **23**, 738–95. *40, 43*

*117. Black, E. C., Robertson, A. C., Hanslip, A. R. and Chiu, W.-G. (1960). Alterations in glycogen, glucose and lactate in rainbow and kamloops trout, *Salmo gairdneri*, following muscular activity. *J. Fish. Res. Bd Can.* **17**, 487–500.

118. Black, E. C. and Tredwell, S. J. (1967). Effect of a partial loss of scales and mucus on carbohydrate metabolism in rainbow trout (*Salmo gairdneri*). *J. Fish. Res. Bd Can.* **24**, 939–53. *46, 47*

119. Black, M. M. and Schwartz, H. M. (1950). South African fish products. XXX.—Seasonal changes in the composition of the pilchard (*Sardina ocellata* Jenyns). *J. Sci. Fd Agric.* **1**, 182–5. *225*

*120. Blanco, M. M., Larru, F. N. and Lobillo, E. (1956). Spectrophotometric determination of iron, manganese, copper, molybdenum, cobalt and total phosphorus in the egg of hake (*Merluccius merluccius* L.). *An. Bromat.* **8**, 315–7.

*121. Blaxter, J. H. S. and Holliday, F. G. T. (1963). The behaviour and physiology of herring and other clupeids. *Adv. mar. Biol.* **1**, 261–293. *69, 104, 116, 117, 155*

*122. Bligh, E. G. and Scott, M. A. (1966). Lipids of cod muscle and the effect of frozen storage. *J. Fish. Res. Bd Can.* **23**, 1025–36. *21, 25*

123. Block, R. J. (1959). The approximate amino acid composition of wild and hatchery trout (*Salvelinus fontinalis*) and some of their principal foods (*Gammarus* and *Hexagenia bilineata*). *Contr. Boyce Thomson Inst. Pl. Res.* **20**, 103–5. *54, 199*

*124. Block, R. J. and Bolling, D. (1945). "The Amino Acid Composition of Proteins and Foods." Charles Thomas, Springfield, Ill.

*125. Block, R. J., Horwitt, M. K. and Bolling, D. (1949). Comparative protein chemistry. The composition of the proteins of human teeth and fish scales. *J. dent. Res.* **28,** *518–24.*

126. Block, R. J. and Weiss, K. W. (1956). "Amino acid Handbook." Charles Thomas, Springfield, Ill. *75*

*127. Bluhm, H. M. and Tarr, H. L. A. (1957). Marine fish muscle nucleic acids. *Can. J. Biochem. Physiol.* **35,** 767–9.

*128. Bocquet, J. (1967). Identification of several sugars in the plasma of a shark, *Scylliorhinus canicula.* *C.r.Séanc. Soc. Biol.* **161,** 836–40.

129. Boddeke, R., Slijper, E. J. and van der Stelt, A. (1959). Histological characteristics of the body-musculature of fishes in connection with their mode of life. *Koninklijke Ned. Akad. van Wetenschappen* Ser. C, **62,** 576–88. *17, 32*

*130. Boehlke, K. W., Church, R. L., Tiemeier, O. W. and Eleftheriou, B. E. (1966). Diurnal rhythm in plasma glucocorticoid levels in channel catfish (*Ictalurus punctatus*). *Gen. comp. Endocrinol.* **7,** 18–21.

131. Boëtius, I. and Boëtius, J. (1967). Studies on the European eel, *Anguilla anguilla* (L.). Experimental induction of the male sexual cycle, its relation to temperature and other factors. *Meddr Danm. Fisk.-og. Havunders.* **4,** 339–405. *222*

132. Bogucki, M. and Trzesinski, P. (1950). Fluctuations in the water and fat content of the cod. *J. Cons. perm. int. Explor. Mer* **16,** 208–10. *173*

*133. Bolognani, L. and Bolognani-Fantin, A. M. (1963). Composition of skin mucus in *Anguilla vulgaris.* *Archo Sci. biol.* **47,** 331–5.

134. Bon, W. F., Swanborn, P. L., Ruttenberg, G. J. C. M. and Dohrn, A. (1964). Comparative investigation of the soluble proteins of the eyelens of fish. *Pubbl. Staz. zool. Napoli* **34,** 59–65. *135, 141*

*135. Bone, Q. (1966). On the function of the two types of myotomal muscle fibre in elasmobranch fish. *J. mar. biol. Ass. U.K.* **46,** 321–49. *20, 33, 34*

*136. Booke, H. E. (1964a). Blood serum protein and calcium levels in yearling brook trout. *Progve Fish Cult.* **26,** 107–10. *123*

137. Booke, H. E. (1964b). A review of variations found in fish serum proteins. *N.Y. Fish Game J.* **11,** 47–57. *94, 135, 141, 164*

138. Booke, H. E. (1965). Increase of serum globulin levels with age in lake whitefish, *Coregonus clupeaformis.* *Trans. Am. Fish. Soc.* **94,** 397–8. *127*

139. Borek, Z. (1958). The contents of lipids and other components in the crucian's (*Carassius carassius* L.) body during hibernation and experimental starvation. *Polskie Archwm Hydrobiol.* **5,** 65–91. *230*

140. Bornstein, P. and Piez, K. A. (1964). A biochemical study of human skin collagen and the relation between intra- and intermolecular cross-linking. *J. clin. Invest.* **43,** 1813–23. *101*

*141. Bose, A. N., Das Gupta, S. K. and Srimani, B. N. (1958). Studies on fish of the Bay of Bengal. 1. Amino acid composition of flesh of Bombay Duck, Ribbon and Shark. *Indian J. vet. Sci.* **28,** 25–6.

*142. Botticelli, C. R., Hisaw, F. L. and Roth, W. D. (1963). Oestradiol-17β, oestrone and progesterone in the ovaries of lamprey (*Petromyzon marinus*). *Proc. Soc. exp. Biol. Med.* **114,** 255–7.

143. Bouck, G. R. and Ball, R. C. (1965). Influence of a diurnal oxygen pulse on fish serum proteins. *Trans. Am. Fish. Soc.* **94,** 363–70. *176*

144. Bowes, J. H., Elliott, R. G. and Moss, J. A. (1955). The composition of collagen and acid-soluble collagen of bovine skin. *Biochem. J.* **61,** 143–50. *101*

*145. Braekkan, O. R. (1955). Role of pantothenic acid in the reproductive cycle of ovaries in fish. *Nature, Lond.* **176,** 598 only. *68, 282*

*146. Braekkan, O. R. (1956). Function of the red muscle in fish. *Nature, Lond.* **178,** 747–8. *20, 24, 27*

*147. Braekkan, O. R. (1958a). Vitamins in Norwegian fish. III. Vitamins in different organs from the most important fish of the cod family (*Gadidae*) caught along the Norwegian coast. *FiskDir. Skr. Serie Teknologiske Undersøkelser* **3** (6), 32 pp. *261, 262*

*148. Braekkan, O. R. (1958b). Vitamins and the reproductive cycle of ovaries in cod (*Gadus morrhua*). *FiskDir. Skr. Serie Teknologiske Undersøkelser* **3** (7), 19pp. *65, 66*

*149. Braekkan, O. R. (1958c). Vitamin B_{12} in marine fish. *Nature, Lond.* **182,** 1386 only. *271*

*150. Braekkan, O. R. (1959). A comparative study of vitamins in the trunk muscles of fishes. *FiskDir. Skr. Serie Teknologiske undersøkelser* **3** (8), 42 pp. *18, 21–25, 27, 30, 96, 151, 200, 281, 282*

151. Braekkan, O. R. (1965). Fish as raw material. *Fiskets Gang* 1964 no. 5, 68–72. *226*

*152. Braekkan, O. R. and Boge, G. (1962a). Vitamin B_6 and the reproductive cycle of ovaries in cod (*Gadus morrhua*).   *Nature, Lond.* **193,** 394–5. *67, 68*

*153. Braekkan, O. R. and Boge, G. (1962b). Further studies on vitamins and the reproductive cycle of ovaries in cod (*Gadus morrhua*). *FiskDir. Skr. Serie Teknologiske undersøkelser* **4** (2), 15pp.

*154. Braekkan, O. R. and Boge, G. (1962c). A comparative study of amino acids in the muscle of different species of fish. *FiskDir. Skr. Serie Teknologiske undersøkelser* **4** (3), 19 pp. *65, 130*

*155. Braekkan, O. R. and Boge, G. (1965). Vitamins in Norwegian fish. IV. Vitamin B_6 and biotin in different organs from Gadidae caught along the Norwegian coast. *FiskDir. Skr. Serie Teknologiske undersøkelser* **4** (12), 11 pp. *20, 25*

*156. Braekkan, O. R., Hansen, K. and Skoglund, T. (1955). Vitamins in Norwegian fish. II. Vitamins in different organs from tuna (*Thunnus thynnus*) caught off the west coast of Norway. *FiskDir. Skr. Serie Teknologiske undersøkelser* 3 (3), 18 pp.

*157. Braekkan, O. R. and Probst, A. (1953). Vitamins in Norwegian fish. I. Nicotinic acid, riboflavin, pantothenic acid, vitamin B_{12} and vitamin A content in whole fish and different organs from fresh herring (*Clupea harengus*) and mackerel (*Scomber scombrus*). *FiskDir. Skr. Serie Teknologiske undersøkelser* 2 (13), 10 pp.

*158. Braganca, B. de M. (1944). Nicotinic acid content of fish. *Ann. Biochem. exp. Med.* 4, 41–4. *147*

159. Brandes, C. H. and Dietrich, R. (1953a). On the distribution of fat in the body of herrings. *Veröff. Inst. Meeresforsch. Bremerh.* 2, (1), 109–21. *36, 37*

160. Brandes, C. H. and Dietrich, R. (1953b). A review of the problem of fat and water content in the edible part of the herring. *Fette Seifen* 55, 533–41. *225*

161. Brandes, C. H. and Dietrich, R. (1956). Fat and water content in redfish. *Fette Seifen AnstrMittel* 58, 433–9. *225*

162. Brandes, C. H. and Dietrich, R. (1958). Observations on the correlations between fat and water content and the fat distribution in commonly eaten fish. *Veröff. Inst. Meeresforsch. Bremerh.* 5, 299–305. *225, 226*

163. Brawn, V. M. (1961a). Aggressive behaviour in the cod (*Gadus callarias* L.). *Behaviour* 18, 107–47. *49, 116*

164. Brawn, V. M. (1961b). Reproductive behaviour of the cod (*Gadus callarias* L.). *Behaviour* 18, 177–98. *49, 116*

165. Brett, J. R. (1956). Some principles in the thermal requirements of fishes. *Q. Rev. Biol.* 31, 75–87. *209*

166. Bridges, C. D. B. (1964a). Variation of visual pigment amongst individuals of an American minnow, *Notemigonus crysoleucas boscii*. *Vision Res.* 4, 233–9. *171, 184, 185*

167. Bridges, C. D. B. (1964b). Effect of season and environment on the retinal pigments of two fishes. *Nature, Lond.* 203, 191–2. *183, 184*

168. Bridges, C. D. B. (1965a). The grouping of fish visual pigments about preferred positions in the spectrum. *Vision Res.* 5, 223–38. *123, 180, 181*

169. Bridges, C. D. B. (1965b). Variability and relationships of fish visual pigments. *Vision Res.* 5, 239–51. *185, 186*

170. Bridges, C. D. B. (1965c). Visual pigments in a fish exposed to different light-environments. *Nature, Lond.* 206, 1161–2. *183*

171. Bridgwater, R. J., Haslewood, G. A. D. and Watt, J. R. (1963). Comparative studies of "bile salts". 17. A bile alcohol from *Chimaera monstrosa*. *Biochem. J.* 87, 28–31. *140*

172. Brocas, J. and Verzár, F. (1961). Measurement of isometric tension during thermic contraction as criterion of the biological age of collagen fibres. *Gerontologia* **5**, 223–7. *128*

*173. Brockerhoff, H., Ackman, R. G. and Hoyle, R. J. (1963). Specific distribution of fatty acids in marine lipids. *Archs Biochem. Biophys.* **100**, 9–12.

174. Brockerhoff, H. and Hoyle, R. J. (1967). Conversion of a dietary triglyceride into depot fat in fish and lobster. *Can. J. Biochem. Physiol.* **45**, 1365–70. *201*

*175. Brooke, R. O., Ravesi, E. M. and Steinberg, M. A. (1962). The composition of commercially important fish taken from New England waters. II. Proximate analysis of butterfish, flounder, pollock and hake, and their seasonal variation. *J. Food Sci.* **27**, 73–6.

176. Brown, G. W. (1964). Urea synthesis in elasmobranchs. *In* "Taxonomic Biochemistry and Serology" (C. A. Leone, ed.) pp. 407–16. The Ronald Press Company, New York. *139.*

*177. Brown, G. W. and Brown, S. G. (1967). Urea and its formation in coelacanth liver. *Science* **155**, 570–2. *139*

*178. Brown, W. D. (1960). Glucose metabolism in carp. *J. cell. comp. Physiol.* **55**, 81–5.

*179. Brown, W. D. (1962). The concentration of myoglobin and haemoglobin in tuna flesh. *J. Food Sci.* **27**, 26–8. *20*

*180. Brown, W. D. (1964). Chemical and physical properties of tuna myoglobins. *First internat. Congr. fd Sci. Technol.* pp. 55–60. Gordon and Breach, New York.

181. von Buddenbrock, W. (1938). What physiological problems are of interest to the marine biologist and his studies of the most important species of fish? Observations on the dying of captured sea-fish and on the lactic acid content of fish blood. *Rapp., P.-v. Réun. Cons. perm. int. Explor. Mer* **51** (4) no. 2, 7pp. *46*

182. Burd, A. C. (1962). Growth and recruitment in the herring of the southern North Sea. *Fishery Invest., Lond. Ser* 2. *Sea Fisheries* **23** (5), 1–40. *97*

*183. Burley, R. W. and Solomons, C. C. (1957). The amino acid composition of fish scale proteins. *S. Afr. ind. Chem.* **11**, 154–7.

*184. Burovina, I. V., Glazunov, V. V., Leont'ev, V. G., Nesterov, V. P., Skul'-skii, I. A., Fleishman, D. G. and Shmitko, M. N. (1963). Content of Li, Na, K, Rb and Cs in muscles of sea organisms of the Barents and Black Seas. *Dokl. Akad. Nauk. SSSR.* **149**, 413–5.

*185. Burovina, I. V., Glazunov, V. V., Leontyev, V. G., Nesterov, N. P. and Skul'skii, I. A. (1964). Alkaline elements in the evolution of sea organisms. *Zh. obshch. Biol.* **25**, 115–23. *138*

*186. Burovina, I. V. and Skul'skii, I. A. (1965). The alkali metals and the chemical specificity of brain tissue. *Dokl. Akad. Nauk. SSSR.* **160**, 236–9.

187. Burrows, R. E. (1964). Effects of accumulated excretory products on hatchery-reared salmonids. *Res. Rep. U.S. Fish Wildl. Serv.* **66,** 12 pp. *49*

*188. Burt, J. R. (1961). Free sugars and sugar phosphates in muscle of chill-stored aquarium cod (*Gadus callarias*). *J. Food Sci.* **26,** 462–8. *41, 42*

*189. Burt, J. R. (1966). Glycogenolytic enzymes of cod (*Gadus callarias*) muscle. *J. Fish. Res. Bd Can.* **23,** 527–38.

190. Burt, J. R. and Jones, N. R. (1961). Changes in sugar phosphates of chilled codling (*Gadus callarias*) muscle. *J. Sci. Fd Agric.* **12,** 344–8. *41, 42*

*191. Burt, J. R. and Stroud, G. D. (1966). The metabolism of sugar phosphates in cod muscle. *Bull. Jap. Soc. scient. Fish.* **32,** 204–12. *41, 42, 49*

*192. Butler, C. (1958). Nutritional value of fish in reference to atherosclerosis and current dietary research. *Comml Fish. Rev.* **20** (7), 7–16.

*193. Butler, D. G. (1967). Effect of ovine prolactin on tissue electrolyte composition of hypophysectomised freshwater eels (*Anguilla rostrata*). *J. Fish. Res. Bd Can.* **24,** 1823–6.

194. Buttkus, H. (1963). Red and white muscle of fish in relation to rigor mortis. *J. Fish. Res. Bd Can.* **20,** 45–58. *17, 20, 30, 31*

*195. Buttkus, H. (1967). Amino acid composition of myosin from trout muscle. *J. Fish. Res. Bd Can.* **24,** 1607–12.

*196. Buttkus, H. and Tarr, H. L. A. (1962). Physical and chemical changes in fish during cold storage. *Fd Technol., Champaign* **16,** 84–8.

*197. Buyanov, N. I. (1963). Determination of the potassium content of fish tissue by the method of flame photometry. *Materialy rybokhozyaistvennyx Issledovanii Severnogo Basseina, Sbornik* no. 1, 59–62.

*198. Cabbat, F. S. and Standal, B. R. (1965). The composition of essential and certain nonessential amino acids in selected Hawaii fish. *J. Food Sci.* **20,** 172–7.

*199. Caillouet, C. W. (1964). Blood lactic acid concentration of unexercised and exercised mature carp in winter and summer. *Iowa St. J. Sci.* **38,** 309–22.

200. Callegarini, C. (1966). Haemoglobins of some freshwater teleosts—electrophoretic study. *Ricerca Scient.* **36,** 59–64. Quoted by *Chem. Abstr.* **64,** 20284b (1966). *122*

*201. Campbell, J. (1935). The non-protein nitrogenous constituents of fish and lobster muscle. *J. biol. Bd Can.* **1,** 179–89.

*202. Cancio, M. (1961). Sodium and potassium in Puerto Rican meats and fish. *J. Am. diet. Ass.* **38,** 341–3.

203. Carey, F. G. and Teal, J. M. (1966). Heat conservation in tuna fish muscle. *Proc. natn. Acad. Sci. U.S.A.* **56,** 1464–9. *209*

204. Carlisle, D. B. and Denton, E. J. (1959). On the metamorphosis of the visual pigments of *Anguilla anguillla* (L). *J. mar. biol. Ass. U.K.* **38,** 97–102. *184*

*205. Carlson, B. M. (1961). A chromatographic analysis of the bound amino acids in lamprey muscle (Petromyzontidae). *J. exp. Zool.* **147,** 43–56. *83, 265*

*206. Carlson, C. J., Thurston, C. E. and Stansby, M. E. (1960). Chemical composition of raw, precooked, and canned tuna. 1. Core sampling methods. *Fd Technol., Champaign* **14,** 477–9.

207. Castell, C. H., Dale, J. and Greenough, M. F. (1959). Spoilage of fish in the vessels at sea: 6. Variations in the landed quality of trawler-caught Atlantic cod and haddock during a period of 13 months. *J. Fish. Res. Bd Can.* **16,** 223–33. *169*

208. Castell, C. H. and MacLean, J. (1964). Rancidity in lean fish muscle. II. Anatomical and seasonal variations. *J. Fish. Res. Bd Can.* **21,** 1361–9. *viii*

209. Causeret, J. (1962). Fish as a source of mineral nutrition. *In* "Fish as Food" (G. Borgstrom, ed.), Vol. 2, Chapter 5, pp. 205–34. Academic Press, New York. *260*

*210. Cedard, L., Fontaine, M. and Nomura, T. (1961). The concentration of oestrogens in the blood of adult salmon (*Salmo salar* L.) in fresh water. *C. r. Séanc. Soc. Biol.* **252,** 2656–7. *112*

*211. Cedard, L. and Nomura, T. (1961). Fluorimetric count after chromatographic separation of oestrogens in the blood of certain teleosts. *Bull. Inst. océanogr. Monaco* no. 1196, 12 pp. *121*

*212. Chan, D. K. O., Chester Jones, I., Henderson, I. W. and Rankin, J. C. (1967). Studies on the experimental alteration of water and electrolyte composition of the eel (*Anguilla anguilla* L.). *J. Endocrinol.* **37,** 297–317. *192, 193, 196*

213. Chance, R. E. (1962). Part I. Amino acid requirements of chinook salmon. Part II. Free amino acids and related compounds in the plasma of chinook salmon and swine. Purdue Univ. Ph.D. Thesis. University Microfilms Inc., Ann Arbor, Michigan, 63–2083. *99, 240*

214. Chance, R. E., Mertz, E. T. and Halver, J. E. (1964). Nutrition of salmonoid fishes. XII. Isoleucine, leucine, valine and phenylalanine requirements of chinook salmon and inter-relations between isoleucine and leucine for growth. *J. Nutr.* **83,** 177–85. *208*

*215. Chang, V. M. and Idler, D. R. (1960). Biochemical studies on sockeye salmon during spawning migration. XII. Liver glycogen. *Can. J. Biochem. Physiol.* **38,** 553–8. *98, 119*

*216. Chang, V. M., Tsuyuki, H. and Idler, D. R. (1960). Biochemical studies on sockeye salmon during spawning migration. XIII. The distribution of phosphorus compounds, creatine and inositol in the major tissues. *J. Fish. Res. Bd Can.* **17,** 565–82. *68*

*217. Cheldelin, V. H. and Williams, R. J. (1942). The B vitamin content of foods *Univ. Tex. Publs* no. 4237, 105–24.

*218. Chesley, L. C. (1934). The concentrations of proteases, amylase and lipase in certain marine fishes. *Biol. Bull. mar. biol. Lab., Woods Hole* **66,** 133–44. *150*

*219. Chester Jones, I. and Phillips, J. G. (1960). Adrenocorticosteroids in fish. *Symp. zool. Soc. Lond.* **1,** 17–32. *143*

*220. Chester Jones, I., Phillips, J. G. and Bellamy, D. (1962). Hormones affecting environmental adjustment. Studies on water and electrolytes in cyclostomes and teleosts with special reference to *Myxine glutinosa* L., (the hagfish) and *Anguilla anguilla* L., (the Atlantic eel). *Gen. comp. Endocrinol. Suppl.* **1,** 36–47.

*221. Chieffi, G. (1962). Integration of reproductive functions. II. Endocrine aspects of reproduction in elasmobranch fishes. *Gen. comp. Endocrinol. Suppl.* **1,** 275–85.

*222. Chieffi, G. and Lupo, C. (1963). Identification of sex hormones in the ovarian extracts of *Torpedo marmorata* and *Bufo vulgaris*. *Gen. comp. Endocrinol.* **3,** 149–52.

223. Chrzan, F. (1950). Investigations on the Baltic cod. *J. Cons. perm. int. Explor. Mer.* **16,** 192–207. *116, 118*

224. Chudova, Z. I. (1961). The role of vitamins A and B_1 in rearing young salmon. *Trudy N.-1. Instuta Rybnogo khozaiistva Soveta Narodnogo Khozaiistva Latviĭskoĭ SSR (Trudy Latv. NIRO)* **3,** 421–9. *209*

*225. Chun, E. H. L. and Doty, P. (1957). Quoted by Doty and Nishihara (1957).

226. Chvapil, M. and Hruza, Z. (1962). Physical and physical-chemical heterogeneity of collagen fibres from rat tail tendon. *Gerontologia* **6,** 102–17. *10*

227. van Citters, R. L. and Watson, N. W. (1968). Coronary disease in spawning steelhead trout, *Salmo gairdnerii*. *Science, N.Y.* **159,** 105–7. *114*

228. Coates, J. A. and Halver, J. E. (1958). Water-soluble vitamin requirements of silver salmon. *Spec. scient. Rep. U.S. Fish Wildl. Serv.* no. 281, 9 pp. *209*

229. Coble, D. W. (1966). Dependence of total annual growth in yellow perch on temperature. *J. Fish. Res. Bd Can.* **23,** 15–20. *210*

*230. Cohen, H., Hamosh, M., Atia, R. and Shapiro, B. (1967). Lysolecithinase in fish muscle. *J. Food Sci.* **32,** 179–81.

*231. Cohen, J. J., Krupp, M. A. and Chidsey III, C. A. (1958). Renal conservation of trimethylamine oxide by the spiny dogfish, *Squalus acanthias*. *Am. J. Physiol.* **194,** 229–35.

232. Comfort, A. (1961). The longevity and mortality of a fish (*Lebistes reticulatus* Peters) in captivity. *Gerontologia* **5,** 209–22. *126, 127*

233. Connell, J. J. (1953). Studies on the proteins of fish skeletal muscle. 2. Electrophoretic analysis of low ionic strength extracts of several species of fish. *Biochem. J.* **55,** 378–88. *132, 133*

*234. Connell, J. J. (1955). Arginase in elasmobranch muscle. *Nature, Lond.* **175,** 562 only.

235. Connell, J. J. (1960). Changes in the actin of cod flesh during storage at −14°. *J. Sci. Fd Agric.* **11,** 515–9. *17*

236. Connell, J. J. (1961). The relative stabilities of the skeletal muscle myosins of some animals. *Biochem. J.* **80,** 503–9. *132*

*237. Connell, J. J. (1963). Sedimentation and aggregation of cod myosin: a re-appraisal. *Biochim. biophys. Acta* **74,** 374–85.

*238. Connell, J. J. (1966). Changes in aldolase activity in cod and haddock during frozen storage. *J. Food Sci.* **31,** 313–6.

*239. Connell, J. J. and Howgate, P. F. (1959a). Studies on the proteins of fish skeletal muscle. 6. Amino acid composition of cod fibrillar proteins. *Biochem. J.* **71,** 83–6. *16, 17*

*240. Connell, J. J. and Howgate, P. F. (1959b). The amino acid composition of some British food fishes. *J. Sci. Fd. Agric.* **10,** 241–4. *130*

241. Conte, F. P. (in the press). Structure and functional pathways of osmoregulation. Excretion and secretion by epithelial tissue. *In* "Fish Physiology" Vol. 1, Chapter 3. Academic Press, London and New York. *138*

242. Conte, F. P., Wagner, H. H., Fessler, J. and Gnose, C. (1966). Development of osmotic and ionic regulation in juvenile coho salmon, *Oncorhynchus kisutch*. *Comp. Biochem. Physiol.* **18,** 1–15. *81*

*243. Cook, A. S. (1931). A study of the occurrence of trimethylamine in marine animals. *Can. Chem. Metall.* **15,** 22 only. *145*

244. Coppini, R. (1967). Study of variations in the chemical composition of the flesh of the mackerel from the middle western Adriatic, particularly with regard to lipids. *Proc. tech. Pap. gen. Fish. Coun. Mediterr.* **8,** technical paper 45, 395–9. *225*

*245. Cordier, G. (1959). Research on the concentration of cardiac glycogen in fresh-water fish. Comparison with marine fish. *C. r. Séanc. Soc. Biol.* **153,** 435–7. *275*

246. Cordier, D., Barnoud, R. and Brandon, A. M. (1957). Study on the blood protein of the dogfish (*Scyllium canicula* L.). Influence of starvation. *C. r. Séanc. Soc. Biol.* **151,** 1912–15. *231*

*247. Cory, R. P. and Wold, F. (1966). Isolation and characterisation of enolase from rainbow trout (*Salmo gairdnerii gairdnerii*). *Biochemistry, N.Y.* (*Biokhimiya*) **5,** 3131–7.

*248. Cowey, C. B. (1965). Amino acids and related substances in fish. *In* "Studies in comparative biochemistry" (K. A. Munday, ed.), Chapter 3, pp. 41–61. Pergamon Press, Oxford. *106, 130, 188, 238*

*249. Cowey, C. B., Daisley, K. W. and Parry, G. (1962). Study of amino acids, free or as components of protein, and of some B vitamins in the tissues of the Atlantic salmon, *Salmo salar*, during spawning migration. *Comp. Biochem. Physiol.* **7,** 29–38. *65, 68, 99, 101, 188, 238*

*250. Cowey, C. B. and Parry, G. (1963). The non-protein nitrogenous constituents of the muscle of parr and smolt stages of the Atlantic salmon (*Salmo salar*). *Comp. Biochem. Physiol.* **8,** 47–51. *82*

*251. Cowgill, U. M., Hutchinson, G. E. and Skinner, H. C. W. (1968). The elementary composition of *Latimeria chalumnae* Smith. *Proc. natn. Acad. Sci. U.S.A.* **60** (2), 456–63.

252. Cowie, W. P. (1968). Identification of fish species by thin-slab polyacrylamide gel electrophoresis of the muscle myogens. *J. Sci. Fd Agric.* **19**, 226–9. *132*

*253. Creac'h, Y. (1964). Free amino acids in the bile of certain cyprinoids. *Bull. Soc. Hist. nat. Toulouse* **99**, 393–6. *223*

254. Creac'h, Y. (1966). Protein thiols and free amino acids of carp tissues during prolonged starvation. *Archs Sci. physiol.* **20**, 115–21. *240, 241*

255. Creac'h, Y. and Cournède, C. (1965). Contribution to the study of enforced starvation in the carp, *Cyprinus carpio* L.; variations in the amount of water and nitrogen in the tissues. *Bull. Soc. Hist. nat. Toulouse* **100**, 361–70. *223, 230*

*256. Creac'h, Y. and Serfaty, A. (1964). The free amino acids in the blood of the common carp. *C. r. Séanc. Soc. Biol.* **158**, 1152–6. *238*

*257. Creac'h, Y. and Serfaty, A. (1965). Proteolysis in the common carp (*Cyprinus carpio* L.) in the course of starvation: importance and localisation. *C. r. Séanc. Soc. Biol.* **159**, 483–6. *224, 238, 240*

*258. Creelman, V. M. and Tomlinson, N. (1959). Biochemical studies on sockeye salmon during spawning migration. VI. Ribonucleic acid and deoxyribonucleic acid. *J. Fish. Res. Bd Can.* **16**, 421–8. *67, 107, 108, 109*

259. Le Cren, E. D. (1958). Observations on the growth of perch (*Perca fluviatilis* L.) over twenty-two years with special reference to the effects of temperature and changes in population density. *J. Anim. Ecol.* **27**, 287–334. *116, 210*

*260. Croston, C. B. (1965). Endopeptidases of salmon caeca: chromatographic separation and some properties. *Archs Biochem. Biophys.* **112**, 218–23.

261. Cruickshank, E. M. (1962). Fat soluble vitamins. *In* "Fish as Food" (G. Borgstrom, ed.). Vol. 2, pp. 175–203. Academic Press, London and New York. *130, 142, 200, 291, 292*

*262. Cserr, H. and Rall, D. P. (1967). Regulation of cerebrospinal fluid [K^+] in the spiny dogfish, *Squalus acanthias*. *Comp. Biochem. Physiol.* **21**, 431–4.

263. Cushing, J. E. (1952). Serological differentiation of fish bloods. *Science, N.Y.* **115**, 404–5. *163*

264. Cushing, J. E. (1964). The blood groups of marine animals. *Adv. mar. Biol.* **2**, 85–131.

265. Dahlberg, M. L., Shumway, D. L. and Doudoroff, P. (1968). Influence of dissolved oxygen and carbon dioxide on swimming performance of largemouth bass and coho salmon. *J. Fish. Res. Bd Can.* **25**, 49–70. *176*

*266. van Dam, L. and Scholander, P. F. (1953). Concentration of haemoglobin in the blood of deep sea fishes. *J. cell. comp. Physiol.* **41**, 522–4. *177*

267. Dambergs, N. (1963). Extractives of fish muscle. 3. Amounts, sectional distribution, and variations of fat, water-solubles, protein and moisture in cod (*Gadus morhua* L.) fillets. *J. Fish. Res. Bd Can.* **20**, 909–18. *6, 119, 122, 123*

268. Dambergs, N. (1964). Extractives of fish muscle. 4. Seasonal variations of fat, water-solubles, protein, and water in cod (*Gadus morhua* L.) fillets. *J. Fish. Res. Bd Can.* **21**, 703–9. *6, 159, 170, 228, 229*

*269. Dambergs, N., Odense, P. and Guilbault, R. (1968). Changes in free amino acids in skeletal muscle of cod (*Gadus morhua*) under conditions simulating gillnet fishing. *J. Fish. Res. Bd Can.* **25**, 935–42.

270. Damodaran, M., Sivaraman, C. and Dhavalikar, R. S. (1956). Amino acid composition of elastoidin. *Biochem. J.* **62**, 621–5. *101*

271. Dannevig, A. (1953). The littoral cod of the Norwegian Skagerak coast. *Rapp. P.-v. Réun. Cons. perm. int. Explor. Mer.* **136**, 7–14. *156, 174*

272. Dannevig, E. H. (1955). Chemical composition of the zones in cod otoliths. *J. Cons. perm. int. Explor. Mer.* **21**, 156–9. *160*

273. Dartnall, H. J. A. (1962). The identity and distribution of visual pigments in the animal kingdom. *In* "The Eye" (H. Davson, ed.), Chapter 18, 367–426 Academic Press, London and New York. *180*

274. Dartnall, H. J. A., Lander, M. R. and Munz, F. W. (1961). Periodic changes in the visual pigment of a fish. *In* "Progress in Photobiology" (*Proceedings of the 3rd international Congress on Photobiology*), pp. 203–213, Elsevier, Amsterdam. *183*

275. Dartnall, H. J. A. and Lythgoe, J. N. (1965). The spectral clustering of visual pigments. *Vision Res.* **5**, 81–100. *180, 181*

276. Das, B. C. (1965). Age-related trends in the blood chemistry and haematology of the Indian carp (*Catla catla*). *Gerontologia* **10**, 47–64. *95, 127*

277. Dawson, A. B. (1933). The relative numbers of immature erythrocytes in the circulating blood of several species of marine fishes. *Biol. Bull. mar. biol. Lab., Woods Hole* **64**, 33–43. *46, 137, 150*

278. Dean, F. D. and Chester Jones, I. (1959). Sex steroids in the lungfish (*Protopterus annectens* Owen). *J. Endocrinol.* **18**, 366–71. *136*

279. Dean, J. M. (1962). A comparative study of carbohydrate metabolism in fish as affected by temperature and exercise. Purdue University Ph.D. Thesis. University Microfilms, Inc., Ann Arbor, Michigan. *46, 212*

*280. Dean, J. M. and Goodnight, C. J. (1964). A comparative study of carbohydrate metabolism in fish as affected by temperature and exercise. *Physiol. Zoöl.* **37**, 280–99. *40, 41, 51*

*281. Deas, C. P. and Tarr, H. L. A. (1949). Amino acid composition of fishery products. *J. Fish. Res. Bd Can.* **7**, 513–21.

282. DeLong, D. C., Halver, J. E. and Mertz, E. T. (1958). Nutrition of salmonoid fishes. VI. Protein requirements of chinook salmon at two water temperatures. *J. Nutr.* **65,** 589–99. *207*

283. Denton, E. J. and Warren, F. J. (1956). Visual pigments of deep-sea fish. *Nature, Lond.* **178,** 1059 only. *180, 182*

284. Denton, E. J. D. and Warren, F. J. (1957). The photosensitive pigments in the retinae of deep-sea fish. *J. mar. biol. Ass. U.K.* **36,** 651–62. *182.*

285. Dessauer, H. C. and Fox, W. (1956). Characteristic electrophoretic patterns of plasma proteins of orders of amphibia and reptilia. *Science, N.Y.* **124,** 225–6. *164, 231*

286. Deuel, H. J. (1957). "The Lipids, their Chemistry and Biochemistry", 3 Volumes. Interscience Publishers Inc., New York and London. *54*

287. DeWilde, M. A. and Houston, A. H. (1967). Haematological aspects of the thermoacclimatory process in the rainbow trout, *Salmo gairdnerii. J. Fish. Res. Bd Can.* **24,** 2267–81. *212*

288. DeWitt, K. W. (1963). Seasonal variations in cod liver oil. *J. Sci. Fd Agric.* **14,** 92–8. *201, 242*

289. Dicker, S. E. (1949). Changes in the extracellular and intracellular fluid phases of muscle during starvation and dehydration in adult rats. *Biochem. J.* **44,** 274–81. *247*

290. Dickerson, J. W. T. and Widdowson, E. M. (1960). Chemical changes in skeletal muscle during development. *Biochem. J.* **74,** 247–57. *88*

291. Dingle, J. R., Hines, J. A. and Neelin, J. M. (1962). Proteins in fish muscle. 17. Fractionation of aqueous extracts with zinc acetate. *J. Fish. Res. Bd Can.* **19,** 591–604. *237*

*292. Diplock, A. T. and Haslewood, G. A. D. (1967). The ubiquinone content of animal tissues. A survey of the occurrence of ubiquinone in vertebrates. *Biochem. J.* **104,** 1004–10. *140*

*293. Doolittle, R. F., Thomas, C. and Stone, W. (1960). Osmotic pressure and aqueous humour formation in dogfish. *Science, N.Y.* **132,** 36–7.

*294. Doty, P. and Nishihara, T. (1957). The molecular properties and thermal stability of soluble collagen. *In* "Recent advances in Gelatin and Glue Research" (G. Stainsby, ed.), pp. 92–9. Pergamon Press, London.

*295. Doyle, J. (1968). Ageing changes in cartilage from *Squalus acanthias* L. *Comp. Biochem. Physiol.* **25,** 201–6. *88*

296. Drilhon, A. (1954). Biological study of several fish blood serum proteins by means of paper electrophoresis. *C. r. Séanc. Soc. Biol.* **148,** 1218–20. *105, 121, 231*

297. Droop, M. R. (1957). Vitamin B_{12} in marine ecology. *Nature, Lond.* **180,** 1041–2. *74*

298. Drury, D. E. and Eales, J. G. (1968). The influence of temperature on histological and radiochemical measurements of thyroid activity in the eastern brook trout *Salvelinus fontinalis* Mitchell. *Can. J. Zool.* **46**, 1–9. *213*

*299. Duchâteau, G. and Florkin, M. (1954). Quantitative composition of non-protein protides in carp muscle. *C. r. Séanc. Soc. Biol.* **148**, 1287–9.

300. Duchâteau, G., Florkin, M. and Jeuniaux, C. (1959). Amino acid composition of the tissues of crustacians. 1. Amino acid composition of the muscles of *Carcinas maenas* L. at the time of migration from sea-water to brackish water and during moulting. *Archs int. Physiol. Biochim.* **67**, 489–500. *188*

301. Duff, G. L. (1929). Factors involved in the production of annual zones in the scales of the cod (*Gadus callarias* Linnaeus). *Contr. Can. Biol. Fish.* **4**, 287–303. *161*

*302. Dugal, L. C. (1967). Hypoxanthine in iced freshwater fish. *J. Fish. Res. Bd Can.* **24**, 2229–39.

303. Dugal, L. P. and Thérien, M. (1947). Ascorbic acid and acclimatisation to cold environment. *Can. J. Res.* **25**, 111–36. *221*

304. Dunlop, H. A. (1955). Management of the halibut fishery of the northeastern Pacific Ocean and Bering Sea. *Internat. Tech. conference on Conservation of Living Resources of the sea*, Rome, United Nations. pp. 222–42. *116, 156*

305. Dunn, M., Camien, M., Eiduson, S. and Malin, R. (1949). The nutritive value of canned foods. 1. Amino acid content of fish and meat products. *J. Nutr.* **39**, 177–85.

*306. Dupont, A. (1958). Amino acid content of Indonesian fresh water fish. *Biochem. Z.* **330**, 174–6.

*307. Dyer, W. J. (1952). Amines in fish muscle. VI. Trimethylamine oxide content of fish and marine invertebrates. *J. Fish. Res. Bd Can.* **8**, 314–24.

*308. Dyer, W. J., Fraser, D. I. and Tibbo, S. N. (1963). Composition and palatability of porbeagle flesh. *J. Fish. Res. Bd Can.* **20**, 1153–8. *21, 23, 25*

*309. Eastoe, J. E. (1957). The amino acid composition of fish collagen and gelatin. *Biochem. J.* **65**, 363–8. *270*

*310. Edelhauser, H. F., Hoffert, J. R. and Fromm, P. O. (1965). In vitro ion and water movement in corneas of rainbow trout. *Invstve Ophth.* **4**, 290–6. *262*

*311. Edisbury, J., Morton, R. A., Simpkins, G. W. and Lovern, J. A. (1938). The distribution of vitamin A and factor A_2. I. *Biochem. J.* **32**, 118–40.

*312. Edström, A. (1964). The ribonucleic acid in the mauthner neuron of the goldfish. *J. Neurochem.* **11**, 309–14. *38*

*313. Eguchi, H., Hashimoto, K. and Matsuura, F. (1960). Comparative studies on two haemoglobins of salmon—III. Amino acid composition. *Bull. Jap. Soc. scient. Fish.* **26**, 810–13. *276*

*314. Ehira, S. and Uchiyama, H. (1967). Change in ribose content of plaice muscle during ice storage. *Bull. Jap. Soc. scient. Fish.* **33**, 136–40.

*315. Eisler, R. and Edmunds, P. H. (1966). Effects of endrin on blood and tissue chemistry of a marine fish. *Trans. Am. Fish. Soc.* **95,** 153–9.

*316. Eleftheriou, B. E., Boehlke, K. W. and Tiemeier, O. W. (1966). Free plasma oestrogens in the channel catfish. *Proc. Soc. exp. Biol. Med.* **121,** 85–8. *111*

317. Eliassen, E., Leivestad, H. and Møller, D. (1960). The effect of low temperatures on the freezing-point of plasma and on the potassium/sodium ratio in the muscles of some boreal and subarctic fishes. *Årbok Univ. Bergen Matematisk-Naturvitenskapelig serie* paper no. 14, 24 pp. *218, 219*

*318. Ellinger, G. M. and Boyne, E. B. (1965). Amino acid composition of some fish products and casein. *Br. J. Nutr.* **19,** 587–92.

319. Embody, G. C. (1934). Relation of temperature to the incubation periods of eggs of four species of trout. *Trans. Am. Fish. Soc.* **64,** 281–92. *69, 210*

*320. Engel, D. W. and Davis, E. M. (1964). Relationship between activity and blood composition in certain marine teleosts. *Copeia* (3), 586–7 (no volume number). *148, 149, 150*

*321. Enger, P. S. (1964). Ionic composition of the cranial and labyrinthine fluids and saccular D.C. potentials in fish. *Comp. Biochem. Physiol.* **11,** 131–7.

*322. Enomoto, Y. (1967). On the effect of the somatotropic hormone to the urine electrolytes of rainbow trout. *Bull. Jap. Soc. scient. Fish.* **33,** 71–3.

*323. Enomoto, N., Izumi, T. and Tomiyasu, Y. (1961). Studies on the external mucous substance of fishes. IV. Amino acid composition of the protein of the external mucous substance from some fishes. *Bull. Jap. Soc. scient. Fish.* **27,** 606–8.

*324. Enomoto, N., Nagatake, H. and Tomiyasu, Y. (1963). Studies on the external mucous substance of fishes. VIII. Quantitative analysis of the mucus-polysaccharide from some fishes. 2. Basic and acidic sugar composition. *Bull. Jap. Soc. scient. Fish.* **29,** 542–5.

*325. Enomoto, N., Nakagawa, H., Matsuda, K. and Tomiyasu, Y. (1966). Sialic acids in the external mucous substance and the cartilage of fishes. *Bull. Jap. Soc. scient. Fish.* **32,** 442–5.

*326. Enomoto, N. and Tomiyasu, Y. (1962). Studies on the external mucous substance of fishes. VII. Quantitative analysis of the mucus-polysaccharide from some fishes. 1. Neutral sugar composition. *Bull. Jap. Soc. scient. Fish.* **28,** 510–13.

*327. von Euler, U. S. and Fänge, R. (1961). Catecholamines in nerves and organs of *Myxine glutinosa, Squalus acanthias,* and *Gadus callarias. Gen. comp. Endocrinol.* **1,** 191–4.

*328. Everson, I. and Ralph, R. (1968). Blood analyses of some Antarctic fish. *Bull. Br. antarc. Surv.* no. 15, 59–62. *220*

*329. Fagerlund, U. H. M. (1967). Plasma cortisol concentration in relation to stress in adult sockeye salmon during the freshwater stage of their life cycle. *Gen. comp. Endocrinol.* **8,** 197–207. *40, 110, 115, 121*

*330. Fahlén, G., Falck, B. and Rosengren, E. (1965). Monoamines in the swim-bladder of *Gadus callarias* and *Salmo irideus*. *Acta physiol. scand.* **64,** 119–26.

331. Falkmer, S. and Matty, A. J. (1966). Blood sugar regulation in the hagfish, *Myxine glutinosa*. *Gen. comp. Endocrinol.* **6,** 334–46. *251*

*332. Falkmer, S. and Winbladh, L. (1964). Some aspects of the blood sugar regulation of the hagfish, *Myxine glutinosa*. *In* "The Structure and Metabolism of the Pancreatic Islets." (S. E. Brolin, B. Hellman and H. Knutson, eds.), pp. 33–43. Pergamon Press, London. *46, 99, 137*

*333. Farberov, V. G. (1964). Influence of cobalt feeding on fish growth and accumulation of vitamin B_{12} in carp liver. *Vestn. Sel'skokhoz Nauki, Vses. Akad. Sel'skokhoz Nauk* **9** (6), 82–3. Quoted by *Chem. Abstr.* **62,** 5617g, (1964).

334. Farkas, T. and Herodek, S. (1964). The effect of environmental temperature on the fatty acid composition of crustacean plankton. *J. Lipid Res.* **5,** 369–73. *216, 217*

335. Farris, D. A. (1958). Diet-induced variation in the free amino acid complex of *Sardinops caerula*. *J. Cons. perm. int. Explor. Mer* **23,** 235–44. *152, 199*

336. Faustov, V. S. and Zotin, A. I. (1965). Changes in the heat of combustion of the eggs of fishes and amphibians during development. *Dokl. Akad. Nauk SSSR.* **162,** 965–8. *71*

337. Fenderson, O. C., Everhart, W. H. and Muth, K. M. (1968). Comparative agonistic and feeding behaviour of hatchery-reared and wild salmon in aquaria. *J. Fish. Res. Bd Can.* **25,** 1–14. *53*

338. Fenn, W. O. (1939). The fate of potassium liberated from muscles during activity. *Am. J. Physiol.* **127,** 356–73. *43*

339. Fenn, W. O. and Cobb, D. M. (1936). Electrolyte changes in muscle during activity. *Am. J. Physiol.* **115,** 345–56. *43*

340. Field, J. and Peiss, C. N. (1949). Tissue respiration in the polar cod (*Boreogadus saida*) as a function of temperature. *Fedn Proc. Fedn Am. Socs exp. Biol.* **8,** 44–5. *212*

*341. Field, J. B., Elvehjem, C. A. and Juday, C. (1943). A study of the blood constituents of carp and trout. *J. biol. Chem.* **148,** 261–9.

342. Fine, J. M., Boffa, G. A. and Drilhon, A. (1964). Electrophoretic and immunological study of serum proteins of the marine lamprey (*Petromyzon marinus* L.). *C. r. Séanc. Soc. Biol.* **158,** 2021–5. *121*

343. Fine, J. M., Drilhon, A., Boffa, G. A. and Amouch, P. (1965). The types of transferrins in certain migratory fish. *In* "Protides of the biological fluids" (Proceedings of the 12th colloquium, Bruges, 1964), (H. Peeters, ed.), pp. 165–7. Elsevier, Amsterdam. *135, 167*

*344. Fischer, W. and Güthert, H. (1968). On the zinc content of the endocrine pancreas tissue and of the musculature of the trembling ray, *Torpedo marmorata* and *Torpedo ocellata*. *Hoppe-Seyler's Z. physiol. Chem.* **349**, 573–4.

*345. Fish, G. R. (1960). The comparative activity of some digestive enzymes in the alimentary canal of tilapia and perch. *Hydrobiologia* **15**, 161–78. *50, 130, 204, 254*

346. Fisher, H. and Griminger, P. (1963). Ageing and food restriction: changes in body composition and hydroxyproline content of selected tissues. *J. Nutr.* **80**, 350–4. *232*

*347. Fisher, L. R. (1964). Vitamin A, carotenoids and total lipids in the livers of some elasmobranchs. *Mar. Res.* no. 2, 18 pp. *91, 95, 96, 124, 291*

348. Fitton Jackson, S. (1957). Structural problems associated with the formation of collagen fibrils *in vivo*. *In* "Connective Tissue" (R. E. Tunbridge, ed.), pp. 77–85. Blackwell, Oxford. *128*

349. Fixsen, M. A. B. and Roscoe, M. H. (1940). Tables of the vitamin content of human and animal foods. II. *Nutr. Abstr. Rev.* **9**, 795–861, *290*

350. Fleming, A. M. (1960). Age, growth and sexual maturity of cod (*Gadus morhua* L.) in the Newfoundland area, 1947–1950. *J. Fish. Res. Bd Can.* **17**, 775–809. *116*

351. Fleming, W. R., Scheffel, K. G. and Linton, J. R. (1962). Studies on the gill cholinesterase activity of several cyprinodontid fishes. *Comp. Biochem. Physiol.* **6**, 205–13. *144*

352. Fleming, W. R., Stanley, J. G. and Meier, A. H. (1964). Seasonal effects of external calcium, oestradiol and ACTH on the serum calcium and sodium levels of *Fundulus kansae*. *Gen. comp. Endocrinol.* **4**, 61–7. *62*

353. Florkin, M. and Schoffeniels, E. (1965). Euryhalinity and the concept of physiological radiation. *In* "Studies in Comparative Biochemistry" (K. A. Munday, ed.), pp. 6–40. Pergamon Press, Oxford. *188*

*354. Follett, B. K. and Heller, H. (1964). The neurohypophysial hormones of lungfishes and amphibians. *J. Physiol., Lond.* **172**, 92–106. *136*

*355. Fomin, S. V., Romanjuk, N. M. and Khvoynitskaya, M. A. (1937). The ascorbic acid contents of the tissues of various fish. *Ukr. biokhem. Zh.* **10**, 365–78. *147, 169, 291*

*356. Fontaine, M., Callamand, O. and Vibert, R. (1950). Physiology of salmon. *Ext. Sta Cent. Hydrobiol.* **3**, 15–26. *106*

*357. Fontaine, M. and Hatey, J. (1953). Contribution to the study of glucose metabolism in the salmon (*Salmo salar*) at different stages of its development and of its migrations. *Physiologia comp. Oecol.* **3**, 37–52. *98, 119, 250, 275*

358. Forrester, C. R. and Alderdice, D. F. (1966). Effects of salinity and temperature on embryonic development of the Pacific cod (*Gadus macrocephalus*). *J. Fish. Res. Bd Can.* **23,** 319–40. *69, 210*

359. Fowler, L. G. and Wood, E. M. (1966). Effect of type of supplemental dietary fat on chinook salmon fingerlings. *Progve Fish Cult.* **28,** 123–7. *53, 54*

*360. Fox, D. L. and Crozier, G. F. (1965). Absence or singular specificity of carotenoids in some lower fishes. *Science, N.Y.* **150,** 771–3. *142*

*361. Fraenkel, G. (1954). The distribution of vitamin B_t (carnitine) throughout the animal kingdom. *Archs Biochem. Biophys.* **50,** 486–95.

362. Franzini-Armstrong, C. and Porter, K. R. (1964). Sarcolemmal invaginations constituting the T system in fish muscle fibres. *J. Cell Biol.* **22,** 675–96. *14*

*363. Fraser, D. I., Dingle, J. R., Hines, J. A., Nowlan, S. C. and Dyer, W. J. (1967). Nucleotide degradation, monitored by thin-layer chromatography, and associated postmortem changes in relaxed cod muscle. *J. Fish. Res. Bd Can.* **24,** 1837–41.

*364. Fraser, D. I., Dyer, W. J., Weinstein, H. M., Dingle, J. R. and Hines, J. A. (1966). Glycolytic metabolites and their distribution at death in the white and red muscle of cod following various degrees of antemortem muscular activity. *Can. J. Biochem. Physiol.* **44,** 1015–33. *7, 24, 25, 29, 31*

*365. Fraser, D. I., Mannan, A. and Dyer, W. J. (1961). Proximate composition of Canadian Atlantic fish. III. Sectional differences in the flesh of a species of chondrostei, one of chimaerae and of some miscellaneous teleosts. *J. Fish. Res. Bd Can.* **18,** 893–905. *7*

*366. Fraser, D. I., Punjamapirom, S. and Dyer, W. J. (1961). Temperature and the biochemical processes occurring during rigor mortis in cod muscle. *J. Fish. Res. Bd Can.* **18,** 641–4.

*367. Freed, J. (1965). Changes in activity of cytochrome oxidase during adaptation of goldfish to different temperatures. *Comp. Biochem. Physiol.* **14,** 651–9. *213*

368. Freedland, R. A. (1967). Effect of progressive starvation on rat liver enzyme activities. *J. Nutr.* **91,** 489–95. *253*

*369. Freeman, H. C. and Idler, D. R. (1966). Transcortin binding of cortisol in Atlantic salmon (*Salmo salar*) plasma. *Gen. comp. Endocrinol.* **7,** 37–43.

370. Fry, F. E. J. (1957). The aquatic respiration of fish. *In* "The Physiology of Fishes" (M. E. Brown, ed.), Vol. 1, Chapter 1, pp. 1–63. Academic Press, London and New York. *213*

371. Fry, F. E. J. (1964). Animals in aquatic environments: fishes. *In* "Handbook of Physiology" Section 4, pp. 715–28. American Physiology Society. *209*

372. Frydenberg, O., Møller, D., Naevdal, G. and Sick, K. (1965). Haemoglobin polymorphism in Norwegian cod populations. *Hereditas* **53,** 257–71. *166*

373. Frydenberg, O., Nielsen, J. T. and Sick, K. (1967). The population dynamics of the haemoglobin polymorphism of the cod. *Ciênc. Cult., S. Paulo* **19**, 111–17. *165*

374. Fujii, Y. (1954). Chemical studies on atka mackerel meat. *Bull. Fac. Fish. Hokkaido Univ.* **5**, 253–76. *261*

*375. Fujii, Y. (1965). Biochemical study on DNA of tunas. *Bull. Tokai reg. Fish. Res. Lab.* **42**, 39–98. *87, 167*

376. Fujii, Y., Mimoto, K. and Higasa, S. (1960). Biochemical studies on tuna. V. Base composition of DNA of tuna testis. *Rep. Nankai reg. Fish. Res. Lab.* **12**, 23–32. *130*. Quoted in *Chem. Abstr.* **57**, 14301a (1962). *130*

*377. Fujikawa, K. and Naganuma, H. (1936). Chemical composition of sardine, *Sardinia melanosticta* (C & V) from Tyôsen. I. Comparative study on dark muscle and white muscle. *Bull. Jap. Soc. scient. Fish.* **5**, 95–102. *19, 21, 24, 25*

*378. Fujimaki, M. and Kojô, K. (1953). Handling effect upon biochemical change in the fish muscle immediately after catch—II. Changes of acid-soluble phosphorus compounds of frigate mackerel muscle. *Bull. Jap. Soc. scient. Fish.* **19**, 499–504.

379. Fujiya, M. (1961). Use of electrophoretic serum separation in fish studies. *J. Wat. Pollut. Control Fed.* **33**, 250–7. *231*

*380. Fukai, R. and Meinke, W. W. (1959). Some activation analysis of six trace elements in marine biological ashes. *Nature, Lond.* **184**, 815–6.

381. Fukuda, H. (1958). On the blood sugar of fresh water fish. *Bull. Jap. Soc. scient. Fish.* **23**, 782–4. *150, 175*

*382. Fukuda, S. and Hirami, Y. (1955). Studies on vitamin B_1 of foods. Part I. Vitamin B_1 content in eyeballs of fishes from province of Tosa. *J. agric. Chem. Soc. Japan* **29**, 247–51. *287*

383. Gambell, R. and Messtorff, J. (1964). Age determination in the whiting (*Merlangius merlangus* L.) by means of the otoliths. *J. Cons. perm. int. Explor. Mer* **38**, 393–404. *160*

384. Ganguly, D. N. and Nag, A. C. (1964). On the organization of the myomeric musculature of some benthonic teleostean fishes with special reference to the functional morphology. *Anat. Anz.* **115**, 418–46. *1, 148*

*385. Garcia, M. D., Lovern, J. A. and Olley, J. (1956). The lipids of fish. 6. The lipids of cod flesh. *Biochem. J.* **62**, 99–107.

386. Garside, E. T. (1959). Some effects of oxygen in relation to temperature on the development of lake trout embryos. *Can. J. Zool.* **37**, 689–98. *69*

387. Garside, E. T. (1966a). Effects of oxygen in relation to temperature on the development of embryos of brook trout and rainbow trout. *J. Fish. Res. Bd Can.* **23**, 1121–34. *210*

388. Garside, E. T. (1966b). Developmental rate and vertebral number in salmonids. *J. Fish. Res. Bd Can.* **23**, 1537–51. *155, 210*

389. Gas-Baby, N., Laffont, J. and Labat, R. (1967). Physiological and histological proof of the regeneration of the cardiac branch of the vagus nerve in the carp. *J. Physiol., Paris* **59**, 39–42. *211*

390. Al-Gauhari, A. E. I. (1958). On the blood sugar in *Clarias lazera* C. et V. *Z. vergl. Physiol.* **41**, 26–34. *45, 50, 92, 123, 252*

391. Geiger, E. and Borgstrom, G. (1962). Fish protein—nutritive aspects. *In* "Fish as Food" (G. Borgstrom, ed.), Vol. 2, Chapter 2, pp. 29–114. Academic Press, London and New York. *99, 124, 198, 260, 261, 265*

*392. Geiger, S. E., Roberts, E. and Tomlinson, N. (1962). Dogfish gelatin. *J. Fish. Res. Bd Can.* **19**, 321–6. *10*

*393. George, J. C. (1962). A histophysiological study of the red and white muscles of the mackerel. *Am. Midl. Nat.* **68**, 487–94. *17, 21, 31*

394. George, J. C. and Bokdawala, F. D. (1964). Cellular organization and fat utilization in fish muscle. *J. Anim. Morph. Physiol.* **11**, 124–32. *17, 21, 31*

395. Gerking, S. D. (1959). Physiological changes accompanying ageing in fishes. *Ciba Fdn Colloq. Ageing* **5**, 181–211. *126*

396. Gerking, S. D. (1960). Evidence of ageing in fishes. *In* "The Biology of Aging" (B. L. Strehler, ed.), Symposium, Gatlinburg, 1957, Publ. no. 6, Amer. Inst. of biol. Sciences, Washington. *127*

397. Ghittino, P. and Leon, J. I. (1963). Histological and histochemical features of fatty liver degeneration in hatchery brook trout (*Salvelinus fontinalis*). *Atti Soc. ital. Sci. vet.* **17**, 569–74. *53, 54, 55*

398. Gillespie, A. L. (1898). 4.—Changes in the digestive activity of the secretions of the alimentary canal of the salmon in different conditions. *Fishery Board for Scotland. Rep. of investigations on the life history of salmon* pp. 23–35. *98, 254*

*399. Giroud, A., Leblond, C. P., Ratsimamanga, R. and Géro, E. (1938). The normal level of ascorbic acid. *Bull. Soc. Chim. biol.* **20**, 1079–87. *292*

*400. Gjessing, E. T. (1963). Free amino acids in hard herring roe. Variation during the ripening process. *FiskDir. Skr. Serie Teknologiske Undersøkelser* **4** (7), 8 pp. *65, 99*

401. Gohar, H. A. F. and Latif, A. F. A. (1961a). The histology of the alimentary tract in representative scarid and labrid fishes (from the Red Sea). *Publs mar. biol. Stn Ghardaqa* **11**, 95–126. *203, 223*

402. Gohar, H. A. F. and Latif, A. F. A. (1961b). The carbohydrases of some scarid and labrid fishes. *Publs mar. biol. Stn Ghardaqa* **11**, 127–46. *205*

403. Gohar, H. A. F. and Latif, A. F. A. (1961c). Gut lipase of some scarid and labrid fishes (from the Red Sea). *Publs mar biol. Stn Ghardaqa* **11**, 215–34. *205*

404. Gohar, H. A. F. and Latif, A. F. A. (1963). Digestive proteolytic enzymes of some scarid and labrid fishes (from the Red Sea). *Publs mar. biol. Stn Ghardaqa* **12**, 3–42. *205*

*405. Goldbeck, C. G. (1947). Some studies on the content of thiamine and anti-thiamine factor in fishery products. *Comml Fish. Rev.* **9** (8), 13–21.

406. Goldspink, G. (1965). Cytological basis of decrease in muscle strength during starvation. *Am. J. Physiol.* **209**, 100–4. *247*

407. Goldspink, G. (1966). An attempt at estimating extrafibre fluid in small skeletal muscles by a simple physical method. *Can. J. Physiol. Pharmacol.* **44**, 765–75. *230*

*408. Goldstein, L. and Forster, R. P. (1965). The role of uricolysis in the production of urea by fishes and other aquatic vertebrates. *Comp. Biochem. Physiol.* **14**, 567–76.

409. Goldstein, L., Hartman, S. C. and Forster, R. P. (1967). On the origin of trimethylamine oxide in the spiny dogfish, *Squalus acanthias. Comp. Biochem. Physiol.* **21**, 719–22. *145, 288*

410. Golovanenko, L. F. (1964). Types of haemoglobin in ontogenesis of the sturgeon (*Acipenser güldenstadti*). *Izv. Gos. Nachn.-Issled. Ozern. i Rechn. Rybn. Khoz.* **58**, 128–34. Quoted in *Chem. Abstr.* **63**, 7396h (1965). *94*

*411. Gomazkova, V. S. (1963). Alkaline phosphatase of olfactory epithelium of some freshwater fishes. *Materialy po Biol. i Gidrolog. Volzhskikh. Vodokhranilishch, Akad Nauk SSSR, Inst. Biol. Vnutr. Vod, Sb. Statei* pp. 99–102. Quoted in *Chem. Abstr.* **63**, 2161f (1965).

*412. Gomes, M. P. N. C. and Trincão, C. (1966). Content of vitamin B_2 in some fishes and molluscs of the Portuguese coast. *Sangre, Santiago*, **11**, 99–100.

*413. Gonzalez-Diaz, C., Fernandez, O. and Cravioto, R. O. (1948). Nutritive value of fresh fish eaten in the City of Mexico. *An. Esc. nac. Cienc. biol., Méx.* **5**, 283–90.

*414. Goodwin, T. W. (1951). 5. Carotenoids in fish. *Biochem. Soc. Symp.* **6**, 63–81.

*415. Gordon, M. S. (1957). Observations on osmoregulation in the Arctic char (*Salvelinus alpinus* L.). *Biol. Bull. mar. biol. Lab., Woods Hole* **112**, 28–33. *192*

416. Gordon, M. S. (1959). Ionic regulation in the brown trout (*Salmo trutta* L.). *J. exp. Biol.* **36**, 227–52. *122, 123*

417. Gordon, M. S. (1968). Oxygen consumption of red and white muscles from tuna fishes. *Science, N.Y.* **159**, 87–90. *31*

418. Gottfried, H. (1964). The occurrence and biological significance of steroids in lower vertebrates. A review. *Steroids* **3**, 219–42. *136, 259*

*419. Gottfried, H., Hunt, S. V., Simpson, T. H. and Wright, R. S. (1962). Sex hormones in fish. The oestrogens of cod (*Gadus callarias*). *J. Endocrinol.* **24**, 425–30. *120*

*420. de Gouveia, A. J. A., Gouveia, A. P., Correira, J. A. and Fonseca, M. H. R. (1956). Fish from the coast of Angola. I. Analytical study of species from the fisheries at Luanda. *Garcia de Orto* **4**, 531–55. Quoted in *Chem. Abstr.* **51**, 14143h (1957).

421. Graham, M. (1924). The annual cycle in the life of the mature cod in the North Sea. *Fishery Invest., Lond. Ser.* 2. *Sea Fisheries* **6** (6), 77 pp. *120, 171*

*422. Grajcer, D. and Idler, D. R. (1961). Testosterone, conjugated and 'free', in the blood of spawned Fraser River sockeye salmon (*Oncorhynchus nerka*). *Can. J. Biochem. Physiol.* **39,** 1585–93.

*423. Grajcer, D. and Idler, D. R. (1963). Conjugated testosterone in the blood and testes of spawned Fraser River sockeye salmon (*Oncorhynchus nerka*). *Can. J. Biochem. Physiol.* **41,** 23–9.

424. Grant, P. T. and Reid, K. B. M. (1968). Isolation and a partial amino acid sequence of insulin from the islet tissue of cod (*Gadus callarias*). *Biochem. J.* **106,** 531–41. *278*

*425. Gras, J., Gautheron, D. and Henry, J. C. (1967). Phosphorylated fractions and free nucleotides of various organs of rainbow trout (*Salmo gairdnerii* Rich.). *C. r. hebd Séanc. Acad. Sci., Paris* Ser. D, **265,** 1547–9

426. Gras, J., Reynaud, R., Gamoty, L., Frey, J. and Henry, J. C. (1967a). Biochemical study of fishes. 1. Six-monthly variations in the water and protein content of the muscle tissue of rainbow trout (*Salmo gairdnerii* Rich). *Experienta* **23,** 430–1. *229*

*427. Gras, J., Reynaud, R., Gamoty, L., Frey, J. and Henry, J. C. (1967b). Biochemical study on fishes. 2. Six-month variation in the content of glycogen, total lipids and minerals in muscle tissue of rainbow trout (*Salmo gairdnerii* Rich). *Experientia* **23,** 431–2.

*428. Gray, I. E. and Hall, F. G. (1930). Blood sugar and activity in fishes with notes on the action of insulin. *Biol. Bull. mar. biol. Lab., Woods Hole* **58,** 217–23. *45, 150*

*429. Gray, D. J. S., Novellie, L. and Shuttleworth, R. G. (1951). Recovery of water-soluble nutritional factors from fish livers. *J. Sci. Fd Agric.* **2,** 91–4.

430. Green, J. W. and Hoffman, J. F. (1953). A study of isotonic solutions for the erythrocytes of some marine teleosts and elasmobranchs. *Biol. Bull. mar. biol. Lab., Woods Hole* **105,** 289–95. *138*

431. Greene, C. W. (1904). Physiological studies of the chinook salmon. II. A study of the blood and serous liquids by the freezing-point method. *Bull. Bur. Fish., Wash.* **24,** 445–56. *119, 188*

432. Greene, C. W. (1919). Biochemical changes in the muscle tissue of king salmon during the fast of spawning migration. *J. biol. Chem.* **39,** 435–56. *226, 242, 243*

433. Greene, C. W. (1926). The physiology of the spawning salmon. *Physiol. Rev.* **6,** 201–41. *98, 114*

*434. Gregory, R. W. (1968). Occurrence of fructose in trout seminal plasma. *Trans. Am. Fish. Soc.* **97,** 203–4.

435. Gross, J. and Budowski, P. (1966). Conversion of carotenoids into vitamins A_1 and A_2 in two species of freshwater fish. *Biochem. J.* **101,** 747–54. *74, 200, 291*

436. Gross, J., Highberger, J. H. and Schmitt, F. O. (1955). Extraction of collagen from connective tissue by neutral salt solutions. *Proc. natn. Acad. Sci. U.S.A.* **41**, 1–7. *10*

437. Gruger, E. H., Nelson, R. W. and Stansby, M. E. (1964). Fatty acid composition of oils from 21 species of marine fish, freshwater fish and shellfish. *J. Am. Oil Chem. Soc.* **41**, 662–7. *145, 146, 201*

438. Gulland, G. L. (1898). 3.—The minute structure of the digestive tract of the salmon, and the changes which occur in it in fresh water. *Fishery Bd for Scotland: Rep. of investigations on the life history of salmon.* H.M.S.O. pp. 13–22. *98, 114, 223*

439. Gunter, G., Sulya, L. L. and Box, B. E. (1961). Some evolutionary patterns in fishes' blood. *Biol. Bull. mar. biol. Lab., Woods Hole* **121**, 302–6. *137*

440. Gustavson, K. H. (1953). Hydrothermal stability and intermolecular organization of collagens from mammalian and teleost skins. *Svensk kem. Tidskr.* **65**, 70–6. *215*

441. Hall, F. G. (1928). Blood concentration in marine fishes. *J. biol. Chem.* **76**, 623–31. *46*

442. Hall, F. G. (1930). The ability of the common mackerel and certain other marine fishes to remove dissolved oxygen from sea water. *Am. J. Physiol.* **93**, 417–21. *149, 150*

*443. Hall, F. G. and Gray, I. E. (1929). The haemoglobin concentration of the blood of marine fishes. *J. biol. Chem.* **81**, 589–94. *137, 148, 177*

444. Hall, F. G., Gray, I. E. and Lepkovsky, S. (1926). The influence of asphyxiation on the blood constituents of marine fishes. *J. biol. Chem.* **67**, 549–54. *46*

445. Halver, J. E. (1957). Nutrition of salmonoid fishes. III. Water-soluble vitamin requirements of chinook salmon. *J. Nutr.* **62**, 225–43. *209*

446. Halver, J. E. (in the press). "Fish Nutrition". Academic Press, London and New York.

447. Halver, J. E., DeLong, D. C. and Mertz, E. T. (1957). Nutrition of salmonoid fishes. V. Classification of essential amino acids for chinook salmon. *J. Nutr.* **63**, 95–105. *208*

*448. Hamaguchi, H., Ohta, N., Onuma, N. and Kawasaki, K. (1960). Studies in inorganic constituents in biological materials (xiv). *J. chem. Soc. Japan.* **81**, 921–4.

449. Hammond, B. R. and Hickman, C. P. (1966). The effect of physical conditioning on the metabolism of lactate, phosphate, and glucose in rainbow trout, *Salmo gairdneri*. *J. Fish. Res. Bd Can.* **23**, 65–83. *48*

450. Hamoir, G. (1953). Myoglobin from carp muscle. *Nature, Lond.* **171**, 345–6. *21*

451. Hamoir, G. (1955). Fish proteins. *Adv. Protein Chem.* **10**, 227–88. *29, 30*

*452. Hane, S. and Robertson, O. H. (1959). Changes in plasma 17-hydroxycortico-steroids accompanying sexual maturation and spawning of the Pacific salmon (*Oncorhynchus tschawytscha*) and rainbow trout (*Salmo gairdnerii*). *Proc. natn. Acad. Sci. U.S.A.* **45**, 886–93. *111*

*453. Haning, Q. C. and Thompson, A. M. (1965). A comparative study of tissue carbon dioxide in vertebrates. *Comp. Biochem. Physiol.* **15**, 17–26.

454. Hanlon, D. P. (1960). The effect of potassium deficiency on the free amino acid pattern of the muscle tissue of protein maintained *Fundulus heteroclitus*. *Biol. Bull. mar. biol. Lab., Woods Hole* **118**, 79–83. *188*

*455. Hanna, M. Y. (1962). Effect of starvation on carbohydrate content of tissues and on relative weights of organs of *Clarias lazera*. *Z. vergl. Physiol.* **45**, 315–21. *252*

*456. Hanson, A. (1966). Differences in the value of N-acetyl histidine in fresh-water and marine teleosts. *C. r. Séanc. Soc. Biol.* **160**, 265–8. *147, 263*

457. Harkness, M. L. R., Harkness, R. D. and James, D. W. (1958). The effect of a protein-free diet on the collagen content of mice. *J. Physiol., Lond.* **144**, 307–13. *102, 232*

458. Harkness, R. D., Marko, A. M., Muir, H. M. and Neuberger, A. (1954). The metabolism of collagen and other proteins of the skin of rabbits. *Biochem. J.* **56**, 558–69. *101*

459. Harrington, W. F. and von Hippel, P. H. (1961). The structure of collagen and gelatin. *Adv. Protein Chem.* **16**, 1–138. *136*

*460. Harrison, M. T., McFarlane, S., Harden, R. M. and Wayne, E. (1965). Nature and availability of iodine in fish. *Am. J. clin. Nutr.* **17**, 73–7.

*461. Hartmann, M., Medem, F. G., Kuhn, R. and Bielig, H. J. (1947). Investigations on the fertilizing materials of rainbow trout. *Z. Naturf.* **2B**, 330–349. *266*

*462. Häsänen, E. and Miettinen, J. K. (1963). Caesium-137 content of fresh-water fish in Finland. *Nature, Lond.* **200**, 1018–9.

463. Hashimoto, K. and Matsuura, F. (1959). Multiple haemoglobins in fish. *Bull. Jap. Soc. scient. Fish.* **24**, 719–23. *135*

464. Hashimoto, K. and Matsuura, F. (1960a). Multiple haemoglobins in fish. II. *Bull. Jap. Soc. scient. Fish.* **26**, 354–60. *135*

465. Hashimoto, K. and Matsuura, F. (1960b). Comparative studies on two haemoglobins of salmon—V. Change in proportion of two haemoglobins with growth. *Bull. Jap. Soc. scient. Fish.* **26**, 931–7. *94*

*466. Hashimoto, Y., Yamada, S. and Mori, T. (1953). Animal protein factor (APF) and vitamin B_{12} in marine products—I. Aquatic animals. *Bull. Jap. Soc. scient. Fish.* **19**, 135–40.

467. Haskell, D. C. and Griffiths, R. (1956). Growth in relation to sex among brook trout. *N.Y. Fish Game J.* **3**, 93–107. *117*

468. Haslewood, G. A. D. (1966). Comparative studies of bile salts. Myxinol disulphate, the principal bile salt of hagfish (*Myxinidae*). *Biochem. J.* **100**, 233–7. *140*

469. Haslewood, G. A. D. (1967a). "Bile Salts". Methuen, London. *140, 141*

470. Haslewood, G. A. D. (1967b). Bile salt evolution. *J. Lipid Res.* **8**, 535–50. *140*

*471. Hastings, W. H. and Spencer, C. F. (1952). Determinations of free and bound ascorbic acid in fishery products. *J. mar. Res.* **11**, 241–4.

*472. Hata, M. and Hata, M. (1967). Fatty acid composition of esters in fish liver. II. Eel (*Anguilla japonica*) liver and *Channa argus* (Cantor) liver. *Tohoku J. agric. Res.* **18**, 267–73.

*473. Hatano, M., Zama, K. and Igarashi, H. (1962). Lipids of salmonoid fishes. V. Acetone-soluble lipid from dark-coloured muscle of dog salmon *Oncorhynchus keta*. *Bull. Fac. Fish. Hokkaido Univ.* **13**, 107–111.

474. Hawkins, A. D., Chapman, K. J. and Symonds, D. J. (1967). Spawning of haddock in captivity. *Nature, Lond.* **215**, 923–5. *116*

*475. Haws, T. G. and Goodnight, C. J. (1962). Some aspects of the haematology of two species of catfish in relation to their habitats. *Physiol. Zoöl.* **35**, 8–17.

476. Hayes, F. R. (1930a). The metabolism of developing salmon eggs. I. The significance of hatching and the role of water in development. *Biochem. J.* **24**, 723–34. *70*

477. Hayes, F. R. (1930b). The metabolism of developing salmon eggs. II. Chemical changes during development. *Biochem. J.* **24**, 735–45. *71, 72*

478. Hayes, F. R., Wilmot, I. R. and Livingstone, D. A. (1951). The oxygen consumption of the salmon egg in relation to development and activity. *J. exp. Zool.* **116**, 377–95. *71*

*479. Heath, A. G. and Pritchard, A. W. (1965). Effects of severe hypoxia on carbohydrate energy stores and metabolism in two species of freshwater fish. *Physiol. Zoöl.* **38**, 325–34. *149, 175*

480. Hegsted, D. M., Milner, J. P., Wilson, D. and Ginna, P. (1953). Changes in muscle water and composition induced by protein depletion in rat at two environmental temperatures. *Am. J. Physiol.* **172**, 14–18. *247*

481. Heincke, F. (1898). "The Natural History of Herrings." 223 pp. Otto Salle, Berlin. *152, 153*

482. Hempel, G. and Blaxter, J. H. S. (1961). The experimental modification of meristic characters in herring (*Clupea harengus* L.). *J. Cons. perm. int. Explor. Mer* **26**, 336–46. *155, 156, 157*

483. Henschel, J. (1936). Water economy and osmoregulation of plaice and flounder. *Wiss. Meeresunters.* **22**, 91–121. *187*

484. Herrera, J. and Muñoz, F. (1957). Biological considerations on the chemical composition of the sardine (*Sardina pilchardus* Walb) from Castellón. *Investigación pesq.* **7**, 33–48. *169, 170, 225, 243, 261*

485. Herrera, J. and Muñoz, F. (1963). Chemical composition of the red mullet (*Mullus barbatus* L.) of Castellón and biological considerations concerning the same. *Investigación pesq.* **23**, 91–113. *120*

486. Hess, A. F., Bills, C. E., Weinstock, M. and Rivkin, J. (1927). Difference in calcium level of the blood between the male and female cod. *Proc. Soc. exp. Biol. Med.* **25**, 349–50. *60*

*487. Hevesy, G., Lockner, D. and Sletten, K. (1964). Iron metabolism and erythrocyte formation in fish. *Acta physiol. scand.* **60**, 256–66.

488. Hewitt, E. R. (1937). Recent work on fatty livers in trout. *Progve Fish Cult.* **27**, 11–15. *53*

*489. Hibi, H. and Hotta, K. (1957). Riboflavin content of fish organs. *Vitamins, Kyoto* **13**, 172–3.

490. Hickling, C. F. (1930). The natural history of the hake. *Fishery Invest., Lond.* Ser. 2, **12** (1), 78 pp. *91, 127, 174*

491. Hickling, C. F. (1933). The natural history of the hake, Part IV. Age-determination and the growth-rate. *Fishery Invest., Lond.* Ser. 2, **13** (2), 120 pp. *116*

492. Hickling, C. F. (1934). Seasonal changes in the ovary of the immature hake, *Merluccius merluccius* L. *J. mar. biol. Ass. U.K.* **20**, 443–61. *171*

493. Higashi, H. (1961). Vitamins in fish—with special reference to edible parts. *In* "Fish as Food" (G. Borgstrom, ed.), Vol. 1, Chapter 13, pp. 411–86. Academic Press, London and New York. *23, 25, 38, 95, 124, 151, 221, 268, 282, 287, 292*

*494. Higashi, H. and Hirai, H. (1948). The nicotinic acid content of fish. *Bull. Jap. Soc. scient. Fish.* **13**, 129–32.

*495. Higashi, H., Hirao, S., Shimizu, K., Yamada, J. and Kikuchi, R. (1953a). Studies on fluctuation of the vitamin A content in fishes—I. Study on vitamin A in the dogfish, *Squalus suckleyi*. *Bull. Jap. Soc. scient. Fish.* **18**, 310–18.

*496. Higashi, H., Hirao, S., Shimizu, K., Yamada, J. and Kikuchi, R. (1953b). Studies on fluctuation of the vitamin A content in fishes—II. Study on vitamin A in sharks. *Bull. Jap. Soc. scient. Fish.* **18**, 349–52.

*497. Higashi, H., Hirao, S., Yamada, J. and Kikuchi, R. (1957). Vitamin A in lamprey, *Entosphenus japonicus*. *Coll. Repr. Tokai reg. Fish. Res. Lab.* **B-261**, 237–45. *38*

*498. Higashi, H., Hirao, S., Yamada, J. and Kikuchi, R. (1958). Vitamin contents in the lamprey, *Entosphenus japonicus* Martens. *J. Vitam.* **4**, 88–99. *38, 252*

*499. Higashi, H., Hirao, S., Yamada, J. and Kikuchi, R. (1962). Studies on fluctuation of the vitamin A content in fishes—V. Some notes on vitamin A in rainbow trout. *Bull. Jap. Soc. scient. Fish.* **28**, 715–21. *55*

500. Higashi, H., Hirao, S., Yamada, J., Kikuchi, R. and Noguchi, H. (1960). Fluctuation of vitamin A in fish. IV. Vitamin A of eel. *Bull. Tokai reg. Fish. Res. Lab.* **28**, 217–30. *55*

*501. Higashi, H., Murayama, S. and Tabei, K. (1959). Riboflavin contents in the liver of fish. *Bull. Jap. Soc. scient. Fish.* **25**, 680–86.

*502. Higashi, H., Murayama, S., Yanase, M. and Tabei, K. (1959a). The pantothenic acid content of fish and shellfish. *Bull. Jap. Soc. scient. Fish.* **24**, 770–75. *282*

*503. Higashi, H., Murayama, S., Yanase, M. and Tabei, K. (1959b). The folic acid content of fish and shellfish. *Bull. Jap. Soc. scient. Fish.* **24**, 776–80.

*504. Higginbotham, A. C. and Meyer, D. K. (1948). Determination of the physical condition of fish. I. Some blood analyses of the southern channel catfish. *Q. J. Fla Acad. Sci.* **11**, 119–24. *255*

505. Hiner, R. L., Hankins, O. G., Sloane, H. S., Fellers, C. R. and Anderson, E. E. (1953). Fibre diameter in relation to tenderness of beef muscle. *Fd Res.* **18**, 364–76. *85*

*506. Hirao, S., Murayama, S., Yanase, M., Yamada, J., Kikuchi, R., Tabei, K., Kisaka, K. and Enomoto, Y. (1958a). Study on the green meat of tuna—I. Quantitative differences of vitamin B group and mineral between the green and the normal meat of precooked tuna. *Bull. Jap. Soc. scient. Fish.* **24**, 671–5.

*507. Hirao, S., Murayama, S., Yanase, M., Yamada, J., Kikuchi, R., Tabei, K., Kisaka, K. and Enomoto, Y. (1958b). Study on the green meat of tuna—II. Quantitative differences of vitamin B group and mineral in kidney between green and normal bodies of yellowfin tuna. *Bull. Jap. Soc. scient. Fish.* **24**, 676–8.

*508. Hirao, S., Yamada, J. and Kikuchi, R. (1954a). Vitamin A in fish meat—I. Variation in the vitamin A content in fish meat by the anatomical locality. *Bull. Jap. Soc. scient. Fish.* **19**, 1047–59. *38*

*509. Hirao, S., Yamada, J. and Kikuchi, R. (1954b). Vitamin A in fish meat—II. Variation in the vitamin A content in fish meat by the body side. *Bull. Jap. Soc. scient. Fish.* **20**, 736–40. *38, 39*

*510. Hirao, S., Yamada, J. and Kikuchi, R. (1955a). Vitamin A in fish meat—III. Individual fluctuation in the vitamin A content in fish meat. *Bull. Jap. Soc. scient. Fish.* **20**, 853–9.

*511. Hirao, S., Yamada, J. and Kikuchi, R. (1955b). Relation between chemical constituents of rainbow trout eggs and the hatching rate. *Bull. Jap. Soc. scient. Fish.* **21**, 240–3. *56, 69, 70, 285*

*512. Hirao, S., Yamada, J. and Kikuchi, R. (1955c). Vitamin A in fish meat—IV. Vitamin A content in the skin of fishes. *Bull. Jap. Soc. scient. Fish.* **21**, 454–7. *39*

*513. Hirao, S., Yamada, J. and Kikuchi, R. (1959). Vitamin A in fish flesh. *Bull. Tokai reg. Fish. Res. Lab.* **25**, 49–65.

514. Hoar, W. S. (1955). Seasonal variations in the resistance of goldfish to temperature. *Trans. R. Soc. Can.* Ser. 3, Sec. 5, **49**, 25–34. *85, 171*

515. Hoar, W. S. (1957). The gonads and reproduction. *In* "The Physiology of Fishes" (M. E. Brown, ed.). Vol. 1, pp. 287–321. Academic Press, London and New York. *117*

516. Hoar, W. S. (1965). Comparative physiology: hormones and reproduction in fishes. *A. Rev. Physiol.* **27**, 51–70. *120, 121, 136, 171*

*517. Hoar, W. S. and Barberie, M. (1945). Distribution of riboflavin in fresh and processed fish. *Can. J. Res.* **23E**, 8–18. *96, 285*

518. Hoar, W. S. and Cottle, M. K. (1952a). Dietary fat and temperature tolerance of goldfish. *Can. J. Zool.* **30**, 41–8. *52, 217*

519. Hoar, W. S. and Cottle, M. K. (1952b). Some effects of temperature acclimatization on the chemical constitution of goldfish tissues. *Can. J. Zool.* **30**, 49–54. *216, 217, 221*

*520. Hochachka, P. W. and Sinclair, A. C. (1962). Glycogen stores in trout tissues before and after stream planting. *J. Fish. Res. Bd Can.* **19**, 127–36. *49, 203, 251*

521. Hodgkin, A. L. and Horowicz, P. (1959). Movements of Na and K in single muscle fibres. *J. Physiol., Lond.* **145**, 405–32. *43*

*522. Hogan, J. W. and Knowles, C. O. (1968). Some enzymatic properties of brain acetylcholinesterase from bluegill and channel catfish. *J. Fish. Res. Bd Can.* **25**, 615–23.

523. Holden (1955). Ring formation in the scales of *Tilapia variabilis* Boulenger and *Tilapia esculenta* Graham from Lake Victoria. *Rep. E. Afr. Freshwat. Fish. Res. Org. for* 1954–5, pp. 36–40. *160*

524. Holmes, E. G. (1965). Changes in the composition of sheep muscle during malnutrition and cobalt deficiency. *Q. J. exp. Physiol.* **50**, 203–13. Quoted in *Chem. Abstr.* **63**, 4726c (1965). *232*

525. Holton, R. W., Blecker, H. H. and Onore, M. (1964). Effect of growth temperature on the fatty acid composition of a blue-green alga. *Phytochemistry* **3**, 595–602. *216*

*526. Hoogland, P. L. (1953). The B-vitamins of cod and haddock. *Prog. Rep. Atlant. Cst Stns* **55**, 11–13.

*527. Hoogland, P. L. (1956). The B-vitamins in cod and haddock. *Stud. Stns Fish. Res. Bd Can.* no. 439, 4 pp.

*528. Hoogland, P. L., Freeman, H. C., Truscott, B. and Waddell, A. E. (1961). The amino acid composition of cod tropomyosin. *J. Fish. Res. Bd Can.* **18**, 501–12.

*529. Hoppe-Seyler, F. A. and Schmidt, W. (1927). For the knowledge of γ-butyrobetaines. *Z. Biol.* **87**, 69–71.

*530. Horiguchi, Y. and Kashiwada, K. (1953). Biochemical studies on skipjack (*Katsuwonus vagans*)—V. Distribution of phosphorus in pyloric coeca. *Bull. Jap. Soc. scient. Fish.* **19**, 733–6.

*531. Horiguchi, Y., Kashiwada, K. and Kakimoto, D. (1953). Biochemical studies on skipjack, *Katsuwonus vagans*—II. Contents of inorganic substances in pyloric coeca. *Bull. Jap. Soc. scient. Fish.* **18**, 279–82.

*532. Horisaka, K. (1964). Free histidine and its derivatives in different fish muscles. II. On the isolation of histidines and their derivatives from the muscle of *Thunnus alalunga, Pneumatophorus japonicus japonicus, Katsuwonus pelamis, Cyprinus carpio, Carassius carassius* and *Parasilurus asotus. J. Biochem., Tokyo* **56**, 607–10.

533. Hornell, J. and Nayudu, M. R. (1923). A contribution to the life-history of the Indian sardine, with notes on the plankton of the Malabar coast. *Madras Fish. Bull.* **17**, 129–97. *65, 91, 116*

*534. Houston, A. H. (1959). Osmoregulatory adaptation of steelhead trout (*Salmo gairdneri* Richardson) to sea water. *Can. J. Zool.* **37**, 729–48.

*535. Houston, A. H. and Madden, J. A. (1968). Environmental temperature and plasma electrolyte regulation in the carp, *Cyprinus carpio. Nature, Lond.* **217**, 969–70. *218*

536. Houston, A. H. and Threadgold, L. T. (1963). Body fluid regulation in smolting Atlantic salmon. *J. Fish. Res. Bd Can.* **20**, 1355–69. *80, 81*

537. Howes, G. B. (1894). On synostosis and curvature of the spine in fishes, with especial reference to the sole. *Proc. zool. Soc. Lond.* (no volume number), 95–101. *x*

*538. Huggel, H., Kleinhaus, A. and Hamzehpour, M. (1963). Blood composition of *Salmo gairdneri irideus* and *Squalius cephalus. Revue suisse Zool.* **70**, 286–90.

539. Hughes, G. M. (1966). The dimensions of fish gills in relation to their function. *J. exp. Biol.* **45**, 177–95. *148*

*540. Hughes, R. B. (1958). Volatile amines of herring flesh. *Nature, Lond.* **181**, 1281–2.

*541. Hughes, R. B. (1959a). Chemical studies on the herring (*Clupea harengus*). 1.—Trimethylamine oxide and volatile amines in fresh, spoiling and cooked herring flesh. *J. Sci. Fd Agric.* **10**, 431–6. *95, 169*

*542. Hughes, R. B. (1959b). Chemical studies on the herring (*Clupea harengus*). II. The free amino-acids of herring flesh and their behaviour during post-mortem spoilage. *J. Sci. Fd Agric.* **10**, 558–64. *96, 99, 277*

*543. Hughes, R. B. (1960a). Chemical studies on the herring (*Clupea harengus*). III.—The lower fatty acids. *J. Sci. Fd Agric.* **11**, 47–53.

*544. Hughes, R. B. (1960b). Chemical studies on the herring (*Clupea harengus*). IV.—Creatine in herring flesh, and its behaviour during heat processing. *J. Sci. Fd Agric.* **11**, 700–5.

*545. Hughes, R. B. (1963). Chemical studies on the herring (*Clupea harengus*). VII.—Collagen and cohesiveness in heat-processed herring, and observations on a seasonal variation in collagen content. *J. Sci. Fd Agric.* **14**, 432–41. *102, 103*

*546. Hughes, R. B. (1964). Chemical studies on the herring (*Clupea harengus*). X.—Histidine and free sugars in herring flesh. *J. Sci. Fd Agric.* **15**, 293–9.

547. Hulet, W. H., Masel, S. J., Jodrey, L. H. and Wehr, R. G. (1967). The role of calcium in the survival of marine teleosts in dilute sea water. *Bull. mar. Sci. Gulf Caribb.* **17**, 677–88. *189*

*548. Humbel, R. E. and Crestfield, A. M. (1965). Isolation and partial structural analysis of insulin from the separate islet tissue of *Lophius piscatorius*. *Biochemistry, N.Y.* **4**, 1044–8. *278*

549. Hunn, J. B. (1964). Some patho-physiologic effects of bacterial kidney disease in brook trout. *Proc. Soc. exp. Biol. Med.* **117**, 383–5. *121*

550. Hunn, J. B. (1967). Bibliography on the blood chemistry of fishes. *Res. Rep. U.S. Fish Wildl. Serv.* **72**, 32 pp. *260*

551. Hunn, J. B. and Fromm, P. O. (1966). In vivo uptake of radioiodide by rainbow trout. *J. Wat. Pollut. Control Fed.* **38**, 1981–5. *207*

552. Hunn, J. B. and Reineke, E. P. (1964). Influence of iodine intake on iodine distribution in trout. *Proc. Soc. exp. Biol. Med.* **115**, 91–3. *207*

*553. Hunn, J. B. and Robinson, P. F. (1966). Some blood chemistry values for five Chesapeake Bay area fishes. *Chesapeake Sci.* **7**, 173–5. *148, 151*

*554. Hunter, A. (1929). The creatine content of the muscles and some other tissues in fishes. *J. biol. Chem.* **81**, 513–23.

555. Huxley, H. E. (1957). The double array of filaments in cross-striated muscle. *J. biophys. biochem. Cytol.* **3**, 631–48. *16*

*556. Høygaard, A. and Rasmussen, H. W. (1939). Vitamin C sources in Eskimo food. *Nature, Lond.* **143**, 943 only.

557. Idler, D. R. and Bitners, I. (1958). Biochemical studies on sockeye salmon during spawning migration. II. Cholesterol, fat, protein and water in the flesh of standard fish. *Can. J. Biochem. Physiol.* **36**, 793–98. *110, 118*

558. Idler, D. R. and Bitners, I. (1959). Biochemical studies on sockeye salmon during spawning migration. V. Cholesterol, fat, protein and water in the body of the standard fish. *J. Fish. Res. Bd Can.* **16**, 235–41. *225, 230*

*559. Idler, D. R. and Bitners, I. (1960). Biochemical studies on sockeye salmon during spawning migration. IX. Fat, protein and water in the major internal organs and cholesterol in the liver and gonads of the standard fish. *J. Fish. Res. Bd Can.* **17**, 113–22. *105, 110*

*560. Idler, D. R., Fagerlund, U. H. M. and Ronald, A. P. (1960). Isolation of pregn-4-ene-17α, 20β-diol-3-one from the plasma of Pacific salmon (*Oncorhynchus nerka*). *Biochem. biophys. Res. Commun.* **2**, 133–7.

*561. Idler, D. R. and Freeman, H. C. (1965). A demonstration of an impaired hormone metabolism in moribund Atlantic cod (*Gadus morhua* L.). *Can. J. Biochem. Physiol.* **43**, 620–3. *115*

*562. Idler, D. R., Freeman, H. C. and Truscott, B. (1964). Steroid hormones in the plasma of spawned Atlantic salmon (*Salmo salar*) and a comparison of their determination by chemical and biological assay methods. *Can. J. Biochem.* **42**, 211–18.

*563 Idler, D. R., Ronald, A. P. and Schmidt, P. J. (1959a). Isolation of cortisone and cortisol from the plasma of Pacific salmon (*Oncorhynchus nerka*). *J. Am. chem. Soc.* **81**, 1260–1.

*564. Idler, D. R., Ronald, A. P. and Schmidt, P. J. (1959b). Biochemical studies on sockeye salmon during spawning migration. VII. Steroid hormones in plasma. *Can. J. Biochem. Physiol.* **37**, 1227–38. *114*

*565. Idler, D. R., Schmidt, P. J. and Bitners, I. (1961). Isolation and identification of adrenosterone in salmon (*Oncorhynchus nerka*) plasma. *Can. J. Biochem. Physiol.* **39**, 1653–4.

*566. Idler, D. R., Schmidt, P. J. and Ronald, A. P. (1960). Isolation and identification of 11-ketotestosterone in salmon plasma. *Can. J. Biochem. Physiol.* **38**, 1053–7.

*567. Idler, D. R., Schmidt, P. J. and Ronald, A. P. (1962). Isolation of 20β-dihydrocortisone from sockeye salmon (*Oncorhynchus nerka*) plasma. *Can. J. Biochem. Physiol.* **40**, 549–53.

*568. Idler, D. R. and Truscott, B. (1966). Identification and quantification of testosterone in peripheral plasma of skate. *Gen. comp. Endocrinol.* **7**, 375–83. *121*

569. Idler, D. R., Truscott, B., Freeman, H. C., Chang, V., Schmidt, P. J. and Ronald, A. P. (1963). In vivo metabolism of steroid hormones by sockeye salmon. (A). Impaired hormone clearance in mature and spawned Pacific salmon (*Oncorhynchus nerka*). (B) Precursors of 11-ketotestosterone. *Can. J. Biochem. Physiol.* **41**, 875–87. *115*

570. Idler, D. R. and Tsuyuki, H. (1958). Biochemical studies on sockeye salmon during spawning migration. 1. Physical measurements, plasma cholesterol, and electrolyte levels. *Can. J. Biochem. Physiol.* **36**, 783–91. *110*

*571. Idler, D. R. and Tsuyuki, H. (1959). Biochemical studies on sockeye salmon during spawning migration. VIII. Androgen content of testes. *J. Fish. Res. Bd Can.* **16**, 559–60.

*572. Igarashi, H., Zama, K., Hatano, M. and Takama, K. (1962). Lipids of flounder. 1. Acetone-soluble lipids from fresh flounder, *Hippoglossus dubius.* *Bull. Jap. Soc. scient. Fish.* **28**, 518–21.

*573. Igarashi, H., Zama, K. and Katada, M. (1957a). Lipids of the muscle of tuna, *Thunnus orientalis*—I. Acetone-soluble lipid of the ordinary muscle. *Bull. Jap. Soc. scient. Fish.* **22**, 787–90.

*574. Igarashi, H., Zama, K. and Katada, M. (1957b). Lipids of the muscle of tuna, *Thunnus orientalis*—II. Acetone-soluble lipid of the dark-coloured muscle. *Bull. Jap. Soc. scient. Fish.* **22**, 791–4. *20*

*575. Igarashi, H., Zama, K. and Katada, M. (1957c). Lipids of the muscle of tuna, *Thunnus orientalis*—III. Lecithins of the dark-coloured and ordinary muscles. *Bull. Jap. Soc. scient. Fish.* **23**, 273–7.

*576. Igarashi, H., Zama, K. and Katada, M. (1957d). Lipids of the muscle of tuna, *Thunnus orientalis*—IV. Cephalins of the dark-coloured and ordinary muscles. *Bull. Jap. Soc. scient. Fish.* **23**, 278–81.

*577. Igarashi, H., Zama, K. and Katada, M. (1960a). Egg lipids of a carp, *Cyprinus carpio*. 1. Fatty oil from carp egg. *Bull. Jap. Soc. scient. Fish.* **26**, 326–9.

*578. Igarashi, H., Zama, K. and Katada, M. (1960b). Egg lipids of a carp, *Cyprinus carpio*. 2. Lecithin from carp egg. *Bull. Jap. Soc. scient. Fish.* **26**, 1128–31.

*579. Ikeda, S., Sato, M. and Kimura, R. (1963). Biochemical studies on L-ascorbic acid in aquatic animals—II. Distribution in various parts of fish. *Bull. Jap. Soc. scient. Fish.* **29**, 765–70.

*580. Ikeda, S. and Shimeno, S. (1967). Studies on glucose-6-phosphatase of aquatic animals—1. Properties of hepatic glucose-6-phosphatase of fishes. *Bull. Jap. Soc. scient. Fish.* **33**, 104–11.

*581. Ikeda, S. and Taguchi, T. (1966). Improved assay method and levels of vitamin E in fish tissues. *Bull. Jap. Soc. scient. Fish.* **32**, 346–51. *292*

582. Iles, T. D. and Wood, R. J. (1965). The fat/water relationship in North Sea herring (*Clupea harengus*), and its possible significance. *J. mar. biol. Ass. U.K.* **45**, 353–66. *226, 227*

*583. Ingalls, R. L., Klocke, J. F., Rafferty, J. P., Greensmith, R. E., Chang, M. L., Tack, P. I. and Ohlson, M. A. (1950). Nutritive value of fish from Michigan waters. *Tech. Bull. Mich. (St. Coll.) agric. Exp. Stn* **219**, 24 pp.

*584. Innami, S. and Kubota, M. (1960). Riboflavin content of fish-eggs. *Rep. natn. Inst. Nutr., Tokyo* pp. 73–4.

*585. Intengan, C. L., Alejo, L. G., Concepcion, I., Corpus, V. A., Salud, R. D., del Rosario, I., Gomez, R. and Henson, J. (1956). Composition of Philippine foods. V. *Philipp. J. Sci.* **85**, 203–13.

586. Inui, Y. and Ohshima, Y. (1966). Effect of starvation on metabolism and chemical composition of eels. *Bull. Jap. Soc. scient. Fish.* **32**, 492–501. *224, 250, 251, 256, 257*

587. Irie, T., Yokoyama, T. and Yamada, T. (1967). Calcification of fish otolith caused by food and water. *Bull. Jap. Soc. scient. Fish.* **33**, 24–6. *160*

588. Ironside, J. I. M. and Love, R. M. (1958). Studies on protein denaturation in frozen fish. 1.—Biological factors influencing the amounts of soluble and insoluble protein present in the muscle of the North Sea cod. *J. Sci. Fd Agric.* **9**, 597–604. *4, 5, 103, 104, 236*

589. Irvine, D. G., Newman, K. and Hoar, W. S. (1957). Effects of dietary phospholipid and cholesterol on the temperature resistance of goldfish. *Can. J. Zool.* **35,** 691–709. *214*

590. Jacquot, R. (1961). Organic constituents of fish and other aquatic animal foods. *In* "Fish as Food" (G. Borgstrom, ed.), Vol. 1, Chapter 6, pp. 145–209. Academic Press, London and New York. *120, 142, 150, 169, 174, 225*

591. Jacquot, R. and Creac'h, P. V. (1950). Fish proteins and their nutritive value. *Congr. intern. étude sur le role du poisson dans l'alimentation* pp. 11–58. *260*

*592. Jaffé, W. G., Nolberga, B., Embden, C., Garcia, S., Olivares, H. and Gross, M. (1956). Composition of Venezuelan fishes. *Archos. venez. Nutr.* **7,** 163–6.

*593. Jakoubek, B. and Edström, J. E. (1965). RNA changes in the Mauthner axon and myelin sheath after increased functional activity. *J. Neurochem.* **12,** 845–9. *48*

594. Jamieson, A. (1967). New genotypes in cod at Greenland. *Nature, Lond.* **215,** 661–2. *167*

*595. Jangaard, P. M., Ackman, R. G. and Sipos, J. C. (1967). Seasonal changes in fatty acid composition of cod liver, flesh, roe, and milt lipids. *J. Fish. Res. Bd Can.* **24,** 613–27. *65, 95, 122, 124, 170*

596. Jangaard, P. M., Brockerhoff, H., Burgher, R. D. and Hoyle, R. J. (1967). Seasonal changes in general condition and lipid content of cod from inshore waters. *J. Fish. Res. Bd Can.* **24,** 607–12. *91, 122*

597. Jankowsky, H. D. and Korn, H. (1965). The influence of the adaptation temperature on the mitochondria content of fish muscle. *Naturwissenschaften* **52,** 642–3. *213*

*598. Janssens, P. A. and Cohen, P. P. (1968). Biosynthesis of urea in the aestivating African lungfish and in *Xenopus laevis* under conditions of water-shortage. *Comp. Biochem. Physiol.* **24,** 887–98.

599. Jared, D. W. and Wallace, R. A. (1968). Comparative chromatography of the yolk proteins of teleosts. *Comp. Biochem. Physiol.* **24,** 437–43. *135*

600. Javaid, M. Y. and Anderson, J. M. (1967). Influence of starvation on selected temperature of some salmonids. *J. Fish. Res. Bd Can.* **24,** 1515–9. *209*

*601. Jensen, C. E. and Vilstrup, T. (1954). Determination of some inorganic substances in the labyrinthine fluids. *Acta chem. scand.* **8,** 697–8.

602. Jensen, V. (1937). Studies in blood groups in fishes (cod). *Z. Rassenphysiol.* **9,** 22–5. *163*

*603. Jofre, I. J. and Izquierdo, J. A. (1967). The concentrations of adrenaline and noradrenaline in the brain and the heart of the goldfish, *Carassius auratus.* *J. Pharm. Pharmac.* **19,** 340–1.

*604. Johansen, J., Fänge, R. and Johannessen, M. W. (1962). Relations between blood, sinus fluid and lymph in *Myxine glutinosa* L. *Comp. Biochem. Physiol.* **7,** 23–8.

605. Johnston, C. E. and Eales, J. G. (1967). Purines in the integument of the Atlantic salmon (*Salmo salar*) during parr-smolt transformation. *J. Fish. Res. Bd Can.* **24,** 955–64. *80*

606. Johnston, C. E. and Eales, J. G. (1968). Influence of temperature and photoperiod on guanine and hypoxanthine levels in skin and scales of Atlantic salmon (*Salmo salar*) during parr-smolt transformation. *J. Fish. Res. Bd Can.* **25,** 1901–9. *80*

*607. Johnston, P. V. and Roots, B. I. (1964). Brain lipid fatty acids and temperature acclimation. *Comp. Biochem. Physiol.* **11,** 303–9. *217*

*608. Jonas, R. E. E. and Bilinski, E. (1965). Ketone bodies in the blood of salmonoid fishes. *J. Fish. Res. Bd Can.* **22,** 891–8.

*609. Jonas, R. E. E. and Bilinski, E. (1967a). Glycerylphosphoryl choline and related compounds in rainbow trout muscle stored at −4°C. *J. Fish. Res. Bd Can.* **24,** 273–80.

*610. Jonas, R. E. E. and Bılinski, E. (1967b). Phospholipase A activity in rainbow trout muscle. *J. Fish. Res. Bd Can.* **24,** 2555–62.

*611. Jonas, R. E. E. and MacLeod, R. A. (1960). Biochemical studies on sockeye salmon during spawning migration. X. Glucose, total protein, non-protein nitrogen and amino acid nitrogen in plasma. *J. Fish. Res. Bd Can.* **17,** 125–6. *99. 119*

612. Jonas, R. E. E., Sehdev, H. S. and Tomlinson, N. (1962). Blood pH and mortality in rainbow trout (*Salmo gairdnerii*) and sockeye salmon (*Oncorhynchus nerka*). *J. Fish. Res. Bd Can.* **19,** 619–24. *47*

613. Jones, B. W. (1966). The cod and the cod fishery at Faroe. *Fishery Invest., Lond.* Ser. II, **25** (5), 32 pp. *173*

*614. Jones, N. R. (1954a). Taurine in fresh and iced skeletal muscle of codling (*Gadus callarias*). *Biochem. J.* **56,** xxii only.

*615. Jones, N. R. (1954b). Factors affecting the free amino acid composition of fresh and iced skeletal muscle of North Sea codling (*Gadus callarias*). *Biochem. J.* **58,** xlvii–xlviii. *238*

*616. Jones, N. R. (1956). Free sugar estimation in codling (*Gadus callarias*) muscle. *Biochem. J.* **62,** 7p–8p.

*617. Jones, N. R. (1958a). Post-mortem changes in acid-soluble nucleotides of rested codling (*Gadus callarias*) muscle at 0°. *Biochem. J.* **68,** 9p only.

*618. Jones, N. R. (1958b). The estimation of free sugars in skeletal muscle of codling (*Gadus callarias*) and herring (*Clupea harengus*). *Biochem. J.* **68,** 704–8.

619. Jones, N. R. (1958c). Free sugars in chill-stored trawled codling muscle. *J. Sci. Fd Agric.* **9,** 672–7. *41, 42*

*620. Jones, N. R. (1959a). The free amino-acids of fish. II.— Fresh skeletal muscle from lemon sole (*Pleuronectes microcephalus*). *J. Sci. Fd Agric.* **10,** 282–6. *188, 238*

*621. Jones, N. R. (1959b). Pyruvic acid in the skeletal muscle of fresh and chill-stored trawled codling (*Gadus callarias*). *J. Sci. Fd Agric.* **10**, 472–4.

*622. Jones, N. R. and Murray, J. (1957). Nucleotides in the skeletal muscle of codling (*Gadus callarias*). *Biochem. J.* **66**, 5p–6p. *41, 42*

*623. Jones, N. R. and Murray, J. (1960). The acid-soluble nucleotides of codling (*Gadus callarias*) muscle. *Biochem. J.* **77**, 567–75. *41, 42, 43, 49*

*624. Jones, N. R. and Murray, J. (1961). Nucleotide concentration in codling (*Gadus callarias*) muscle passing through *rigor mortis* at 0°. *Z. vergl. Physiol.* **44**, 174–83.

*625. Jones, N. R. and Murray, J. (1966). Nicotinamide adenine dinucleotide (NAD) and reduced NAD in living and chill-stored dying muscle of cod, *Gadus callarias*. *Bull. Jap. Soc. scient. Fish.* **32**, 197–203.

626. Jonsson, J. (1953). On the Icelandic stock of cod during the years 1928–53. *Rapp. P.-v. Réun. Cons. perm. int. Explor. Mer* **136**, 51–7. *210*

627. Jordan, D. S. (1963). "The Genera of Fishes and a Classification of Fishes." Reprinted with a new foreword by G. S. Myers, index by H. M. Smith and L. P. Schultz. Stanford University Press, California. *x, 406–9* (Appendix A).

628. Jordan, H. E. and Speidel, C. C. (1930). Blood formation in cyclostomes. *Am. J. Anat.* **46**, 355–92. *136, 137*

*629. Joshi, N. V., Barnabas, J. and Barnabas, T. (1958). Amino acid composition of edible muscles. *Indian J. med. Res.* **46**, 345–50.

*630. Joshi, S. and Magar, N. G. (1955). Nutritive value of some Bombay fish—III. Phospholipids in fish. *J. Univ. Bombay* **23** (5), 27–33.

*631. Joshi, S., Master, F. and Magar, N. G. (1953). Nutritive value of some Bombay fish. Part 1. Distribution of non-protein nitrogen extractives, and thiamine, riboflavin and niacin. *Indian. J. med. Res.* **41**, 431–9.

632. Joubert, D. M. (1955). Growth of muscle fibre in the foetal sheep. *Nature, Lond.* **175**, 936 only. *85*

633. Kafuku, T. (1950). "Red muscles" in fishes. 1. Comparative anatomy of the scombroid fishes of Japan. *Jap. J. Ichthyol.* **1**, 89–100. *19*

*634. Kakimoto, D. (1957a). Studies on B-vitamins in pyloric coeca of skipjack—II. P-amino benzoic acid (PABA) and riboflavin. *Bull. Jap. Soc. scient. Fish.* **22**, 577–82.

*635. Kakimoto, D. (1957b). Studies on B-vitamins of pyloric coeca of skipjack, *Katsuwonus vagans*—IV. On vitamin B_{12}. *Bull. Jap. Soc. scient. Fish.* **22**, 634–6.

*636. Kakimoto, D. and Kanazawa, A. (1957). Studies on B-vitamins in pyloric coeca of skipjack—I. Thiamine, nicotinic acid, folic acid, biotin and pantothenic acid. *Bull. Jap. Soc. scient. Fish.* **22**, 574–6.

*637. Kakimoto, D. and Kanazawa, A. (1959a). Studies on folic acid and folinic acid of fishes. *Bull. Jap. Soc. scient. Fish.* **24**, 933–6.

*638. Kakimoto, D. and Kanazawa, A. (1959b). Studies on folic acid and folinic acid of *Cyprinus carpio*. *Bull. Jap. Soc. scient. Fish.* **25**, 431–4.

*639. Kakimoto, D., Kanazawa, A. and Kashiwada, K. (1957). Amino acid composition of the pyloric coeca of skipjack, *Katsuwonus vagans*. *Bull. Jap. Soc. scient. Fish.* **22**, 631–4.

*640. Kamra, S. K. (1966). Effect of starvation and refeeding on some liver and blood constituents of Atlantic cod (*Gadus morhua* L.). *J. Fish. Res. Bd Can.* **23**, 975–82. *251, 252*

641. Kaneko, T., Takeuchi, M., Ishii, S., Higashi, H. and Kikuchi, T. (1967a). Effect of dietary lipids on fish under cultivation—III. Effect of methyl esters of highly unsaturated fatty acids, methyl linoleate and methyl palmitate on the fatty acid composition of rainbow trout flesh lipids. *Bull. Jap. Soc. scient. Fish.* **33**, 47–55. *201*

642. Kaneko, T., Takeuchi, M., Ishii, S., Higashi, H. and Kikuchi, T. (1967b). Effect of dietary lipids on fish under cultivation—IV. Changes of fatty acid composition in flesh lipids of rainbow trout on non-feeding. *Bull. Jap. Soc. scient. Fish.* **33**, 56–8. *242*

*643. Kanemitsu, T. and Aoe, H. (1958). On the studies of carotenoids of the salmon—II. Determination of muscle pigment. *Bull. Jap. Soc. scient. Fish.* **24**, 555–8. *36, 38, 96, 122*

*644. Kansyuk, R. P. (1967). Comparative evaluation of the activity and thermal stability of digestive enzymes of some fish in the northwestern part of the Black Sea. *Obmen Veshchestv. Biokhim. Ryb., Akad. Nauk SSSR, Min. Ryb. Khoz. SSSR, Ikhtiol. Kom.* pp. 209–14. Quoted in *Chem. Abstr.* **69**, 1001n (1968).

*645. Kapeller-Adler, R. and Krael, J. (1930). Investigation of the nitrogen distribution in the muscle of different classes of animals. I. *Biochem. Z.* **221**, 437–60.

*646. Karrick, N. L. (1955). Vitamin content of fishery byproducts part 2— Vitamin B_{12} in Pacific sardine (*Sardinops coerulea*) organs and riboflavin, nicotinic acid, and vitamin B_{12} in albacore tuna (*Germo alalunga*) organs. *Comml Fish. Rev.* **17**, (2), 8–11.

647. Karrick, N. L., Clegg, W. and Stansby, M. E. (1956). Composition of fresh-water fish—No. 1. *Comml Fish. Rev.* **18** (2), 13–16. *173*

648. Karrick, N. L. and Thurston, C. E. (1964). Proximate composition of silver salmon. *J. agric. Fd Chem.* **12**, 282–4. *36*

*649. Karrick, N. L. and Thurston, C. E. (1968). Proximate composition and sodium and potassium contents of four species of tuna. *Fish. Ind. Res.* **4** (2) 73–81.

650. Karst, H. (1965). Vitamin A regulation in the pike perch (*Lucioperca lucioperca*) and some other freshwater fishes in Germany. *Int. Z. Vitam Forsch.* **35**, 328–41. Quoted in *Chem. Abstr.* **64**, 11600b (1966). *200*

651. Kashiwada, K. (1952). Studies on the enzymes of skipjack, *Katsuwonus vagans*, entrails.—1. On the seasonal variation of proteolytic enzyme activity in pyloric coeca. *Bull. Jap. Soc. scient. Fish.* **18**, 151–4. *204*

*652. Kasinova, N. E. (1961). Mineral content of fish meat. *Vop. Pitan.* **20**, 74–7.

*653. Kassemsarn, B.-O., Sanz Perez, B., Murray, J. and Jones, N. R. (1963). Nucleotide degradation in the muscle of iced haddock (*Gadus aeglefinus*), lemon sole (*Pleuronectes microcephalus*), and plaice (*Pleuronectes platessa*). *J. Food Sci.* **28**, 28–37.

*654. Katada, M., Zama, K. and Igarashi, H. (1959). Studies on the phosphatide of aquatic animals—XIX. Lipids of the body tissues of herring, *Clupea pallasii*. *Bull. Jap. Soc. scient. Fish.* **24**, 905–8.

*655. Katada, M., Zama, K. and Igarashi, H. (1960). Lipids of the muscle of tuna, Thynnus orientalis—VII. Distribution of lipids in dark-coloured muscle, ordinary muscle, and several other tissues. *Bull. Jap. Soc. scient. Fish.* **26**, 425–9.

656. Katayama, T., Ikeda, N. and Harada, K. (1965). Carotenoids in sea breams, *Chrysophrys major*, Temminck & Schlegel—1. *Bull. Jap. Soc. scient. Fish.* **31**, 947–52. *51, 200, 201*

*657. Kato, T., Shinjo, S. and Shimada, T. (1968). Isolation and properties of ferratin from tuna fish (*Thunnus obesus*) spleen. *J. Biochem., Tokyo* **63**, 170–5.

*658. Kawakita, Y. (1956). Distribution of lipids in the central nervous system of some vertebrates. *J. Biochem., Tokyo* **43**, 111–18.

659. Kawatsu, H. (1966). Studies on the anaemia of fish.—1. Anaemia of rainbow trout caused by starvation. *Bull. Freshwat. Fish. Res. Lab., Tokyo* **15**, 167–73. *255, 256*

660. Keiz, G. (1959). The relationship between the fat content of the liver of the carp (*Cyprinus carpio*) and the season, food and sex, as well as to the content of fat-soluble vitamin A. *Naturwissenschaften* **46**, 610 only. *120*

661. Kelly, K. O. (1969). Factors affecting the texture of frozen fish. *In* "Freezing and Irradiation of Fish" (R. Kreuzer, ed.), 339–42. Fishing News (Books), London. *93*

662. Kelly, P. B., Reiser, R. and Hood, D. W. (1958). The effect of diet on the fatty acid composition of several species of freshwater fish. *J. Am. Oil Chem. Soc.* **35**, 503–5. *146, 201*

*663. Kenyon, A. J. (1967). The role of the liver in the maintenance of plasma proteins and amino acids in the eel, *Anguilla anguilla* L., with reference to amino acid deamination. *Comp. Biochem. Physiol.* **22**, 169–75.

*664. Ketz, H. A., Assmann, G. and Witt, H. (1960). The sodium, potassium and glucose contents of serum and erythrocytes in birds and fish. *Acta biol. med. germ.* **4**, 598–605.

18**

665. Keys, A., Brozek, J., Mickelsen, O., Henschel, A. and Taylor, H. (1947). Total body fluid, fat and active tissue in starvation and subsequent rehabilitation. *Fedn Proc. Fedn Am. Socs exp. Biol.* **6**, 142 only. *230*

666. Khailov, M. M. (1962). An electrophoretic investigation of the plasma proteins from the blood of gadoid fish. *Trudy murmansk biol. Inst.* **4**, 202–7. *231*

*667. Khalid, Q., Mirza, A. S. and Khan, A. H. (1968). The fatty acid composition of edible marine fish oils. *J. Am. Oil Chem. Soc.* **45**, 247–9.

668. Khalil, F. and Abdel-Messeih, G. (1959). Effect of starvation on contents of water, nitrogen and lipids of tissues of *Varanus griseus*, Daud. *Z. vergl. Physiol.* **42**, 410–4. *223*

669. Khawaja, D. K. and Jafri, A. K. (1967). Biochemical changes in the muscle of the freshwater murrel, *Ophicephalus punctatus*, Bloch during growth. *Broteria* **36** (3–4), 71–84. *91*

*670. Khorana, M. L., Sarma, M. L. and Giri, K. V. (1942). Investigations on the food value of fish and other marine products. *Indian J. med. Res.* **30**, 315–18.

*671. Kiermeir, A. (1939). On the blood sugar of freshwater fish. *Z. vergl. Physiol.* **27**, 460–91. *46, 92, 150, 202, 251*

*672. Kilborn, L. G. and MacLeod, J. J. R. (1920). Observations on the glycogen content of certain invertebrates and fishes. *Q. J. exp. Physiol.* **12**, 317–30.

673. Kinne, O. and Kinne, E. M. (1962). Rates of development in embryos of a cyprinodont fish exposed to different temperature-salinity-oxygen combinations. *Can. J. Zool.* **40**, 231–53. *69, 210*

*674. Kisch, B. (1930). Research on urea in selachians. *Biochem. Z.* **225**, 197–207. *144*

675. Kishinouye, K. (1923). Contributions to the comparative study of the so-called scombroid fishes. *J. Coll. Agric. imp. Univ. Tokyo* **8**, 293–475. *18, 19, 31*

*676. Kitamikado, M., Takahashi, T., Noda, H., Morishita, T. and Tachino, S (1965). Digestibility of dietary components in young yellow tail, *Seriola quinqueradiata* T and S. *Bull. Jap. Soc. scient. Fish.* **31**, 133–7.

677. Kitamura, S., Suwa, T., Ohara, S. and Nakagawa, K. (1967). Studies on vitamin requirements of rainbow trout—II. The deficiency symptoms of fourteen kinds of vitamin. *Bull. Jap. Soc. scient. Fish.* **33**, 1120–5. *187, 208*

*678. Klawe, W. L., Barrett, I. and Klawe, B. M. H. (1963). Haemoglobin content of the blood of six species of scombroid fishes. *Nature, Lond.* **198**, 96 only. *148*

*679. Klethi, J. and Mandel, P. (1965). Eye lens nucleotides of different species of vertebrates. *Nature, Lond.* **205**, 1114–5.

680. Klicka, J. (1965). Temperature acclimation in goldfish: lack of evidence for hormonal involvement. *Physiol. Zoöl.* **38**, 177–89. *213*

*681. Klocke, J. F., Porter, T., Tack, P. I., Leffler, E., Henry, N. S. and Nitchals, R. (1946). Nutritive value of fish from Michigan waters. I. Nicotinic acid of lake herring, carp, common suckers, and burbot. *Fd Res.* **11**, 179–86.

*682. Klocke, J. F., Tack, P. I., Ohlson, M. A., Nitchals, R., Leffler, E. and Henry, N. S. (1947). Nutritive value of fish from Michigan waters. II. Thiamin of lake herring, carp, common sucker, burbot, and smelt. *Fd Res.* **12**, 36–43.

*683. Klungsøyr, M., and Boge, G. (1953). B-vitamins in herring organs. *Meld. SSF* (1), pp. 10–13.

684. Knipprath, W. G. and Mead, J. F. (1965). Influence of temperature on the fatty acid pattern of muscle and organ lipids of the rainbow trout (*Salmo gairdneri*). *Fish. Ind. Res.* **3**, 23–7. *217*

*685. Knipprath, W. G. and Mead, J. F. (1968). The effect of the environmental temperature on the fatty acid composition and on the *in vivo* incorporation of 1-^{14}C-acetate in goldfish (*Carassius auratus* L.). *Lipids* **3**, 121–8. *217*

686. Kobrle, V. and Chvapil, M. (1962). Amount of ultrafiltrable and collagen-bound hydroxyproline in different organs of the rat during ageing. *Physiologia bohemoslov.* **11**, 243–48. *128*

687. Koch, H. J. A., Bergström, E. and Evans, J. C. (1964). The microelectric separation on starch gel of the haemoglobins of *Salmo salar* L. *Meded. K. vlaam. Acad.* **26** (9), 1–33. *94*

688. Koch, H. J. A., Evans, J. C. and Bergström, E. (1959). Sodium regulation in the blood of parr and smolt stages of the Atlantic salmon. *Nature. Lond.*, **184**, 283 only. *81, 190*

689. Koch, H. J. A., Wilkins, N. P., Bergström, E. and Evans, J. C. (1967). Studies on multiple components of the haemoglobins of *Salmo salar* L. *Meded. K. vlaam. Acad.* **29**, 1–16. *166*

*690. Kodicek, E. (1940). Estimations of nicotinic acid in animal tissues, blood and certain foodstuffs. 2. Applications. *Biochem. J.* **34**, 724–35.

*691. Koizumi, C., Kawakami, H. and Nonaka, J. (1967). Studies on 'green' tuna —III. Relation between 'greening' and trimethylamine oxide concentration in albacore meat. *Bull. Jap. Soc. scient. Fish.* **33**, 131–5. *38*

*692. de Koning, A. J. (1966). Phospholipids of marine origin. 1. The hake (*Merlucius capensis*, Castelnau). *J. Sci. Fd Agric.* **17**, 112–7.

693. Kono, T. and Colowick, S. P. (1961). Isolation of skeletal muscle cell membrane and some of its properties. *Archs Biochem. Biophys.* **93**, 520–33. *16*

694. Kono, T., Kakuma, F., Homma, M. and Fukuda, S. (1964). The electron-microscopic structure and chemical composition of the isolated sarcolemma of the rat skeletal muscle cell. *Biochim. biophys. Acta* **88**, 156–76. *12, 86*

*695. Konosu, S., Hashimoto, K. and Matsuura, F. (1958). Chemical studies on the red muscle ('Chiai') of fishes—XI. Amino acid composition of tuna myoglobin. *Bull. Jap. Soc. scient. Fish.* **24**, 563–6.

*696. Konosu, S., Katori, S., Ota, R., Eguchi, S. and Mori, T. (1956). Amino acid composition of fish muscle protein. *Bull. Jap. Soc. scient. Fish.* **21**, 1163–6. *130, 265*

*697. Konosu, S. and Matsuura, F. (1960). Tryptophan content of fish meat. *Bull. Jap. Soc. scient. Fish.* **26,** 1040–9.

*698. Konosu, S., Özay, M. and Hashimoto, Y. (1964). Free amino acids in the muscle of a few species of fish. *Bull. Jap. Soc. scient. Fish.* **30,** 930–4.

*699. Kooyman, G. L. (1963). Erythrocyte analysis of some Antarctic fishes. *Copeia* (2), 457–9. *220*

700. Kordyl, E. (1951). Chemical composition of the Baltic cod and herring in relation to the degree of sexual maturity. *Pr. morsk. Inst. ryb. Gdyni* (6), 145–58. Quoted in *World fish. Abstr.* **4** (6), UDC 637–502–7. *119, 243*

*701. Korzhenko, V. P. (1966). Variations in amino acid composition of gonads in the course of ovo- and spermatogeny in *Oncorhynchus keta*, Walbaum. *Dokl. Akad. Nauk SSSR* **171,** 237–9. *66, 99, 100, 101, 125*

702. Korzhenko, V. P. and Novikov, G. G. (1967). Amino acid composition of total muscle protein in fish. *Obmen Veshchestv Biokhim. Ryb., Akad. Nauk SSSR, Min. Ryb. Khoz. SSSR, Ikhtiol. Kom.* pp. 247–53. Quoted in *Chem. Abstr.* **69,** 1002p (1968). *102*

703. Kosmina, V. V. (1966). Electrophoretic changes in protein of blood serum of fish during prolonged starvation. *J. Hydrobiol.* **2** (4), 74–7. *232, 234, 235*

704. Kostuichenko, V. A. (1961). Age and rate of growth of the goby (*Neogobius melanostomus* Pallas). *Trudy Azovo-Chernomorskogo nauchno-issledovatelskogo instituta rybnogo khozyaictva i okeanografii* (19), 45–59. *117*

705. Kotlyarevskaya, N. V. (1967). Hatching dates of *Misgurnus fossilis* L. as affected by oxygen conditions. *Dokl. (proc.) Acad. Sci. U.S.S.R., Biological Sciences Section* **177,** 746–9 (English translation). *69*

706. Krauel, K. K. and Ridgway, G. J. (1963). Immunoelectrophoretic studies of red salmon (*Oncorhynchus nerka*) serum. *Int. Archs Allergy appl Immun.* **23,** 246–53. *105*

*707. Kringstad, H. and Folkvord, S. (1949). The nutritive value of cod roe and cod liver. *J. Nutr.* **38,** 489–502.

*708. Kringstad, H. and Thoresen, F. (1940). On the occurrence of the anti-pellagra vitamin, nicotinic acid (-amide) in a group of foodstuffs. *Nord. Med.* **8,** 2248–50.

709. Krishnamoorthi, K. P. (1958). Changes in the free amino acids in the different stages of the fish, *Labeo fimbriatus* (Bloch), *Mystus seenghala* (Sykes) and *Boleophthalmus boddaerti* (Day). *J. zool. Soc. India* **10,** 49–53. *65*

710. Krivobok, M. N. (1964). On the role of the liver in the maturation of the ovaries of the Baltic herring, *Clupea harengus membras* L. *Vop. Ikhtiol.* **4,** 483–94. *62, 63, 92*

711. Krogh, A. (1937). Osmotic regulation in freshwater fishes by active absorption of chloride ions. *Z. vergl. Physiol.* **24,** 656–66. *191*

*712. Kruchakova, F. A. (1952). Alkali and alkaline-earth metals and iron in the muscles of certain fish and invertebrates of the Black Sea. *Trudy Karadagskoi Biologicheskoi Stantsii Nauk SSSR* (12), 111–15. *7*

*713. Kubo, S. (1957). On fish tropomyosin. I. Isolation and amino acid composition. *Bull Fac. Fish. Hokkaido Univ.* **8**, 147–57.

714. Kubo, T. (1955). Changes of some characteristics of blood of smolts of *Oncorhynchus masou* during seaward migration. *Bull. Fac. Fish. Hokkaido Univ.* **6**, 201–7. *81*

*715. Kubota, M. and Kimura, S. (1967). Skin collagen of the great blue shark. *Bull. Jap. Soc. scient. Fish.* **33**, 338–42.

716. Kubota, Z. and Ono, T. (1965). Morphology of the Japanese loach, *Misgurnus anguillicaudatus* (Cantor)—V. Geographical variation of the number of vertebrae. *J. Shimonoseki Univ. Fish.* **14**, 41–52. *153, 154*

*717. Kuindshi, N. N. (1962). Ascorbic acid content of some types of fish of the Ob basin. *Vop. Pitan.* **21**, 83–4.

718. Kutscher, F. and Ackermann, D. (1933). The comparative biochemistry of vertebrates and invertebrates. *A. Rev. Biochem.* **2**, 355–76. *24, 29, 143, 145, 288*

*719. Kuwabara, S. (1957). Acetylcholine (ACh) cycle in the electric organ of fish. *J. Shimonoseki Coll. Fish.* **6**, 149–240.

*720. Kwon, T. W. and Olcott, H. S. (1965). Tuna muscle aldolase—1. Purification and properties. *Comp. Biochem. Physiol.* **15**, 7–16.

721. Lagios, M. D. (1965). Seasonal changes in the cytology of the adenohypophysis, testes, and ovaries of the black surfperch, *Embiotoca jacksoni*, a viviparous percomorph fish. *Gen. comp. Endocrinol.* **5**, 207–21. *171*

722. Lagler, K. F., Bardach, J. E. and Miller, R. R. (1962). 'Ichthyology'. John Wiley & Sons, New York. *116, 138, 200, 203*

*723. Lahiry, N. L. and Proctor, B. E. (1956). The microbiological determination of the essential amino acids in fish protein. *Fd Res.* **21**, 87–90.

*724. Lahlou, B. (1967). Urinary excretion in a euryhaline fish, the flounder (*Platichthys flesus* L.): characteristics of normal urine in fresh water and sea water and effects of changing the surroundings. *Comp. Biochem. Physiol.* **20**, 925–38. *192, 193, 197*

*725. Landgraf, R. G. (1953). Technical note no. 27—Alaska pollock: proximate composition; amino acid, thiamine, and riboflavin content; use as mink feed. *Comml Fish. Rev.* **15** (7), 20–2.

726. Lane, J. P., Hill, W. S. and Learson, R. J. (1966). Identification of species in raw processed fishery products by means of cellulose polyacetate strip electrophoresis. *Comml Fish. Rev.* **28** (3), 10–13. *132*

*727. Lange, R. and Fugelli, K. (1965). The osmotic adjustment in the euryhaline teleosts, the flounder, *Pleuronectes flesus* L. and the three-spined stickleback, *Gasterosteus aculeatus* L. *Comp. Biochem. Physiol.* **15**, 283–92. *145, 190, 191, 192, 193, 195, 288*

728. Lankester, R. (1871). On the occurrence of haemoglobin in the muscles of molluscs and the distribution of it in the living organism. *Pflügers Arch. ges. Physiol.* **4**, 315–20. *28*

*729. Lauter, C. J., Brown, E. A. B. and Trams, E. G. (1968). Composition of plasma lipoproteins of the spiny dogfish *Squalus acanthias*. *Comp. Biochem. Physiol.* **24**, 243–7.

730. Lavagna, M. F. (1954). Biochemistry of fish lenses: comparative study of the water content of animal lenses. *Bull. Soc. Ophtal. Fr.* pp. 45–51, *262*

*731. Lazarow, A. and Berman, J. (1947). The production of diabetes in the toadfish with alloxan. *Biol. Bull. mar. biol. Lab., Woods Hole* **93**, 219 only.

732. Lecal, J. (1958). Influence of the salinity factor on the serum proteins of *Blennius pavo*. *C. r. Séanc. Soc. Biol.* **152**, 1492–4. *121, 187*

733. Lee, J. Y. (1962). Data on the application of serological methods to the study of races and populations of teleosteans. Univ. of Paris, thesis for Doctor in Natural Sciences, pp. 1–33. *163*

*734. Leivestad, H., Andersen, H. and Scholander, P. F. (1957). Physiological response to air exposure in codfish. *Science, N.Y.* **126**, 505 only. *44, 45*

*735. Leloup-Hatey, J. (1960). The influence of enforced exercise on the concentration of plasma corticosteroids in a teleost: the carp (*Cyprinus carpio* L.). *J. Physiol., Paris* **52**, 145–6. *40, 43*

*736. Leontiev, V. G. and Skul'skii, I. A. (1966). Comparative investigation of sodium and potassium distribution within the body of animals. *Zh. evolyutsionnoi biokhimii i Fiziologii* **2**, 206–13.

*737. Lepkovsky, S. (1930). The distribution of serum and plasma proteins in fish. *J. biol. Chem.* **85**, 667–73.

*738. Levine, P. T., Glimcher, M. J., Seyer, J. M., Huddleston, J. I. and Hein, J. W. (1966). Noncollagenous nature of the proteins of shark enamel. *Science, N.Y.* **154**, 1192–3.

739. Lewis, M. S. and Piez, K. A. (1964). The characterization of collagen from the skin of the dogfish shark, *Squalus acanthias*. *J. biol. Chem.* **239**, 3336–40. *101*

740. Lewis, R. W. (1962). Temperature and pressure effects on the fatty acids of some marine ectotherms. *Comp. Biochem. Physiol.* **6**, 75–89. *217*

741. Lewis, R. W. (1967). Fatty acid composition of some marine animals from various depths. *J. Fish. Res. Bd Can.* **24**, 1101–15. *179*

*742. Lie, J. and Lunde, G. (1940). Vitamin B_1 in some Norwegian foods. *Nord. Med.* **8**, 2250–2.

743. de Ligny, W. (1969). Serological and biochemical studies of fish populations. *Oceanogr. mar. Biol.* **9**, (in the press). *163*

744. Liljemark, A. (1969). Influence of freezing and cold storage on the submicro-scopical structure of fish muscle. *In* "Freezing and Irradiation of Fish" (R. Kreuzer, ed.) 40-145, *12*. Fishing News (Books), Ltd., London.

745. Lindsey, C. C. (1958). Modification of meristic characters by light duration in kokanee, *Oncorhynchus nerka. Copeia* (2), 134–6. *156*

*746. Linzel, W., Pfeiffer, H. and Zippel, I. (1939). Investigation on trimethyl-amine. IV. Report on the occurrence of trimethylamine oxide in the muscle of freshwater fish. *Biochem. Z.* **301**, 29–36.

747. Liu, R. K. and Walford, R. L. (1966). Increased growth and life-span with lowered ambient temperature in the annual fish, *Cynolebias adloffi. Nature, Lond.* **212**, 1277–8. *211*

748. Loeb, J. (1911). The role of salts in the preservation of life. *Science, N.Y.* **34**, 653–65. *138*

749. Loeb, J. and Wasteneys, H. (1912). On the adaptation of fish (*Fundulus*) to higher temperatures. *J. exp. Zool.* **12**, 543–57. *214*

*750. Lopez-Matas, A. and Fellers, C. R. (1948). Composition and nutritive value of fresh, cooked, and processed swordfish. *Fd Res.* **13**, 387–96.

*751. Loughlin, M. E. and Teeri, A. E. (1960). Nutritive value of fish. II. Biotin, Folic acid, Pantothenic acid, and free amino acids of various salt-water species. *Fd Res.* **25**, 479–83.

752. Love, R. M. (1954). Post-mortem changes in the lenses of fish eyes: assess-ment of storage time and fish quality. *J. Sci. Fd Agric.* **5**, 566–72. *262*

753. Love, R. M. (1957). The biochemical composition of fish. *In* "The Physiology of Fishes" (M. E. Brown, ed.), Vol. 1, Chapter 10, pp. 401–18. Academic Press, London and New York. *259*

754. Love, R. M. (1958a). Studies on the North Sea cod. I. Muscle cell dimensions. *J. Sci. Fd Agric.* **9**, 195–8. *2, 85, 87*

*755. Love, R. M. (1958b). Studies on the North Sea cod. II. Deoxyribose nucleic acid in the musculature. *J. Sci. Fd Agric.* **9**, 199–203. *3, 86, 107*

756. Love, R. M. (1958c). Studies on the North Sea cod. III. Effects of starvation. *J. Sci. Fd Agric.* **9**, 617–20. *211, 222, 223, 225, 228, 230, 243, 244*

757. Love, R. M. (1960). Water content of cod (*Gadus callarias* L.) muscle. *Nature, Lond.* **185**, 692 only. *89, 91, 159*

758. Love, R. M. (1962a). Isolation of and direct analysis of uncontaminated muscle cell contents. *Nature, Lond.* **196**, 593–4. *12, 13*

759. Love, R. M. (1962b). The measurement of 'condition' in North Sea cod. *J. Cons. perm. int. Explor. Mer.* **27**, 34–42. *89, 174, 175, 224*

760. Love, R. M. (1966). The freezing of animal tissue. *In* 'Cryobiology' (H. T. Meryman, ed.), Chapter 7, pp. 317–405. Academic Press, London and New York. *131*

761. Love, R. M., Lavéty, J. and Steel, P. J. (1969). The connective tissues of fish. II. Gaping in commercial species of frozen fish in relation to rigor mortis. *J. Fd Technol.* **4**, 39–44. *8, 147, 148*

762. Love, R. M., Lovern, J. A. and Jones, N. R. (1959). The chemical composition of fish tissues. *Spec. Rep. Fd Invest. Bd D.S.I.R.* **69**, 62 pp. *259*

763. Love, R. M. and Olley, J. (1965). Cold-storage deterioration in several species of fish, as measured by two methods. *In* "The Technology of Fish Utilization" (R. Kreuzer, ed.), pp. 116–7. Fishing News (Books) Ltd., London. *131*

764. Love, R. M. and Robertson, I. (1967). Studies on the North Sea Cod. IV. Effects of starvation, 2. Changes in the distribution of muscle protein fractions. *J. Sci. Fd Agric.* **18**, 217–20. *5, 51, 104, 236*

765. Love, R. M., Robertson I. and Strachan, I. (1968). Studies on the North Sea cod. VI. Effects of starvation. 4. Sodium and potassium. *J. Sci. Fd. Agric.* **19**, 415–22. *3, 58, 87, 88, 106, 211, 222, 243–7, 249*

766. Lovern, J. A. (1932a). Fat metabolism in fishes. I. General survey of the fatty acid composition of the fats of a number fishes, both marine and freshwater. *Biochem J.* **26**, 1978–84. *145*

*767. Lovern, J. A. (1932b). Fat metabolism in fishes. II. The peritoneal, pancreatic and liver fats of the sturgeon (*Acipenser sturio*). *Biochem. J.* **26**, 1985–8. *146, 201*

768. Lovern, J. A. (1934a). Fat metabolism in fishes. IV. Mobilization of depôt fat in the salmon. *Biochem. J.* **28**, 1955–60. *65, 124, 242*

769. Lovern, J. A. (1934b). Fat metabolism in fishes. V. The fat of the salmon in its young freshwater stages. *Biochem. J.* **28**, 1961–3. *146*

770. Lovern, J. A. (1935). Fat metabolism in fishes. VII. The depôt fats of certain fish fed on known diets. *Biochem. J.* **29**, 1894–7. *146, 201*

771. Lovern, J. A. (1937). Fat metabolism in fishes. XI. Specific peculiarities in depôt fat composition. *Biochem. J.* **31**, 755–63. *142.*

772. Lovern, J. A. (1938a). Fat metabolism in fishes. XII. Seasonal changes in the composition of herring fat. *Biochem. J.* **32**, 676–80. *95, 105, 170, 242*

773. Lovern, J. A. (1938b). Fat metabolism in fishes. XIII. Factors influencing the composition of the depôt fat of fishes. *Biochem. J.* **32**, 1214–24. *91, 201, 216, 242*

774. Lovern, J. A. (1939). Captive eels. Some observations on their behaviour. *Salm. Trout Mag.* **94**, 56–7. *230*

775. Lovern, J. A. (1942). The composition of the depôt fats of aquatic animals. *Spec. Rep. Fd Invest. Bd D.S.I.R.* **51**, 72 pp. *65, 81, 118, 139, 147, 201, 202, 272*

776. Lovern, J. A. (1950). Some causes of variation in the composition of fish oils. *J. Soc. Leath. Trades Chem.* **34**, 7–21. *216*

777. Lovern, J. A. (1958). The nutritional significance of fish lipids. *Proc. Nutr. Soc.* **17**, 161–6. *142*

778. Lovern, J. A. (1964). The lipids of marine organisms. *Oceanogr. mar. Biol.* **2**, 169–91. *142*

779. Lovern, J. A., Edisbury, J. R. and Morton, R. A. (1933). Variations in vitamin A content of fish-liver oils, with particular reference to seasonal fluctuations in the potency of halibut-liver oil. *Biochem. J.* **27**, 1461–9. *95, 172, 291*

*780. Lovern, J. A. and Sharp, J. G. (1933). The diet of the halibut and intensity of feeding, in relation to the vitamin A potency of the liver oil. *Biochem. J.* **27**, 1470–2.

*781. Ludány, G. v. (1936). Vitamin C in freshwater fishes and freshwater crabs. *Biochem. Z.* **284**, 108–10.

782. Lühmann, M. and Mann, H. (1957). Organ weights in the carp. *Arch. Fisch-Wiss.* **8**, 1–11. *84, 203*

*783. Lukton, A. and Olcott, H. S. (1958). Content of free imidazole compounds in the muscle tissue of aquatic animals. *Fd Res.* **23**, 611–18. *23, 24, 147, 151, 266, 268*

784. Lundbeck, J. (1953). German market investigations on cod, mainly in the north-eastern area. *Rapp. P.-v. Réun. Cons. perm. int. Explor. Mer.* **136**, 33–9. *156*

*785. Lunde, G. (1939). Recent research on the vitamins in fish and fish products. *Angew. Chem.* **52**, 521–4.

*786. Lunde, G. and Kringstad, H. (1938). Vitamin B factors in roe and fish liver. *Tidsskr. HermetInd.* pp. 184–90 (no volume number).

*787. Lunde, G., Kringstad, H. and Olsen, A. (1938). Research on the content of vitamin B_1 and B_2 in several food products, especially fish and fish products. *Avhand. norske Vidensk.-Akad.* 1. *Mat.-Naturv. Klasse* (7), 51 pp.

*788. Lupo, C. and Chieffi, G. (1963). Oestrogens and progesterone in ovaries of the marine teleost *Conger conger*. *Nature, Lond.* **197**, 596 only.

*789. Lyengar, R. and Schlenk, H. (1967). Wax esters of mullet (*Mugil cephalus*) roe oil. *Biochemistry, N.Y.* **6**, 396–402.

*790. McBean, R. L., Neppel, M. J. and Goldstein, L. (1966). Glutamate dehydrogenase and ammonia production in the eel (*Anguilla rostrata*). *Comp. Biochem. Physiol.* **18**, 909–20.

791. McBride, J. R., Fagerlund, U. H. M., Smith, M. and Tomlinson, N. (1965). Post-spawning death of Pacific salmon: sockeye salmon (*Oncorhynchus nerka*) maturing and spawning in captivity. *J. Fish. Res. Bd Can.* **22**, 775–82. *114*

*792. McBride, J. and MacLeod, R. A. (1956a). The sodium and potassium content of British Columbia sea foods. II. Some commercially important fresh fish. *Prog. Rep. Pacif. Cst Stns* **105**, 19–21. *88*

*793. McBride, J. R. and MacLeod, R. A. (1956b). Sodium and potassium in fish from the Canadian Pacific coast. *J. Am. diet. Ass.* **32**, 636–8. *244*

794. McBride, J. R., MacLeod, R. A. and Idler, D. R. (1959a). Identity of the gel factor in herring solubles and means of overcoming its effect. *J. agric. Fd Chem.* **7,** 646–50. *102, 169*

795. McBride, J. R., MacLeod, R. A. and Idler, D. R. (1959b). Proximate analysis of Pacific herring (*Clupea pallasii*) and an evaluation of Tester's "fat factor". *J. Fish. Res. Bd Can.* **16,** 679–84. *102, 122, 123*

*796. McBride, J. R., MacLeod, R. A. and Idler, D. R. (1960). Seasonal variation in the collagen content of Pacific herring tissues. *J. Fish. Res. Bd Can.* **17,** 913–18. *102, 104, 169*

*797. MacCallum, W. A., Jaffray, J. I., Churchill, D. N., Idler, D. R., and Odense, P. H. (1967). Post-mortem physicochemical changes in unfrozen Newfoundland trap-caught cod. *J. Fish. Res. Bd Can.* **24,** 651–78.

*798. MacCallum, W. A., Jaffray, J. I., Idler, D. R. and Churchill, D. N. (1969). Condition of Newfoundland fish and its influence on quality after single and double freezing: inshore, trap-caught cod. *In* "Freezing and Irradiation of Fish" (R. Kreuzer, ed.) 56–63. Fishing News (Books) Ltd., London.

*799. McCartney, T. H. (1965). The influence of age and sex on the total serum cholesterol level in brown trout. *Fish. Res. Bull. N.Y.* **28,** 42–3. *96, 121*

*800. McCartney, T. H. (1966). Monthly variations of the serum total cholesterol of mature brown trout. *Fish. Res. Bull. N.Y.* **29,** 72–5. *121*

801. McCartney, T. H. (1967). Monthly variations of the serum total cholesterol and serum total lipid-phosphorus of mature brown trout. *Fish. Res. Bull. N.Y.* **30,** 42–5. *63, 64, 110, 116, 117, 121*

*802. McCay, C. M. (1931). Phosphorus distribution, sugar, and haemoglobin in the blood of fish, eels, and turtles. *J. biol. Chem.* **90,** 497–505. *112, 114, 150*

803. McCay, C. M. and Tunison, A. V. (1937). (No title). *Rep. Cortland Hatch. N.Y. St. Conserv. Dep. for year* 1936, no. 5. *53*

804. McCay, C. M., Tunison, A. V., Crowell, M. and Paul, H. (1936). The calcium and phosphorus content of the body of the brook trout in relation to age, growth, and food. *J. biol. Chem.* **114,** 259–63. *73, 207*

*805. McColl, J. D. and Rossiter, R. J. (1952a). A comparative study of the lipids of the vertebrate central nervous system. I. Brain. *J. exp. Biol.* **29,** 196–202.

*806. McColl, J. D. and Rossiter, R. J. (1952b). A comparative study of the lipids of the vertebrate central nervous system. II. Spinal cord. *J. exp. Biol.* **29,** 203–10.

*807. McFarland, W. N. and Munz, F. W. (1958). A re-examination of the osmotic properties of the Pacific hagfish, *Polistotrema stouti. Biol. Bull. mar. biol. Lab., Woods Hole* **114,** 348–56. *46, 137*

808. McFarland, W. N. and Munz, F. W. (1965). Codominance of visual pigments in hybrid fishes. *Science, N.Y.* **150,** 1055–7. *183.*

809. McHugh, J. L. (1954). The influence of light on the number of vertebrae in the grunion, *Leuresthes tenuis*. *Copeia* 23–5. *156*

*810. McIntyre, J. M., Waisman, H. A., Henderson, L. M. and Elvehjem, C. A. (1941). Nicotinic acid content of meat and meat products. *J. Nutr.* **22**, 535–40.

811. Mackie, I. M. (1968). Species identification of cooked fish by disc electrophoresis. *Analyst, Lond.* **93**, 458–60. *132*

*812. McKnight, I. M. (1966). A haematological study on the mountain whitefish. *Prosopium williamsoni*. *J. Fish. Res. Bd Can.* **23**, 45–64. *122*

*813. MacLeod, J. J. R. and Simpson, W. W. (1927). The immediate post-mortem changes in fish muscle. *Contr. Can. Biol. Fish.* **3**, 439–56. *221*

*814. MacLeod, R. A., Jonas, R. E. E. and McBride, J. R. (1958). Variations in the sodium and potassium content of the muscle tissue of Pacific salmon with particular reference to migration. *Can. J. Biochem. Physiol.* **36**, 1257–68. *88, 106, 245, 246*

*815. MacLeod, R. A., Jonas, R. E. E. and Onofrey, E. (1960). A biochemical study of coho salmon (*Oncorhynchus kisutch*) maturing sexually in an aquarium. *J. Fish. Res. Bd Can.* **17**, 323–5.

*816. MacLeod, R. A., Jonas, R. E. E. and Roberts, E. (1963). Glycolytic enzymes in the tissues of a salmonoid fish (*Salmo gairdnerii gairdnerii*). *Can. J. Biochem. Physiol.* **41**, 1971–81.

*817. MacPherson, N. L. (1932). Studies in the behaviour of the carbohydrates and lactic acid of the muscle of the haddock (*Gadus aeglefinus*) after death. *Biochem. J.* **26**, 80–7.

818. MacPherson, N. L. (1933). Vitamin A concentration of cod liver oil correlated with age of cod. *Nature, Lond.* **132**, 26–7. *95*

819. MacPherson, N. L. (1937). Newfoundland cod liver oil. *Serv. Bull. Div. Fish. Res. Newfoundld* **3**, 43 pp. *173*

820. Magnin, E. (1960). Research on the blood protein of *Acipenser sturio* L. from the Gironde. *Annls Stn cent. Hydrobiol. appl.* **8**, 183–8. 122

821. Mairs, D. F. and Sindermann, C. J. (1960). Intraspecies variability in electrophoretic patterns of fish serum. *Anat. Rec.* **137**, 377–8. *164*

*822. Malins, D. C., Wekell, J. C. and Houle, C. R. (1965). Composition of the diacyl glyceryl ethers and triglycerides of the flesh and liver of the dogfish (*Squalus acanthias*). *J. Lipid Res.* **6**, 100–5. *201*

*823. Malvin, R. L., Cafruni, E. J. and Kutchai, H. (1965). Renal transport of glucose by the aglomerular fish *Lophius americanus*. *J. cell. comp. Physiol.* **65**, 381–4.

824. Mancuso, V. M. (1964). Protein typing of some authentic fish species by disc electrophoresis. *J. Ass. off. agric. Chem.* **47**, 841–4. *132*

825. Manery, J. F. (1954). Water and electrolyte metabolism. *Physiol. Rev.* **34**, 334–417. *11*

826. Manery, J. F. (1962). Minerals in nonosseous connective tissues (including the blood, lens and cornea). *In* "Mineral Metabolism" (C. F. Comar and F. Bronner, eds.), Vol. 1 part B, Chapter 13, pp. 551–608. Academic Press, London and New York. *101*

*827. Mankikar, S. R. and Sohonie, K. (1960). Essential amino acids, tyrosine and cystine content of purified proteins of Bombay fish. *J. Univ. Bombay* **29**, 82–5.

828. Mann, H. (1961). Fish cultivation in Europe. *In* "Fish as Food" (G. Borgstrom, ed.), Vol. 1, Chapter 3, pp. 77–102. Academic Press, London and New York. *91, 116, 205*

829. Mannan, A., Fraser, D. I. and Dyer, W. J. (1961). Proximate composition of Canadian Atlantic fish. I. Variation in composition of different sections of the flesh of Atlantic halibut (*Hippoglossus hippoglossus*). *J. Fish. Res. Bd Can.* **18**, 483–93. *36*

830. Manwell, C. (1963). Foetal and adult haemoglobins of the spiny dogfish, *Squalus suckleyi*. *Archs Biochem. Biophys.* **101**, 504–11. *94*

*831. de Marco, C. and Antonini, E. (1958). Amino-acid composition of haemoglobin from *Thunnus thynnus*. *Nature, Lond.* **181**, 1128 only.

*832. Maren, T. H. (1962). Ionic composition of cerebrospinal fluid and aqueous humour of the dogfish, *Squalus acanthias*. 1. Normal values. *Comp. Biochem. Physiol.* **5**, 193–200.

833. Markert, J. R. and Vanstone, W. E. (1966). Pigments in the belly skin of coho salmon (*Oncorhynchus kisutch*). *J. Fish. Res. Bd Can.* **23**, 1095–7. *80*

834. Marsh, M. C. (1902). Haemoglobin estimations and blood counts in fishes. *Wash. med. Ann.* **1**, 397–8. *55*

835. Marshall, N. B. (1965). "The Life of Fishes". 402 pp. Weidenfeld and Nicolson, London. *31, 36, 109, 116, 136, 138, 143, 148, 198, 210*

836. Martin, N. V. (1966). The significance of food habits in the biology, exploitation, and management of Algonquin Park, Ontario, lake trout. *Trans. Am. Fish. Soc.* **95**, 415–22. *51, 199*

837. Masoro, E. J. (1967). Skeletal muscle lipids. III. Analysis of the functioning of skeletal muscle lipids during fasting. *J. biol. Chem.* **242**, 1111–4. *242*

838. Master, F. and Magar, N. G. (1954). Studies in the nutritive value of Bombay fish. Part 2. Amino acid composition. *Indian J. med. Res.* **42**, 509–13.

*839. Masukawa, T., Sako, S. and Nagata, S. (1957). Thiamine content of the red muscle 'Chiai' of fishes. *Vitamins, Kyoto* **13**, 13 only. *23*

*840. Matsubara, T. and Chuda, K. (1937). On the vitamin C (ascorbic acid) content of freshwater fish tissue. *Mitt. med. Akad. Kyoto* **21**, 849–74.

*841. Matsumoto, F. (1950). The distribution of lecithine in the various parts of sardine [*Sardina melanosticta*] body. *Bull. Jap. Soc. scient. Fish.* **16**, 303–5. *38*

*842. Matsumoto, J. (1965). Role of pteridines in the pigmentation of chromatophores in cyprinid fish. *Jap. J. Zool.* **14**, 45–94.

*843. Matsuura, F., Baba, H. and Mori, T. (1953). Chemical studies on the red muscle ('Chiai') of fishes—I. Occurrence of arginase in the red muscle of fishes. *Bull. Jap. Soc. scient. Fish.* **19**, 893–8. *19, 20*

*844. Matsuura, F. and Hashimoto, K. (1954). Chemical studies on the red muscle ('Chiai') of fishes—II. Determinations of the content of haemoglobin, myoglobin and cytochrome c in the muscles of fishes. *Bull. Jap. Soc. scient. Fish.* **20**, 308–12. *19, 20, 21*

*845. Matsuura, F. and Hashimoto, K. (1959). Chemical studies on the red muscle ('Chiai') of fishes—X. A new method for determination of myoglobin. *Bull. Jap. Soc. scient. Fish.* **24**, 809–15.

*846. Matsuura, F., Kogure, T. and Fukui, G. (1952). Methionine contents of muscle proteins of various aquatic animals. *Bull. Jap. Soc. scient. Fish.* **17**, 359–62. *21*

*847. Matsuura, F., Konosu, S., Ota, R., Katori, S. and Tanaka, K. (1955). Chemical studies on the red muscle ('Chiai') of fishes—III. Comparative studies of amino acid contents in the protein of the ordinary and the red muscle of fishes by microbiological assay. *Bull. Jap. Soc. scient. Fish.* **20**, 941–5. *25, 26*

*848. Matty, A. J. (1959). Thyroid protein-bound iodine of a teleost fish (*Scarus guacamaia*). *J. Endocrinol.* **19**, 353–8. *95, 278*

849. May, A. W. (1967). Fecundity of Atlantic cod. *J. Fish. Res. Bd Can.* **24**, 1531–51. *90*

*850. Mega, A. (1965). A study on vitamin E in marine products (Report no. 2). Determination of the vitamin E content of fish and shellfish from the Sea of Japan. *Rep. Hokkaido Inst. Publ. Health* **15**, 93–7. *291, 292*

851. Meisner, H. M. and Hickman, C. P. (1962). Effect of temperature and photoperiod on the serum proteins of the rainbow trout, *Salmo gairdneri. Can. J. Zool.* **40**, 127–30. *123*

852. Mellgren, S. I. and Mathisen, J. S. (1966). Oxidative enzymes, glycogen and lipid in striated muscle. A histochemical study in the Atlantic hagfish (*Myxine glutinosa* L.). *Z. Zellforsch. mikrosk. Anat.* **71**, 169–88. *24, 30, 31*

*853. Mengi, T. (1965). Modifications of the chemical composition of the maturing ovary of the Baltic cod. *Kieler Meeresforsch.* **21**, 107–21. 65

854. Menten, M. L. (1927). Changes in the blood sugar of the cod, sculpin, and pollock during asphyxia. *J. biol. Chem.* **72**, 249–53. *45*

*855. van der Merwe, R. P. and Kapp, L. (1961). Determination of lead in fish and fish products. *15th. Ann. Rep. Fish. Indust. Res. Inst., Cape Town.* pp. 50–51.

856. Meyer, D. K., Westfall, B. A. and Platner, W. S. (1956). Water and electrolyte balance of goldfish under conditions of anoxia, cold and inanition. *Am. J. Physiol.* **184**, 553–6. *245*

857. Mezincescu, M. D. and Strugali, H. (1958). The partition of water in muscles and liver between the extra- and intracellular spaces and its variations. *Acad. rep. populare Romîne, Inst. biochemie, Studii cercetări biochimie* **1**, 141–53. Quoted in *Chem. Abstr.* **53**, 11574 (1959). *88*

*858. Miles, H. M. and Smith, L. S. (1968). Ionic regulation in migrating juvenile coho salmon, *Oncorhynchus kisutch. Comp. Biochem. Physiol.* **26**, 381–98.

*859. Miller, R. B., Sinclair, A. C. and Hochachka, P. W. (1959). Diet, glycogen reserves and resistance to fatigue in hatching rainbow trout. *J. Fish. Res. Bd Can.* **16**, 321–8. *39, 40, 41, 43, 202*

860. Milroy, T. H. (1908). Changes in the chemical composition of the herring during the reproductive period. *Biochem. J.* **3**, 366–89. *98*

*861. Minakowski, W. and Nowicka, Z. (1962). Total content of L-ascorbic acid during the embryonal development of the common pike (*Esox lucius* L.) eggs. *Zesz. nauk. wyzsz. Szk. roln. Olsztyn.* **12**, 49–54. *74*

*862. Mirsky, A. E. and Ris, H. (1951). The desoxyribonucleic acid content of animal cells and its evolutionary significance. *J. gen. Physiol.* **34**, 451–62. *140*

863. Mitchell, W. A. (1883). "On the place of fish in a hard-working diet." Clowes, London. *174.*

*864. Miyahara, S. (1952). Polarography of inorganic substances in marine animals—I. Separation and determination of cobalt. *Bull. Jap. Soc. scient. Fish.* **18**, 273–5.

865. Moiseev, P. (1955). Fluctuations in the commercial fish populations of the north-western Pacific in relation to environmental and other factors. *Intern. tech. Conf. of living Resources of the Sea*, pp. 266–89. United Nations, Rome. *210*

866. Mollison, P. L. (1946). Observations on cases of starvation at Belsen. *Br. med. J.* **1**, 4–8. *230*

*867. Mori, T., Hashimoto, Y. and Komata, Y. (1956). B-vitamins content in the muscle of fish. *Bull. Jap. Soc. scient. Fish.* **21**, 1233–5. *27*

*868. Mori, T., Hashimoto, Y. and Maeda, Y. (1954). Animal protein factor (APF) and vitamin B_{12} in marine products —V. Variations in the vitamin B_{12} content of marine animals in the spoilage (part 2). *Bull. Jap. Soc. scient. Fish.* **20**, 604–9.

*869. Mori, T., Konosu, S. and Miyagawa, S. (1957). Choline content of the muscle of aquatic animals. *Bull. Jap. Soc. scient. Fish.* **23**, 282–4. *19, 20*

*870. Morishita, T., Noda, H., Kitamikado, M., Takahashi, T. and Tachino, S. (1964). On the activity of the digestive enzymes in cultured fish. *J. Fac. Fish. pref. Univ. Mie–Tsu* **6**, 239–46. *84*

*871. Morre, J. and Barret, J. (1963). Potassium content of various fisheries products with a view to measuring the radioactivity of food. *Revue Trav. Inst. (scient. tech.) Pêch. marit.* **27**, 235–40.

*872. Morris, B. (1959). The proteins and lipids of the plasma of some species of Australian fresh and salt water fish. *J. cell. comp. Physiol.* **54**, 221–30.

*873. Morris, D., Bull, G. and Hebb, C. O. (1965). Acetylcholine in the electric organ of *Torpedo*. *Nature, Lond.* **207**, 1295.

*874. Morris, R. (1965). Studies on salt and water balance in *Myxine glutinosa* L. *J. exp. Biol.* **42**, 359–71. *137*

875. Morris, R. W. (1965). Seasonal changes in metabolism of four south temperate marine fishes. *Trans. R. Soc. N.Z.* **6**, 141–52.

876. Morton, R. A. and Creed, R. H. (1939). The conversion of carotene to vitamin A_2 by some freshwater fishes. *Biochem. J.* **33**, 318–24. *200*

*877. Motais, R., Romeu, F. G. and Maetz, J. (1965). Mechanism of euryhalinity. Comparative study of flounder (euryhaline) and Ballan wrasse during transfer into fresh water. *C. r. Séanc. Soc. Biol.* **261**, 801–4. *187*

*878. Motais, R., Romeu, F. G. and Maetz, J. (1966). Exchange diffusion effect and euryhalinity in teleosts. *J. gen. Physiol.* **50**, 391–422. *192, 193*

*879. Motelică, I. (1961). Action of insulin on the blood glucose of the carp (II). *Studii Cerc. Biol.* **13**, 535–47.

*880. Mounib, M. S. and Eisan, J. S. (1968). Uricolytic enzymes in cod sperm. *Can. J. Physiol. Pharmacol.* **46**, 283–4.

881. Mugiya, Y. (1964). Calcification in fish and shellfish—III. Seasonal occurrence of a pre-albumin fraction in the otolith fluid of some fish, corresponding to the period of opaque zone formation in the otolith. *Bull. Jap. Soc. scient. Fish.* **30**, 955–67. *160, 232*

882. Mugiya, Y. (1965). Calcification in fish and shell-fish—IV. The differences in nitrogen content between the translucent and opaque zones of otolith in some fish. *Bull. Jap. Soc. scient. Fish.* **31**, 896–901. *160*

883. Muñoz, F. (1961). A comparative chemical study on the African hakes, *Merluccius merluccius* L. and *Merluccius senegalensis* Cadenat. *Investigación pesq.* **19**, 37–53. *260*

884. Munro Fox, H. (1954). (No title to this paper). *Nature, Lond.* **173**, 850 only. *150, 179*

885. Munz, F. W. (1957). Photosensitive pigments from retinas of deep-sea fishes. *Science, N.Y.* **125**, 1142–3. *182*

886. Munz, F. W. (1958). Photosensitive pigments from the retinae of certain deep-sea fishes. *J. Physiol., Lond.* **140**, 220–35. *182*

887. Munz, F. W. (1959). The photosensitive retinal pigments of fishes from relatively turbid coastal waters. *J. gen. Physiol.* **42**, 445–59. *183*

888. Munz, F. W. (1964). The visual pigments of epipelagic and rocky-shore fishes. *Vision Res.* **4**, 441–54. *181, 183*

889. Munz, F. W. and Morris, R. W. (1965). Metabolic rate of the hagfish, *Eptatretus stoutii* (Lockington 1878). *Comp. Biochem. Physiol.* **16**, 1–6. *89*

*890. Murachi, S. (1959). Haemoglobin content, erythrocyte sedimentation rate and haematocrit of the blood in the young of the carp (*Cyprinus carpio*). *J. Fac. Fish. Anim. Husb. Hiroshima Univ.* **2**, 241–7. *93, 255*

*891. Murayama, S. and Tabei, K. (1956). Studies on the vitamin B group (B_1, B_2, B_6 and B_{12}) in the pyloric appendages of fishes. *Bull. Jap. Soc. scient. Fish.* **22**, 136–43.

*892. Murayama, S. and Yanase, M. (1961). The amounts of chemical constituents of eyed eggs of rainbow trout from various sources. *Bull. Tokai reg. Fish. Res. Lab.* **31**, 311–16. *56*

*893. Murayama, S., Yanase, M. and Tabei, K. (1959). Vitamin B contents of tissues of red salmon (*Oncorhynchus nerka*). *Bull. Tokai reg. Fish. Res. Lab.* **25**, 67–79.

*894. Murray, J. and Jones, N. R. (1957). Post-mortem changes in acid-soluble nucleotides of rested codling (*Gadus callarias*) muscle at 0°. *Biochem. J.* **68**, 9p. only.

*895. Murray, R. W. and Potts, W. T. W. (1961). The composition of the endolymph, perilymph and other body fluids of elasmobranchs. *Comp. Biochem. Physiol.* **2**, 65–75.

896. Møller, D., Naevdal, G. and Valen, A. (1966). Report on work with blood analyses for population research. *Fisken Hav.* (2), 17 pp. *165*

*897. Nace, P. F. (1955). Arterial blood sugar content of toadfish, intact and treated with alloxan or adrenal steroids. *Biol. Bull. mar. biol. Lab., Woods Hole* **109**, 366 only.

*898. Nace, P. F., Moule, M. L. and Schuh, J. E. (1964). The normal blood sugar of the toadfish. *Can. J. Physiol. Pharmacol.* **42**, 225–32. *99, 221*

899. Nace, P. F. and Schuh, J. E. (1961). Environmental temperature change and blood sugar change in the toadfish, *Opsanus tau*. *Biol. Bull. mar. biol. Lab., Woods Hole* **121**, 401 only. *221*

*900. Nagase, G. (1964). Contribution to the physiology of digestion in *Tilapia mossambica* Peters: digestive enzymes and the effects of diets on their activity. *Z. vergl. Physiol.* **49**, 270–84. *203, 204*

*901. Nagayama, F. (1961a). Enzymatic studies on the glycolysis in fish muscle— III. Contents of glycolytic intermediates. *Bull. Jap. Soc. scient. Fish.* **27**, 1014–7. *7, 24, 25*

*902. Nagayama, F. (1961b). Enzymatic studies on the glycolysis in fish muscle— V. Differences of phosphorylase activity due to the part and the freshness of muscle. *Bull. Jap. Soc. scient. Fish.* **27**, 1022–5.

*903. Nagayama, F. (1961c). Enzymatic studies on the glycolysis in fish muscle— VI. Phosphoglucomutase. *Bull. Jap. Soc. scient. Fish.* **27**, 1026–8.

*904. Nagayama, F. (1961d). Enzymatic studies on the glycolysis in fish muscle—VII. Phosphoglucose isomerase and lactic dehydrogenase. *Bull. Jap. Soc. scient. Fish.* **27,** 1029–31.

*905. Nagayama, F., Saito, Y. and Hayashi, M. (1967). Distribution of β-glucuronidase in fish. *Bull. Jap. Soc. scient. Fish.* **33,** 1132–5.

906. Naito, K. and Wilt, F. H. (1962). The conversion of vitamin A_1 to retinene$_2$ in a freshwater fish. *J. biol. Chem.* **237,** 3060–4. *183*

907. Nakagome, J. (1965). On the seasonal variation of swimming layer of yellowfin tuna, big-eyed tuna and blue marlin in the area of Caroline and Marshall Islands—V. Relation between seasonal variation of depth of swimming layer and that of depth of water temperature layer. *Bull. Jap. Soc. scient. Fish.* **31,** 785–8. *209*

908. Nakagome, J., Tsuchiya, H., Suzuki, S., Tanaka, S., Sakakibara, T. and Honda, H. (1965a). Age composition of Atlantic tunas related with distribution of water temperature and distance from land. I. Yellowfin tuna. *Bull. Jap. Soc. scient. Fish.* **31,** 97–100. *216*

909. Nakagome, J., Tsuchiya, H., Suzuki, S., Tanaka, S., Sakakibara, T. and Honda, H. (1965b). Age composition of Atlantic tunas related with distribution of water temperature and distance from land—II. Albacore. *Bull. Jap. Soc. scient. Fish.* **31,** 101–4. *216*

*910. Nakano, T. (1960). Studies on the physiological chemistry of phosphorus compounds in fish muscle—II. On the individual and regional variations of phosphorus compounds contents in fish muscle. *Bull. Jap. Soc. scient. Fish.* **26,** 1192–7.

*911. Nakano, T. (1961). Studies on the physiological chemistry of phosphorus compounds in fish muscle. VIII. The effect of urethane on phosphorus compounds in muscle of mackerel. *Bull. Jap. Soc. scient. Fish.* **27,** 1095–9. *23, 24, 29*

*912. Nakano, T. and Tomlinson, N. (1967). Catecholamine and carbohydrate concentrations in rainbow trout (*Salmo gairdnerii*) in relation to physical disturbance. *J. Fish. Res. Bd Can.* **24,** 1701–15. *40, 46*

913. Nakano, T. and Tsuchiya, Y. (1960). Studies on the physiological chemistry of phosphorus compounds in fish muscle. I. Distribution of various phosphorus compounds in fish muscle. *Bull. Jap. Soc. scient. Fish.* **26,** 1095–8. *29*

914. Nakatani, R. E. (1957). Changes in the inorganic phosphate and lactate levels in blood plasma and muscle tissue of adult steelhead trout after strenuous swimming. *Tech. Rep. Sch. Fish. Univ. Wash.* **30,** 14 pp. *40, 42*

*915. Namiki, S. (1933). The cholesterol content of fish muscle. *J. Biochem., Tokyo* **18,** 163–71.

*916. Nanba (Namba), K. and Kariya, T. (1967). The blood lactic acid levels of carp in the different environments. *Tohoku J. agric. Res.* **18,** 275–9.

*917. Nasedkina, Ye. A. and Meshcheryakova, L. S. (1966). Amount of free amino acid in the meat of some deep water fish of the Bering Sea. *Izv. vyssh. ucheb. Zaved., Pishchevaya Tekhnologiya* (3), 63–4.

*918. Natarajan, M. V. and Sreenivasan, A. (1961). Proximate and mineral composition of freshwater fishes. *Indian J. Fish.* **8,** 422–9.

*919. Nazir, D. J. and Magar, N. G. (1963). Chemical composition of mackerel (*Rastrelliger kanagurta*) and changes in the nutritive value during storage. *Indian Jnl Technol.* **1,** 247–9.

*920. Nazir, D. J. and Magar, N. G. (1964). Determination of ubiquinone and tocopherol in some tissues of shark (*Carcharias ellioti* Day). *Biochem. J.* **90,** 268–70.

921. Neave, F. (1958). The origin and specification of *Oncorhynchus*. *Trans. R. Soc. Can.* **52,** 25–39. *141, 142*

922. Needham, D. M. (1926). Red and white muscle. *Physiol. Rev.* **6,** 1–27. *17*

923. Neilands, J. B. (1947). The conversion of carotene to vitamin A in the fish. *Archs Biochem.* **13,** 415–9. *200*

*924. Neilands, J. B., Sirny, R. J., Sohljell, I., Strong, F. M. and Elvehjem, C. A. (1949). The nutritive value of canned foods. II. Amino acid content of fish and meat products. *J. Nutr.* **39,** 187–202.

925. Nemeth-Csoka, M. (1965). Collagen fibres. V. Age-dependent modification of connective tissue (chemical and morphological investigations compared). *Acta histochem.* **20,** 65–81. *128*

*926. Nesterov, V. P. and Skul'skii, I. A. (1965). A comparative investigation of the distribution of Li, Na, K, Rb, and Cs in the muscle tissue of marine animals. *Zhurnal evolutsionnoi Biokhimii i Fiziologii* **1,** 151–6. *138*

*927. Nevenzel, J. C., Rodegker, W., Mead, J. F. and Gordon, M. S. (1966) Lipids of the living coelacanth, *Latimeria chalumnae*. *Science, N.Y.* **152,** 1753–4. *142*

*928. Ney, P. W., Deas, C. P. and Tarr, H. L. A. (1950). Amino acid composition of fishery products (II). *J. Fish. Res. Bd Can.* **7,** 563–6.

929. Nikolsky, G. V. (1963). "The Ecology of Fishes", 352 pp. Translated by L. Birkett. Academic Press, London and New York. *97, 112, 116, 117, 152, 154, 199, 209, 241*

930. Nimmi, M. E., de Guia, E. and Bavetta, L. A. (1965). Changes in the quantity and nature of collagen in rabbit skin as a function of age. *Nature, Lond.* **207,** 865–6. *128*

931. Nishihara, H. (1967). Studies on the fine structure of red and white fin muscles of the fish (*Carassius auratus*). *Arch. histol. jap.* **28,** 425–47. *17, 20, 30*

*932. Nitta, T., Taguchi, F. and Mori, T. (1948). On the vitamin content of fish products. *Bull. Jap. Soc. scient. Fish.* **13,** 153–4.

*933. Nixon, D. A. (1965). The glycogen and meso-inositol concentrations in the muscle and liver in the elasmobranch *Scyliorhinus stellaris*. *Pubbl. Staz. zool. Napoli* **34**, 515–20. *278*

*934. Noda, H. (1967a). Studies on various phosphatases of the fishes. III. Changes in the activities of phosphatases during development of rainbow trout, *Salmo irideus*. *J. Fac. Fish. pref. Univ. Mie-Tsu* **7**, 57–64. *74*

*935. Noda, H. (1967b). Studies on various phosphatases of the fishes. IV. Effect of growth upon phosphatases activities of rainbow trout, *Salmo irideus*. *J. Fac. Fish. pref. Univ. Mie-Tsu* **7**, 65–71.

936. Noda, H. (1967c). Studies on various phosphatases of the fishes. V. Variation in four phosphatases activities during fasting of rainbow trout, *Salmo irideus*. *J. Fac. Fish. pref. Univ. Mie-Tsu* **7**, 73–80. *254*

937. Noda, H. and Tachino, S. (1965). Studies on various phosphatases of fishes. II. Distribution of phosphatases in fish organs. *J. Fac. Fish. pref. Univ. Mie-Tsu* **6**, 303–11. *151*

*938. Noguchi, E. (1932). On the urea-content of muscle of marine animals. *Bull. Jap. Soc. scient. Fish.* **1**, 121–3.

939. Nomura, M. (1963). Studies on reproduction of rainbow trout, *Salmo gairdneri*, with special reference to egg taking.—V. Development of gonads and size of fish spawned firstly. *Bull. Jap. Soc. scient. Fish.* **29**, 976–84. *116*

940. Nottingham, P. M. (1952). The alkaline hydrolysis and hydrolytic products of fish protein. Ph.D. thesis, University of Aberdeen, Scotland. *238*

941. Nursall, J. R. (1956). The lateral musculature and the swimming of fish. *Proc. zool. Soc. Lond.* **126**, 127–43. *11*

942. Nyman, L. (1965). Species specific proteins in freshwater fishes and their suitability for a "protein taxonomy". *Hereditas* **53**, 117–26. *164*

943. Odense, P. H., Allen, T. M. and Leung, T. C. (1966). Multiple forms of lactate dehydrogenase and aspartate aminotransferase in herring (*Clupea harengus harengus* L.). *Can. J. Biochem. Physiol.* **44**, 1319–26. *167*

944. Odense, P., Bordeleau, A. and Guilbault, R. (1966). Tolerance levels of cod (*Gadus morhua*) to low salinity. *J. Fish. Res. Bd Can.* **23**, 1465–7. *117*

945. Ogata, T. and Mori, M. (1963). A histochemical study of hydrolytic enzymes in muscle fibres of various animals. *J. Histochem. Cytochem.* **11**, 645–52. *23, 24*

*946. Ogino, C. and Konno, K. (1950). On the content of cholesterol and phosphatide of the brain of carp. *Bull. Jap. Soc. scient. Fish.* **15**, 830–2. *95*

*947. Ogino, C. and Yasuda, S. (1962). Changes in inorganic constituents of developing rainbow trout eggs. *Bull. Jap. Soc. scient. Fish.* **28**, 788–91. *79*

*948. Oglesby, L. M. and Bannister, A. C. (1959). Sodium and potassium in salt-water fish. *J. Am. diet. Ass.* **35**, 1163–4.

*949. Oglesby, R. T. and Weiss, C. M. (1963). Some biochemical constituents of fish tissue, with special reference to brains. *Trans. Am. Fish. Soc.* **92**, 168–70.

*950. Oguri, M. (1968). Urinary constituents of snake-head fish, with special reference to urine sugar. *Bull. Jap. Soc. scient. Fish.* **34,** 6–10.

*951. Oguri, M. and Takada, N. (1965). pH, calcium level and osmotic concentration of the urine in the snake-head fish, *Channa argus*. *Bull. Jap. Soc. scient. Fish.* **31,** 293–6.

*952. Oguri, M. and Takada, N. (1966). Effects of some hormonic substances on the urinary and serum calcium levels of the snake-head fish, *Channa argus*. *Bull. Jap. Soc. scient. Fish.* **32,** 28–31. *267*

*953. Oguri, M. and Takada, N. (1967). Serum calcium and magnesium levels of goldfish, with special reference to the gonadal maturation. *Bull. Jap. Soc. scient. Fish.* **33,** 161–6. *61, 62, 267*

954. Ohsawa, W. and Tsukuda, H. (1964). Composition and heat tolerance of serum proteins of goldfish acclimated to different temperatures. *J. Biol. Osaka City Univ.* **15,** 31–8. *214*

*955. Okada, I., Osakabe, I., Kuratomi, Y. and Sekine, E. (1953). On the studies of glutathion in the marine products: part 2. Polarographic determination of glutathion in carp and whale. *J. Tokyo Univ. Fish.* **39,** 185–91. *20*

*956. Okumura, N., Otsuki, S. and Aoyama, T. (1959). Studies on the free amino acids and related compounds in the brains of fish, amphibia, reptiles, aves and mammal by ion exchange chromatography. *J. Biochem., Tokyo* **46,** 207–12.

*957. Olley, J. and Duncan, W. R. H. (1965). Lipids and protein denaturation in fish muscle. *J. Sci. Fd Agric.* **16,** 99–104.

*958. Olley, J. and Lovern, J. A. (1954). The lipids remaining in the flesh of the haddock after extraction by acetone and ethanol-ether. *Biochem. J.* **57,** 610–19.

*959. Olley, J. and Lovern, J. A. (1960). Phospholipid hydrolysis in cod flesh stored at various temperatures. *J. Sci. Fd Agric.* **11,** 644–52. *36*

*960. Olley, J., Pirie, R. and Watson, H. (1962). Lipase and phospholipase activity in fish skeletal muscle and its relationship to protein denaturation. *J. Sci. Fd Agric.* **13,** 501–16. *260*

961. Olley, J., Stephen, E., Farmer, J. and Robertson, I. (1967). A critical look at two objective tests for cold storage deterioration. *J. Fd Technol.* **2,** 207–16. *132*

962. Ono, T., Nagayama, F. and Masuda, T. (1960). Studies on the fat metabolism of fish muscles. 4. Effects of the components in foods on the culture of rainbow trout. *J. Tokyo Univ. Fish.* **46,** 97–106. *53, 54, 55*

963. Orton, J. H. (1929). Reproduction and death in invertebrates and fishes. *Nature, Lond.* **123,** 14–15. *89, 126*

964. Otterbech, F. (1953). The cod population of the Oslofjord. *Rapp. P.-v. Réun. Cons. perm. int. Explor. Mer* **136,** 15–21. *116, 160*

*965. Oya, T. and Hirosawa, H. (1936). The content of the ascorbic acid in the marine animals and products. *Bull. Jap. Soc. scient. Fish.* **5,** 195–98.

*966. Paniaotova, M. and Bail'ozov, D. (1960). The composition of various freshwater and sea fish. *Nauchi Trudove Bulgarska Akademiya Nauk* **2,** 113–9.

967. Parker, R. R., Black, E. C. and Larkin, P. A. (1959). Fatigue and mortality in troll-caught Pacific salmon (*Oncorhynchus*). *J. Fish. Res. Bd Can.* **16,** 429–48. *47*

968. Parker, R. R. and Vanstone, W. E. (1966). Changes in chemical composition of central British Columbia pink salmon during early sea life. *J. Fish. Res. Bd Can.* **23,** 1353–84. *88, 226*

969. Parker, T. J. and Haswell, W. A. (1940). "A Textbook of Zoology", Vol. 2, 6th. Ed., 758 pp. MacMillan, London. *137*

970. Parks, T. B. and Rose, E. R. (1933). The copper, iron and manganese content of fish. *J. Nutr.* **6,** 95–8. *21, 144*

*971. Parry, G. (1961). Osmotic and ionic changes in blood and muscle of migrating salmonids. *J. exp. Biol.* **38,** 411–27. *106, 190, 192–5*

*972. Partmann, W. (1954). The first post-mortem changes in the muscular tissue of fish. *Arch. FischWiss.* **5,** 159–70.

973. Parvatheswararao, V. (1967). Some mechanisms underlying thermal acclimation in a freshwater fish, *Etroplus maculatus* (Teleostei). *Comp. Biochem. Physiol.* **21,** 619–26. *221, 291*

974. Patashnik, M. (1966). New approaches to quality changes in fresh chilled halibut. *Comml Fish. Rev.* **28** (1), 1–7. *93*

*975. Pathak, S. P. and Reddy, B. R. (1962). The component acids of the fats of some Indian freshwater fishes. *Biochem. J.* **85,** 618–20.

976. Patterson, H. R. and Hutton, K. E. (1965). Race-specific erythrocyte antigen of chinook salmon. *Progve Fish Cult.* **27,** 51 only. *163*

977. Pavlov, J. P. (1902). "The Work of the Digestive Glands", translated by W. P. Thompson, p. 35. Charles Griffin, London. *203*

*978. Pavlovic, V., Kekic, H., Mladjenovic, O. and Vukotic, N. (1961). Blood sugar and the concentration of glycogen in the liver, heart and muscle in certain species of fish from the Adriatic Sea. *Rapp. P.-v. Réun. Commr int. Explor. Scient. Mer Méditerr.* **18,** 279–81.

*979. Pawar, S. S. and Magar, N. G. (1965). Biochemical changes in catfish, tilapia and mrigal fish during rigor mortis. *J. Food Sci.* **30,** 121–5.

980. Peachey, L. D. (1965). The sarcoplasmic reticulum and transverse tubules of the frog's sartorius. *J. Cell. Biol.* **25,** 209–31. *14*

981. Pearse, A. S. and Achtenberg, H. (1917). Habits of yellow perch in Wisconsin lakes. *Bull. Bur. Fish., Wash.* **36,** 297–366. *211*

*982. Pennock, J. F., Morton, R. A., Lawson, D. E. M. and Laidman, D. L. (1962). Quinones and related compounds in fish tissues. *Biochem. J.* **84**, 637–40.

983. Pequignot, J. and Serfaty, A. (1965). Influence of salinity on the respiration of teleostean tissues. *Experientia* **21**, 227–30. *189*

*984. Pequignot, J. and Serfaty, A. (1966). Variations in salinity in eels. Alterations of the QO_2 and the concentrations of cations of liver and kidney tissues. *Experientia* **22**, 121–4. *84, 193, 194*

*985. Pequin, L. and Serfaty, A. (1966). Glutamic acid and nitrogen excretion in the common carp, *Cyprinus carpio* L. *Comp. Biochem. Physiol.* **18**, 141–9.

986. Peterson, D. H., Jäger, H. K., Savage, G. M., Washburn, G. N. and Westers, H. (1966). Natural coloration of trout using xanthophylls. *Trans. Am. Fish. Soc.* **95**, 408–14. *201*

*987. Petkovitch, T. A. (1965). On the chemical elemental composition of the plankton-eating fish of the Black Sea. *Gidrobiol. Zh.* **1**, 53–6.

988. Petkovitch, T. A. (1967a). Trace elements in organs and tissues of some plankton-eating and benthos-eating fish in the northwestern part of the Black Sea. *Obmen Veshchestv Biokhim. Ryb. Akad. Nauk SSSR, Min. Ryb. Khoz. SSSR, Ikhtiol. Kom.* 279–83 (no volume number). Quoted in *Chem. Abstr.* **69**, 1004r (1968). *200, 280*

*989. Petkovitch, T. A. (1967b). Elemental chemical composition of bone tissue of Black Sea plankton-feeding and benthos-feeding fishes. *Dopov. Akad. Nauk ukr. RSR* **2**, Ser. B, 142–6.

*990. Petrenko, I. N. and Karasikova, A. A. (1958). The amino acid composition of the proteins in the process of maturing of the sexual products in sprat from the Gulf of Riga. *Dokl. Akad. Nauk SSSR* **122**, 1071–2. *66, 99, 100*

*991. Phillips, A. M. (1958). The organic composition of brook and brown trout blood. *Progve Fish Cult.* **20**, 114–6.

*992. Phillips, A. M. and Brockway, D. R. (1958). The inorganic composition of brown trout blood. *Progve Fish Cult.* **20**, 58–61.

993. Phillips, A. M., Livingston, D. L. and Dumas, R. F. (1960). Effect of starvation and feeding on the chemical composition of brook trout. *Progve Fish Cult.* **22**, 147–54. *225, 243*

994. Phillips, A. M., Livingston, D. L. and Poston, H. A. (1966). The effect of changes in protein quality, calorie sources and calorie levels upon the growth and chemical composition of brook trout. *Fish. Res. Bull. N.Y.* **29**, 6–14. *203*

*995. Phillips, A. M., Lovelace, F. E., Brockway, D. R. and Balzer, G. C. (1953). The nutrition of trout. *Fish. Res. Bull. N.Y.* **16**, 46 pp. *84, 205, 206, 251, 253*

996. Phillips, A. M., Lovelace, F. E., Podoliak, H. A., Brockway, D. R. and Balzer, G. C. (1955). The nutrition of trout. *Fish. Res. Bull. N.Y.* **18**, 52 pp. *186, 187, 206, 207, 208*

997. Phillips, A. M., Lovelace, F. E., Podoliak, H. A., Brockway, D. R. and Balzer, G. C. (1956). The nutrition of trout. *Fish. Res. Bull. N.Y.* **19,** 56 pp. *52, 54, 92, 174, 207, 208, 211*

*998. Phillips, A. M., Podoliak, H. A., Brockway, D. R. and Balzer, G. C. (1957a). The nutrition of trout. *Fish. Res. Bull. N.Y.* **20,** 61 pp. *206, 207, 211*

*999. Phillips, A. M., Podoliak, H. A., Brockway, D. R. and Vaughn, R. R. (1957b). The nutrition of trout. *Fish. Res. Bull. N.Y.* **21,** 93 pp. (Year of publication not given in this report; 1957 is the 'year' covered. Usually the reports are published in the year following.)

1000. Phillips, A. M., Podoliak, H. A., Dumas, R. F. and Thoesen, R. W. (1958). The nutrition of trout. *Fish. Res. Bull. N.Y.* **22,** 87 pp. *52, 53, 55, 72, 202*

*1001. Phillips, A. M., Podoliak, H. A., Livingston, D. L., Dumas, R. F. and Hammer, G. L. (1961). (No title). *Fish. Res. Bull. N.Y.* **24,** 76 pp. *49*

1002. Phillips, A. M., Podoliak, H. A., Livingston, D. L., Dumas, R. F. and Thoesen, R. W. (1960). The nutrition of trout. *Fish. Res. Bull. N.Y.* **23,** 83 pp. *207, 211*

1003. Phillips, A. M., Podoliak, H. A., Poston, H. A., Livingston, D. L., Booke, H. E. and Hammer, G. L. (1962). (No title). *Fish. Res. Bull. N.Y.* **25,** 57 pp. *73, 77*

1004. Phillips, A. M., Podoliak, H. A., Poston, H. A., Livingston, D. L., Booke, H. E., Pyle, E. A. and Hammer, G. L. (1963). (No title). *Fish. Res. Bull. N.Y.* **26,** 93 pp. *189, 227*

*1005. Phillips, A. M., Podoliak, H. A., Poston, H. A., Livingston, D. L., Booke, H. E., Pyle, E. A. and Hammer, G. L. (1964). The nutrition of trout. *Fish. Res. Bull. N.Y.* **27,** 111 pp. *61, 63, 69, 119, 218*

*1006. Phillips, J. G. (1959). Adrenocorticosteroids in fish. *J. Endocr.* **18,** xxxvii.

*1007. Phillips, J. G. and Chester Jones, I. (1957). The identity of adrenocortical secretions in lower vertebrates. *J. Endocrinol.* **16,** iii only.

*1008. Phillips, J. G., Chester Jones, I., Bellamy, D., Greep, R. O., Day, L. R. and Holmes, W. N. (1962). Corticosteroids in the blood of *Myxine glutinosa* L. (Atlantic hagfish). *Endocrinology* **71,** 329–31.

*1009. Phillips, J. G., Holmes, W. N. and Bondy, P. K. (1959). Adrenocortico-steroids in salmon plasma (*Oncorhynchus nerka*). *Endocrinology* **65,** 811–18.

*1010. Picos, C. and Jules, V. G. (1962). Coagulation of carp blood. *Acta hydrobiol., Krakow* **4,** 413–20.

*1011. Pickford, G. E. and Grant, F. B. (1967). Serum osmolality in the coel-acanth, *Latimeria chalumnae*: urea retention and ion regulation. *Science, N.Y.* **155,** 568–70. *139*

1012. Pickford, G. E., Pang, P. K. T., Stanley, J. G. and Fleming, W. R. (1966). Calcium and fresh-water survival in the euryhaline cyprinodonts, *Fundulus kansae* and *Fundulus heteroclitus*. *Comp. Biochem. Physiol.* **18,** 503–9. *189*

*1013. Piez, K. A. (1965). Characterization of a collagen from codfish skin containing three chromatographically different α chains. *Biochemistry, N.Y.* **4,** 2590–6.

*1014. Piez, K. A., Eigner, E. A. and Lewis, M. S. (1963). The chromatographic separation and amino acid composition of the subunits of several collagens. *Biochemistry, N.Y.* **2,** 58–66.

*1015. Piez, K. A. and Gross, J. (1960). The amino acid composition of some fish collagens: the relation between composition and structure. *J. biol. Chem.* **235,** 995–8. *10*

1016. Pine, E. K. and Holland, J. F. (1966). Heterogeneity in the composition of human collagen. *Archs Biochem. Biophys.* **115,** 95–101. *128*

1017. Piper, R. G. and Stephens, R. F. (1962). A comparative study of the blood of wild and hatchery-reared lake trout. *Progve Fish Cult.* **24,** 81–4. *55*

1018. Pitt, G. A. J. (1964). A survey of the chemistry of visual pigments. *Expl Eye Res.* **3,** 316–26. *186*

*1019. Plack, P. A. (1964). Retinal in eggs, blood and liver. *Expl Eye Res.* **3,** 383–7.

*1020. Plack, P. A. and Kon, S. K. (1961). A comparative survey of the distribution of vitamin A aldehyde in eggs. *Biochem. J.* **81,** 561–70. *67*

*1021. Plack, P. A., Kon, S. K. and Thompson, S. Y. (1959). Vitamin A_1 aldehyde in the eggs of the herring (*Clupea harengus* L.) and other marine teleosts. *Biochem. J.* **71,** 467–76

*1022. Plack, P. A. and Woodhead, P. M. J. (1966). Vitamin A compounds and lipids in the blood of the cod *Gadus morhua* from the Arctic in relation to gonadal maturation. *J. mar. biol. Ass. U.K.* **46,** 547–59. *67, 95, 124, 173, 200, 252*

*1023. Plack, P. A., Woodhead, A. D. and Woodhead, P. M. J. (1961). Vitamin A compounds in the ovaries of the cod, *Gadus morhua* L., from the Arctic. *J. mar. biol. Ass. U.K.* **41,** 617–30. *67*

*1024. Platner, W. S. (1950). Effects of low temperature on magnesium content of blood, body fluids and tissues of goldfish and turtle. *Am. J. Physiol.* **161,** 399–405. *177, 218, 280*

*1025. Plisetskaya, E. M. (1967). Respiration and glycogen in lamprey brain. *Evol. Neirofiziol. Neirokhim., Akad. Nauk SSSR. Otd. Fiziol.* pp. 149–55. Quoted in *Chem. Abstr.* **68** (1), 1161u (1968).

1026. Podoliak, H. A. (1965). Some effects of stress on the osmotic tolerance of fingerling brown trout. *Fish. Res. Bull. N.Y.* **28,** 71–8. *189*

1027. Podoliak, H. A. and McCormick, J. H. (1967). Absorption of dissolved strontium by brook trout. *Fish. Res. Bull. N.Y.* **30,** 5–13. *207*

1028. Pora, E. A. (1936a). On the chemical and physico-chemical differences in the blood according to the sexes in *Labrus bergylta*. *C. r. Séanc. Soc. Biol.* **121,** 102–5. *119, 120*

1029. Pora, E. A. (1936b). On the chemical and physico-chemical differences in the blood of the two sexes of the elasmobranchs. *C. r. Séanc. Soc. Biol.* **121,** 105–7. *124*

1030. Pora, A. E. and Precoop, O. (1960). On the question of studying excretory processes in freshwater fishes. Part III. Excretion of metabolic products in carp during starvation and various feeding conditions. *Vop. Ikhtiol.* **16,** 175–82. *256*

1031. Pora, E. A., Sildan, N. and Wittenberger, C. (1965). Muscle cholinesterase in fish. *Stud. Univ. Babes-Bolyai, Ser. Biol.* (1), 85–7. *20*

1032. Pora, E. A., Wittenberger, C. and Gábos, M. (1964). Ascorbic acid in the muscle of carp. *Stud. Univ. Babes-Bolyai, Ser. Biol.* (1), 111–6. *25*

1033. Poston, H. A. (1966a). Effect of water temperature on levels of serum protein components of brown trout. *Fish. Res. Bull. N.Y.* **29,** 25–7. *124*

1034. Poston, H. A. (1966b). Effect of sex and reproductive stage on haemoglobin levels in brown trout. *Fish. Res. Bull. N.Y.* **29,** 28–9.

*1035. Pottinger, S. R. and Baldwin, W. H. (1940). The content of certain amino acids in the edible portions of fishery products. *Proc. Pacif. Sci. Congr.* **3,** 453–9.

*1036. Pottinger, S. R. and Baldwin, W. H. (1946). The content of certain amino acids in seafoods. *Comml Fish. Rev.* **8** (8), 5–9.

1037. Potts, W. T. W., Foster, M. A., Rudy, P. P. and Howells, G. P. (1967). Sodium and water balance in the cichlid teleost, *Tilapia mossambica.* *J. exp. Biol.* **47,** 461–70. *198*

*1038. Pradhan, S. V. (1961). A study of blood of a few Indian fishes. *Proc. Indian Acad. Sci.* **54B,** 251–6. *93*

*1039. de Prailauné, S. (1955). On the haemoglobin of the coelacanth. *C. r. Séanc. Soc. Biol.* **149,** 655–8. *137*

*1040. Preston, A. (1960). Red blood values in the plaice (*Pleuronectes platessa* L.). *J. mar. biol. Ass. U.K.* **39,** 681–7. *93*

1041. Privol'nev, T. I. and Brizinova, P. N. (1964). Melting points of fats in fishes. *Izv. Gos. Nauchn.-Issled. Inst. Ozern. i Rechn. Rybn. Khoz.* **58,** 45–57. *127, 217*

*1042. Proctor, B. E. and Bhatia, D. S. (1950). Effect of high-voltage cathode rays on amino acids in fish muscle. *Fd Technol., Champaign* **4,** 357–61.

1043. Protasov, V. R. (1964). Some features of the vision of fishes. *Akad. Nauk. SSSR, Inst. Morfologii Zhivotnykh* 29–48. *186*

*1044. Pyke, M. and Wright, M. D. (1941). Vitamin content of salmon. *Nature, Lond.* **147,** 267 only.

1045. Pyle, E. A. (1965). Maintenance of relative swimming performance among brook trout grouped by initial swimming performance. *Fish. Res. Bull. N.Y.* **28,** 55–9. *117*

1046. Pyle, E. A., Poston, H. A. and Livingston, D. L. (1967). The effect of enforced exercise upon the growth and chemical composition of fingerling brook trout. *Fish. Res. Bull. N.Y.* **30,** 52–4. *48*

*1047. Qudrat-i-Khuda, M., Rahman, K. M. and Khan, N. A. (1964). Fish and fish products. Part IV. Evaluation of certain important types of fish for their valuable constituents and essential amino acids. *Scientific Researches, East Reg. Laboratories, P.C.S.I.R., Dacca* **1,** 49–56. *261*

1048. Rabaey, M. (1965). Comparative study of tissue proteins (lens and muscle) in fish. *In* "Protides of the Biological Fluids", 12th Colloquium, 1964 (H. Peeters, ed.), pp. 273–7. Elsevier, Amsterdam. *135, 141, 167*

1049. Rae, B. B. (1967a). The food of cod in the North Sea and on west of Scotland grounds. *Mar. Res.* (1), 68 pp. *84, 98, 170, 190, 199*

1050. Rae, B. B. (1967b). The food of cod on Faroese grounds. *Mar. Res.* (6), 23 pp. *171*

1051. Rakow, D. (1963). On the feeding habits of fishes and their effect on the quality of the fish flesh. *Archiv. Lebensmittelhyg.* **14,** 261–3. *173, 199*

*1052. Rapson, W. S. and Schwartz, H. M. (1944). South African fish products. Part III. The stonebass (*Polyprion americanus,* Bl. and Schn.). *J. Soc. chem. Ind., Lond.,* (*b*) **63,** 18–21T.

*1053. Rapson, W. S., Schwartz, H. M., Molteno, C. J. and van Rensburg, N. J. (1944). South African fish products. Part IV. The snoek (*Thyrsites atun,* Euphr.) *J. Soc. chem. Ind., Lond.,* (*b*) **63,** 21–3 T.

*1054. Rapson, W. S., Schwartz, H. M. and van Rensburg, N. J. (1944). South African fish products. Part VI. The stockfish or hake (*Merluccius capensis,* Cast.). *J. Soc. chem. Ind., Lond.,* (*b*) **63,** 313–6 T.

*1055. Rapson, W. S., Schwartz, H. M. and van Rensburg, N. J. (1945a). South African fish products. Part XI. The Kabeljou (*Sciaena hololepidota,* Lacep.) the geelbek (*Atractoscion aequidens,* C. and V.) and the baardman (*Umbrina capensis,* Pappe). *J. Soc. chem. Ind., Lond.,* (*b*) **64,** 7–11 T.

*1056. Rapson, W. S., Schwartz, H. M. and van Rensburg, N. J. (1945b). South African fish products. Part XII. The red gurnard (*Chelidonichthys capensis,* C. and V.). *J. Soc. chem. Ind., Lond.,* (*b*) **64,** 44–46 T.

1057. Rapson, W. S., Schwartz, H. M. and van Rensburg, N. J. (1945c). South African fish products. Part XIII. The jacopever, *Sebastichthys capensis* (Gmelin), and the sancord, *Helicolenus maculatus* (C. and V.). *J. Soc. chem. Ind., Lond.,* (*b*) **64,** 47–50 T.

*1058. Rasmussen, R. A. and Rasmussen, L. E. (1967). Some observations on the protein and enzyme levels and fractions in normal and stressed elasmobranchs. *Trans. N.Y. Acad. Sci.* **29** Ser. II, 397–413. *40, 189*

1059. Rasquin, P. and Hafter, E. (1951). Age changes in the testis of the teleost, *Astyanax mexicanus. J. Morph.* **89,** 397–407. *126*

1060. Rass, T. S. (1964). Changes in eye size and body coloration in secondary deep-sea fishes. *In* "Fishes of the Pacific and Indian oceans, Biology and Distribution". (T. S. Rass, ed.) Moscow. Translated from Russian, Israel programme for scientific translations, Jerusalem, 1966. *179*

*1061. Rausch-Stroomann, J. G. and Breckwoldt, M. (1963). The mineral content of sea fish. *Medizin Ernähr*. **4**, 240–4.

1062. Raven, H. C. (1939). On the anatomy and evolution of the locomotor apparatus of the nipple-tailed ocean sunfish (*Masturus lanceolatus*). *Bull. Am. Mus. nat. Hist.* **76**, 143–50. *33*

1063. Rayner, M. D. and Keenan, M. J. (1967). Role of red and white muscles in the swimming of the skipjack tuna. *Nature. Lond.* **214**, 392–3. *34*

1064. Read, L. J. (1968). Ornithine-urea cycle enzymes in early embryos of the dogfish *Squalus suckleyi* and the skate *Raja binoculata*. *Comp. Biochem. Physiol.* **24**, 669–74. *139*

*1065. Reay, G. A. (1939). The nitrogen extractives of fish. *Rep. Fd Invest. Bd* 1938, 87–9. *146, 202*

1066. Reiser, R., Stevenson, B., Kayama, M., Choudhury, R. B. R. and Hood, D. W. (1963). The influence of dietary fatty acid and environmental temperature on the fatty acid composition of teleost fish. *J. Am. Oil Chem. Soc.* **40**, 507–13. *145, 217*

1067. Ridgway, G. J., Cushing, J. E. and Durall, G. L. (1961). Serological differentiation of populations of sockeye salmon, *Oncorhynchus nerka*. *Bull. int. N. Pacif. Fish. Commn* **3**, 5–10. *163*

1068. Ridgway, G. J. and Klontz, G. W. (1961). Blood types in Pacific salmon. *Bull. int. N. Pacif. Fish. Commn* **5**, 49–55. *163*

1069. Ridgway, G. J., Klontz, G. W. and Matsumoto, C. (1962). Intraspecific differences in serum antigens of red salmon demonstrated by immunochemical methods. *Bull. int. N. Pacif. Fish. Commn* **8**, document no. 396. *105*

1070. Riedel, D. (1961). World fisheries. *In* "Fish as Food" (G. Borgstrom, ed.), Vol. 1, Chapter 2, pp. 41–75. Academic Press, London and New York.

1071. Rigby, B. J. (1968). Amino acid composition and thermal stability of the skin collagen of the Antarctic icefish. *Nature, Lond.* **219**, 166–7. *216*

1072. Ringer, S. (1883). Concerning the influence of saline media on fish, etc. *J. Physiol., Lond.* **5**, 98–115. *188*

1073. Ripley, E. and Bolomey, R. A. (1946). The relation of the biology of the soupfin shark to the liver yield of vitamin A. *Fish Bull. Calif.* **64**, 39–72. *91, 95, 105*

1074. Robertson, I., Love, R. M. and Cowie, W. P. (1967). Studies on the North Sea cod. V.—Effects of starvation, 3. Electrophoresis of the muscle myogens. *J. Sci. Fd Agric.* **18**, 563–5. *141, 234, 237*

*1075. Robertson, J. D. (1954). The chemical composition of the blood of some aquatic chordates, including members of the tunicata, cyclostomata and osteichthyes. *J. exp. Biol.* **31**, 424–42. *137, 144*

*1076. Robertson, J. D. (1960). Studies on the chemical composition of muscle tissue. 1. The muscles of the hagfish, *Myxine glutinosa* L., and the roman eel, *Muraena helena* L.   *J. exp. Biol.* **37**, 879–88.

*1077. Robertson, J. D. (1966). Osmotic constituents of the blood plasma and parietal muscle of *Myxine glutinosa* L. *In* "Some Contemporary Studies in Marine Science" (H. Barnes, ed.), pp. 631–44. George Allen and Unwin Ltd., London.

1078. Robertson, O. H. (1961). Prolongation of the life span of kokanee salmon (*Oncorhynchus nerka kennerlyi*) by castration before beginning of gonad development. *Proc. natn. Acad. Sci. U.S.A.* **47**, 609–21. *115, 117, 126, 127*

1079. Robertson, O. H., Hane, S., Wexler, B. C. and Rinfret, A. P. (1963). The effect of hydrocortisone on immature rainbow trout (*Salmo gairdnerii*). *Gen. comp. Endocrinol.* **3**, 422–36. *115, 211, 223, 233*

*1080. Robertson, O. H., Krupp, M. A., Favour, C. B., Hane, S. and Thomas, S. F. (1961). Physiological changes occurring in the blood of the Pacific salmon (*Oncorhynchus tschawytscha*) accompanying sexual maturation and spawning. *Endocrinology* **68**, 733–46. *99, 106, 111, 112, 113, 114, 119, 252*

*1081. Robertson, O. H., Krupp, M. A., Thomas, S. F., Favour, C. B., Hane, S. and Wexler, B. C. (1961). Hyperadrenocorticism in spawning migratory and nonmigratory rainbow trout (*Salmo gairdnerii*); comparison with Pacific salmon (genus *Oncorhynchus*). *Gen. comp. Endocrinol.* **1**, 473–84. *111, 114*

1082. Robertson, O. H. and Wexler, B. C. (1957). Pituitary degeneration and adrenal tissue hyperplasia in spawning Pacific salmon. *Science, N.Y.* **125**, 1295–6. *114*

*1083. Robin, E. D., Murdaugh, H. V. and Weiss, E. (1964). Acid-base, fluid and electrolyte metabolism in the elasmobranch. 1. Ionic composition of erythrocytes, muscle and brain. *J. cell. comp. Physiol.* **64**, 409–18. *139*

1084. Robinson, P. F. and Schwartz, F. J. (1965). A revised bibliography of papers dealing with the oyster toadfish, *Opsanus tau*. *Contr. Chesapeake biol. Lab.* **284**, 18 pp. *148*

*1085. Ronold, O. A. and Jakobsen, F. (1947). Trimethylamine oxide in marine products. *J. Soc. chem. Ind., Lond.* **66**, 160–6. *169*

1086. Root, R. W. (1931). The respiratory function of the blood of marine fishes. *Biol. Bull. mar. biol. Lab., Woods Hole* **61**, 427–56. *148, 149*

1087. Roots, B. I. and Prosser, C. L. (1962). Temperature acclimation and the nervous system in fish. *J. exp. Biol.* **39**, 617–29. *213, 214*

*1088. Rosenberg, H., Ennor, A. H., Hagerman, D. D. and Sugai, S. (1962). L-threonine ethanolamine phosphate: a compound newly isolated from fish. *Biochem. J.* **84**, 536–41.

*1089. Roubal, W. T. (1967). Oxidative deterioration of flesh lipids of Pacific cod (*Gadus macrocephalus*). *J. Am. Oil Chem. Soc.* **44**, 325–7.

*1090. Roy, A. and Sen, P. B. (1941). The estimation of cystine, tyrosine and tryptophane in some common edible fishes of Bengal. *Ann. Biochem. exp. Med.* **1**, 321–4.

1091. Rumen, N. M. and Love, W. E. (1963). The six haemoglobins of the sea lamprey (*Petromyzon marinus*). *Archs Biochem. Biophys.* **103**, 24–35. *166*

1092. Ruud, J. T. (1954). Vertebrates without erythrocytes and blood pigment. *Nature, Lond.* **173**, 848–50. *129, 150, 177, 179, 220*

1093. Ruud, J. T. (1958). Vertebrates without blood pigment: a study of the fish family Chaenichthyidae. *Int. Congr. Zool.* **15**, 526–8. *177, 178*

*1094. Saad, F., Kominz, D. R. and Laki, L. (1959). A study of the tropomyosins of three cold-blooded vertebrates of different classes. *J. biol. Chem.* **234**, 551–5.

*1095. Saha, K. C. (1939). Distribution of free and total ascorbic acid in the liver and muscle of Bengal freshwater fish. *J. Indian chem. Soc.* **16**, 511–14.

*1096. Saha, K. C. (1941). Nicotinic acid content of fish. *Ann. Biochem. exp. Med.* **1**, 75–8.

*1097. Saito, K. (1954a). Biochemical studies on fish blood—I. On the morphological property of blood-corpuscles. *Bull. Jap. Soc. scient. Fish.* **19**, 1134–8.

*1098. Saito, K. (1954b). Biochemical studies on the fish blood.—II. On the elements of blood coagulation and coagulation time. *Bull. Jap. Soc. scient. Fish.* **19**, 1139–43.

*1099. Saito, T., Arai, K. and Yajima, T. (1959). Studies on the organic phosphates in muscle of aquatic animals—VII. Changes in purine nucleotides of red lateral muscle of fish. *Bull. Jap. Soc. scient. Fish.* **25**, 573–5. *20, 23*

*1100. Sakaguchi, M., Fujita, M. and Simidu, W. (1964). Studies on muscle of aquatic animals XXXXIII. Creatine and creatinine contents in fish muscle extractives. *Bull. Jap. Soc. scient. Fish.* **30**, 999–1002. *25, 29*

*1101. Sakaguchi, M. and Simidu, W. (1965). Studies on muscle of aquatic animals —XXXXV. Variation with season and growth in nitrogenous extractives of mackerel muscle. *Bull. Jap. Soc. scient. Fish.* **31**, 72–5.

1102. Salvatore, F., Zappia, V. and Costa, C. (1965). Comparative biochemistry of deamination of L-amino acids in elasmobranch and teleost fish. *Comp. Biochem. Physiol.* **16**, 303–9. *139*

1103. Sanders, B. G. (1964). Electrophoretic studies of serum proteins of three trout species and the resulting hybrids within the family salmonidae. *In* "Taxonomic Biochemistry and Serology" (C. A. Leone, ed.), pp. 673–9. The Ronald Press Company, New York. *164*

*1104. Sano, T. (1960a). Haematological studies of the culture fishes in Japan. 2. Seasonal variation of the blood constituents of rainbow trout. *J. Tokyo Univ. Fish.* **46**, 67–75.

1105. Sano, T. (1960b). Haematological studies of the culture fishes in Japan. 3. Changes in blood constituents with growth of rainbow trout. *J. Tokyo Univ. Fish.* **46**, 77–87. *118*

1106. Sano, T. (1962a). Haematological studies of the culture fishes in Japan. 5. Application of a protein refractometer on fish serum. *J. Tokyo Univ. Fish.* **48,** 99–104. *235*

1107. Sano, T. (1962b). Haematological studies of the culture fishes in Japan. 6. Variation in blood constituents of Japanese eel, *Anguilla japonica,* during starvation. *J. Tokyo Univ. Fish.* **48,** 105–9. *235, 256*

*1108. Sanz Perez, B. and Jones, N. R. (1962). Effects of tetracycline antibiotics on the products of anserinase action in chill stored haddock (*Gadus aeglefinus*) muscle. *J. Food Sci.* **27,** 69–72.

*1109. Sasa, S. (1958). Chemical studies on herring meat (1). *Bull. Fac. Fish. Hokkaido Univ.* **8,** 319–45.

*1110. Sasa, S. (1959). Chemical studies on herring meat (2). *Bull. Fac. Fish. Hokkaido Univ.* **9,** 329–64.

*1111. Satomi, Y. (1966). Nucleic acid and phospholipid content of silver carp (*Hypophthalmichthys molitrix*), crucian carp (*Carassius carassius*) and carp (*Cyprinus carpio*) grown together in fertilized ponds. *Bull. Freshwat. Fish. Res. Lab., Tokyo* **16,** 113–32.

*1112. Sautier, P. (1946a). Thiamine assays of fishery products. *Comml Fish. Rev.* **8** (2), 17–19.

*1113. Sautier, P. (1946b). Riboflavin assays of fishery products. *Comml Fish. Rev.* **8** (3), 19–21.

1114. Sawyer, W. H. (1966). Diuretic and natriuretic responses of lungfish (*Protopterus aethiopicus*) to arginine vasotocin. *Am. J. Physiol.* **210,** 191–7. *136*

1115. Sawyer, W. H. and Pickford, G. E. (1963). Neurohypophysial principles of *Fundulus heteroclitus*: characteristics and seasonal changes. *Gen. comp. Endocrinol.* **3,** 439–45. *172*

1116. Schaefer, A. A. (1925). The number of blood corpuscles in fishes in relation to starvation and seasonal cycles. *J. gen. Physiol.* **7,** 341–3. *171*

1117. Schaefer, H. (1962). Free amino acids and related compounds in the body muscle of freshly caught marine bony fishes. *Helgoländer wiss. Meeresunters.* **8,** 257–75. *151, 221*

1118. Schaub, M. C. (1963). The ageing of collagen in the striated muscle. *Gerontologia* **8,** 16–35. *128*

1119. Schimke, R. T. (1962). Differential effects of fasting and protein-free diets on levels of urea cycle enzymes in rat liver. *J. biol. Chem.* **237,** 1921–4. *253*

1120. Schleusing, G. and Nöcker, J. (1960). Influence of potassium deficiency and exercise on the extracellular and intracellular mineral content of the skeletal muscle of trained and untrained animals. *Medsche Welt, Stuttg.* 1579–83. *43*

1121. Schmidt, J. (1917). *Zoarces viviparus* L. and local races of the same. *C. r. Trav. Lab. Carlsberg* **13,** 279–396. *152*

1122. Schmidt, J. (1919). Racial studies in fishes. III. Diallel crossings with trout (*Salmo trutta* L.). *J. Genet.* **9,** 61–7. *153*

1123. Schmidt, J. (1930). Racial investigations. X. The Atlantic cod (*Gadus callarias* L.) and local races of the same. *C. r. Trav. Lab. Carlsberg* **18** (6), 72 pp. *153, 154, 155*

*1124. Schmidt, P. J. and Idler, D. R. (1962). Steroid hormones in the plasma of salmon at various stages of maturation. *Gen. comp. Endocrinol.* **2**, 204–14. *110, 112, 121*

*1125. Schmitt, A., Siebert, G. and Bottke, I. (1966). Comparative study on dipeptidase activities in fish tissues. *Arch. Fisch Wiss.* **17**, 50–60. *254*

*1126. Scholander, P. F. and van Dam, L. (1957). The concentration of haemoglobin in some cold water Arctic fishes. *J. cell. comp. Physiol.* **49**, 1–4. *177, 221*

1127. Scholander, P. F., van Dam, L., Kanwisher, J. W., Hammel, H. T. and Gordon, M. S. (1957). Supercooling and osmoregulation in Arctic fish. *J. cell. comp. Physiol.* **49**, 5–24. *218, 219*

1128. Scholander, P. F., Flagg, W., Walters, V. and Irving, L. (1953). Climatic adaptation in Arctic and tropical poikilotherms. *Physiol. Zoöl.* **26**, 67–92. *212*

*1129. Schormüller, J. (1939). On the occurrence of vitamin B_2 (lactoflavin). *Z. Unters. Lebensmittel* **77**, 1–17.

*1130. von Schroeder, W. (1890). On the formation of urea in shark. *Hoppe-Seyler's Z. physiol. Chem.* **14**, 576–98.

*1131. Schtsherbina, M. A. (1962). Content of amino acid in raw protein in pond fish and several feeds. *Vop. Prudov. Rybovod.* **11**, 5–13. Quoted in Hepher, B. and Chervinski, J. (1965). *Bamidgeh* **17**, 31–46.

*1132. Schuh, J. E. and Nace, P. F. (1961). Seasonal changes in blood sugar and related phenomena in the toadfish, *Opsanus tau*. *Biol. Bull. mar. biol. Lab., Woods Hole* **121**, 406 only. *169, 221*

1133. Schwanzara, S. A. (1967). The visual pigments of freshwater fishes. *Vision Res.* **7**, 121–48. *180*

1134. Scott, D. P. (1962). Effect of food quantity on fecundity of rainbow trout, *Salmo gairdneri*. *J. Fish. Res. Bd Can.* **19**, 715–30. *223*

*1135. Seagran, H. L. (1953). Technical note no. 25—Amino acid content of salmon roe. *Comml Fish. Rev.* **15** (3), 31–4.

*1136. Seagran, H. L., Morey, D. E. and Dassow, J. A. (1954). The amino acid content of roe at different stages of maturity from the five species of Pacific salmon. *J. Nutr.* **53**, 139–49. *66*

*1137. Secondat, M. and Diaz, D. (1942). Research on blood lactic acid in freshwater fish. *C. r. hebd. Séanc. Acad. Sci., Paris* **215**, 71–3. *40, 47*

*1138. Seshadri, B. (1964). Effect of insulin on blood glucose level in the fish *Ophiocephalus striatus* (Bloch). *J. Anim. Morph. Physiol.* **11**, 302–8.

*1139. Severin, S. E. and Vul'fson, P. L. (1959). Nitrogen extractive substances of fish muscle. *Biochemistry N.Y.* (*Biokhimiya*) **24**, 923–9.

1140. Shanks, W. E. and Halver, J. E. (1960). Indispensable amino acids for sockeye salmon and rainbow trout. *Fedn Proc. Fedn Am. Socs exp. Biol.* **19,** 11 only. *208*

*1141. Shanta, N. and Motelica, I. (1962). Investigation of the vitamin C content of carp. *Revue Biol., Buc.* **7,** 137–47. Quoted in *Chem. Abstr.* **58,** 3708b (1963). *291, 292*

*1142. Sharp, J. G. (1935). Glycogenolysis in fish-liver at low temperatures. *Biochem. J.* **29,** 854–9.

*1143. Sharratt, B. M., Chester Jones, I. and Bellamy, D. (1964). Water and electrolyte composition of the body and renal functions of the eel (*Anguilla anguilla* L.). *Comp. Biochem. Physiol.* **11,** 9–18. *82, 120, 192, 193, 195, 196*

*1144. Shell, E. W. (1961). Chemical composition of blood of smallmouth bass. *Res. Rep. U.S. Fish Wildl. Serv.* **57,** 36 pp.

1145. Shewan, J. M. (1951). The chemistry and metabolism of the nitrogenous extractives in fish. *Biochem. Soc. Symp.* **6,** 28–48. *146, 151, 221*

1146. Shewan, J. M. (1953). The nitrogenous extractives from fresh fish muscle. II.—Comparison of several gadoid and elasmobranch species. *J. Sci. Fd Agric.* **4,** 565–8. *143*

1147. Shewan, J. M. (1955). The nitrogenous extractives from fresh fish muscle. III.—Comparison of several flat fishes and members of the herring-mackerel group. *J. Sci. Fd Agric.* **6,** 99–104. *151*

*1148. Shewan, J. M. and Jones, N. R. (1957). Chemical changes occurring in cod muscle during chill storage and their possible use as objective indices of quality. *J. Sci. Fd Agric.* **8,** 491–8.

*1149. Shimada, K. and Tanaka, E. (1936). Distribution of inositol in fish. *Bull. Jap. Soc. scient. Fish.* **4,** 305–6.

*1150. Shimeno, S. and Ikeda, S. (1967). Studies on glucose-6-phosphatase of aquatic animals.—II. The enzyme activities in fish tissues. *Bull. Jap. Soc. scient. Fish.* **33,** 112–6.

*1151. Shimizu, Y. and Higasa, S. (1960). Biochemical studies on the growth and maturation of fish. XII. Some notes on riboflavins in the liver and the kidney of tunas and marlins. *Rep. Nankai reg. Fish. Res. Lab.* **12,** 33–44.

*1152. Shimizu, Y. and Higasa, S. (1961). Biochemical studies on the growth and maturation of fish. XIII. Some notes on riboflavins in the bile of tunas and marlins. *Rep. Nankai reg. Fish. Res. Lab.* **13,** 47–51.

*1153. Shimma, Y. and Taguchi, H. (1964a). A comparative study on fatty acid composition of fish. *Bull. Jap. Soc. scient. Fish.* **30,** 179–88.

*1154. Shimma, Y. and Taguchi, H. (1964b). A comparative study on fatty acid compositions of wild and cultivated 'Ayu', sweet smelt (*Plecoglossus altivelis*). *Bull. Jap. Soc. scient. Fish.* **30,** 918–25. *55*

*1155. Shmerling, Z. G. (1965). Isolation and properties of DNA of sturgeon oocytes. *Biokhimiya* **30,** 113–23.

*1156. Shorland, F. B. (1953). New Zealand fish oils. 6. Seasonal variations in the composition of New Zealand groper (*Polyprion oxygeneios*) liver oil. *Biochem. J.* **54**, 673–7. *252*

1157. Shubnikov, D. A. (1959). The use of the fat content and blood analysis data as an aid in searching for the Atlanto-Scandian herring during the summer. *Ryb. Khoz.* **35** (3), 12–14. *149*

*1158. Shuster, C. Y., Froines, J. R. and Olcott, H. S. (1964). Phospholipids of tuna white muscle. *J. Am. Oil Chem. Soc.* **41**, 36–41.

1159. Sick, K. (1961). Haemoglobin polymorphism in fishes. *Nature, Lond.* **192**, 894–6. *94, 164, 165*

1160. Sick, K., Westergaard, M. and Frydenberg, O. (1962). Haemoglobin pattern and chromosome number of American, European and Japanese eels (*Anguilla*). *Nature, Lond.* **193**, 1001–2. *166*

*1161. Siddiqi, M. A. (1966). A comparative study of some biochemical constituents in different tissues of some freshwater teleosts. II. Total cholesterol. *Sci. Cult.* **32**, 136–8.

*1162. Siddiqi, M. A. (1967). Seasonal variations in ascorbic acid content and calcium content of different tissues of *Ophicephalus punctatus* Bloch. *Indian J. exp. Biol.* **5**, 54–5. *122, 291*

1163. Siebert, G. (1962). Studies on proteolysis in fish tissues. *21st. meeting of Research Group of the Food Industry, Bonn* October 10th and 11th 1962. *254*

*1164. Siebert, G. and Bottke, I. (1963). Enzymes in the body cavities of fishes. *Arch. FischWiss.* **14**, 57–68.

*1165. Siebert, G., Malortie, R. and Beyer, R. (1962). Digestive enzymes of freshly-caught cod. *Arch. FischWiss.* **13**, 21–34.

1166. Siebert, G. and Schmitt, A. (1965). Fish tissue enzymes and their role in the deteriorative changes in fish. *In* "The Technology of Fish Utilization" (R. Kreuzer, ed.), pp. 47–52. Fishing News (Books) Ltd., London. *254*

*1167. Siebert, G., Schmitt, A. and Bottke, I. (1964). Enzymes of the amino acid metabolism in cod musculature. *Arch. FischWiss.* **15**, 233–44. *98, 222*

1168. Siebert, G., Schmitt, A., Malortie, R. V. and Adloff, E. (1960). Thermal denaturation of enzyme proteins of cold-blooded animals. *Experientia* **16**, 491–2. *213*

1169. Simidu, W. (1961). Nonprotein nitrogenous compounds. *In* "Fish as Food" (G. Borgstrom, ed.), Vol. 1, Chapter 11, pp. 353–84. Academic Press, London and New York. *288*

*1170. Simpson, T. H., Wright, R. S. and Gottfried, H. (1963). Steroids in the semen of dogfish (*Squalus acanthias*). *J. Endocrinol.* **26**, 489–98.

*1171. Simpson, T. H., Wright, R. S. and Hunt, S. V. (1963). Sex hormones in fish. Part II. The oestrogens of *Scyliorhinus caniculus*. *J. Endocrinol.* **26**, 499–507. *112*

*1172. Simpson, T. H., Wright, R. S. and Renfrew, J. (1964). *J. Endocrinol.* **31**, 11–20.

*1173. Sindermann, C. J. and Mairs, D. F. (1961). Blood properties of prespawning and postspawning anadromous alewives (*Alosa pseudoharengus*). *Fishery Bull. Fish Wildl. Serv. U.S.* **61**, 145–51 (Fishery Bulletin 183). *104, 106, 192*

1174. Sipos, J. C. and Ackman, R. G. (1964). Association of dimethyl sulphide with the 'blackberry' problem in cod from the Labrador area. *J. Fish. Res. Bd Can.* **21**, 423–5. *199*

1175. Slicher, A. M. (1961). Endocrinological and haematological studies in *Fundulus heteroclitus* (Linn.). *Bull. Bingham oceanogr. Coll.* **17**, art. 3, 55 pp. *55, 121, 124, 188*

1176. Smallwood, W. M. (1916). Twenty months of starvation in *Amia calva*. *Biol. Bull. mar. biol. Lab., Woods Hole* **31**, 453–64. *222, 255*

1177. Smelser, G. K. (1962). Corneal hydration. Comparative physiology of fish and mammals. *Investve Ophth.* **1**, 11–32. *143*

1178. Smirnova, L. I. (1962). Seasonal blood changes in fish of the Rybinsk reservoir. *Vop. Ikhtiol.* **2** Vyp. 4 (25), 677–86. *104, 170, 177, 255*

1179. Smirnova, L. I. (1965). Blood indices of the burbot during prolonged total fasting and subsequent feeding. *Dokl. (Proc.) Acad. Sci. U.S.S.R., Biological Sciences Sections* (English translation) **160**, 107–9. *255, 256*

1180. Smit, H. (1967). Influence of temperature on the rate of gastric juice secretion in the brown bullhead, *Ictalurus nebulosus*. *Comp. Biochem. Physiol.* **21**, 125–32. *211*

1181. Smith, A. C. and Goldstein, R. A. (1967). Variation in protein composition of the eye lens nucleus in ocean whitefish, *Caulolatilus princeps*. *Comp. Biochem. Physiol.* **23**, 533–9. *167*

1182. Smith, H. W. (1929). The composition of the body fluids of elasmobranchs. *J. biol. Chem.* **81**, 407–19. *139*

*1183. Smith, H. W. (1931a). The absorption and excretion of water and salts by the elasmobranch fishes. 1. Freshwater elasmobranchs. *Am. J. Physiol.* **98**, 279–95. *139, 144, 145, 289*

*1184. Smith, H. W. (1931b). The absorption and excretion of water and salts by the elasmobranch fishes. II. Marine elasmobranchs. *Am. J. Physiol.* **98**, 296–310. *139*

1185. Smith, H. W. (1935). The metabolism of the lung-fish. I. General considerations of the fasting metabolism in active fish. *J. cell. comp. Physiol.* **6**, 43–67. *222*

*1186. Smith, L. S. (1966). Blood volumes of three salmonids. *J. Fish. Res. Bd Can.* **23**, 1439–46.

1187. Smith, S. (1952). Studies in the development of the rainbow trout (*Salmo irideus*). II. The metabolism of carbohydrates and fats. *J. exp. Biol.* **29**, 650–66. *72*

1188. Snieszko, S. F. (1961). Microhaematocrit values in rainbow trout, brown trout, and brook trout. *Progve Fish. Cult.* **23**, 114–19. *121*

*1189. Snyder, D. G. (1958). Amino acid composition of the protein and inorganic constituents of the ash of pollock fish scales. *Comml Fish. Rev.* **20** (8), 4–9.

1190. Sobel, H., Hewlett, M. J., Hoshek, S. and Sacker, I. M. (1967). Effect of starvation on hyaluronic acid and extractable protein in skin of mice. *Am. J. Physiol.* **212**, 773–6. *232, 233*

1191. Sohn, B. I., Carver, J. H. and Mangan, G. F. (1961). Composition of commercially-important fish from New England waters. Part 1—proximate analysis of cod, haddock, Atlantic Ocean perch, butterfish and mackerel. *Comml Fish. Rev.* **23** (2), 7–10. *260*

*1192. Sokabe, H., Mizogami, S., Murase, T. and Sakai, F. (1966). Renin and euryhalinity in the Japanese eel, *Anguilla japonica*. *Nature, Lond.* **212**, 952–3.

*1193. Solomons, C. (1955). Proteins in fish scale. *S. Afr. J. med. Sci.* **20**, 27–8.

*1194. Söremark, R. (1967). Vanadium in some biological specimens. *J. Nutr.* **92**, 183–90.

*1195. Sorvachev, K. F. (1957). Changes in proteins of carp blood serum during hibernation. *Biokhimiya* **22**, 872–8. *230, 231, 232, 251*

1196. Sréter, F. A. (1963). Cell water, sodium, and potassium in stimulated red and white mammalian muscles. *Am. J. Physiol.* **205**, 1295–8. *43*

1197. Sréter, F. A. and Friedman, S. M. (1958). The effect of muscular exercise on plasma sodium and potassium in the rat. *Can. J. Biochem. Physiol.* **36**, 333–8. *43*

*1198. Stanley, J. G. and Fleming, W. R. (1964). Excretion of hypertonic urine by a teleost. *Science, N.Y.* **144**, 63–4.

*1199. Stanley, J. G. and Fleming, W. R. (1967). The effect of hypophysectomy on the electrolyte content of *Fundulus kansae* held in fresh water and sea water. *Comp. Biochem. Physiol.* **20**, 489–97. *191, 192, 193, 197*

1200. Stansby, M. E. (1967). Fatty acid patterns in marine, freshwater, and anadromous fish. *J. Am. Oil Chem. Soc.* **44**, 64 only. *147*

*1201. Stapleton, R. P. (1968). Trace elements in tissues of the calico bass, *Paralabrax clathratus* (Girard). *Bull. Sth. Calif. Acad. Sci.* **67**, 49–58.

1202. Steen, J. B. and Berg, T. (1966). The gills of two species of haemoglobin-free fishes compared to those of other teleosts—with a note on severe anaemia in an eel. *Comp. Biochem. Physiol.* **18**, 517–26. *276*

1203. Steffens, W. (1964). Comparative anatomical-physiological investigation of wild and pond carp. *Z. Fisch.* **12**, 725–800. Quoted in *Chem. Abstr.* **65**, (3), 4320d (1966). *55*

1203a. Sterne, J., Hirsch, C. and Pele, M.-F. (1968). Troubles of sugar metabolism following feeding exclusively on glucose in the fish "*Carassius auratus*". *Path. Biol., Paris* **16**, 639–47.

19*

*1204. Steven, D. M. (1948). Studies on animal carotenoids. I. Carotenoids of the brown trout (*Salmo trutta* Linn.). *J. exp. Biol.* **25**, 369–87. *50, 201*

*1205. Steven, D. M. (1949). Studies on animal carotenoids. II. Carotenoids in the reproductive cycle of the brown trout. *J. exp. Biol.* **26**, 295–303. *67, 201*

1206. Stevens, E. D. (1968). The effect of exercise on the distribution of blood to various organs in rainbow trout. *Comp. Biochem. Physiol.* **25**, 615–25. *31, 46*

1207. Stevens, E. D. and Black, E. C. (1966). The effect of intermittent exercise on carbohydrate metabolism in rainbow trout, *Salmo gairdnerii*. *J. Fish. Res. Bd Can.* **23**, 471–85. *40, 41, 42*

1208. Stewart, N. E., Shumway, D. L. and Doudoroff, P. (1967). Influence of oxygen concentration on the growth of juvenile largemouth bass. *J. Fish. Res. Bd Can.* **24**, 475–94. *176*

1209. Stielau, W. J., Freedland, R. A. and Meyer, J. H. (1965). Effects of B-vitamin deficiencies and of starvation on liver enzyme activities of growing rats. *J. Nutr.* **87**, 109–16. *253*

1210. Stirling, W. (1886). On red and pale muscles in fishes. *Rep. Fishery Bd Scotl.* **4**, Appendix F no. IX, pp. 166–71. *17*

*1211. Strack, E., Schwaneberg, H. and Wannschaff, G. (1937). On the basic constituents of lamprey. *Hoppe-Seyler's Z. physiol. Chem.* **247**, 52–62.

1212. Stroganov, N. S. (1956). Physiological adaptability of fish to the temperature of the surrounding medium. *Akad. Nauk SSSR, Zoologicheskii Institut* 108 pp. M. Roublev, translator. Published for the National Science Foundation, Washington, D.C. by the Israel Programme for Scientific Translations, Jerusalem, 1962. *117, 212*

*1213. Sugii, K. and Kinumaki, T. (1968). Distribution of vitamin E in a few species of fish. *Bull. Jap. Soc. scient. Fish.* **34**, 420–28.

*1214. Sugimura, K., Taira, H., Hoshino, N., Ebisawa, H. and Nagahara, T. (1954). The amino acid content of fish muscle protein. *Bull. Jap. Soc. scient. Fish.* **20**, 520–4.

*1215. Sulya, L. L., Box, B. E. and Gunter, G. (1960). Distribution of some blood constituents in fishes from the Gulf of Mexico. *Am. J. Physiol.* **199**, 1177–80.

1216. Summerfelt, R. C., Lewis, W. M. and Ulrich, M. G. (1967). Measurement of some haematological characteristics of the goldfish. *Progve Fish. Cult.* **29**, 13–20. *121*

1217. Sumner, F. B. and Fox, D. L. (1935a). Studies of carotenoid pigments in fishes. II. Investigations of the effects of coloured backgrounds and of ingested carotenoids on the xanthophyll content of *Girella nigricans*. *J. exp. Zool.* **71**, 101–23. *50*

1218. Sumner, F. B. and Fox, D. L. (1935b). Studies of carotenoid pigments in fishes. III. The effects of ingested carotenoids upon the xanthophyll content of *Fundulus parvipinnis*. *Proc. natn. Acad. Sci. U.S.A.* **21**, 330–40. *200*

*1219. Sundararaj, B. I., Kumar, M., Narasimhan, P. V., Prasad, M. R. N., Venkitasubramanian, T. A. and Malethy, J. (1966). Effects of starvation and glucose administration on carbohydrate metabolism of saccus vasculosus and liver of *Notopterus notopterus* (Teleostei). *Indian J. exp. Biol.* **4**, 1–3.

1220. Sutton, A. H. (1968). The relationship between ion and water contents of cod (*Gadus morhua* L.) muscle. *Comp. Biochem. Physiol.* **24**, 149–61. *106, 230, 246, 247*

*1221. Suyama, M. (1958). Changes in the amino acid composition of protein during the development of rainbow trout eggs. *Bull. Jap. Soc. scient. Fish.* **13**, 789–92. *70, 76*

*1222. Suyama, M. (1959). Biochemical studies on the eggs of aquatic animals—I. *Bull. Jap. Soc. scient. Fish.* **25**, 48–51.

*1223. Suyama, M. (1966). Changes in amino acid composition of proteins during development of puffer eggs. *Bull. Jap. Soc. scient. Fish.* **32**, 533–5. *77*

*1224. Suyama, M., Koike, J. and Suzuki, K. (1960). Studies on the glycolysis and the formation of ammonia in the muscle and blood of elasmobranchs. *J. Tokyo Univ. Fish.* **46**, 51–65.

1225. Suyama, M. and Ogino, C. (1958). Changes in chemical compositions during development of rainbow trout eggs. *Bull. Jap. Soc. scient. Fish.* **23**, 785–8. *71*

*1226. Suyama, M. and Tokuhiro, T. (1954a). Urea content and ammonia formation of the muscle of cartilaginous fishes—II. *Bull. Jap. Soc. scient. Fish.* **19**, 935–8.

*1227. Suyama, M. and Tokuhiro, T. (1954b). Urea content and ammonia formation of the muscle of cartilaginous fishes. III. The distribution of urea and trimethylamine oxide in different parts of the body. *Bull. Jap. Soc. scient. Fish.* **19**, 1003–6. *146, 289, 290*

*1228. Suzuki, K. (1966). Colorimetric determination of cholesterol of fish oil by ferric chloride method. *J. Tokyo Univ. Fish.* **52**, 61–70.

*1229. Suzuki, K., Hayakawa, T., Hasegawa, Y., Iketomi, T. and Yagi, M. (1957). Manganese content of foods in Japan. I. *Rep. natn. Inst. Nutr. Tokyo* p. 31 only. (No vol. number).

1230. Svetovidov, A. N. (1948). "Fauna of U.S.S.R." Fishes. **9** (4), Gadiformes. Academy of Sciences of the USSR. Translated from Russian by the National Science Foundation, Washington D.C. and Smithsonian Institution, 1962. pp. 168–91 on the various species of cod. *173*

*1231. Swaminathan, M. (1944). Nicotinic acid content of Indian foodstuffs. *Indian J. med. Res.* **32**, 39–46.

*1232. Swaminathan, M. (1946). Vitamin B_1 (Thiamin) content of Indian foodstuffs. *Indian J. med. Res.* **34**, 289–97.

1233. Swift, D. R. and Pickford, G. E. (1965). Seasonal variations in the hormone content of the pituitary gland of the perch, *Perca fluviatilis* L. *Gen. comp. Endocrinol.* **5**, 354–65. *172*

*1234. Taarland, T., Mathiesen, E., Øvsthus, Ø. and Braekkan, O. R. (1958). Nutritional values and vitamins of Norwegian fish and fish products. *Tidsskr. HermetInd.* **44**, 405–12.

*1235. Taguchi, T. and Ikeda, S. (1968). Studies on the properties of fish actomyosin—III. Lecithin found in the actomyosin from fish muscle. *Bull. Jap. Soc. scient. Fish.* **34**, 339–43.

*1236. Takada, K. and Nishimoto, J. (1958). Studies on the choline in fish—I. Content of choline and the similar substances in fishes. *Bull. Jap. Soc. scient. Fish.* **24**, 632–5.

*1237. Takagi, M., Murayama, H. and Endo, S. (1967). Trimethylamine and trimethylamine oxide contents of fish and marine invertebrates. *Bull. Fac. Fish. Hokkaido Univ.* **18**, 261–7.

*1238. Takahashi, T. Unpublished work, quoted by Gustavson, K. H. (1956). "The Chemistry and Reactivity of Collagen" p. 225. Academic Press, London and New York.

*1239. Takahashi, T., Ishino, A., Tanaka, T., Takei, M. and Yokoyama, W. (1957). Studies on the properties of shark skin as the raw material for manufacturing leather. *Bull. Tokai reg. Fish. Res. Lab.* **15**, 95–238.

1240. Takahashi, T. and Shiokawa, A. (1953). Physico-chemical studies on the skin and leather of marine animals—IV. On the water in shark skin. *Bull. Jap. Soc. scient. Fish.* **18**, 333–40. *226*

*1241. Takahashi, T. and Yokoyama, W. (1949). Chemical study on placoid scale. *Bull. Jap. Soc. scient. Fish.* **14**, 223–6.

*1242. Takahashi, T. and Yokoyama, W. (1954a). Physico-chemical studies on the skin and leather of marine animals.—X. On the protein in shark skin. *Bull. Jap. Soc. scient. Fish.* **20**, 411–20. *38*

*1243. Takahashi, T. and Yokoyama, W. (1954b). Physico-chemical studies on the skin and leather of marine animals.—XII. The content of hydroxyproline in the collagen of different fish skins. *Bull. Jap. Soc. scient. Fish.* **20**, 525–9. *215*

*1244. Takama, K., Zama, K. and Igarashi, H. (1966). Lipids of Alaska pollack (*Theragra chalcogramma*). *Bull. Fac. Fish. Hokkaido Univ.* **17**, 133–8.

1245. Tallan, H. H. (1962). A survey of the amino acids and related compounds in nervous tissue. *In* "Amino Acid Pools" (J. T. Holden, ed.), pp. 472, 476, 478 and 481. Elsevier, Amsterdam. *129*

*1246. Tamura, O., Yasuda, M. and Fujiki, T. (1962). Method for judging the physiological condition of fish by the quantitative changes of the blood characters. 1. *Bull. Jap. Soc. scient. Fish.* **28**, 504–9.

*1247. Tarr, H. L. A. (1950). The acid-soluble phosphorus compounds of fish skeletal muscle. *J. Fish. Res. Bd Can.* **7**, 608–12.

*1248. Tarr, H. L. A. (1953). The Maillard reaction in flesh foods. *Fd Technol., Champaign* **8**, 15–19.

*1249. Tarr, H. L. A. and Leroux, M. (1962). Acid-soluble phosphorus compounds and free sugars in fish muscle and their origin. *Can. J. Biochem. Physiol.* **40**, 571–89.

*1250. Tashima, L. and Cahill, G. F. (1965). Fat metabolism in fish. *In* "Handbook of Physiology" (A. E. Renold and G. F. Cahill, eds.), Section 5: Adipose Tissue, pp. 55–8. Williams and Wilkins, Baltimore. *250*

*1251. Teeri, A. E., Loughlin, M. E. and Josselyn, D. (1957). Nutritive value of fish. I. Nicotinic acid, riboflavin, vitamin B_{12} and amino acids of various saltwater species. *Fd Res.* **22**, 145–50.

1252. Templeman, W. and Andrews, G. L. (1956). Jellied condition in the American plaice *Hippoglossoides platessoides*. *J. Fish. Res. Bd Can.* **13**, 147–82. *230, 238, 245, 250*

*1253. Testa, C. and Simongini, G. (1960). Determination of trimethylamine oxide in piscine species from the Adriatic. *Atti Soc. ital. Sci. vet.* **14**, 469–73.

1254. Thomas, J. D. (1964). Studies on the growth of trout, *Salmo trutta*, from four contrasting habitats. *Proc. zool. Soc. Lond.* **142**, 459–509. *172*

1255. Thomas, J. E. (1964). Organ systems in adaptation: the digestive system. *In* "Handbook of Physiology" (D. B. Dill, ed.), Section 4: Adaptation to the Environment. Williams and Wilkins, Baltimore. *203*

1256. Thomas, M. L. H. and McCrimmon, H. R. (1964). Variability in paper electrophoretic patterns of the serum of landlocked sea lamprey, *Petromyzon marinus* Linnaeus. *J. Fish. Res. Bd Can.* **21**, 239–46. *121, 231*

*1257. Thommen, H. and Gloor, U. (1965). Presence of keto-carotenoids in the trout. *Naturwissenschaften* **52**, 161–2.

*1258. Thompson, M. H. (1964). Determination of sodium and potassium in fish and other marine products. *J. Ass. off. agric. Chem.* **47**, 701–7.

1259. Thompson, M. H. and Farragut, R. N. (1965). Amino acid composition of the alewife (*Alosa pseudoharengus*). *Fish. Ind. Res.* **3**, 47–53. *233*

1260. Thompson, R. R. (1967). Disc electrophoresis method for the identification of fish species. *J. Ass. off. agric. Chem.* **50**, 282–5. *132*

*1261. Thorson, T. B. (1959). Partitioning of body water in sea lamprey. *Science, N.Y.* **130**, 99–100.

*1262. Thurston, C. E. (1958a). Variation in composition of southeastern Alaska pink salmon. *Fd Res.* **23**, 619–25. *6, 245*

*1263. Thurston, C. E. (1958b). Sodium and potassium in the edible portions of 34 spp. of fish. *Comml Fish. Rev.* **20** (1), 1–5.

*1264. Thurston, C. E. (1958c). Sodium and potassium content of 34 species of fish. *J. Am. diet. Ass.* **34**, 396–9.

1265. Thurston, C. E. (1958d). Changes in composition of sole during refrigeration. *Comml Fish. Rev.* **20** (8), 21–2. *58*

*1266. Thurston, C. E. (1961a). Proximate composition of nine species of rockfish. *J. Food Sci.* **26**, 38–42.

*1267. Thurston, C. E. (1961b). Proximate composition and sodium and potassium contents of four species of commercial bottom fish. *J. Food Sci.* **26**, 495–8. *88*

*1268. Thurston, C. E. (1961c). Proximate composition of nine species of sole and flounder. *J. agric. Fd Chem.* **9**, 313–6. *245*

1269. Thurston, C. E. (1962). Physical characteristics and chemical composition of two sub-species of lake trout. *J. Fish. Res. Bd Can.* **19**, 39–44. *6, 21, 36, 129*

*1270. Thurston, C. E. and Groninger, H. S. (1959). Composition changes in Puget Sound pink salmon during storage in ice and refrigerated brine. *J. agric. Fd Chem.* **7**, 282–4. *6, 58, 122, 123*

*1271. Thurston, C. E. and MacMaster, P. P. (1960). Variations in chemical composition of different parts of halibut flesh. *Fd Res.* **25**, 229–36. *4, 6, 21, 24*

1272. Thurston, C. E. and Newman, H. W. (1962). Proximate composition changes in sockeye salmon (*Oncorhynchus nerka*) during spawning migration. *Fish. Ind. Res.* **2**, 15–22. *105, 106*

*1273. Thurston, C. E. and Osterhaug, K. L. (1960). Sodium content of fish flesh. *J. Am. diet. Ass.* **36**, 212–5.

*1274. Thurston, C. E., Stansby, M. E., Karrick, N. L., Miyauchi, D. T. and Clegg, W. C. (1959). Composition of certain species of freshwater fish. II. Comparative data for 21 species of lake and river fish. *Fd Res.* **24**, 493–502.

1275. Thurston, R. V. (1967). Electrophoretic patterns of blood serum proteins from rainbow trout (*Salmo gairdneri*). *J. Fish. Res. Bd Can.* **24**, 2169–88. *55, 104*

1276. Tilik, Z. E. (1932). Changes in the chemical composition of the flesh of the svir salmon in relation to spawning migration. *Izv. vses. Inst. ozern. rechn. ryb.* **14**, 133–48. Quoted in *Comml Fish. Abstr.* **18** (12), p. 13 (1965). *98, 243*

*1277. Todd, W. R., Laastuen, L. E. and Thomas, A. E. (1967). Effect of amino acid imbalance on liver glycogen levels in young salmon. *Comp. Biochem. Physiol.* **23**, 431–5.

*1278. Tohyama, Y., Tetsumoto, S., Fukuya, S. and Yamada, S. (1941). Studies on fish in Japan as a source of insulin. *Bull. Jap. Soc. scient. Fish.* **10**, 153–5.

*1279. Tomlinson, N., Arnold, E. S., Roberts, E. and Geiger, S. E. (1961). Observations on post-mortem biochemical changes in fish muscle in relation to rigor mortis. *J. Fish. Res. Bd Can.* **18**, 321–36. *42, 43*

*1280. Tomlinson, N. and Creelman, V. M. (1960). On the source of free ribose formed post mortem in the muscle of ling cod (*Ophiodone longatus*). *J. Fish. Res. Bd Can.* **17**, 603–6.

*1281. Tomlinson, N., Creelman, V. M. and Reid, K. G. (1960). The phosphorus-containing fractions of sterile ling cod muscle during storage at 0°C. *J. Fish. Res. Bd Can.* **17**, 371–6.

1282. Tomlinson, N. and Geiger, S. E. (1962). Glycogen concentration and post-mortem loss of adenosine triphosphate in fish and mammalian skeletal muscle. A review. *J. Fish. Res. Bd Can.* **19,** 997–1003. *275*

*1283. Tomlinson, N., Geiger, S. E. and Kay, W. W. (1965). Sodium, potassium and magnesium concentration and weight changes in fish stored in refrigerated sea water in relation to biochemical changes associated with rigor mortis. *J. Food Sci.* **30,** 126–34. *41–3*

*1284. Tomlinson, N., McBride, J. R. and Geiger, S. E. (1967). The sodium, potassium and water content of the flesh of sockeye salmon (*Oncorhynchus nerka*) in relation to sexual development and starvation. *J. Fish. Res. Bd Can.* **24,** 243–8. *114, 245*

*1285. Tomoda, M. and Hotta, K. (1957). Riboflavin content of the dark muscle of fishes. *Vitamins, Kyoto* **13,** 417–8. *151*

1286. Trout, G. C. (1954). Otolith growth of the Barents Sea cod. *Rapp. P.-v. Réun. Cons. perm. int. Explor. Mer* **136,** 89–102. *126*

1287. Trout, G. C. (1967). The Bear Island cod: migrations and movements. *Fishery Invest., Lond.* Ser. II, **21** (6), 51 pp. *90, 171, 174*

1288. Trout, G. C. (1958). Otoliths in age determination. *Spec. Publs int. Commn N.W. Atlant. Fish.* (1), 207–14. *161*

1289. Tsuchiya, T. (1961). Biochemistry of fish oils. *In* "Fish as Food" (G. Borgstrom, ed.), Vol. 1, Chapter 7, pp. 211–58. Academic Press, London and New York. *272*

1290. Tsuchiya, Y. and Kunii, K. (1960). Studies on the influence of treatments immediately after catching upon the quality of fish flesh.—V. Determination of lactic acid in fish muscle. *Bull. Jap. Soc. scient. Fish.* **26,** 284–8. *29*

1291. Tsukuda, H. (1960). Temperature adaptation in fishes. III. Temperature tolerance of the guppy, *Lebistes reticulatus*, in relation to the rearing temperature before and after birth. *Biol. J. Nara Women's Univ.* (10), 11–14. *213*

1292. Tsukuda, H. (1961). Temperature acclimatization on different organization levels in fishes. *J. Inst. Polytech. Osaka Cy Univ.,* Section D, Biology **12,** 15–45. *117, 213*

*1293. Tsukuda, N. and Amano, K. (1966a). Studies on the discoloration of red fishes—1. Content of carotenoid pigments in eighteen species of red fishes. *Bull. Jap. Soc. scient. Fish.* **32,** 334–45.

*1294. Tsukuda, N. and Amano, K. (1966b). Studies on the discoloration of red fishes—II. The discoloration of the three species during ice and freeze storage. *Bull. Jap. Soc. scient. Fish.* **32,** 522–9.

*1295. Tsunoo, S., Horisaka, K., Motonishi, K. and Takeda, J. (1964). On the ophidin in the muscle of the sea-snake, *Laticauda semifasciata* and *laticaudata*. *J. Biochem., Tokyo* **56,** 604–6.

*1296. Tsuyuki, H. and Naruse, U. (1962). On the yellowtail oil—IX. Sphingo-lipid in meat. *Bull. Jap. Soc. scient. Fish.* **28,** 585–8. *20*

*1297. Tsuyuki, H., Naruse, U. and Shionoya, A. (1961). On the yellowtail oil—VII. Lecithin in meats. *Bull. Jap. Soc. scient. Fish.* **27**, 1113–6. *21*

1298. Tsuyuki, H. and Roberts, E. (1965). Zone electrophoretic comparison of muscle myogens and blood proteins of artificial hybrids of salmonidae with their parental species. *J. Fish. Res. Bd Can.* **22**, 767–73. *164*

1299. Tsuyuki, H. and Roberts, E. (1966). Inter-species relationships within the genus *Oncorhynchus* based on biochemical systematics. *J. Fish. Res. Bd Can.* **23**, 101–7. *122, 134, 141, 163*

1300. Tsuyuki, H., Roberts, E. and Kerr, R. H. (1967). Comparative electropherograms of the family Catostomidae. *J. Fish. Res. Bd Can.* **24**, 299–304. *132*

1301. Tsuyuki, H., Roberts, E. and Vanstone, W. E. (1965). Comparative zone electropherograms of muscle myogens and blood haemoglobins of marine and freshwater vertebrates and their application to biochemical systematics. *J. Fish. Res. Bd Can.* **22**, 203–13. *141*

1302. Tsuyuki, H., Uthe, J. F., Roberts, E. and Clarke, L. W. (1966). Comparative electropherograms of *Coregonus clupeaformis*, *Salvelinus namaycush*, *S. alpinus*, *S. malma*, and *S. fontinalis* from the family Salmonidae. *J. Fish. Res. Bd Can.* **23**, 1599–1606. *135*

1303. Tsuyuki, H. and Wold, F. (1964). Enolase: multiple molecular forms in fish muscle. *Science, N.Y.* **146**, 535–7. *132*

1304. Tucker, D. W. (1959). A new solution to the Atlantic eel problem. *Nature, Lond.* **183**, 495–501. *189*

1305. Tunison, A. V., Phillips, A. M., McCay, C. M., Mitchell, C. R. and Rodgers, E. O. (1940). The nutrition of trout. *Fish. Res. Bull. N.Y.* 30 pp. *202*

*1306. Tyler, J. C. (1960). Erythrocyte counts and haemoglobin determinations for two Antarctic notothenid fishes. *Stanford ichthyol. Bull.* **7**, 199–200. *220*

1307. Tåning, Å. V. (1952). Experimental study of meristic characters in fishes. *Biol. Rev.* **27**, 169–93. *152, 155, 156*

1308. Ueda, T., Shimizu, Y. and Simidu, W. (1964). Studies on muscle of aquatic animals—XXXXII. Species difference in fish actomyosin (Part 2). Relation between heat-denaturing point and species. *Bull. Jap. Soc. scient. Fish.* **31**, 352–6. *130, 214*

*1309. Ueda, T., Shimizu, Y. and Simidu, W. (1967). Extractability of fish actin. *Bull. Jap. Soc. scient. Fish.* **33**, 59–64.

*1310. Uesugi, S. and Yamazoe, S. (1964). Acetylcholinesterase activity during the development of the rainbow trout eggs. *Gunma J. med. Sci* **13**, 91–3. *71, 74, 75*

*1311. Umemura, K. (1951). Free amino acids in the fish red muscle. *Medicine and Biology (Japan).* **20**, 1–2.

*1312. Umminger, B. L. (1968). Life below zero. *Yale scient. Mag.* **42** (6), 6–10. *219*

*1313. Ushiyama, H., Fujimori, T., Shibata, T. and Yoshimura, K. (1965). Studies on carbohydrases in the pyloric caeca of the salmon, *Oncorhynchus keta*. *Bull. Fac. Fish. Hokkaido Univ.* **16**, 183–8.

1314. Uthe, J. F., Roberts, E., Clarke, L. W. and Tsuyuki, H. (1966). Comparative electropherograms of representatives of the families Petromyzontidae, Esocidae, Centrarchidae and Percidae. *J. Fish. Res. Bd Can.* **23**, 1663–71. *164*

1315. Uthe, J. F. and Tsuyuki, H. (1967). Comparative zone electropherograms of muscle myogens and blood proteins of adult and ammocoete lamprey. *J. Fish. Res. Bd Can.* **24**, 1269–73. *82, 237*

1316. Vanstone, W. E., Roberts, E. and Tsuyuki, H. (1964). Changes in the multiple haemoglobin patterns of some Pacific salmon, genus *Oncorhynchus*, during the parr-smolt transformation. *Can. J. Physiol. Pharmacol.* **42**, 697–703. *80, 176*

*1317. Vasil'yeva, Y. N., Dyubyuk, N. Y. and Lychnikova, T. D. (1961). Mineral constituents of certain species of fish and a check on the ratio of the content of mineral elements to that of albumen. *Vop. Pitan.* (2), 54–9.

1318. Velankar, N. K. (1965). Free propionic acid in the skeletal muscle of elasmobranchs. *Curr. Sci.* **34**, 586 only. *143*

*1319. Velankar, N. K. and Govindan, T. K. (1958). A preliminary study of the distribution of non-protein nitrogen in some marine fishes and invertebrates. *Proc. Indian Acad. Sci., Section B* **47**, 202–9.

1320. Vellas, F. (1965). Effects of several ecological factors on the activity of uricolytic enzymes of the liver of mirror carp (*Cyprinus carpio* L.). *Ann. Limnol.* **1**, 435–42. *50, 212, 253*

1321. Vellas, F. and Serfaty, A. (1967). Urea excretion in the carp (*Cyprinus carpio* L.). *Archs Sci. physiol.* **21**, 185–92. *256*

*1322. Vendrely, R. and Picaud, M. (1968). Comparative study of the histones of the erythrocytes of different animal species. *Expl Cell. Res.* **49**, 13–24.

*1323. Vendrely, R. and Vendrely, C. (1950). On the absolute concentration of deoxyribose nucleic acid in the cell nuclei of several species of birds and fish. *C. r. hebd. Séanc. Acad. Sci., Paris* **230**, 788–90. *140*

*1324. Venkataraman, R. and Chari, S. T. (1957). Amino-acid composition of some marine fishes. *Indian J. med. Res.* **45**, 77–80.

1325. Vernberg, F. J. and Gray, I. E. (1953). A comparative study of the respiratory metabolism of excised brain tissue of marine teleosts. *Biol. Bull. mar. biol. Lab., Woods Hole* **104**, 445–9. *148, 150*

1326. Vinogradov, A. P. (1953). "The elementary chemical composition of marine organisms." (J. Efron and J. K. Setlow, translators), 647 pp. Sears Foundation, New Haven. *1, 21, 23, 25, 95, 119, 136, 137, 143, 144, 151, 179, 200, 260, 270, 278, 280, 293*

*1327. Viswanathan, R., Bhatt, Y. M., Sreekumaran, C., Doshi, G. R., Gogate, S. S., Bhagwat, A. M. and Unni, C. K. (1966). Mineral content of aquatic foods. *Proc. Indian Acad. Sci., Section B* **64**, 301–13.

1328. Voronova, L. A. (1962). Application of spectral analysis to the determination of potassium and sodium in isolated muscle fibres. *Vest. leningr. gos. Univ., Series Biologii* **17** (21), Biol. no. 4, 86–93. *43*

*1329. Vul'fson, P. L. (1961). Extractable nitrogenous compounds of fish muscle. *Biokhimiya* **26**, 300–4.

1330. Wald, G. (1938). On rhodopsin in solution. *J. gen. Physiol.* **21**, 795–832. *180*

1331. Wald, G. (1947). The chemical evolution of vision. *Harvey Lect.* **41**, 117–60. *180*

1332. Wald, G., Brown, P. K. and Brown, P. S. (1957). Visual pigments and depths of habitat of marine fishes. *Nature, Lond.* **180**, 969–71. *181, 182*

1333. Wedemeyer, G. (1968). Uptake and distribution of Zn^{65} in the coho salmon egg (*Oncorhynchus kisutch*). *Comp. Biochem. Physiol.* **26**, 271–9. *293*

1334. Weiser, M. and Otte, E. (1964). Chemical and histological studies on wild and pond trout. *Wien. tierärztl. Mschr.* **51**, 98–106. *53, 54*

1335. Wessels, J. P. H. and Fisher, H. (1965). Estimation of protein reserves and the nitrogen content of organs in protein-depleted and repleted cocks. *Br. J. Nutr.* **19**, 57–69. *256*

*1336. Wessler, E. and Werner, I. (1957). On the chemical composition of some mucous substances in fish. *Acta chem. scand.* **11**, 1240–7.

*1337. Westöö, G. (1967). Mercury in fish. *Vår Föda* pp. 1–7.

1338. Wharton, D. R. A., Wharton, M. L. and Lola, J. (1965). Blood volume and water content of the male American cockroach, *Periplaneta americana* L. Methods and the influence of age and starvation. *J. Insect Physiol.* **11**, 391–404. *230*

1339. Whitaker, J. R. (1959). Chemical changes associated with ageing of meat with emphasis on the proteins. *Adv. Fd Res.* **9**, 1–60. *101*

1340. Whitworth, W. R. (1968). Effects of diurnal fluctuations of dissolved oxygen on the growth of brook trout. *J. Fish. Res. Bd Can.* **25**, 579–84. *176*

*1341. Wiechers, S. G. and Dreosti, G. M. (1961). The chemical composition of South African fishes. *Memo. Fishg Ind. Res. Inst. Un. S. Afr.* **118**, 18 pp.

*1342. Wikgren, B. J. (1953). Osmotic regulation in some aquatic animals with special reference to the influence of temperature. *Acta zool. fenn.* **71**, 102 pp. *218*

*1343. Wilber, C. G. (1954). Lipids in the northern pike. *Trans. Am. Fish. Soc.* **84**, 150–4.

1344. Wilkins, N. P. (1967a). Polymorphism of whole blood proteins in the cod (*Gadus morhua* L.). *J. Cons. perm. int. Explor. Mer* **31**, 77–88. *163*

1345. Wilkins, N. P. (1967b). Starvation of the herring, *Clupea harengus* L.: survival and some gross biochemical changes. *Comp. Biochem. Physiol.* **23**, 503–518. *222, 242*

1346. Wilkins, N. P. and Iles, T. D. (1966). Haemoglobin polymorphism and its ontogeny in herring (*Clupea harengus*) and sprat (*Sprattus sprattus*). *Comp. Biochem. Physiol.* **17**, 1141–58. *94, 104, 135*

1347. Williams, P. M. (1965). Fatty acids derived from lipids of marine origin. *J. Fish. Res. Bd Can.* **22**, 1107–22.

1348. Wilson, S. and Dixon, G. H. (1961). A comparison of cod and bovine insulins. *Nature, Lond.* **191**, 876–9. *278*

1349. Wilson, S. H., Hill, H. Z. and Hoagland, M. B. (1967). Physiology of rat-liver polysomes. Protein synthesis by stable polysomes. *Biochem. J.* **103**, 567–72. *232*

1350. Winberg, G. G. (1961). New information on metabolic rate in fishes. *Vop. Ikhtiol.* **1**, 157–65. *212*

1351. Wittenberger, C. (1960). "Studies on the Physiology of the Striated Muscle of Teleosteans." Dissertation for degree of Candidate of Biological Sciences, Univ. Babes-Bolyai, Cluj. *30*

*1352. Wittenberger, C. (1968). Alterations of the carbohydrate metabolism in trout, induced by effort and hypoxia. *Rev. Roumaine de Biol.* **13**, 131–7.

1353. Wittenberger, C. and Diaciuc, I. V. (1965). Effort metabolism of lateral muscles in carp. *J. Fish. Res. Bd Can.* **22**, 1397–1406. *31, 40–43*

1354. Wittenberger, C. and Oros, I. (1961). Research on the physiology of teleost striped muscle. V. Contributions to the study of lateral muscles in several marine fish. *Studii Cerc. Biol.* **12**, 333–41. *30*

1355. Wittenberger, C. and Vitca, E. (1966). Variation of the glycogen content in the lateral muscles of the carp during work performed by isolated muscles and during starvation. *Studia Univ. Babes-Bolyai, Series Biologica* (2), 117–23. *30*

1356. Wohlschlag, D. E. (1963). An Antarctic fish with unusually low metabolism. *Ecology* **44**, 557–64. *212*

1357. Wood, E. M., Yasutake, W. T., Woodall, A. N. and Halver, J. E. (1957). The nutrition of salmonoid fishes. 1. Chemical and histological studies of wild and domestic fish. *J. Nutr.* **61**, 465–77. *53, 55*

1358. Wood, E. M., Yasutake, W. T., Halver, J. E. and Woodall, A. N. (1960). Chemical and histological studies of wild and hatchery salmon in fresh water. *Trans. Am. Fish. Soc.* **89**, 301–7. *55*

*1359. Wood, J. D. (1958). Biochemical studies on sockeye salmon during spawning migration. IV. The non-protein nitrogenous constituents of the muscle. *Can. J. Biochem. Physiol.* **36**, 833–8. *99*

*1360. Wood, J. D., Duncan, D. W. and Jackson, M. (1960). Biochemical studies on sockeye salmon during spawning migration. XI. The free histidine content of the tissues. *J. Fish. Res. Bd Can.* **17**, 347–51. *99*

1361. Woodall, A. N. and LaRoche, G. (1964). Nutrition of salmonoid fishes. XI. Iodide requirements of chinook salmon. *J. Nutr.* **82**, 475–82. *208*

1362. Woodhead, A. D. and Ellett, S. (1966). Endocrine aspects of ageing in the guppy, *Lebistes reticulatus* Peters—1. The thyroid gland. *Exp. Gerontol.* **1**, 315–30. *127*

1363. Woodhead, A. D. and Woodhead, P. M. J. (1965). Seasonal changes in the physiology of the Barents Sea cod, *Gadus morhua* L., in relation to its environment. I. Endocrine changes particularly affecting migration and maturation. *Spec. Publs. int. Commn N.W. Atlant. Fish.* **6**, 691–715. *61, 109, 110, 213*

1364. Woodhead, P. M. J. (1968). Seasonal changes in the calcium content of the blood of Arctic cod. *J. mar. biol. Ass. U.K.* **48**, 81–91. *61, 160*

1365. Woodhead, P. M. J. and Woodhead, A. D. (1959). The effects of low temperatures on the physiology and distribution of the cod, *Gadus morhua* L., in the Barents Sea. *Proc. zool. Soc. Lond.* **133**, 181–99. *209, 219*

1366. Woodhead, P. M. J. and Woodhead, A. D. (1964). Seasonal changes in the physiology of the cod in relation to its environment. II. Physiological reactions of cod, *Gadus morhua* L., to low temperatures. *ICNAF Environmental Symposium*, Rome, contribution no. F–6B. *219*

1367. Woodhead, P. M. J. and Woodhead, A. D. (1965). Seasonal changes in the physiology of the Barents Sea cod, *Gadus morhua* L., in relation to its environment. II. Physiological reactions to low temperatures. *Spec. Publs int. Commn N.W. Atlant. Fish.* **6**, 717–34. *219*

*1368. Wotiz, H. H., Botticelli, C. R., Hisaw, F. L. and Olsen, A. G. (1960). Oestradiol 17-β, oestrone and progesterone in the ovaries of dogfish (*Squalus suckleyi*). *Proc. natn. Acad. Sci. U.S.A.* **46**, 580–3.

*1369. Wurtziger, J. and Hensel, G. (1967). Cholesterol content of fish fillets as a means of determining fish species. *Fette Seifen AnstrMittel* **69**, 937–42. *269*

*1370. Yakovleva, Z. A. (1964). Mineral composition of fishes caught in southern and central areas of the Atlantic and verification of the correlation between mineral elements and protein contained therein. *Vop. Pitan.* **23**, 57–60.

*1371. Yamada, J. (1962). Vitamin A in *Entosphenus tridentatus* Gairder. *Bull. Tokai reg. Fish. Res. Lab.* **33**, 33–4.

1372. Yamada, J. (1964). Histochemical observations of fish muscle—I. Distribution of fat in important food fish. *Bull. Tokai reg. Fish. Res. Lab.* **39**, 21–8. *261*

*1373. Yamagata, M., Horimoto, K. and Nagaoka, C. (1968). On the distribution of trimethylamine oxide in the muscles of yellowfin tuna. *Bull. Jap. Soc. scient. Fish.* **34**, 344–50. *23*

*1374. Yamakawa, T., Sugii, K., Iwasaki, K., Kinumaki, T. and Higashi, H. (1963). Vitamin D contents in fish. *Vitamins, Tokyo* **27**, 269–78.

1374a. Yamamura, Y. (1949a). Study on the vitamin A in "Aburazame" liver. (II). Distribution of A in each lobe. *Bull. Jap. Soc. scient. Fish.* **15**, 611–14. *38*

1374b. Yamamura, Y. (1949b). Studies on the vitamin A in "Aburazame" liver. (III). Difference by external and inner layer of the liver. *Bull. Jap. Soc. scient. Fish.* **15**, 635–7. *38*

1375. Yamamura, Y. and Kondo, S. (1949). Study on the vitamin A in "Aburazame" liver (I). *Bull. Jap. Soc. scient. Fish.* **15**, 7–12. *38*

*1376. Yamamura, Y. and Muto, S. (1961). Change of vitamin A and carotenoids during development of the salmon eggs. *Bull. Tokai reg. Fish. Res. Lab.* **19**, 171–9. *74*

1377. Yamanaka, H., Yamaguchi, K., Hashimoto, K. and Matsuura, F. (1967). Starch-gel electrophoresis of fish haemoglobins—III. Salmonoid fishes. *Bull. Jap. Soc. scient. Fish.* **33**, 195–203. *94, 122, 135*

1378. Yamanaka, H., Yamaguchi, K. and Matsuura, F. (1965). Starch gel electrophoresis of fish haemoglobins—II. Electrophoretic patterns of haemoglobin of various fishes. *Bull. Jap. Soc. scient. Fish.* **31**, 833–9. *135*

1379. Yamashita, H. (1967). Haematological study of a species of rockfish, *Sebastiscus marmoratus*—I. The effect of chlorinity on the moisture content and specific gravity of blood, serum protein and erythrocyte counts. *Bull. Jap. Soc. scient. Fish.* **33**, 81–90. *119, 187*

*1380. Yanase, M. (1952). Studies on the vitamin B_{12} of aquatic animals. I. The vitamin B_{12} content of fishes (1). *Bull. Jap. Soc. scient. Fish.* **17**, 389–92.

*1381. Yanase, M. (1953). Studies on the vitamin B_{12} of aquatic animals. II. The vitamin B_{12} content of fish (2). *Bull. Jap. Soc. scient. Fish.* **18**, 629–35. *271*

*1382. Yanase, M. (1955). Studies on vitamin B_{12} of aquatic animals. VI. The vitamin B_{12} level in the gastric and intestinal contents of fish. *Bull. Jap. Soc. scient. Fish.* **21**, 197–204.

*1383. Yanase, M. (1956). The vitamin B_6 content of fish meat. *Bull. Jap. Soc. scient. Fish.* **22**, 51–5. *96, 147, 151, 284*

*1384. Yanase, M. (1958). The vitamin B_6 content of fish liver. *Bull. Tokai reg. Fish. Res. Lab.* **22**, 53–6. *130*

*1385. Yanni, M. (1961). Studies on carbohydrate content of the tissues of *Clarias lazera*. *Z. vergl. Physiol.* **45**, 56–60. *98, 120*

1386. Yanni, M. (1962). Effect of starvation on contents of water and lipides of tissues of *Clarias lazera*. *Z. vergl. Physiol.* **45**, 390–5. *223*

*1387. Yanni, M. (1964). The assimilation of fructose and galactose in the different tissues of *Clarias lazera*. *Z. vergl. Physiol.* **49**, 130–7.

*1388. Young, E. G. and Inman, W. R. (1938). The protein of the casing of salmon eggs. *J. biol. Chem.* **124**, 189–93.

1389. Young, E. G. and Lorimer, J. W. (1960). The acid-soluble collagen of cod skin. *Archs Biochem. Biophys.* **88**, 373–81. *101, 243*

*1390. Young, E. G. and Lorimer, J. W. (1961). A comparison of the acid-soluble collagens from the skin and swim bladder of the cod. *Archs Biochem. Biophys.* **92,** 183–90.

*1391. Young, E. G. and Smith, D. G. (1956). The amino acids in the ichthulo-keratin of salmon eggs. *J. biol. Chem.* **219,** 161–4.

*1392. Yudaev, N. A. (1950). Content of histidine, carnosine and anserine in the muscles of some fish. *Dokl. Akad. Nauk SSSR* **70,** 279–82. *147*

1393. Yur'eva, V. I. and Mel'kova, L. A. (1967). Electrophoretic fractionation of proteins in the sarcoplasm of fish, and the amino acid composition of the fractions. *Obmen. Veshchestv Biokhim. Ryb, Akad. Nauk SSSR, Min. Ryb. Khoz. SSSR, Ikhtiol. Kom.* pp. 260–3. Quoted in *Chem. Abstr.* **69,** 1003q (1968). *130*

*1394. Yurkowski, M. and Brockerhoff, H. (1965). Lysolecithinase of cod muscle. *J. Fish. Res. Bd Can.* **22,** 643–52. *253*

1395. Zadunaisky, J. A. (1966). The location of sodium in the transverse tubules of skeletal muscle. *J. Cell. Biol.* **31,** C11–C16. *14*

*1396. Zama, K. (1963a). Studies on the phospholipids of aquatic animals. *Mem. Fac. Fish. Hokkaido Univ.* **11,** (1), 73 pp. *21, 29*

*1397. Zama, K. (1963b). Lipids of pollack heart. 1. Acetone-soluble lipid from heart of pollack, *Theragra chalcogramma. Bull. Fac. Fish. Hokkaido Univ.* **13,** 181–5.

*1398. Zama, K., Hatano, M. and Igarashi, H. (1966a). Lipids of salmonoid fishes. VIII. Acetone-soluble lipid from heart of chum salmon, *Oncorhynchus keta. Bull. Fac. Fish. Hokkaido Univ.* **17,** 123–6.

*1399. Zama, K., Hatano, M. and Igarashi, H. (1966b). Lipids of salmonoid fishes. IX. Conjugated lipids from heart of chum salmon, *Oncorhynchus keta. Bull. Fac. Fish. Hokkaido Univ.* **17,** 127–32.

*1400. Zama, K., Katada, M. and Igarashi, H. (1959). Egg lipids of a salmon, *Oncorhynchus keta*—II. Conjugated lipids from salmon eggs. *Bull. Jap. Soc. scient. Fish.* **24,** 739–42. *76*

*1401. Zama, K., Takama, K. and Igarashi, H. (1967). Lipids of salmonoid fishes, X. Lipids from spleen of silver salmon, *Oncorhynchus kisutch,* and red salmon. *O. nerka. Bull. Fac. Fish. Hokkaido Univ.* **18,** 102–9.

1402. Zharov, V. L. (1965). Body temperature of tuna (Thunnidae) and other perciform fishes of the tropical Atlantic. *Vop. Ikhtiol.,* **5** (1), 157. Translated in *Fedn Proc. Fedn Am. Socs exp. Biol.* **25** (2), T291–4. *48*

1403. Ziecik, M. and Slawinski, O. (1965). Chemical and weight composition of the edible parts and waste of the tench (*Tinca tinca*) during an annual cycle. *Zesz. nauk. wyzsz. Szk. roln. Olsztyn.* **20,** 17–36. Quoted in *Chem. Abstr.* **64,** 14644b (1966). *119*

*1404. Zigman, S., Munro, G. and Lerman, S. (1965). A study of the DNA of dogfish corneal epithelium. *Investve Ophth.* **4,** 222–5.

1405. Zilva, S. S., Drummond, J. C. and Graham, M. (1924). The relation of the vitamin A potency of the liver oil to the sexual condition and age of the cod. *Biochem. J.* **18,** 178–81. *252*

*1406. Zore, V. A. and Tichonova, E. I. (1963). Simultaneous spectral determination of lead, copper and tin in fresh fish and some preserves. *Gig. Sanit.* **28** (2), 58–60.

*1407. Zydowo, M. and Purzycka, J. (1964). Comparative studies on glutamine content in animal tissues. *Acta biochim. pol.* **11,** 165–8.

SUBJECT INDEX

A

Absorption of nutrients from the environment, 205–7
Actin, preparation from fish muscle, 16, 17
Active fish, starvation in, 231
Activity, intrinsic, 147
Adaptive resistance to freezing, 219
Aggression, 49
  in hatchery fish, 53
Ageing, 126–8
Ammocoete-adult change in lampreys, 82
Anatomical distribution of substances, 1
Aquarium, effects of keeping in, 49–51
Artificially propagated eggs, difference from normal, 55, 56
Ash,
  general, 261
  in marine and freshwater fish, 143
  in starvation, 225–30, 243, 244
  seasonal variation in, 169–70
Ash/protein relations, 227

B

Bile salts, evolution of, 140
Body shape in fish from different grounds, 156, 158
Body temperature, raising above ambient, 48
Bones, contamination of sample with, 1
Buoyancy in relation to lipid distribution, 36, 142, 143

C

Carbohydrates,
  accumulation in ovary, 98
  in the diet, effect of, 202, 203
  in maturation, 98, 99
  in starvation, 250–2
Carotene, conversion to vitamin A, 200

Castration, prolongation of life by, 115, 126
Cell dimensions,
  in different regions of the musculature, 1–4
  in relation to body length, 85, 86
Cell walls, relationship with myocommata, 8
  nature of, 86
Cessation of feeding on capture, 51
Clearance of steroids after spawning, 115
Coelacanth, chemistry of the, 142
Cold-water species, low haemoglobin in, 177–9
Collagen deposition during maturation, 102
Cone shapes in the musculature of active fish, 148
Connective tissue,
  proportion in 'pure' muscle, 7, 8
  thermal denaturation of, in relation to hydroxyproline content, 215
  thickening of, during maturation, 102
Critical size for maturation, 97
Cushing's syndrome, similarity in spawning fish, 114

D

Dark muscle, 17
  and activity of fish, 26
  cell dimensions of, 2, 4, 17, 18
  chemical differences from white muscle, 20
  deep and superficial, 19, 26
  distribution along body, 19
  function of, 26
  proportion in the tail, 7
  similarity to heart muscle, 30
  similarity to liver, 27, 28
Date of spawning in different geographical localities, 159